LIB051005 R3/78

FRASER UNIVERSITY LIBRARY

D1133112

The Pattern of
Animal Communities

Aerial view of part of Wytham North Hill (looking north-west), with farmland beyond. West of the old London to Gloucester coach road on the left are young forest plantings, east of it deciduous woodland and scrub with enclaves of farm fields. Limestone grassland in bottom foreground and in centre. (Photo Hunting Surveys. 30 April 1960)

THE PATTERN OF
ANIMAL
COMMUNITIES

Charles S. Elton

*With photographs
mainly by D. A. Kempson
and the Author*

LONDON: METHUEN & CO LTD
NEW YORK: JOHN WILEY & SONS INC

First published in Great Britain in 1966
by Methuen and Co Ltd, 11 New Fetter Lane, London EC4
© 1966 Charles S. Elton
Printed in Great Britain by
Butler and Tanner Ltd, Frome and London

To

THOMAS PARK

*whose laboratory experiments have
thrown so much light on Nature*

Contents

.

Plates

Text Figures

Preface

THE ECOLOGICAL SURVEY on which this book is based began to be planned in 1942, and since 1945 has been mainly centred upon Oxford University's estate at Wytham Woods, where a rich series of habitats from open ground and limestone to woodland with many springs and marshes interspersed occupies a hill set in riverine surroundings. Here biological research workers from the University have accumulated a considerable body of knowledge, some of which I have arranged in a general setting that allows one to comprehend some of the inter-related parts of the whole system. It is also intended to provide a framework for understanding animal communities elsewhere. The ecological inquirer is, more than most scientific people, apt to find himself lost in a large labyrinth of interrelations and variables. The dictionary defines a labyrinth as 'an intricate structure of inter-communicating passages, through which it is difficult to find one's way without a clue'. This could equally be a figurative description of plant and animal communities. The present book seeks to provide a plan of construction of the labyrinth and a few new clues that may help the inquirer to know where he is on the general ecological map.

In presenting this blue-print of animal communities I have avoided giving long lists of species such as the botanist, with his smaller kingdom, can handle fairly well. Instead, I have indicated the nature and scale of the different communities and used examples to illustrate the ideas. It is to be understood, however, that a full ecologically organized index of all available records from Wytham Woods (as well as a great many from elsewhere), together with a collection of specimens of many of the animals and plants concerned, is kept in the Wytham Ecological Survey at the Bureau of Animal Population. And although a good many scientific papers about animal life at Wytham have already been published, a very large body of information in the Survey still remains to be published in detail in special journals, while a great deal of information also needs to be kept on permanent record there.

Several things should be said about this mountain of ecological ore, the first being that it has been mined along many separate lodes, by different people in different scientific departments and for different purposes. Not all of it has been drawn upon here, and in particular I have made no attempt to describe or assess the whole of the intense and continued population analyses of mammals (in the

Bureau of Animal Population), of birds (in the Edward Grey Institute of Field Ornithology) and of oak-tree insects (in the Hope Department of Entomology). That is to say, I have used some of this information but with another object, and not in order to discuss directly the natural control of populations; though some ideas on this subject have come out as an extra dividend from the ecological survey itself. And it has become evident that this highly refined kind of research on population dynamics could benefit from a more systematic description of the habitats of the populations concerned. Besides the work of the three main groups mentioned above, a good deal was done at Wytham earlier on by the Department of Forestry, and smaller amounts come from the Department of Agriculture, the Department of Zoology and the Department of Botany. A notable amount of research at Wytham has been done by visitors from other countries, especially at the Bureau of Animal Population, and this has added a most valuable and stimulating element of variety. Thus, substantial field work on populations or communities has been done by research graduates and more senior ecologists from New Zealand, Australia, Canada, Southern Rhodesia, the United States, Japan, Denmark and Jugoslavia.

It would have been impossible to carry out an investigation on this scale without help from a great many people for which I am deeply grateful. Many individuals are acknowledged in the text or in the Notes, and will not be recapitulated here, and I hope they will not think that this lessens my appreciation of their cooperation. I am especially indebted to others who have been more closely associated with my work. In the general planning of the Ecological Survey I was helped by Professor R. S. Miller, then a research student, with whom I have kept in touch across the Atlantic during the past fifteen years and who has greatly influenced my ideas. He has kindly read this book before publication. Similarly I have shared a great deal of fertile discussion with Professor C. Overgaard Nielsen, during the period he was at Oxford and later at the Molslaboratoriet in Denmark. In the executive work of the Survey Miss Brenda Macpherson (now Mrs Sladen) greatly assisted me from 1951 to 1956, when the standard indexing methods were being evolved; Mr S. W. Hurry was my assistant in 1960; and Mr C. A. Elbourn has been my assistant since 1961. Mr Elbourn has given me help in a great many ways during the preparation of this book, and his grasp of the detailed methods of the Survey has proved invaluable. Mrs E. Young helped me greatly in the indexing work of the Survey for some years.

Among the research staff of the Bureau of Animal Population I also wish particularly to thank Mr H. N. Southern and Miss K. Paviour-Smith (now Mrs Southern), whose knowledge of Wytham Woods is so comprehensive. Mr Southern was the first ecologist to begin regular research there after the last war. Mrs Southern has prepared and kindly allowed me to use in Ch. 15 an analysis of bracket fungi and their beetle inhabitants. Other members of the staff have also given me unstinted help during this long task. On all photographic matters I have been aided by Mr D. A. Kempson, who has contributed many of the pictures in this book and whose high standards of technique are well known. Mr K. T. Marsland has been a standby in many ways, and Mrs M. Marsland has faultlessly typed the main text of the book. The Bureau's office and library have also played a necessary part. In the former Miss C. M. Gibbs and others (including especially Mrs C. Nightingale) have looked after a variety of tasks for me, and in the latter I am especially grateful to the library secretary, Mrs J. M. Dunkley, for many services.

Those who have engaged in ecological work at Wytham owe a great deal to the late Mr H. D. Meads, who was responsible for wardening the woods, keeping meteorological records and many other activities there; and to the Head Forester, Mr H. Probitts, who has taken an interest in the scientific research as well as giving all kinds of practical help.

The Wytham Ecological Survey has been supported since 1951 by grants from the Nature Conservancy, and I am most grateful to it and to its successive Directors-General, Captain C. Diver and Mr E. M. Nicholson, for support and for giving me a free hand with the research over such a long period. The Conservancy's grants towards other research in the Bureau of Animal Population have also contributed much to the results. I am glad to say that the habitat classification evolved and tested in Wytham Woods has now been adopted by the Conservancy and built into the management plans for National Nature Reserves, through the patient efforts of Mr T. Huxley and Dr E. Duffey, both of whom had worked at Wytham while at the Bureau.

I am very grateful to Dr R. R. Askew for advice and information about oak gall insects (Ch. 10) and to Professor M. Lloyd for allowing me to use his records of insects visiting ivy flowers (Ch. 13). I have not been able to acknowledge individually all those who have identified animals for which records are cited, though they have been mentioned wherever there might otherwise be any doubt about the correctness of the identifications. Special tribute should be paid to the magnificent British collections of the Hope Department of Entomology, which have been of major assistance, and I wish to thank Professor G. C. Varley and his staff for their patient help and for many courtesies.

The plan on which the photographs have been chosen needs an explanation. I have included pictures of most of the main habitat components that are discussed in Ch. 4, and nearly all the terrestrial and some of the fresh-water ones receive treatment later in the book. But certain habitats are not fully covered in the text, either because inadequate information exists about their communities (conifer woodland is the chief example), because the information exists but is unsuitable for this kind of analysis (ponds), or because there are already authoritative text-books about them (large lakes, the intertidal zone of the seashore). Nevertheless I believe there is justification for having photographs of the whole range of British land and fresh-water animal habitats in one place.

For the use of air photographs I wish to thank the following. Hunting Surveys Ltd took vertical air photographs of the whole Wytham Woods area in the springs of 1953 and 1960, and also a special series of oblique photographs in the latter year. Their field operations and choice of methods resulted in a very fine record of this area that will increase in value with the passage of time, and which has been a substantial help in our research on the ground. Their photographs are used for the Frontispiece and Plates 6, 7, 8, 69, 75 and 81. Through the courtesy of the Nature Conservancy, I was allowed access to a series of vertical photographs of Wytham Woods taken by Dr J. K. S. St. Joseph in June 1961, two of which (Plates 9 and 10) I have used here by permission of the Committee for Aerial Photography, University of Cambridge. Aerofilms Ltd have supplied Plates 67 and 82, and Messrs C. H. Wood (Bradford) Ltd Plate 5. The last had previously appeared in the *Journal of Animal Ecology* (C. H. Mortimer and E. B. Worthington, 1942, 11 : 245). Mr H. N. Southern has kindly allowed the use of an unpublished photograph (Plate 60) of a tawny owl and its prey; Miss E. M. O. Laurie (now Mrs Isserlis) that of a woodland pond (Plate 64); and Mrs Grattan that of a photograph (Plate 78) published by her father, Dr A. H. Church. Copyright of photographs taken by D. A. Kempson and the author is held by the Bureau of Animal Population, with the exception of Plates 1, 2, 4, 11, 17-19, 22-25, 66, 68 and 77 which are the author's own copyright. Acknowledgement is made to the following publishers for permission to use illustrations: Springer Verlag (Plate 32); Hutchinson (Plates 33 and 85); The American Association for the Advancement of Science (Fig. 10); the Botanical Society of the British Isles (Figs. 11-14); Svenska Skogsvårdsföreningen (Fig. 22). To all the authors, editors and publishers involved who have permitted the use of photographs and of text figures I offer thanks. Professor R. S. Miller gave permission to reproduce two maps (Figs. 23 and 24) from his thesis. Figs. 20 and 27 are the result of field work by Mr Elbourn and drawing by Mr A. J. Dunford at the Bureau of Animal Population. The latter has assisted with several other text figures.

I am especially grateful to my wife for her steady encouragement and for carefully reading each chapter as it was written.

Bureau of Animal Population
Department of Zoological Field Studies
Botanic Garden, Oxford
2 December 1964

CHAPTER 1

Patterns in Nature

MOST PEOPLE have learned to see, on an atlas or in reality (often now from an aeroplane), the shape and pattern of the great geographical zones of a continent, the climatic belts of the world or the zones along the sea-coast; and they will be familiar also with the appearance of a small-scale map (or again, the country itself from the air), with its repetition of certain component features like rivers, ponds, woods, fields, roads and the settlements of man (Plates 1 and 5). We carry this consciousness of repeated patterns down to still smaller parts of the landscape, whether natural or influenced by human control and management – for example zones by the roadside of road surface, grass verge, ditch, hedgerow and field; the same species of plant (oak or ash or pine or potato) making a vegetation pattern of individuals, or similarly the same species of animal or groups of animals (cattle, the earth castings of moles, rookeries, anthills and so on). All this consciousness of pattern, much of it quite familiar pattern, so pervades our minds that it may often seem a commonplace phenomenon – 'quite simple', as the ordinary empirical Englishman is fond of saying, because he does not wish to have to consider burdensome complications or causes. So one might speak of being alive or growing old or autumn colours or the periodic return of the sun or moon. Yet how many people who spread out a single sheet of the One-Inch Ordnance Survey map, or travel in a train for quarter of an hour, are aware that in such a bit of patterned landscape alone there may be more than ten thousand different kinds of wild plants and animals living fairly permanently, in some sort of balance of growth and metabolism and altogether in astronomical numbers of individuals?

In the last few decades ecologists have reached a stage where they are beginning to try and explore the distribution of animals within this pattern of habitats. In order to do this at all, we have to classify and analyse the habitat patterns down to quite small units, find out what communities of animals live in each sort of place, and how the different communities interact with their own bit of landscape and with one another. It is a very long and difficult job to do. This book records a modest beginning, during which I have thought carefully for twenty years about the best methods of classifying habitats for the purpose, and have applied the ideas in a particular place – Wytham Woods – which provides the greater part of the examples upon which I shall draw.

It will be necessary at this point to explain that 'pattern' is a word that has grown through several different meanings, to end up (for the present) in that favourite meaning that ecologists have rather widely adopted and that I have used above – the repetition of certain component shapes to form a connected or inter-spersed 'design'. When we decorate our houses we may be satisfying this deep consciousness of natural pattern by introducing derived or new designs and arrangements and motifs into our artificial surroundings. But 'design', with its overtones of human, to some extent also still of divine, purpose, is for the present ecological discussion an equivocal word, though it has constantly to be borne in mind that an enormous amount of the ecological pattern we see in this country and many others gets its form partly from human management and is not natural or at least is only semi-natural. And this may frequently be so without our realizing the past historical influences that brought it about. The great dictionaries inevitably lag so far behind the current practice of living language that the latest and perhaps commonest meaning of pattern is not yet enshrined in all of them. In earlier days the word connoted a single model to be copied or ideal to be followed. So we find in Spenser's 'Hymn in Honour of Beauty':

> It seems that he before his eyes had placed
> A goodly pattern, to whose perfect mould
> He fashioned them as comely as he could;
> That now so fair and seemly they appear,
> As nought may be amended anywhere.

However it is easy to suppose that from this idea of making other copies from a unique thing, naturally arose the notion of repeated pattern, and at a more complex level the intermingling of many separate components into a com-posite whole – 'a vast pattern of patterns' as Smuts once said of the world as a whole.

One more general thing needs to be said about patterns in nature. When one thinks of a pattern it is usually with some idea of regularity in its arrangement such as might be seen in a Greek key-pattern frieze, or a wallpaper, in an orchard or even a hazel coppice. This idea of regularity comes, I imagine, from the original feeling of perfection attached to the word. But in natural ecological systems it is unusual for exact regularity to occur. We find the repetition of com-ponent parts, but not a replication of identical ones, nor at exact intervals. Each is a little or even a good deal different from the rest. This could not be otherwise in any biological system, but the inherent variability of ecological communities produces the most complex and plastic of all such systems. Nevertheless the essential repetition is there – as we may easily see and feel with the trees of a pine wood, a nesting colony of gannets on sea rocks, the tussocks of a *Molinia* grass moor or the sequence of spring flushes on the sides of a hill. The repetition of the component parts of the main category pine, gannet, tussock or spring flush is the important thing. (The differences between individual component units are also important, as will be shown, and combine with the major pattern to set up some overwhelmingly important processes affecting the balance of populations and communities.) Throughout this book I shall deliberately stretch the meaning of pattern, as is already done by a great many ecologists, to include all three kinds of arrangements that may occur: regular orderly spacings of units, irregular spacings, or mixtures of the two: provided, that is, they involved the replication at intervals of similar component habitats and the animal communities in them. The fact is, there is no other convenient short word for the purpose, because most people have never analysed nature from this point of view, and so have not evolved a convenient language for it. I think there is less of what Audy[15] has termed 'esoteric obfuscation' in employing a familiar word in one of its special senses, than in inventing some terrible new one for the purpose. With this general explanation, I hope the reader will not find it inconsistent or contradictory to be told about 'regular patterns' and 'irregular patterns', bearing in mind all the time that one is dealing with the repetition of similar kinds of situations each with a characteristic community of animal species, together with the interweaving of these into a whole complex ecosystem.

The traveller, the naturalist and the poet have often written about the face of nature that a person ordinarily sees as he passes through or pauses in wild country, canoes up a river or sails on the ocean. They are describing the outer appearance (and its special significance to them) of rocks and earth, plant life, the air with its clouds and translucence, the surface of water – and a little of the animal life. The first four together form the great maze of habitats for animals that covers the earth's crust. Over a great deal of country the rocks and earth are of course themselves almost hidden by vegetation. A. H. Church[69] wrote of the Oxford countryside (shortly before its full entry into the machine age): 'Trees or grass clothe the visible surface of the land, in close canopy or as thick undergrowth; animal life beyond a few birds and the animals maintained by man, is conspicuously inconspicuous.' Yet there are over twenty-five thousand species of animals of all kinds in the British Isles and perhaps a third of that number may occur in the countryside that Church described. He did not make this remark just because he was a botanist. Go for a walk in the woods with a naturalist: although you will assuredly see some animals, even conspicuous ones – let us say meadow brown butterflies, a green woodpecker, a swarm of flies dancing close over a stream, or bumble-bees visiting flowers – any idea that you are really seeing the animal population as a whole is quickly found to be an illusion. The caterpillar of the butterfly (which itself may be invisible on a cold, windy day) lives low down among grass by day, climbing higher to feed by night; the woodpecker (which in any case is only visible now and then) subsists by pecking out its food from dead wood or under bark, or inside mounds of the yellow ant which is entirely subterranean in habits; the larvae of the flies may live hidden in damp soil or under water, while the adults may only be swarming for a few days in the year; and the bees are probably storing honey and pollen in an underground nest whither they retire at night. This huge world of animal populations is mostly hidden from ordinary observation by a *curtain of natural cover*: it begins to be fully revealed only when you look on the undersides of the leaves of a beech or sycamore tree, strip the loose bark from a dead log or dig into its rotting sapwood, turn over a stone or a dead rabbit or the litter of dying leaves – or go out at night with a mothing lamp. And there are many hundreds of animals that cannot easily be detected at all or properly counted without special methods of extracting them from the soil or other medium in which they live.

To see the life of even one kind of animal in nature wholly and continuously will tax the extreme resource and endurance of an observer. Few people see more than a fragment of it. The forests of the Amazon probably contain the richest land fauna anywhere in the world. Yet Alfred Russel Wallace frequently refers in his *Narrative of Travels on the Amazon and Rio Negro*[533] to the difficulty of getting to the right place at the right season or in suitable weather, and his harvest of specimens and field observations was gathered at great personal cost. He wrote (the time was June 1848): 'Thus it is that travellers who crowd into one description all the wonders and novelties which it took them weeks and months to observe, must produce an erroneous impression on the reader, and cause him, when he visits the spot, to experience much disappointment. As an instance of what is meant, it may be mentioned that during the first week of our residence in Pará, though constantly in the forest in the neighbourhood of the city, I did not see a single humming-bird, parrot or monkey. And yet, as I afterwards found, humming-birds, parrots, and monkeys are plentiful enough in the neighbourhood of Pará; but they require looking for, and a certain amount of acquaintance with them is necessary in order to discover their haunts, and some practice is required to see them in the thick forest, even when you hear them close by you.' Animal populations, then, are partly detectable with ease, and partly hidden from our senses, because the overwhelmingly greater mass of them is hidden under some kind of cover, and most of the detectable ones are seen for short periods only before they again vanish. Rocks and earth, vegetation, air and water combine to form a vast *container* of animal life, an enormous labyrinth or at any rate (as in the oceans) a largely inaccessible place in which animals settle their affairs out of reach of our direct observation.

I have mentioned the intermittent appearance of animals as they emerge from and return to cover. This is what we see ourselves, but it is also a really fundamental experience between the animals themselves – speaking of the majority of species, and more especially of the smaller ones. The universal organization of animal communities into some kind of food-chain system, with the species at each consumer level usually pursued by predators at a higher consumer level, and often by parasitoid insects seeking to lay their eggs – all this could not exist without the presence of cover. For cover offers a means of escape, or of puzzling and diverting a pursuer with alternative pathways; and when the relative sizes of enemy and prey are taken into account, cover provides also a number of absolute refuges.[127] But in so far as an active animal cannot remain alive very long, or breed or disperse its population if it sits indefinitely in the safety of a refuge, the chase is constantly renewed. And it is easy to see, indeed it has been proved in laboratory experiments as well, that the balance of skills between the prey and the enemy is very finely adjusted. It is undoubtedly a fact that an overwhelming majority of species have had their behaviour modified in evolution to take account of the attacks of enemies within a system of cover, usually fairly complex cover. This is not, of course, necessarily to say that enemies always control the numbers of their prey at the present day. The statement also needs substantial qualification in three respects. First, there are many animals that escape detection, not by escaping into a maze or a refuge, but by resembling some part of their environment: protective coloration, structure and behaviour carry the principle of cover into the open, as it were, and probably with much less loss of energy. But even this class of animals is closely linked with the nature of its habitat, with small-scale scenery against which it is camouflaged. The second class of animals is a large one: these come out in the dark. We perhaps do not know very much about the efficacy of darkness as cover. Simply because it is a difficult barrier to our own sight it is not necessarily so also to all other kinds of animals. One could imagine a long-continued evolutionary 'struggle' between a daylight enemy and prey which eventually exhausted all the possibilities of a balance of offensive and defensive adaptations, so that coming out at night became the last adaptation of all. The third class of animals includes those that are comparatively free from enemies, through size and strength, either of the individual or the herd, or else have managed to be quite inedible or to live in some place where there just are no effective enemies at all.

The elusiveness of most animals is not just an accidental limitation of our own senses and skill, or of our large size, though it is much enhanced by them. Whatever size we were and whatever increased acuity we possessed (short of clairvoyance) we should still notice the discontinuous appearances of most wild animals within the field of our perception. This is of course partly because in any case the activity of animals is interrupted by short periods of rest, and rest takes place more often than not under or against cover. And there are quite long periods of disappearance brought about by hibernation or from being for a time in the egg or pupal stage only. But the usual reason is just that the activity is not continuously visible. If we were as small as ants, say, then instead of watching a rabbit jump from its burrow and dash to cover in a patch of thorn pursued by a stoat, we might be watching a springtail one millimetre long jumping from behind a group of soil particles pursued by a rove-beetle into a patch of fungus mycelial threads. In all except a few communities cover is paramount in the life of animals, protection from climatic extremes and from water loss being additional reasons for this. So when we look at the patterned landscape we are looking at a very complicated structure of cover, within and to a lesser extent outside and around which are living a very large number of animals, with populations interspersed to form communities, highly dependent on the kind of structure that the cover provides. Within this pattern of cover the species network is maintained as an enormous production machine in which the members of most food-chains meet in staccato contact. It seems most probable that without the damping effect of cover upon all these feeding contacts the whole system would soon break down or at any rate become very simplified. And in so far as this cover structure is itself partly edible, we must suppose that there must be limiting arrangements that do prevent animals from eating themselves out of house and home. These general statements about cover are intended to give force and special emphasis to *habitat structure* in the life of animals, for this is one of the features that makes their ecology intrinsically so different from that of vegetation itself.

One may suppose that the general elusiveness of wild animals, and the difficulty of counting most of them accurately, was one of the reasons why population ecology has appeared so lately on the scientific scene. Yet one may still wonder why it was about 2000 years before civilized man, profoundly involved in aspects of nature around him, began to pay sustained attention to counting wild animal populations. Why count stars and not animals? In the second century B.C., Hipparchus made a list of more than a thousand stars; but it was not until the last quarter of the nineteenth century A.D. that biologists started to make censuses of wild animals in a scientific manner, by straining water through fine nets to count the plankton organisms. And it was not until the first decade of the present century that a systematic attempt was made by the great pioneer marine ecologist C. G. J. Petersen, to measure the populations of a whole community in order to study the productivity of flatfish in Danish coastal waters. Yet numbers are fascinating in themselves, the stocktaking of flocks and herds is more ancient than science, and there has been anxious thought about the size and growth of human populations for the last two hundred years. There is no word in our language to describe the formations or communities of animal life, in the way that 'vegetation' does for plants. You can't very well write about the 'animation' of the British Isles! Instead we have to use 'fauna', a mock-Latin invention of the eighteenth century. The reason for this deficiency is that you cannot just walk about with a notebook and describe animal life as a whole. Most of it is not visible at all, and certainly not in solid-looking masses, except in a few zones like the seashore or some of the mixed ungulate herds of the African plains or the penguin rookeries of Antarctica. We have scores of native botanical terms like herbage, grassland, scrub, woodland, moor and marsh, but lack a similar set of ordinary words for the corresponding entities of animal communities. And the neo-classical terms coined by some ecologists for the purpose are like the 'laboured jets of darkness to show the way through sunlight' of which C. E. Montague wrote, when describing the efforts of a colonel to explain the Infantry Training Manual to his men. The only terms we have naturally in our language are for groups of particular kinds of animals that happen to aggregate, like rookery, herd, flock, swarm, school and so on. But these apply to social phenomena really, that are not typical of how most animals live, nor applicable to whole communities, in which the animals move about most of the time in open order, interspersed, and their movements interweaving, while from time to time there occur those dramatic contacts that keep the ecological wheels turning. Plants seldom occur in open systems, except during new colonization or in extreme habitats like deserts or the Arctic, or in open water.

The dream of really knowing some day what animal populations are doing behind the curtain of cover originally came to me from gazing at the intricate pattern of landscape out of railway train windows, from walking slowly in woods, from observing the extraordinary polygonal markings of Arctic fjaeldmark soils and vegetation, from lying flat at the edge of ponds and trying to decipher their lay-out, and from analysing sand-dunes, sea-cliff slopes and rocky shores. This dream contains a wish to understand how many kinds of animals there are in each habitat, that is, the scale of communities; how, if at all, the different parts of the pattern have separate communities; how these can be defined and classified; how these separate aspects of the whole system are related and interact; what prevents the animals from completely destroying the vegetable and possibly other parts of the landscape, that is, what preserves the balance of numbers among them (uneasy balance though it may be). Such aims and interests are analogous to those felt by a physiologist who tries to visualize the interplay of tissues in organs, and of organs in a body; or the organic chemist who wants to understand the complex arrangement of parts, the molecular patterns, in a compound. The objective is to get out a ground-plan of an organized system containing innumerable different

27

parts, arranged in a hierarchy of recognizable and repeated patterns that are pro-duced, maintained or changed by potentially violent dynamic forces that do not normally operate at full power. The means of making such a blue-print of natural habitats and communities is, in the case of an ecologist, an ecological survey. This is by no means just a matter of registration and enumeration. It is not a static task but an exciting study of processes in nature.

CHAPTER 2

Ecological Survey

THE FIRST SURVEY of a great ecological system was that done by François Forel on Lac Leman (usually marked on our maps as the Lake of Geneva) in the later years of the nineteenth century.[162] The author recalls how as a boy his interest first became riveted upon the lake when his father showed him the sites of the famous Neolithic lake villages at Morges. This was thirty-seven years before the appearance of the first volume of his lucid three-volume monograph in 1892. The other two volumes came out in 1895 and 1904, the last containing the biological material. This whole project seems to have owed much of its strategic plan also to his father, to whom the book is dedicated. It was an enormous enterprise covering and linking together all the chief aspects of a very large lake that could be studied at that period. Starting from the geography, geology and glaciology, the wind-generated waves and the surface circulation, and the turn-over of water brought about by vertical temperature changes in spring and autumn, he passes on by way of vegetation and the microplankton to the invertebrate life at various depths from shallow water right down to the deepest zone below the limit of light. Finally there are disquisitions upon human history, fish and fisheries, the types of vessels used on the lake, and even a census of the swan population.

Far from being just an interesting encyclopaedic medley of information such as Humboldt might have produced a century before, this scholarly book presents a broad account of how the different features of a big lake are integrated into a whole working system, in which the flora and fauna form part of the network of channels for matter and energy. No one has since attempted anything quite so comprehensive, though naturally this field of ecology has extended vastly with the later researches of limnologists into all kinds of special problems. There is something educated and free from dogma in Forel's treatment that one misses in many monographs of the present day. His viewpoint is summarized in the following passage (Vol. 3, 1904): 'Ce que je vois de plus admirable quand je contemple la nature, c'est sa simplicité. Au premier abord tout paraît compliqué; a l'étude tout s'ordonne et s'unifié.' Elsewhere he remarks: 'C'est vers l'unité qu'elle tend.' But I am sure this unity of which he speaks was not a single severe abstraction, but rather a panoramic view of all the main processes going on in a lake that did not at the same time conceal the smaller complexities that are interwoven in them. It is refreshing to be told (in 1904) that the innumerable processes in a large lake can all be fitted into simple ideas of process and interchange, for if this is true (and it has been mostly borne out by later discoveries, perhaps especially well exemplified by the modern work of Ruttner[417]) we may hope to make the same true simplifications in terrestrial systems that still seem to us rather inchoate and endlessly ramifying. One example of Forel's ecological insight is the way he realized the dynamic interdependence of the plankton and the profundal, deep-water communities. Though neither has any species in common each plays an interlocking role in the circulation of organic matter in the lake, in turn dependent upon the thermal circulation and the action of surface winds, themselves functions of the climate and topography of the lake basin. These are the ABC of modern hydrobiologists, but were not common notions in the nineteenth century.

The next attempt at a comprehensive study of a large ecosystem was C. G. J. Petersen's survey of marine life of the Danish coasts and inland salt fjords. His investigations started with the dredging of shallow waters in 1883-7, early essays in the tagging of flatfish and many other aspects of fisheries research, and the invention in 1896 of a primitive bottom-sampler attached to a long pole. By the year 1908 he was able to undertake his first general quantitative survey of animal communities on the sea-bottom, which culminated in the first of a series of great monographs in 1911.[383] This first survey was done in collaboration with Boysen Jensen, who was mainly responsible for the study of suspended organic matter; while Petersen handled the sampling of the bottom fauna, now with the famous Petersen Grab, a dredge which enabled a tenth of a square metre of the sea-bottom to be cut out and hauled up together with all the slower-moving animals living in it. Censuses were made at many points on the coast but there is special interest attached to those in the Limfjord – a series of shallow salt-water lakes and channels in Jutland that are almost land-locked, though communicating with the sea on either coast. Here the chief zones of life are the water, the eel-grass (*Zostera*) beds in the shallow water down to four or five metres, and the bottom deposits composed of a few millimetres of brown partly organic fluff overlying black methane-producing mud. This fluffy layer was thought to come chiefly from the decay of the eel-grass in the zone above, a conclusion later substantiated more fully by Boysen Jensen.[247] The richness of this source of organic material is indicated by Petersen's statement in 1918,[382] that *Zostera* on some 2000 nautical square miles of the Danish shallow coastal water was estimated to produce a total of about four times as much dry matter each year as all the field and meadow hay in Denmark.

Here already was a clear conception of the two great divisions of any ecological system, into that based directly upon green plants (in the sea, at any rate upon chlorophyll-producing plants, whatever their superficial colour), and the other division, whose resource is chiefly the decaying organic matter, usually plant but sometimes animal. The motive for this great survey was an economic interest in measuring the food resources available to fish, particularly plaice, but the execution of it meant a study of the whole of the marine communities. It was decided, however, that plankton did not play an important part in feeding the bottom-living animals, and so it was not much studied, being already pretty well known from earlier work. The eel-grass fauna was also collected, but not counted or weighed. The more recondite problems of the microflora and microfauna of the bottom were not explored at all. It seems likely that the accident that this great pioneer ecologist was primarily interested in fish as a crop for man led him to undertake an investigation of the food-chains leading up to them, and therefore to a study of whole communities. (Similarly Hardy[211] in the early 1920s worked out a parallel food-chain story for the herring and sea plankton in the North Sea.) But Petersen's ideas for carrying all this out were far ahead of his time, for he not only saw the need to survey the communities and try to find how they varied with the nature of the substratum, but he did this by a census of populations. He also comprehended very clearly some of the chief processes of flow and balance in the ecosystem as a whole, though perhaps not at this date stating them very formally – his general résumé published seven years later[382] does so more fully. For example, he perceived that *Zostera* had a double role as a food resource for animals: a small direct effect upon animals attached to it (these being mostly a summer outburst chiefly of small molluscs browsing upon the 'fur' of epiphytic algae using the eel-grass as a support); and a larger and far more important one in the form of organic debris or 'litter' for the bottom animals to eat. Further, it was not enough to count and weigh animals: 'In order to carry the principle of metabolism as far as possible, we must also endeavour to understand, on what materials and what quantities this bottom-fauna is nourished' – that is find out how to convert the censuses and the biomass into a changing rate of productivity, eventually in physiological as well as ecological terms. Oh rare ecologist, who could perceive all this in 1911! A colleague of Petersen's, H. Blegvad,[32] continued these censuses of bottom animals and compared them also with estimates of fish populations in Limfjord and various other places. In the quiet 'backwater' of Thisted Bredning in Limfjord, where the original ecological surveys had been done, annual measurements were made from 1910 to 1924, and these revealed extraordinary fluctuations in the biomass of the bottom fauna, principally but not only in the smaller species of bivalve molluscs. This extended Petersen's picture of communities into another dimension.

In 1949 A. C. Hardy[212] made an illuminating comparison between the history of research in marine ecology and that on land communities. He suggested that the earlier development of the former could be explained mainly by the pressure of interest in marine fisheries and the large resources available for research into their whole environment. And he stressed some of the intrinsic difficulties of studying the hidden and mobile world below the surface, remarking: 'What would the land ecologist say if his woods and meadows changed position overnight?' But it needs to be added that the variety and complexity of habitat structures is far greater on land than in the sea (or in fresh-water), also the number of species of animals living together is much higher. We could justifiably ask: 'What would the marine ecologist say if he had to study a wood in which one small stream had more species of animals living in it than on the whole of the Dogger Bank; or a meadow in whose litter and soil there were more species than in the North Sea's plankton?'

About the same time that Petersen's surveys were being assembled Victor Shelford was putting together his information about *Animal communities in temperate America as illustrated in the Chicago region: a study in animal ecology*, published in 1913.[439] This was the first synoptic description of communities in the temperate forest belt, near a large lake, and the first systematic attempt to codify terrestrial animal communities at all. As a reconnaissance, a deliberate attempt to knit a mass of fragmentary separate details into a single picture with some fifty component communities, it was a fine pioneer feat. As he remarks: 'Though man is a land inhabitant, all the best work along these and many other lines has been done upon aquatic animals.' And it is fascinating to find Petersen in a 1918 footnote,[382] making much the same remark from the other end: 'It might perhaps seem more natural to compare the fauna of the sea bottom with the fauna upon land; as a matter of fact, however, strange as it may seem, there does not exist any survey of animal communities on land based on quantitative investigations of the commoner species.' Shelford did not count animals, and indeed remarked of his own survey that 'the quantity of life has been little studied. While it is evident that some habitats have more animals than others, we have no exact data.' Although much has been done to mend this situation in recent times, the statement could still stand for much of our knowledge of forest life in any part of the world – communities which are undoubtedly among the richest and most complex on earth. It is less to be wondered at when it is realized that Shelford's survey ranged over such a wide series of habitats: streams and rivers; ponds and lakes with their marginal zones of marsh and shore and bog; grassland; and a dozen kinds of scrub and woodland. Here and there some extra habitats like logs and carrion are also noticed. The details about each community are rather meagre and patchy. Nevertheless the plan is a clear and grand one, and the examples are often very interesting, indeed the text bears the stamp of good teaching material rather than of sustained research. These descriptions are an early example of the American tradition of ecological writing, staccato and non-conjunctive.

One may wonder why Forel's studies gave rise to a whole sub-science in ecology, that of limnology (a name he invented himself), and Petersen laid the groundwork for later investigations of fish populations and marine productivity, while Shelford's survey on the other hand seems to have remained somewhat stranded, away from the intellectual stream. I think the probable reason for this is an important one, which has a sharp bearing on ideas about ecological survey. Shelford certainly saw that terrestrial and aquatic communities are organized into food-chains and what Thienemann later called consumer layers. Not unnaturally, for that time, he also supposed that this structure of the community provided also the ordinary checks on numbers – a Darwinian concept. He also knew that there could be abrupt changes in numbers, but explained these solely by external shocks from the weather, with consequential repercussions through the food-chains. We were, after all, still enveloped in these notions in the early 1920s. They imply states of dynamic balance and recovery in the community, as do his excellent observations upon ecological succession. Nevertheless Shelford had a mainly physiological view that concentrated more on the limitations of habitat for species than upon any intrinsic properties of the species network, that is, ideas about tolerance limits and behaviour rather than about populations, interchange and flow. 'If we knew', he wrote, 'the physiological life histories of a majority of animals, most other ecological problems would be easy of solution.' This dream has certainly not been realized yet! Again, 'Ecology is that branch of general physiology which deals with the organism as a whole' or 'an ecological classification is a classification upon a physiological basis'. And with this emphasis upon the restriction of species to their narrower ecological zones, he immediately ran against the difficulty of dealing with species that move about frequently from one zone to another.

I have dealt rather closely with Shelford's ideas, partly because his work had the enormous merit of trying to see a very large and complicated bit of landscape as a whole, with its plant and animal communities arranged in the order of ecological succession; partly also because it had at first a great influence upon my own ideas as to what an ecological survey is for and about. Although my own early drive towards community ecology at the age of seventeen was a personal and internal one, it was set alight for several years by Shelford's book, which I actually carried with me in my knapsack in the course of an Oxford expedition to Spitsbergen in 1921 that I was fortunate enough to be able to accompany. It was partly to try and apply Shelford's method of treatment to the Arctic that I undertook a survey of the barrens of Bear Island and parts of West Spitsbergen and a smaller island called Prince Charles Foreland (all now contained in the Viking name of Svalbard), with the collaboration in the field of Victor Summerhayes, botanist to the expedition. This was one of the earliest joint surveys of the kind, and although at that date it was still inevitably dominated by the excellent classifications of plant ecologists, and, as mentioned above, by the methods of Shelford, it enabled some useful harmonization of the associations of plants and animals to be achieved, and some older concepts to be looked at afresh. In 1923 and again in 1924, I accompanied the Oxford expeditions to Spitsbergen led by George Binney which not only explored the main island but also the extremely barren and at that time rather inaccessible islands to the north of it, within Lat. 80° and 81° N., and in regions where the polar ice-pack frequently pushes right against the land even in summer. During these two expeditions I undertook the whole of the ecological survey, both of vegetation and of animals, as well as investigating some of the curious physiographical patterns of frost-shattered rocks and soils. Summerhayes undertook all the subsequent work at home upon the plants. From this three-summer survey a fairly clear picture of the patterns of communities emerged,[489, 490] the chief omission being the extraction from litter and soils of the rich microfauna of microscopic mites and springtails, discovered (at any rate in other Arctic lands like Greenland and Canada) by Marie Hammer twenty years later.[205]

The Spitsbergen archipelago, about the size of England and Wales, lies on the northern continental shelf of Europe, yet is like an oceanic island, having apparently received most of its animal life, and probably many of its plants, by accidental immigration across the sea (or even, as with reindeer, sometimes across the frozen winter sea),[231] previous glaciation having erased most of the flora and fauna. This isolation has, for example, prevented two important northern animals, the lemming and the Arctic hare, from arriving at all. A magnificent instance of accidental immigration by air, though quite unsuccessful as a piece of colonization, was observed by Binney's three sledge parties on North-East Land in August 1924, when a vast swarm of aphids and hover-flies was blown some 800 miles from the spruce forest of northern Europe across the Barents Sea on to the frozen centre of the island.[123] Therefore, to the ecological poverty of the High Arctic brought about by a very severe climate and barren soils, has been added the limitation due to geographical isolation, and these two things together make the animal communities very simple indeed. The vegetation does reach a respectable mixture of species in some places, albeit highly tenanted by lichens and mosses, and not in closed community except where birds from the sea have manured the ground, or the climate (as in the heart of the longer fjords) is relatively sunny. This poverty in species made it possible to carry out a fairly good primary ecological survey in spite of the inaccessible nature of much of the country, where one might be lucky to reach some spot and yet have to leave it within a few hours. The comparison of a large number of different localities was, however, helped by the fact that most of the inland mountain and plateau country has a permanent covering of ice and snow, so that one was dealing mostly with a narrower coastal fringe on which this sparse life had been able to establish itself.

Even after the first summer's work it had begun to dawn upon me that merely to look for zonal species, the indicators or 'characteristic' species of each community, was really to put nature into a physiological strait-jacket, and to leave out most of the really important processes at work in an ecosystem. In fact, such restricted species are often rather the specialized ones, valuable enough to the biologist for that reason – especially if his main interest is in the evolution of adaptation – but not necessarily the most important parts of the ecological system they are living in, not the main cogs in the *heavy machinery* of the place. It is not entirely easy to recall in retrospect the exact development of one's ideas forty years before, but I think it was above all the extraordinary, often dramatic, influence of Arctic sea-birds upon the plant growth around or below their nesting sites on cliff scree and tundra that first brought home this idea. As everyone knows, the poverty of terrestrial life in the High Arctic contrasts with the almost fabulous richness of marine pelagic life based on phytoplankton growth in the continuous daylight of summer and the abundance of mineral nutrients washed off the land or brought by upwelling currents. The sea-birds, themselves innumerable, feed on the pelagic crustacea and fish, a few also indirectly by harvesting the labours of other birds. In the Subarctic of northern Norway one can see plenty of green vegetation on the hills, in Spitsbergen the ordinary tundra is dull and brownish in colour; but where sea-birds have come to nest its greenness matches that of Norway, as can be tested by means of a standard colour chart. At these sea-bird colonies, especially at the base of any cliffs occupied by guillemots or puffins, there will be seen not only green grass and surprising natural gardens of flowers like white saxifrage and scurvy-grass, but often a luxuriant growth of them. Here at a glance one could visualize the whole chain of transfer from the diatoms of the phytoplankton, passing through the zooplankton chain, to birds feeding principally on crustacea or fish, to the enrichment of terrestrial vegetation with the nutrients from bird guano, and even to the greater richness of invertebrate life in the meadow or turf so formed. And this could even happen in an otherwise barren countryside of frost-shattered surface rocks carrying only scattered flowering plants – in the most sterile landscapes of all, only scattered plants of the pale yellow Arctic poppy.

From the observations of a later Oxford expedition in 1933, we can get a notion of the enormous volume of this traffic from sea to land during the 24-hour daylight of the Arctic summer with its almost continual activity of sea-birds round the clock. At the head of Icefjord, a long fjord on West Spitsbergen, lies the Nordenskiold Glacier, with a two-mile front coming down to the sea in Klaas Billen Bay and continually breaking off in icebergs and brash. Close under these active ice-cliffs was noticed a concentrated flock of sea-birds, chiefly kittiwake gulls, *Rissa tridactyla*, but also many fulmar petrels, *Fulmarus glacialis*, both of which pick their food out of the top inch or two of water. They were assembled in a brown-coloured patch about fifty yards wide near the centre of the glacier. This marked an upwelling of plankton species usually found at greater depths and so provided a convenient place for studying and measuring the feeding of the birds. Such local vertical circulation by a glacier face, though not entirely understood, seems to be brought about partly by the fresh-water glacier stream entering the sea,[484] and also (as later work on a similar spot in West Greenland has suggested) by the melting ice moving away from the glacier face.[214] Anyway, it makes available a rich source of marine food usually inaccessible to surface-feeding birds though not to diving species like guillemots and puffins. The plankton here contained among other animals great numbers of a species of Euphausiid crustacean, *Thysanoessa inermis*, that was the chief food of the birds. This Euphausiid itself lives upon smaller crustacea such as copepods, which feed on diatoms, the main plant source in Arctic phytoplankton. Hartley and Fisher[215] set out to try and calculate how many *Thysanoessa* were being removed every day from this one patch of ice-strewn sea by the kittiwakes, of which there were one or two thousand present at any one time, journeying from the nearest large colonies about thirty miles away. These gulls made altogether over 15,000 visits per 24-hour day, each bird on the average probably eating about 370 *Thysanoessa* at a meal – a total removal of over five and a half million a day by this kind of bird alone. This is only the work of one species at one place. By the end of a glacier in another large fjord, Wijde Bay, the same observers found an upwelling containing huge numbers of a planktonic amphipod, *Themisto libellula*, also attended by a large crowd of kittiwakes and fulmars. But there are similarly great flows of material from the sea to vast guillemot colonies and to smaller ones of puffins, little auks and other sea-birds.

This interlocking of species across the boundaries of even the main habitats was especially easy to see in Spitsbergen, but in later years one came across it also everywhere in British communities, and many examples will be given in this book. For example, in Wytham Woods no single kind of mammal is entirely confined to one of the component habitats of the kind that Shelford would have used, or that we ourselves now use. Even the water shrew, *Neomys fodiens*, will live successfully far from water. The mole, *Talpa europaea*, moves equally in the soils of pasture and woodland, and when pressed can swim quite well. The vole *Microtus agrestis*, occupies open grassland, but is also well established in glades and along the woodland edge, and can travel far through the thick woods themselves. These animals are all specialists in their own way, but not confined within any one narrow physiological tolerance limit or habitat boundary. This situation applies no less to many invertebrates, a common example being the large earthworm *Lumbricus terrestris*, main food of the mole, for it inhabits a wide variety of soils in grassland, scrub and deciduous woodland. There are of course also species with relatively restricted habitat that are important in the ecological machinery. Such is the small stag-beetle, *Sinodendron cylindricum*, whose larvae are among the commonest tunnel-makers in rotting wood. Yet this species may be found in conifer as well as deciduous wood, and at all heights from the ground up to the canopy.

Another universal property of the animal species network could also be seen very easily in the Arctic. Because of the general scarcity in the Arctic of food for predatory birds and mammals, most of them range across a wide variety of different habitats. Thus the purple sandpiper, *Erolia maritima*, would be seen feeding on different zones of the drier tundra, at the edge of freshwater lakes and ponds, and also along the seashore. The Arctic fox, *Alopex lagopus*, searches every place where food is available for it, and to which it can get, including the frozen sea-ice in winter, where it follows the polar bear for its leavings. It stands at the apex of the whole terrestrial ecological pyramid in the Arctic. In temperate communities also we find that a great many of the predators like birds, spiders, wasps, lacewings and centipedes may have quite wide habitat tolerance and so their populations help to link the whole species network into one system of production. The problem of ecological survey is therefore to trace these connections wherever they lead, at any rate to trace the quantitatively important ones, while at the same time defining the groupings of species into local communities living in different parts of the system.

It will easily be seen that the notions fostered by this experience of Arctic life were much more in the line of Forel and Petersen (whose work I did not read until some time later) than of Shelford: the expectation of finding a very untidy dynamic, mobile, changing picture in nature rather than a neat physiological arrangement; a world of rather unstable populations in an unstable environment, not a static arrangement of animals limited to habitats created chiefly by plants and vegetation with its special microclimates. Forel summed up his own outlook upon limnology as follows: 'La description de la terre n'est pas l'énumération et la description individuelles de chacune des catégories d'êtres et de choses qui se rencontre sur notre planète; c'est bien plutôt le tableau d'ensemble offert par la réunion de ces diverse catégories, par leurs rapports les unes avec les autres, par les réactions qu'elles reçoivent du milieu dans lequel elles sont plongées, et qu'elles produisent sur le milieu.'[162] But it was not until Alfred Lotka published his *Elements of Physical Biology* in 1925[301] that a general theory of ecological machinery containing physical ideas of energy transformation as well as ecological ideas of population process was available, and by one of the frequent flukes of scientific discovery, his work was seldom read by ecologists until quite recent years, except in connection with one important but special aspect concerned with fluctuations in numbers.

This condensed historical discussion has been concerned with four early attempts to describe the nature of whole ecosystems, and the vegetation and animals in their rightful place in them. They describe very different scenes: a Swiss lake, a Danish sea-fjord, some North American woods and waters, and the habitats of the High Arctic in Spitsbergen. There have been many other smaller ecological surveys, and it is not my purpose to trace their development here. Those of Forel, Petersen, Shelford and ourselves were chosen because of their strategic aim and scale, and to lead up to the ideas I have arrived at in later enterprises. But it should be remarked that the earlier impulse among ecologists towards a broad, integrated survey of some large ecosystem, with its animal populations, has generally slackened in favour of a lot of smaller investigations on a narrower scale – tactical studies becoming more popular than strategical ones. Yet any advance on a huge front like that of community ecology clearly needs both strategy and tactics, a context as well as a scatter of only slightly related sentences or paragraphs. I do not believe that the continued stockpiling of innumerable smaller facts and conclusions about life-histories, distribution, populations, habits, interrelations, habitats, productivity, energy flow and the rest, will automatically build up a balanced picture of nature as a piece of inorganic and organic machinery; any more than the piling up of stones taken out of a large quarry will by itself result in the planning and building of a city. But equally, it would be quite pointless to attempt an ecological survey without having a pretty good selection of information on all such topics to work with. There are already distinct signs that population studies done on one species or a small group of associated species (say a host and its parasites) fairly soon run into difficulties simply caused by the fact that none of these populations operate within a closed system of any kind. It is one of the tasks of an ecological survey to provide the strategic setting for population studies, which is why I largely turned again to the former after a long period engaged in research upon the latter.

These rather general statements lead up to a more formal analysis of the nature of ecological survey and some of the problems it presents. We can start with some quite generally agreed facts. All animal populations form a part of food-chains based upon living or dead organic matter – their resources. Fabre[147] put it more poetically when writing about the glow-worm: 'from the least to the greatest in the zoological progression, the stomach sways the world; the data supplied by food are the chief among all the documents of life.' The simplest food-chain would be one kind of animal with no enemies or parasites, living solely on one species of plant that had no other herbivores eating its tissues. These do exist in nature, though they are rather exceptional. There could also be a plant with no animals of any kind connected with it. These are also exceptional in nature, though under domestication we find a great many exotic plants living in this state because they have not yet got their native dependent animals with them. The gradual arrival of such animals and their establishment upon invading plant species is one of the fascinating phenomena of the present time.[133] Most green plants, except algae, mosses, ferns and horsetails, even when no animal attacks their tissues of leaf, stem or root, may have flowers that are visited by insects and fruits or seeds that are eaten by birds and other animals. But even the simplest situation – one plant with one insect, or the plant with no animals – is not really ecologically insulated from the rest of the community of species. The plant may, and probably does, compete for space with another species whose power of competition is partly affected by herbivorous animals. Experiments have proved[256] that even a moderate infestation of *Aphis fabae* on field beans can reduce the height of stem by a fifth, and the weight of the beans by over four-fifths; while the aftermath of myxomatosis (as well as earlier observations before it) has conclusively shown how decisive is the selective influence of the rabbit on our vegetation.[497] In some maritime plant communities, the ragwort, *Senecio jacobaea*, may only flower at all when rabbit pressure reduces the competitive power of other plants growing with it. But the rabbit does not live on ragwort. Again, every plant that dies contributes material that is a possible resource for animals, either directly or through the intermediate agency of bacteria or fungi. We can say that, for all practical purposes, no species can exist in an area without having some, usually many, relationships with others.

Most food-chains have more than one link, often as many as five or even more, composed of animals preying in turn on other species of animals, each starting from one of the food resources, ultimately plant. A great many animals, in addition, have more than one kind of food. Even at the herbivore level one has only to think of the common partridge, *Perdix perdix*, whose diet faithfully reflects the seasonal changes in such resources as grasses, flowers, insects, corn and various wild seeds[322] (Fig. 9, p. 137) or any bee exploiting the numerous supplies of pollen and honey in different flowers. Predators and parasites may also have several or many different sources of food, predators being especially polyphagous in this way. The tawny owl, *Strix aluco*, in Wytham Woods, whose digestive pellets were examined by Southern[463] harvests not only eleven species of mammals and at least fourteen kinds of birds, but also large numbers of earthworms, and several kinds of beetles. A male badger caught near Oxford in 1935 forcibly illustrates this point: it had in its stomach the feet and other remains of four hedgehogs, a family of very young rabbits from a nest, another young family of some small mammal, larvae and pupae from a nest of bumble bees and one beetle![321] The small Linyphiid spider, *Linyphia triangularis*, whose webs are common on brambles and other vegetation in woodland, were found by Turnbull[509] to catch over 150 sorts of insects, a great many of which were eaten by the spiders. Parasites often have numerous hosts, though there are also a great many that are specific. A survey of parasites of small mammals in a mixed wood near Oxford produced every variant from a roundworm entirely confined to one species of wood-mouse, to a common flea that came on every small rodent, and another that occurred both on the wood-mouse and the mole.[136]

Various terms have been coined for these food relationships, amongst which food-cycle and food-web are the commonest. The idea of a cycle of nutrients through the community has the advantage of conveying a somewhat more dynamic meaning than that of a web, which is a structure and not a process except while it is being made. Miller and I employed a rather wider term, *the species network*, to describe any part of the interlocking system of species.[137] It is designed to take care not only of food relationships, important though they are, but also of all sorts of other relationships that exist between species and contribute to the integration of communities. There may, for example, be competition for space itself, and many other kinds of competitive interference that do not cause death or any immediate transfer of energy and materials from one species to another. Conversely there exist a multitude of ways in which one kind of animal alters the structure of the habitat in ways that improve it for other species. These effects range all the way from historical damage to a tree by insects or mammals resulting in its premature fall and the development of a log community, to rather closely knit arrangements amounting to adaptive symbiosis. The species network is the organic part of the 'world engine' so vividly described by Lotka:[301] 'The picture presented to our minds is that of a gigantic overshot mill wheel, receiving from above the stream of sunlight with its two hundred twenty-seven million gross horsepower – though much of this is spilt without effect – and discharging below its dissipated energy in the form of heat at the general temperature level. . . . But in detail the engine is infinitely complex, and the main cycle contains within itself a maze of subsidiary cycles.'

The interspersed mixture of species that forms the network has some curious properties of its own that can only be mentioned here in passing. One is that a relationship within it does not necessarily imply simultaneous activity of two species or even their coexistence. The nest of a summer migrant bird, for example, is a structure that can be colonized by animals that inhabit old nest debris, and the bird that made it may never re-visit it. A rabbit population may have died out ten years before, but leave innumerable scars and changes behind. The case of the falling tree was mentioned above. Indeed, the essence of most ecological succession is that groups of species happen to prepare the way for others by altering the habitat. A second remarkable property of the species network as such is its capacity (also explored mathematically by Lotka, among others) to generate fluctuations in numbers, quite independently of any external disturbances like weather or catastrophe. We know of two ways in which this can happen: the fluctuations can be self-generated in one species and cause ripples along the network; and there

1. Patterned landscape of the upper valley of the R. Wye, Monmouthshire, seen from the Black Mountains escarpment; with recurrent components of pasture, cornfield, hedge, wood, bracken slope with scattered shrubs, and cottages. (Photo C. S. E. 1 Sept. 1955)

2. The four Terrestrial formation-types: Open Ground (grazed by sheep and rabbits, and with a pattern of ant mounds), bracken Field Type, elder Scrub and ash Wood. Midsummer Hill, Malverns, Herefordshire. (Photo C. S. E. 4 Sept. 1955)

3. Terrestrial formation-types (in heavy frost): *Brachypodium pinnatum* grassland with dead scattered *Pastinaca sativa*, calcareous scrub and young birches, and oak–ash–sycamore–beech wood. Rough Common, Wytham Woods. (Photo C. S. E. 19 Dec. 1961)

4. Zonation from sea to land, St Bride's Haven, Pembrokeshire. Red Devonian sandstone forms the intertidal zone, and also a terrestrial maritime cliff top and slope that is not cultivated. (Photo C. S. E. 27 Aug. 1950)

5. Aerial view of Windermere and the pattern of country around and behind it. (Photo C. H. Wood)

6. Aerial view of Wytham North Hill (looking south-west), with deciduous woodland and scrub surrounded by farmland. Most of the woodland is oak–ash–sycamore, except for conifers in right centre and beeches in left upper centre. (Photo Hunting Surveys. 30 April 1960)

7. Aerial view of Wytham North Hill (looking north-east). The original Great Wood upper left; new forest plantings right centre; limestone grassland in centre; English elms in hedgerow in foreground. (Photo Hunting Surveys. 30 April 1960)

8. An elementary exercise for zoologists: in this aerial view of the country between Cassington (Oxfordshire) and Wytham Woods (lower r. hand corner) there are at least 105 of the habitat components analysed in Ch. 4. (Photo Hunting Surveys. 30 April 1960)

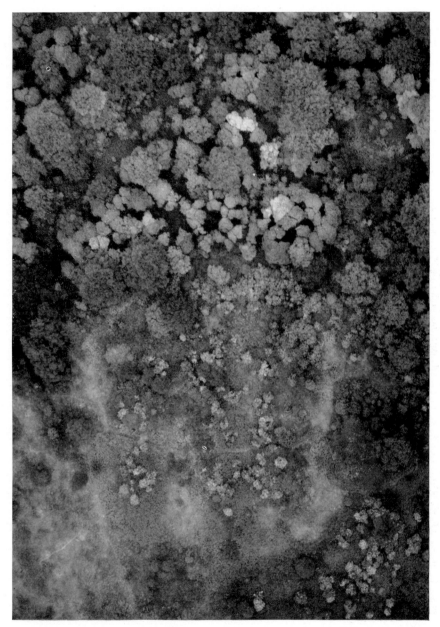

9. Aerial view of four Terrestrial Formation-types on Wytham Hill, from deciduous woodland; through scrub of hawthorn, elder (in flower), etc.; limestone grassland, bracken and bramble; to open ground. (Photo Dr J. K. S. St Joseph. 9 June 1961)

10. Aerial view of the pattern of oak–ash–sycamore woodland in Wytham Woods (mapped in Fig. 20, p. 195). The large glades are mostly of bracken, with bramble. (Photo Dr J. K. S. St Joseph 9 June 1961)

can be an interplay of populations between predator and prey or parasite and host affecting oscillations in numbers.

It is such considerations about the species network that enable us to say that *the ultimate goal of an ecological survey should be to discover and measure the main dynamic relations between all populations of organisms living on an area over some period of time.* 'An ecological survey is not just a catalogue of the biological properties of individual species or a list of species, or a series of censuses. It is, or is heading towards, a synthesis that will describe not only the parts of a complex system but the interaction and balance between them, and the dynamic properties of the system as a whole.'[137] This definition implies of course that all the different habitats and natural resources must be mapped out and classified, so that the pattern of the different centres of action can be recognized. It is here that one begins to notice the great apparent difference between surveys of the sea and large lakes on the one hand, and those of terrestrial communities, which are subject to much more intense patterning of relatively small zones and patches, interspersed and repeated. Though such patterning on a relatively small scale is by no means absent from the great aquatic systems, for instance on intertidal rocky shores, it is on dry land that it reaches its climax of complication. It may strike the reader that it is easier to put out lofty-sounding aims of this kind than to carry them out usefully in fact. Certainly it would be wrong not to face the grave difficulties of drawing up a blue-print for the interwoven lives of several thousand species of animals – for that is the scale of complexity we often encounter even on a square mile or two of any mixed ecosystem on land. Nevertheless, after working continuously on the problem for the last twenty years, I am satisfied that there are useful, practical and effective methods of developing ecological survey on this level. But to carry them out certain conditions must be satisfied, which at this point will only be mentioned briefly, since they are expanded or exemplified in later chapters.

Apart from the special methods of assembling and indexing information about animal communities on this scale, which are summarized in Ch. 5, there are five main practical requirements to be met. The first is an agreed method for *classification of habitats*, simple enough to be used by the ordinary ecologist or naturalist, yet at the same time specifying all the essential kinds of community. Above all, these components of the total pattern must so far as possible correspond to realities in nature, to more or less integrated animal communities. As this topic is dealt with in Ch. 4, it need only be said here that the main criteria are visible or otherwise clearly detectable discontinuities, usually shown by the habitat structure. Such structural boundaries are not only convenient to the ecological surveyor who wishes for research purposes to break down a big system into its component parts, but they also have a great deal of ecological significance to the animals themselves, for example in marking the changes in food resources or cover. But it is necessary also to put in a few arbitrary boundaries particularly for some of the vertical zones. This standard classification keeps in mind two aspects of the relations of the component parts: those within each smaller habitat (relations between species and their physical surroundings, and between each other), and those between different component habitats. The latter category, which is in a way the king-pin in the philosophy of ecological survey, especially on this larger scale, comprises two different classes of event: the migration of members of a species from one locus to another of a similar sort, e.g. log to log, tree to tree, pond to pond; and their movement from the original habitat to a quite different one, e.g. log to flowering shrub, tree canopy to ground, pond to stream – or an extreme case such as the spotted flycatcher, *Muscicapa striata*, coming from the thorn-bush savannahs of Africa to take up summer nesting quarters in this country on the edge of a wood or the porch of a house.

The second consideration is that of *ecological importance*, a concept by means of which it is often possible to pick out certain main events and processes and (for the moment) ignore the rest. Thus one can take earthworms as being master workers and incorporators of dying vegetation in the soil. Perhaps among them will be one or two species larger, stronger and more abundant than the rest. Or some grazing animal, or a dominant canopy-feeding caterpillar, that deeply affects the whole structure of the vegetation, and therefore of many animals. But this method of simplification is far less straightforward than it looks. It might seem the obvious thing to omit all the 'less important' species and concentrate upon the 'important' ones; yet if this process of selection (normal and respectable in science) is applied too heartily to the animal community, the investigator is apt to find himself left with only the ghost of the whole animal community he started to survey, which is after all doing something rather different than was originally intended.

The third and fourth requirements are *time* and *continuity*. There are many scientific tasks that can be speeded up just by putting more research labour into them. Field surveys of communities are not among these. A great many of the processes one is trying to study operate slowly (ecological succession over the years, recovery from some local disaster, fluctuations in numbers of animals). The largely hidden lives of so many animals and the difficulty of knowing all their habitats – even their ordinary food, the vagaries of their activities and the time of appearance of the adult stages (which are often the only clue to the species) according to the weather, and the sheer number of species to be known – make the work slow and to a certain extent dependent upon unplanned opportunities, amongst which are the season and years of abundance, suitable weather, and even the availability of research people with particular flairs for some part of the subject. *Continuity* implies a permanent organization to keep track of the survey, guide it and continuously adjust its outlook and methods to new discoveries. But above all it needs a suitable protected area for the work.

The ideal *place* for a long-term ecological survey on land can, from our experience, be defined fairly well. It should have some of the attributes of wild country, though no one expects to find all of them in our battered island, except in land that is too far from any active centre of learning to be much use in this way. It must be fairly large, because we want a variety of habitats and as big a pool of species as possible, and because it must stand up to really tough erosion from the field ecologists themselves, who usually find it necessary to carry away quite sizeable chunks of the habitat, and certainly quite large fractions of some of the populations! I think one or two square miles is a good size, which gives some opportunities for setting aside areas for experimental alteration of the habitat, as well as studying the existing ones. The choice of an area near Oxford was settled by a great piece of good fortune that came to the University in 1942, with the acquisition from the owner, the late Col. Raymond ffennel, of a large part of Wytham Hill with its surrounding farmlands. Here was a magnificent opportunity to study the whole range of habitats from grasslands to deciduous woodland, from springs to a river with its connected smaller channels, from damp ground to ponds and marshes, with plenty of logs and other small special habitats, and some remarkable differences of soil structure and topography. At that time the implications of such an enterprise still had to be fully comprehended and worked out, but field work began in 1943, with some important population studies of vertebrates by H. N. Southern. My first serious reconnaissance was on 17 April of that year. In general terms, I had thought of the scheme as 'a multiple correlation apparatus for assembling and handling ecological data on a large scale by uniform methods'. These methods were finally streamlined and standardized in 1953, when R. S. Miller and I (with the help of Miss Brenda Macpherson (now Mrs Sladen)) crystallized the habitat classification and designed a punch-card for permanent use, after a solid year of discussions and fertile arguments ranging from general theories of population down to such topics as the meaning of a habitat 'edge', and of 'community' when the participant species are scattered in small separate centres of action. The survey was planned to collect information at three separate levels. First of all, the published information about species in Britain, fortified by a good deal of European work. Secondly, information (mainly from published work) about the fauna of the three-county block (Oxfordshire, Berkshire and Buckinghamshire) in the approximate centre of which Oxford lies. It was thought that if any species was present in this area of 2095 square miles, there was at any rate a chance that it might turn up in or near Wytham Hill, and if it was not already in these counties such occurrence was rather unlikely. Thirdly, the survey in Wytham itself, mostly focused on the hill, but with an eye on later study of the surrounding

43

farmlands and river system. On this square mile or two of country an enormous concentration of ecological effort has taken place during the last twenty years, nearly all of it independent individual research by different members of the University, though with much friendly cooperation between them. Already more is known about the ecology of its animals than of any other bit of land in the world.

CHAPTER 3

Wytham Hill

JUST BEFORE it flows through Oxford, the River Thames makes a great loop to the north, east and then south, running in a wide alluvial valley that still gets partly flooded in winter. In this shepherd's crook of river lie two hills closely connected by a col and shaped rather like a twisted figure of eight, rising about 300 feet above the river level. These are part of the ring of hills that surrounds the basin in which the City of Oxford lies. Inside the river loop the University now possesses 3400 acres of land – or a little over five square miles – of which the wooded part of the hills themselves with some enclaves of park and arable fields form about a third (Frontispiece and Plates 6 and 7). The northern one is Wytham Hill, the southern one Seacourt Hill; but I shall refer to the whole block that runs two and a half miles from north-west to south-east as Wytham Hill, as indeed is general practice nowadays except among geologists. (Seacourt was a medieval village that was formerly at the terminus of a pilgrims' route to a holy well near Binsey[329] but deserted by 1439, even its foundations being now obliterated by a new road, and its name only in general use for a small channel of the Thames network running nearby – the Seacourt Stream.) The slopes and tops of the hill have nearly a thousand acres of scrub and woodland, which once formed part of the larger Cumnor Wood, then owned by the great Abbey of Abingdon, but passing into the hands of private estate owners by the time of the Reformation, except for a number of small freeholdings most of which in turn were swallowed up by the enclosures of the eighteenth and nineteenth centuries.[194]

Any place that has some of the qualities of an island seems to attract one as an ecologist, and this wooded hill set in a ring of farmland, itself bounded on three sides by river, has some of the ecological integrity of an island, and at the same time a really rich variety of habitats and a profusion of species that most islands lack. The village of Wytham, still retaining its external traditional character, derives its name from 'Wihtham', an Anglo-Saxon word found in records of the year 957, and meaning according to Ekblaw[121] 'the ham in the bend'. Here, as elsewhere in Britain, we have an area of land and water whose ecological character is a blend of the absolute possibilities of locality, rocks, soils, climate, wild flora and fauna, with more than a thousand years of mostly unrecorded history of

45

exploitation by man and his domestic animals. Gradually also there has been added the impact of foreign species introduced to Britain such as the pheasant (Roman), the rabbit (Norman), the sycamore (Tudor onwards), the oak marble gall and the American grey squirrel (nineteenth century). By no stretch of the imagination can Wytham Hill be called an entirely natural ecosystem: its rocks quarried for road metal, its timber selectively cut down or pollarded, its oak bark taken for tanning, its dead wood gathered for fuel, its glades cattle-grazed, its predatory animals and birds shot to protect game, some parts deforested for crop lands or heavily scarred by recent forestry fellings and plantings, some old fields allowed to grow back into woodland, the river below controlled since the reign of James I by locks[69] and nowadays artificially stocked with fish (many of which the angler throws back after catching them), its springs piped for water supplies or dammed to make ponds to attract wild-fowl – and its habitats now studied and sometimes modified by ecologists.

This hill might therefore seem a singularly unsuitable place on which to investigate the full-scale workings of nature. Yet a piece of English country that has been exploited by the relatively light pressures of earlier centuries, greatly modifying but never quite destroying the whole range of habitats, still has an extraordinary power of ecological recuperation. Nature resurgent after its exploitation by man can become an active dynamo of ecological process and interaction: vegetation clothing the ground in turn with grassland, scrub and woodland, the filling out of thinned canopy, the accumulation of decaying matter with its exceptionally rich fungal and animal communities, the development of all the intricate natural patterns of species, and the infiltration once more of fresh arrivals from foci of survival in the surrounding countryside. All this can happen if the chance is given to it, and if exploitation has not passed too far into urbanization, or the ruthless uniformity and over-simplification of modern crops and forests, in which many of the dominant plants are not native species and management increasingly attempts the methods of an open-air mass-production factory. In Wytham Woods, the central part of this estate, nearly all the processes of interference mentioned in the examples above have ceased by now, or have become stabilized or are contained within quite circumscribed areas of the hill. In other words there still remains the natural variety, with the modifications imposed by history.

Wytham Hill is not in the very centre of England, yet it is not far from it. The centre, if that term has a meaning in an island so irregularly shaped as Britain, lies some forty miles to the northwards, not far from Shakespeare's country, on the unimpressive low agricultural uplands on which a good many of our rivers have their head-waters. But in all directions Oxford is at least sixty miles from any sea-coast or mountain. It is one of the great inland cross-roads of England – the old coach road from London to Gloucester crossed over the top of Wytham Hill and was in use until the second half of the eighteenth century. Geologically Wytham lies in the middle of a great belt of calcareous Mesozoic strata fifty to a hundred miles wide, stretching from Dorset to the Wash, and north from Lincolnshire into Yorkshire, and containing many alternating rocks of chalk or limestone, with clays and sands as well. Wytham itself is situated between the chalk downlands some fifteen miles to the south, and the Great Oolite plateau of the Cotswold Hills. There is a little capping of thin glacial drift, for the greatest extension of the Pleistocene ice seems to have been only a few miles north of here. These gravelly clays must have come from glacial outwash, and sometimes consist of no more than a scattering of well-worn rounded quartzite pebbles derived from the Trias of north-west England.

The main top of the hill is a beautiful coral reef, part of the Upper Corallian strata. This reef of 'Coral Rag' is partly still *in situ* stratigraphically, a fragment of a raised tropical fringing reef that has been traced for fifty miles down into Wiltshire. Its surface, packed with fossils, is visible in many places, and W. J. Arkell, who has done more than anyone to elucidate the geological structure of the hill,[10] made an interesting comparison between the animal communities of such Jurassic reefs and those surviving in the Red Sea at the present day.[9] Below it, but exposed only in a quarry bottom, is another kind of limestone made from small fragments of the reef re-sorted by sea currents. The soil that develops on the rubbly Coral Rag surface is poor and shallow, except where the glacial vestiges have combined to make richer pockets. Every stage in the colonization of bare soil onwards can be seen on the top: a magnificent pattern of bare ground, ungrazed meadows, scrub and deciduous woodland. The limestone meadow flora is especially rich and attractive, and has many affinities with the chalk grassland so much studied by botanists in past decades and now made scarce by the ploughing up of downland pastures. Below these limestone beds is a thinner stratum of tawny sand, the Calcareous Grit, overlying a deep solid base of Oxford Clay, also calcareous, and notable for the abundance of a massive fossil oyster of the genus *Gryphaea*. The sand beds are the headquarters for the badger and fox, and formerly were also for the rabbit.

The arrangement and nature of these three geological strata have resulted in three very important secondary features. First of all, the porous upper layers absorb the rain, and where the sand and clay meet a wonderful variety of springs, seepages and flushes are found all round the middle of the hill, mostly at 300-400 feet. So while the top is fairly dry (soon recovering after even torrential rains), and in some years can become drought-stricken, the lower region has abundant streams and marshes, and a few ponds also that have been made in the past by damming the streams, which flow down eventually to the Thames, itself an intricate maze of river loops, side channels and ditches. Some of the small springs and streams run through open pastures and others through thick woods, this providing a further facet of variety in the fauna. The reservoir of water inside the hill must be large, for some of the springs have never been known to dry up in the last twenty years. A second consequence of the geological structure has been the washing out and down by these springs of a good deal of the sand itself, to which Arkell[10, 11] attributed the extraordinary displacement of huge rafts of the top coral reef, which have slipped down to form a cambered or tortoise-shaped hilltop

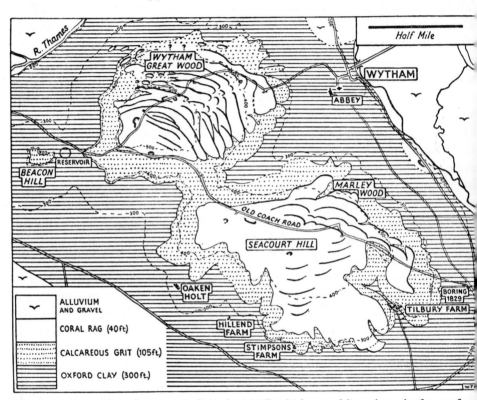

FIG. I. The geological structure of Wytham Hill. Thick curved lines show the fronts of limestone ridges. The main contour of springs and flushes occurs between the sand (stippled) and the clay below. (From W. J. Arkell, 1947)

with a series of broken-off terrace shelves on the sides (Fig. 1). A third effect of all this is that the local soil conditions can be pretty complex, with mixtures of weathered glacial clay, limestone, sands, sands mixed with clay, and the tough clay itself. (Some of the sands are leached of their calcium.) The base of the hill is buried in alluvial deposits of silt and gravel brought by the river. But the main stratification, like an enormous cake with an original icing of glacial drift and a soft 'cream layer' of sand in the middle, dominates the ecosystem. This whole structure dips down to the south-east.

Within the University estate at Wytham the ecological survey has drawn nearly all its material from the wooded, grassy, marshy and spring-fed hill, only so far receiving a scatter of information from the agricultural land and the river system covering the lower ground. Very roughly therefore, the main results come from about two square miles of land. Our 'wilderness', the bits of land set aside for scientific reserves immune from ordinary estate management (though not from all ecological management) strictly speaking covers only about 220 acres, the remaining woodland being under forestry management; but biologists have always been given the additional privilege by the University of working (albeit with less certainty of continuity in the habitat) on the whole of the hill. Under a revised general plan of management there is now assurance that Wytham Woods will be managed in perpetuity with the primary aims of keeping its natural beauty and encouraging ecological variety. To anyone from a big continental country a thousand acres may not sound a very large slice of land to take for a sample of the animal communities in Britain. The United States Forest Service recently created *within one of its existing forests* in Oregon a wilderness area of half a million acres! Nevertheless on this area of two square miles or so there are already known to be living, or at any rate to have been living at some time during the last sixty years, several thousand species of animals. At the date of writing (1964) we actually know of about 3800 species, and allowing for our ignorance still of a good many groups of animals and of certain communities (such as marshes, woodland soil, arable land, meadow vegetation and river) one can hardly believe that there are less than 5000 species altogether, and not improbably a good many more than that. For example, the tally of Diptera, Lepidoptera, Parasitic Hymenoptera and sawflies (Symphyta) is still quite low, and that of the internal parasites of animals almost nil. There is as yet no authoritative estimate for the total number of species of British land and freshwater animals, but it is certainly over 25,000 and rather unlikely ever to rise above 30,000. It can be seen that the estimated fauna of this calcareous south midland hill may be as much as a sixth or a fifth of the British fauna – on an area that is only 1/25,000 of England and 1/60,000 of the British Isles. Such high concentration of species is partly brought about by the exceptionally rich mixture of habitats found at Wytham, but it has been met with also in other small areas such as Wicken Fen, Windsor Forest and Spurn Head peninsula. It raises many questions both scientific and practical.

There are three important ecological systems that are not represented at all near Oxford: maritime, mountain and large lake. And the communities of acid soils such as heaths, moors and bogs are also almost lacking though they become quite common in south Berkshire. Allowing for these big lacunae, the Wytham fauna must contain quite a high percentage of the English animals likely to occur on inland calcareous lowland. Far from being a small sample of the national ecosystem, we find here an almost embarrassingly rich assembly of species, in a bit of landscape which, though beautiful and varied after the manner of the small-scale English scene, is not conspicuously so, and which for many years has carried the reputation among entomologists of lacking many of the really 'exciting' species of insects. A similar thought has been explored by A. H. Church[69] when glorifying the commonplace character of the flora immediately round Oxford: 'Of the British types of vegetation, that of the central plain of England is, again, the most inferior, in variety of forms, as of biological constituents. The local Oxford flora can show no heath-moors, alpine slopes, sand-dunes, shingle beaches or estuarine swamps, which have so attracted ecologists in other directions; it remains characteristically commonplace, sylvestral, agrestal, paludal, with no special developments in any direction, and with little to attract the visitor from other more favoured districts. Yet it is this very commonplace character which constitutes its greatest asset. With the attention no longer distracted by special factors or extreme conditions of soil and water-supply, one may settle down to the examination of just what constitutes the ordinary flora of the river-valleys of the central plain of England, its limitations and its expression in common types which represent the response to a fairly average condition of environmental factors.' And he adds sardonically that 'the plants of an English countryside may have a special scientific interest alike for the inhabitants of Greenland's icy mountains or those of India's coral strand, as conversely the English botanist is expected to be familiar with the ecology of these distant lands'.[69] This brilliant botanist settled down to the patient daily observation and analysis of the vegetation round Oxford (a radius of three miles or to the tops of the near hills) for a period of four years (1921-4), and his three resulting monographs[69, 70] contain more information about the plant ecology of the district than anything written since.

Before saying more about the present habitats on Wytham Hill it is necessary to add a little about the historical background of the present estate, which helps one to understand the peculiar mixture of the natural and artificial occurring there. The investigations of Grayson and Jones,[194] of the Oxford Department of Forestry, have put together a good deal of ecological history from old maps and documents, especially for the eighteenth century onwards. (By a piece of good luck, one set of maps dating from the Enclosure Awards of 1814 and having sketched on them the owner's plans for the new planting of parts of the estate, was rescued by an Oxford librarian from the street dustbin of a private land agent.) The character of Wytham Woods in Saxon times is not directly known, but the land and some of its waters passed to the Abbey of Abingdon by a Saxon royal charter probably of the tenth century, as part of what was then called Cumnor Woods. The earliest known use of the name 'Wytham Woods' was in 1623. For some reason neither these woods, nor Bagley Wood a few miles away, were included in Domesday Book. Although much of the lower land of Wytham soon came under the executive management of manor knights, the Abbey seems to have kept a direct hand upon the woods of the north hill. During the Middle Ages there are only glimpses of the methods of occupation and treatment, from which and by analogy with the known history of other woodlands in the Oxford region, we can suppose that although there was much timber on the hill, it was all or mostly grazed by stock, and inhabited by deer, so that it would more likely be a mixture of woods and rough common or waste, than a solid stand of trees. One reason for this conclusion is that the enclosures made by the various landlords into whose often changing hands much of the land came after the dissolution of the monasteries, were evidently intended to a large extent to preserve the timber from exploitation and to keep out grazing animals or acorn-hunting pigs. In these early days it was quite well understood that woodlands had to regenerate, and we know that in some forests such as Wychwood and Salcey temporary enclosure against deer and cattle, but sometimes only against the latter, was used for this purpose. And a law of 1543 allowed a landlord to enclose for seven years part of any wood after heavy felling or thinning.[363]

At Wytham permanent enclosure by landlords started quite early and went on for about 250 years until its final climax in the first two decades of the nineteenth century. For example the central piece of Wytham Great Wood, the chief stand of trees on the north part of the hill, was enclosed by the owner just before 1555, and was later extended until in the eighteenth century it covered about 260 acres. But we do not know for certain how much of the original woodland was high forest or coppiced, how much low scrub or even the kind of dense canopy of very high scrub or understorey (consisting of hawthorn and maple) that is still found in Wychwood Forest, or what parts were common pasture with patches of scrub and bramble on it. But two examples can be given of how the surviving place names suggest the nature of the original habitat. The eighteenth-century map constructed by Grayson and Jones shows a very broad belt of common pasture land stretching from the bounds of the old Cumnor Wood right across to the present University Farm, the Great Wood lying on the top and slopes north of this. The largest surviving open space of grassland is still known as Rough Common, but it is now surrounded by woodland or scrub that has spread out from Great Wood or been planted in the last century. There is a section of woodland continuous with Great Wood, and stretching north-east as far as the present fields of the University Farm. Two parts of this are called Thorny Croft and Common Piece (the latter originally a bit of common land enclosed in the eighteenth century, called 'My Lady's Common Piece'). 'The 1726 map shows the lower part from Common Piece northwards as divided, though distinctly labelled "Common", and carrying many trees. Several of these dividing banks still exist, and it appears that despite some degree of enclosure, it was relatively well-wooded but subject to rights of pasture.'[194]

Whether the woods were in medieval times 'natural' or 'semi-natural' or partly regressive through grazing or other causes may not matter so much for understanding the present flora and fauna, as is sometimes assumed in discussions about 'primitive' or 'primeval' forest. It is at any rate quite clear that Wytham Woods have not for many centuries been 'virgin', though if given the chance to do so they might well return to something resembling a natural woodland, even if this would be different in composition from the original Saxon forest. What could be more fascinating than to watch this happen and record its progress over a hundred years or more, armed with the methods of modern ecology? But to achieve this would require something a great deal more subtle and broad-based than the curriculum of modern forestry planning. For keeping and building up the variety of the plant and animal life in such a place, whether historically or in the future, it may be just as good to have been situated through the centuries, as Wytham still is, in a region of good and abundant woodlands, than to have inherited a primeval state. This point is well borne out by the occurrence at the present day in Marleywood Plantation (on the south hill of the estate) of isolated populations of three locally very rare species of animals: an ant, *Lasius brunneus*, a beetle, *Prionychus ater*,[135] and a centipede, *Cryptops hortensis*. All three here live in rotting beech trees which were certainly planted not more than about 150 years ago (between 1808 and 1827) when the plantation itself, now a well-established wood of oak, ash, sycamore, English elm and beech, was started on what had been farm fields. The plantation adjoins Marley Wood, which has a much longer history back to the Middle Ages. In the latter, these three species have not so far been discovered, perhaps partly because most of the large old trees were cut out and sold a few years ago. But in Marleywood Plantation, the dying or dead trees concerned are now individually preserved for ecological study (see Ch. 14).

Although Wytham was never part of a very large forest, at any rate after Saxon times, it does lie in a region very rich in trees of woodland and hedgerow and park. In the twelfth and thirteenth centuries much of Oxfordshire was forest. There was then a great chain of Royal Forests extending from Wychwood Forest on the western border of the county across to Woodstock (where some of the ancient oaks survive in Blenheim Park), and thence eastwards to Bernwood Forest (now mostly felled, and a State Forest once more), and finally north-east over to Whittlewood and Salcey Forests on the borders of Buckinghamshire and Northamptonshire. Turner in *Select Pleas of the Forest*[511] states that in the thirteenth century one Warden looked after forests running from Oxford to Stamford Bridge in Lincolnshire. In 1086 the area of Royal Forests in Oxfordshire was 51,000 acres and a hundred years later Wychwood Forest (*sensu lato*) reached its zenith (by additional 'afforestation') at some 70,000 acres; even in 1300 it was still over 50,000 acres.[542] At the present day it is only a remnant surrounded by farmland, but the centre square mile of it is a National Nature Reserve, mostly woodland, and a valuable reservoir of wild species. These forests were the favourite hunting grounds of a long succession of kings and barons. The existence of a Royal Forest does not, of course, in itself imply that the whole was under woodland, only that it was subject to forest law, an intricately interwoven system of rights and prohibitions (mainly of course connected with the king's deer, but also taking account of an immense detail of subsidiary exploitation and conservation of the resources).[511] But there is plenty of independent testimony to the rich and abundant woodlands there, and the forest animals inhabiting them. In any case, forests are all the richer in species if they contain plenty of open glades and green rides. Again, near Oxford there were also Shotover Forest (now defunct), Stowood (still surviving after a fashion as a modern plantation), and Bagley Wood (mainly an oak wood, now strongly diversified by the more artificial experiments of forestry), and others. To the south were what Cox[85] called 'the wild stretches and dense backwoods' of the Chiltern chalk hills, to this day heavily wooded and naturally managed, because the beeches that dominate the forest landscape there are able to regenerate naturally.

Over this long period of a thousand years there must have been a perpetual though often slow process of dispersal and interchange of many species of plants and animals (see Ch. 18), so that any woodland that began to recover its full ecological structure after hard times or was created anew might eventually receive (like Marleywood Plantation) its quota from a pool of species elsewhere amounting, probably, to between a quarter and a half of the British flora and fauna. And we need not look only to active migration, or to the free natural transport provided by wind, water or animal carriage, though these are powerful enough. Throughout the Middle Ages (and to a considerable extent afterwards and above all in the present age of mobility) woodland and other natural products were moved about the country on a surprising scale. From Royal Forests like Wychwood and Shotover there were frequent grants of fuel wood or timber, that were taken in large loads for long distances. Many instances of this can be found in Cox's book on *The Royal Forests of England*.[85] Thus in 1222 the Hospital of St Bartholomew at Oxford took 100 horse-loads of dry wood for fuel from Shotover Forest. About 1230 a large supply of wood fuel from Wychwood Forest was granted to the Dominican Friars of Oxford. Later in the thirteenth century we read of the same thing, of eighty cartloads of brushwood for the king, and of timber taken to Oxford, all from Wychwood. And, to give a small example directly affecting the Wytham area (as we have adopted it for the purpose of ecological survey), the nuns of Godstow nunnery (whose ruins can still be seen by the Thames) were given every day by the Abbey of Abingdon four loads of thorns for fuel from Wytham Woods which lie a mile away.[194] All this transport of dead wood about the countryside must have provided additional opportunities for the dispersal of many kinds of animals and some plants attached to live or dead trees, and sometimes for long distances.

By the sixteenth and seventeenth centuries a rather clearer picture of Wytham Hill begins to be visible, though there are many confusing changes of ownership among the people who replaced the Abbey of Abingdon. The gradual transfer by enclosure of land from the freeholders and tenant farmers has already been mentioned, and eventually the woods, consisting chiefly of oak (*Quercus robur*) ash and elm, became subject to more regular cutting and coppicing. Judging by the plant community that develops at the present day, the woods higher up the hill must have been something like the calcareous ash–oak association described by Tansley[493] as growing on marls, calcareous clays, calcareous sands and thin loams over chalk. Such woods have a good shrub layer of hazel (*Corylus avellana*), young ash (*Fraxinus excelsior*), maple (*Acer campestre*), dogwood (*Cornus sanguinea*), privet (*Ligustrum vulgare*), spindle (*Euonymus europaeus*), elder (*Sambucus nigra*) and wayfaring tree (*Viburnum lantana*), all of which live commonly or in patches locally on the hill, accompanied also by shrub species such as hawthorn (*Crataegus*), guelder rose (*Viburnum opulus*) and other species. Blackthorn, *Prunus spinosa*, is also there, but chiefly abundant on the clay lower down. The characteristic field layer under thicker canopy is dog's mercury, *Mercurialis perennis*, with local societies or mixtures of other species in the less shady places, and a great deal of ground moss. Some of the open fields or common enclosed in past centuries has grown up to resemble almost completely the older woods of which they now form an integral part, and only a very few plants seem to have failed to spread far into the new habitat provided, among them being apparently the herb paris, *Paris quadrifolia*, and meadow saffron, *Colchicum autumnale*. The English elm, *Ulmus procera*, is most abundant on the outskirts of the wood, and where it evidently survived and spread from the hedges in the old enclosures.

At some time after the Tudor period the European sycamore, *Acer pseudoplatanus*, introduced into Britain and planted as an ornamental tree, must have reached Wytham. It is now abundant living on equal terms with the native trees and regenerating of its own accord so that the chief tree mixture on the hill is now an oak–ash–sycamore wood. Left to itself the sycamore would probably settle down eventually to a normal ecological balance in our deciduous woods: A. G. Tansley once remarked to me that it fills a natural position in the woodland structure that is occupied by various other species of maples in North America, though ordinarily only to a rather limited extent in this country by our native common maple, *Acer campestre*. In its native habitats in Europe the sycamore usually seems to occupy a subordinate place in the forest. According to the *Biological Flora* monograph of this species[250] the sycamore did not begin to be used widely in Britain as a timber tree (as distinct from an ornamental species) until the closing years of the eighteenth century, and in all likelihood it formed part of the nineteenth-century planting at Wytham now to be mentioned.

The plans sketched on the 1814 Enclosure Award map were those of the Fifth Earl of Abingdon, who set in train a whole series of ambitious plans to convert parts of the estate into the landscaped ornamental parkland fashionable at that period, with provision also for keeping game. Not all these plans were carried out, but nevertheless a great deal was done and the original pattern of semi-natural woodland, common and farm fields was added to or overlaid by a new design of curved belts and patches of trees, and broad new rides cut in some of the older woods. These plantations included species new to the estate, or foreign ones. The previously existing woodlands were also allowed to complete their spread on to much of the common and waste land, but the large Park remained in agricultural use, chiefly pasture, but with many large trees scattered in it that are still a very fine habitat for animals. The most important trees to be planted at Wytham both scenically and ecologically, were the beeches, *Fagus sylvatica*, which are now quite large and in some instances dead or dying or beginning to rot, so providing (in spite of their relatively small numbers, little over a hundred in all) an unrivalled series of micro-habitats for the fungal and animal communities of rotting wood, as well as patches of beech litter on the ground that contribute to the multiple patterns of the woodland floor.

Details of the remaining history need not be given. After the Fifth Earl's death in 1854, very few further drastic changes were made in the estate for the next ninety years, and little care was put into the management of the woodlands, so that when the University became owners the place had a pleasantly unkempt and wild look, romantic rather than utilitarian, and as a result of the natural power of resurgence already alluded to, presenting a wonderfully diverse pattern of habitats. During this ninety years the rabbit increased very greatly and later on the American grey squirrel arrived. Both these species had major effects upon the vegetation, the rabbit sufficiently to make an impress on the scenery. The belts of elder scrub, now beginning to die of old age but still very beautiful with their arching stems, lavish corymbs of white flowers in summer and heavy bunches of purple berries in autumn, are an ecological feature brought about by the fact that rabbits do not attack their bark. But many trees, especially sycamores and even some large beeches, still show evidence of the heavy ring-barking that used to take place. And the whole balance of the Coral Rag meadows has been changed since rabbits diminished after the myxomatosis pandemic several years ago. A final new influence since 1945, more powerful than the rabbit or grey squirrel, has been the onset on parts of the estate of modern afforestation whose rather weird mixtures and patterns of native and exotic species has, on those parts of the hill affected, imposed a new artificial and simplified chessboard arrangement on the more natural patterns that they obliterate.

The flora of the Wytham area has been studied by a long succession of Oxford botanists, the product of all this collecting being summarized by Druce[106] in *The Flora of Berkshire* in 1897. In this we can trace most of the more striking or uncommon species, but after the manner of most earlier floras no separate localities are given for the common ones. In the last twenty years a certain amount of botanical work has been done again, but any systematic survey of the vegetation by modern methods is still lacking. The information about plant life that does exist has been assembled partly by the Department of Forestry in connection with its management schemes, and notably by E. W. Jones, who has also published lists of Wytham mosses and liverworts.[251] At the same time a great deal of information has been obtained for the Bureau of Animal Population's Ecological Survey.

With attention nowadays turning to the fascinating animal communities of macrofungi in Wytham Woods (see Ch. 15), we are beginning to know a good deal about the species, especially of bracket fungi growing on dying and dead trees. Ground-living toadstools are less well known, and perhaps this is not a very rich place for them, even in wet years. There is here an extraordinarily complex and often little-known world in which these fruiting bodies with their special animal inhabitants, their fungus mycelia growing under bark or in rotting wood, each again with special animal communities, and the ground toadstools with their mycelia in the soil or roots of trees, form as varied a part of the whole ecosystem both in species and populations of fungi and of animals, as that based directly upon green plants. Both in the exact groupings of vascular plants and bryophytes with their associated herbivore-based food-chains, and the communities associated with fungi, botanists have a huge field still to explore at Wytham.

There is a little to be said about the past work done by naturalists upon animals in Wytham, that is, before the intensive ecological investigations of the last two decades. The latter form much of the material drawn upon in later chapters and need hardly be mentioned at this stage. Oxford has a long and distinguished history of entomological work, both professional and amateur; and one of the things that makes possible our ecological survey, as well as much special research, is the fine series of collections of British insects and spiders that are available for consultation in the museum of the Hope Department of Entomology. It is worth remembering that these collections have taken over 145 years to accrue and still much of the taxonomic material is not yet completely understood or finally classified. If the present ecological survey described here could continue for another 125 years, people would probably make even more cautious remarks about its completeness, and certainly about the explanations for many of the phenomena it would have recorded. In such a vast field, one may press on but cannot afford to be impatient. The founder of the Hope Department, the Rev. F. W. Hope, was an undergraduate at Christ Church in the years 1819-22, and during this time collected beetles in the district. Some of his records have been preserved in the form of annotations in a book, among them notes about five species in Wytham Woods. These are of extreme interest, because they include two species now regarded as long extinct in Britain: the largest species of burying-beetle in Europe, *Necrophorus germanicus*, and a stag-beetle, *Platycerus caraboides*.[530] These observations are of more than natural historical interest because they suggest the changeableness of faunas and communities. Many other people must have collected at Wytham, and one only wishes that more of the work of nineteenth-century entomologists had been published or their information adequately preserved on labels. However, from 1904 onwards until after the first World War, there was a remarkable and sustained effort by James Walker and a group of friends to collect and bring together all earlier records of the species of beetles in the Oxford district – being roughly the area within seven miles of the city centre, 'this being the limit at which one can effectively work a district by the aid of one's legs unassisted by a bicycle', as Walker wrote in 1906, when the countryside close to Oxford must still have kept a great deal of the character celebrated about a hundred years ago in poems by Matthew Arnold, though even then he was writing:

> How changed is here each spot man makes or fills!
> In the two Hinkseys nothing keeps the same.

It is not always remembered by scientists how far our earlier geologists and naturalists *walked* and how successfully this enabled them to appreciate and get to know nature. By 1906, 1399 species of beetles, about 61% of the then known British species, had been found in this relatively small bit of country. A long series of reports published by the Ashmolean Natural History of Oxfordshire from 1906 to 1929 added about 750 more, making a total of 2148 or 59·7% of the 3597 British beetles known in 1929. Quite a large amount of this work was done in the Wytham area, but like the botanists Walker did not record in print the localities of the commoner species, confining his details to the more rare and local ones. Of the latter he published notes of over 380 Wytham species, a very useful and important base for later comparisons, especially as in his reports the habitats were often given fairly clearly. Many of his specimens also survive, but their labels are too general and brief to tell us very much. This great effort upon the British Coleoptera has been matched by work in other groups of animals at Oxford, and the summary given in the 1939 volume of the *Victoria County History of Oxfordshire* provides another important reference work, even though it does not include Wytham, since this place is in Berkshire.

We then come to the recent period since 1943, of modern ecology, of frequent visits by day or night – usually by motor transport – to some selected area for intensive field studies, the era of the D.Phil. student and of experiments. By 1964 there had been 150 scientific publications about Wytham, with many more on the way. This modern work is characterized by a strong desire to reduce the incredibly diverse, complex and intricate processes of animal population ecology and behaviour and the nature of communities to objective terms, if possible and where appropriate to quantitative terms, with all the apparatus of census quotas, sample plots, statistical tests, and estimates of marriages, births, deaths and movements among animals. This is of course necessary; it is also wonderful and stimulating if one can digest it and keep pace with the results, which most people nowadays manage to do by becoming specialists. But we should take notice of the plea from Professor Thomas Park[373] in his Presidential address to the Ecological Society of America in 1960 for what he called 'the conservation and development of natural history' as well. He said: 'There is an intellectual reason for natural history far beyond its own intrinsic worth. It is one of the prime sources of insight and knowledge for the modern ecologist. It helps him to visualize a problem and ask a cogent question. In applying analytical methods to ecological problems one does not excommunicate natural history. Rather, one imposes upon it new dimensions of concept and method and thus increases his capacity to interpret events that are otherwise not interpretable through unaided observation.' This advice, coming from one of the greatest ecological experimenters on animal populations, is impressive and timely, and may remind us to respect both the continuing value of naturalists and the solid basis for ecology that they have laid in the past – just as it increases our appreciation of a piece of limestone meadow on Wytham Hill to know that what we stand on was formerly the outpost of a vast fringing reef system stretching across central Europe.

I will conclude this general account by trying to convey some idea of what Wytham Woods looks like, and how it feels to enter and work there in different seasons and weathers. To do this in proper style, one would really have to write a complete tale of the phenological changes round the year, as Church has so brilliantly done for the Oxford district; or a scientific version (if that can be imagined) of Richard Jeffries' *Chronicles of the Hedges*. Here I can only give some impressions, necessary personal ones. Seen from a distance the hill lies low and is dark with woodland, except for the Park (a long valley between the two parts of the hill, with large scattered trees of English elm, oak and ash), and the curious arable field and grassy enclaves near the top that make one sometimes think of John Buchan's *Dancing Floor*. For inhabitants of Oxford it is one of the important parts of the horizon, and the sun sets early behind it. Pack-horses, riders and coaches for many years rode over the crestway near which on the central col there is a small open space among trees called 'The Bowling Alley', whose origin is now unknown. This old coachway is now the favourite walk of university dons, a good many of whom though not scientists are nature lovers; others, like the two walkers who one day passed blindly by me discussing the monetary system of Czecho-slovakia, may obtain their recreation by exercise alone.

On entering the woods one passes into an irregular mixture of oak and ash and elm and sycamore, not always in very dense or high canopy, flanked in open spots by bands of scrub or the vigorous flowering plants of glade or the edge of rides – such as the red campion, *Melandrium rubrum*, or burdock, *Arctium lappa*, or thistles, bramble and tall grasses. On some parts of the hill there are stretches of bracken or oases of bracken–scrub savannah. Through the year is seen in succession a wonderful display of flowering shrubs: white blackthorn blossom on its greyish bare twigs; the goat sallow with golden catkins in the male, and green ones in the female, both visited by many early insects such as bees and flies; flowering masses of the white hawthorn, smelling of fish and attracting a horde of insects also, including a great many beetles; then the flowers of elder, faintly scented and attractive to us, but not so much to insects, though the autumn berries are food for birds and moths; and late in the year the orange and pink fruits of the spindle form brilliant patches against the heavy darkening green of the trees. The oaks hold central place as a habitat for animals. They can be climbed in search of canopy animals, or else one may look at the low-sweeping branches of the older trees, on which at midsummer one may spend several hours collecting the amazingly diverse insect and spider fauna without moving more than a few yards. The leaves of the sycamore, when they are within reach of the ground, provide (from their exotic simplicity of herbivores) a diagrammatic community of animals at work, that can be shown to students just by turning over the leaves under which will be found in favourable seasons an enormous aphid population attended by parasites and preda-tors – of the latter, soldier and sailor beetles (Cantharidae), lacewings and lady-birds and their larvae, the larvae of hover-flies, and spiders. By September the oak leaves are leathery and carry a poor population of insects except for numerous galls, the ash turns yellow just before falling, the sycamores are extensively blotched with leaf spot fungi and are getting brittle, and the beeches turn foxy brown. In October and November the heavy leaf-fall takes place, but nearly all except oak and beech leaves have disappeared by the following summer, eaten by animals and decomposed. Long-lasting into early winter are the tall English elms, flaming pillars of pale golden yellow.

Under the canopy of the mixed deciduous wood a great deal of the ground is hidden by an extensive green sheet of dog's mercury less than a foot high, while dispersed among it or completely replacing it in some patches are other flowering plants like enchanter's nightshade, *Circaea lutetiana*, or *Arum maculatum*. Under the beeches, however, there is usually pure leaf litter. The animal ecologist tuned to the idea of woodland as a whole ecosystem looks with eagerness for fallen logs and partly dying trees or shrubs as a natural and necessary part of his peculiar mental landscape, in which every structure produced in nature has a functional relation to the rest, and nearly always houses some part of the animal life. On rotting wood there appear, not infrequently at rather unpredictable places and times, large populations of bracket fungi belonging to over a score of common species. Forestry, whether from a dim tradition of aristocratic order inherited from the eighteenth century, or from some later notion of sweeping clean the factory floor, tends to remove dead wood, with sword and fire so to speak. When I was discussing with the owner's estate agent the conservation of what afterwards became one of our larger woodland National Nature Reserves, he remarked with a smile: 'We would like a healthy forest, but I expect what we call healthy would not suit you.' Another land agent, musing on the same theme, said: 'I know what kind of wood you want, you want an *untidy* one!' And they did help to provide untidiness, and in a handsome way. On the woodland floor lies a heterogeneous refuse heap fallen mostly from the canopy above: leaf litter, many twigs and remains of tree fruits such as acorns, ash and sycamore samaras and beech mast; with small dead branches and here and there a larger log. Looking under the dog's mercury one finds large earthworm castings, dead snail shells, the runways of mice and moles, and perhaps occasionally a small corpse of dead mammal or bird. In the peak of summer there can often be heard a light patter from the excreta of oak moth caterpillars hitting the vegetation and ground. By day the lower tree trunks are rather bare of active animal life, but after dark these trunks become important highways up and down between the canopy and the ground and support a massive traffic of insects, spiders, harvestmen, centipedes and slugs. But the abounding life of the litter and soil is only properly revealed by extraction in special apparatus, and the crop of minute animals obtained in this way never ceases to astonish. Through this complex structure of cover and in search of various foods quite a large population of birds is dispersed, but as Wallace remarked (see Ch. 1), 'a certain amount of acquaintance with them is necessary in order to discover their haunts and some practice is required to see them in the thick forest, even when you hear them close to you'.

Here and there one encounters small fast-running streams in heavy shade and quite devoid of green plants, so that the animals living in them derive their ultimate food resource from the fallen leaves of trees – a kind of aquatic litter. Or one walks into the edge of a woodland marsh with vegetation almost head-high in summer and a very different fauna, for these marshes are in glades and have rich plant life. On top of the hill the open parts on shallower limestone soils are graced with a particularly beautiful series of meadows, parts of which (before the rabbits died off of myxomatosis) used to be grazed into turf with many delicate flowers which now have to compete with much stronger grass growth. There is every degree of complexity from meadow and mat vegetation containing nearly a hundred species of plants, to places that have pure stands of false brome grass, *Brachypodium pinnatum*. Many of the flowers are brilliant, and nothing can excel the appearance of viper's bugloss, *Echium vulgare*, one of the borage family, with its bright blue flowers and pink and blue stamens, on which have settled brown-streaked large skipper butterflies, *Ochlodes venata*, and red-spotted dark green burnet moths, *Zygaena filipendulae*. Parts of the open ground have been cultivated or kept as pasture, and older stretches of the latter still carry a pattern of mounds and underground highways of the yellow ant, *Lasius flavus*. Down by the slow muddy River Thames there is a special riparian zone, half meadow and half marsh, and in some of the pastures near it one can hear the cries of curlews in spring, and is reminded of Matthew Arnold's description of 'Wytham flats' in his poem 'Thyrsis'.

The hill has very many variations on all these themes, as well as further themes that have not yet been mentioned, and some that have not even been explored. To know thoroughly these few square miles would really need more days and nights and less sleep than any one person can contemplate. The weather, the time of year, the time of day or night, the extraordinary fluctuations in numbers that many species undergo, one's own variations in receptivity and fatigue, all complicate scientifically, yet enrich personally, the experience of community ecology. On many days of cold weather, and through much of the winter anyhow, there is extremely little invertebrate life to be seen unless one strips away the cover; and the summer migrant birds have gone. Even in good weather bird life tends to droop into silence in the middle part of the day, and the greatest activity of most of the mammals and an enormous number of the invertebrates is at night. The microclimate on a hill system with this peculiar shape and with slopes in all aspects, varies to a striking degree, sometimes from yard to yard, and one learns the decisive control that wind exercises upon the life and behaviour of flying insects.

CHAPTER 4

The Classification of Habitats

IN THE GAME of chess, counted by most people as capable of stretching parts of the intellect pretty thoroughly, there are are only two sorts of squares, each replicated thirty-two times, on which only twelve species of players having among them six different forms of movement and two colours perform in populations of not more than eight of any one sort. On Wytham Hill, described in the last chapter as a small sample of midland England on mostly calcareous soils but with a full range of wetness, there are something like a hundred kinds of 'habitat squares' (even taken on a rather broad classification, and ignoring the individual habitat units provided by hundreds of separate species of plants) most of which are replicated inexactly thousands of times, though some only once or twice, and inhabited altogether by up to 5000 species of animals, perhaps even more, and with populations running into very many millions. Even the Emperor Akbar might have felt hesitation in playing a living chess game on the great courtyard of his palace near Agra, if each square had contained upwards of two hundred different kinds of chessmen. What are we to do with a situation of this magnitude and complexity? It seems, indeed it certainly is, a formidable operation to prepare a blueprint of its organization that can be used scientifically. However, that is what I have been trying to do, and the primary ideas about it are set forth in this chapter.

First of all, let us consider some of the attitudes that zoologists take up before this problem. The first and commonest is to ignore it. Definition of habitats, or rather lack of it, is one of the chief blind spots in zoology, and I shall enlarge on this question in the next chapter. Nothing but time and the slow drift of ideas can change it very much. If Aristotle's zoological survey be considered as the first high-powered attempt to bring order into our understanding of the animal kingdom, it has taken 2300 years in its development to the present stage at which the inhabitants of many countries expect to be able to find out for themselves or with expert help the name of a species and its position in the zoological hierarchy. In Britain we take it for granted that it is possible to assign to most of our animals not only an agreed name, but a 'taxonomic position' – that is, a context, often referable in theory at any rate to an evolutionary relationship. And we have enormous institutions like the British Museum of Natural History continuously engaged on this work. But historical progress in the classification of the animal kingdom has been interrupted by more than one scientific Dark Age during which the subject was ignored or its advance brought to a halt, sometimes for centuries. I think we are still in a Dark Age of this kind with regard to the classification and definition of animal habitats, and any attempt to steer out of it must inevitably appear in some ways crude and contain errors of judgement.

There is, secondly, the belief that such questions can be left to the geographer. This view was expressed to me once by a teacher of that subject to whom the ecological survey at Wytham had been explained: 'What you need is a geographer to pull it together for you!' But geography concerns itself chiefly with much broader classifications of earth and water and climate, and with the relation between man himself and his crops and landscape, and is a blunt tool for defining habitats that may at the lower end occupy areas as small as half a square foot, or – as with the bodies of animals as habitats for parasites – even less. Thirdly, it is often held that the job of classifying habitats has already been done by plant ecologists, in so far as they have set up a whole series of plant associations based on plant succession, relation to soils and so on, and since the food-chains of the animal community ultimately depend on these plants. But experience has been that although vegetation is a highly important element in defining where animals live and in what their resources consist, the details of plant associations are frequently difficult to apply in a relevant way; and at the same time many aspects of habitat structure and in particular some of the forms of dead organic matter (not to mention many human artefacts) are largely omitted or given slight attention by plant ecologists, though they become essential in studying animal habitats. It therefore seemed a good idea to try and think out a general system of classification, using ideas from many other branches of science, and arranging the results so that all possible animal habitats would be included within the system. In doing this one is following an old Chinese proverb that says: 'Listen to all, plucking a feather from every passing goose, but follow no one absolutely.'

The aim of such classification is not merely to produce a formal series of units or names that can be conveniently pigeon-holed (even though a 'pigeon hole' would in fact be one of the units we might use). It is to provide a mental context or panorama that will enable an ecologist to realize where the particular habitat he studies fits on to other ones, and how their communities interact. For whatever population groups we choose for study in the field, it is quite certain that very few of them are really closed systems, and we need to be able to tackle the dilemma that the larger the area of ground you take as a unit for study in order to cut down these 'edge effects', the more complex it becomes internally. An analogy from

63

organic chemistry may make this point clearer. One of the formulae for the chemical HEOD of which the insecticide dieldrin mainly consists runs as follows: '1 : 2 : 3 : 4 : 10 : 10-hexachloro-6 : 7-epoxy-1 : 4 : 4a : 5 : 6 : 7 : 8 : 8a-octahydro-exo-1 : 4-endo-5 : 8-dimethanonaphthalene.' Fifty years ago only small fragments of such a chemical structure would have been known at all, just as we still know ecology mainly in small fragments, which are interesting in themselves but becoming embarrassingly numerous. It was of course necessary during the development of organic chemistry to classify the various kinds of unit and work out their relationships one by one; but to understand the properties of the final 'community' of chemical components (e.g. the property that wheat seeds 'dressed' with dieldrin can kill not only certain insects that attack wheat, but also wood-pigeons and many other birds, as well as acting as a chain poison to kill owls and hawks and foxes) it has to be studied as a larger whole whose properties can only be partly predicted from the sum of its parts.

Any ecological classification of habitats needs to fulfil three requirements. The first is to divide up the landscape and its species network into different components that can be defined by discontinuities in the field; the second is that components of one kind should be recognizably similar though they can never be exactly so; and the third is that they should have some ecological meaning, that is contain groups of species that form communities in some real sense of the term. As already pointed out (Ch. 2) one of the criteria for finding such meaning is that each habitat contains a characteristic kind of resources upon which its community is based. At the same time we shall expect always to find inter-communication not only between components of the same kind separated by different ones, but between components of diverse kinds. Where there are no convenient natural discontinuities, we have not hesitated to use certain arbitrary limits (thus the height of a man, say 6 foot, is taken as the upper limit of the field layer) provided they are useful and can be defined without difficulty. This sort of procedure is inherent in any classification, and its necessary limitations are well expressed in a remark by Smuts:[460] 'We do not wish to spread Nature on a sort of Procrustes bed of our concepts and cut off here and there what appears surplus or unnecessary or even non-existent to our subjective standards. Our experience is largely fluid and plastic, with little that is rigid and with much that is indefinite about it. We should as far as possible withstand the temptation to pour this plastic experience into the moulds of our hard and narrow preconceived notions, and even at the risk of failing to explain precisely all that we experience we should be modest and loyal in the handling of that experience.'

Reverting to the simile used at the beginning, we can now see that a chess game does not fairly illustrate the difficulties of studying animal communities in their natural setting. For whereas in chess the two players are completely responsible for the evolution and results of the game, animal populations are already geared to work according to their own rather set rules, they are living chessmen adapted to survive by their own efforts in mixed communities of other species, and therefore the problem is not to explore all the theoretical possibilities of interaction but to find out what types of interaction exist as the end-products of a highly selective evolutionary process. The Emperor Akbar, or his regimental sergeant-major, might well have been able to handle a multiple game of living chess if the various groups on each square were already well-drilled platoons or companies with predictable patterns of behaviour. Our main trouble is that although we know that species have a genetically built-in schedule of drill that may grow with experience, we are usually ignorant of what the responses will be, and the number of species is very large. Nevertheless populations and communities do have sufficient regulatory arrangements to make it unnecessary for the ecologist to understand the whole workings of the system when he is looking at its broad classification. The game of polo provides a better illustration of this situation, partly because it is an internally regulated play of forces operated by living organisms; but also because historically it is known to have been played with enormously larger numbers of players. The present game has four men and four ponies a side. But in the early fourteenth century the Spanish traveller Pero Tafur[290] described a form of polo near Cairo, in which there were about a thousand horsemen on each side under the Sultan, the modern game being only a very simplified 'model' of the earlier more realistic exercise, in which the Sultan's son had to be restrained from cutting down one of his opponents with his sword! We might draw from this history the moral that many ecologists are drawing from the present trends in their subject: that a simplified model provides a better game, but lacks a good many of the real properties that the natural struggle for existence in the field has got [1].

Some of the considerations influencing the scale on which one can usefully make a general classification of habitats have already been mentioned. So far as possible we need a uniform and practical method of recording habitats that can be used equally by the naturalist or zoologist studying a particular species or a small group of them, and by anyone trying to assemble information about whole communities. There are on the one hand reasons for keeping a pattern of rather large components, one being the wide degree of movement and interchange shown for example by predators; on the other hand we also want to avoid having just vague generalities, or deploying groups of species so large as to be almost incomprehensible and clumsy to handle. The answer to this dilemma is clearly to construct a hierarchy of habitats which can include both the larger and the smaller elements in one description. When the present methods were being finally crystallized[137] in 1951-2, another practical criterion had to be kept in mind: the application of the system to a convenient form of punch-card. For it was decided that only by means of standard punch-cards could the information about species and communities be accumulated and associated in an orderly way. In a more advanced and clear-cut subject, or in one that is intrinsically simple like the county distribution of species, some kind of machine punch-card can supply as many subdivisions as are needed. But at the pioneer stage of a habitat classification into which some alterations are bound to be introduced as the result of working experience, it is necessary to use a needle-sorted punch-card (Fig. 4; see Ch. 5) with plenty of blank space to receive additional unclassified information that in the long run provides new material for perfecting the interpretation of communities. The use of hand-sorted species punch-cards in turn requires a decision about the most convenient size of card to handle in packs, and this was fixed at 4 by 6 inches, with 92 holes along the edges, of which 60 are available for coding the habitat classification, the rest being re- served for other biological information, for localities and for certain operational needs. Eight of the habitat holes refer to plant or parts of the plant, so that 52 remain for coding the main hierarchy of habitats. With these holes there are over 1200 real combinations that are usable, though not all of these are equally useful. Some little ingenuity was required to fit all this jigsaw puzzle together in such a way that the mechanical limitations did not impose too much slavery on the reali- ties we were trying to codify. Here I shall only give a condensed summary of the main features, which are discussed more fully in separate chapters.

The classification originally devised has so far stood up quite well to hard use, though a few changes and additions have been made that are incorporated in the following account. But since it was intended primarily to apply to an inland and lowland place little weight was then given to the subdivision of maritime and montane zones and patterns. More has been done in that direction since then by conservation officers of the Nature Conservancy in the course of trials of this method of classification for making primary surveys and inventories of animal habitats in National Nature Reserves, and I have also included some remarks on them in later chapters. Our own classification depends on four main categories: *Habitat Systems*, where suitable divided laterally into *Formation-types* and stratified into *Vertical Layers*, with a small series of *Qualifiers* to take care of some other important subdivisions of the systems and formation-types. Beyond this it is per- fectly possible to add any desired amount of information about plant species and communities, soil types, and so on, and such information is of great value not only in amplifying the picture of the habitat, but in making a bridge to plant ecology. On the other hand, a great deal of zoological field work is done under circum- stances where such desirable details either cannot be recorded properly at all or in the time available; and there is not general agreement among plant ecologists about either the nature or the names of some of the vegetation units, and the same can be said about soil science. Classification of these two aspects was therefore omitted from the punch-holes, but recorded where possible on the rest of the card, or by reference elsewhere.

The seven *Habitat Systems* include everything between low-tide mark of the sea and the uppermost free-living animals in the atmosphere, the latter being a more real ecological limit than the former, if we exclude from the picture astronauts, human or animal. There is, of course, much interchange across low-tide mark both by marine and terrestrial species and the sea is included formally on account of this. In order to give a fairly real picture, I shall describe in turn each System with its subsidiary parts.

The *Terrestrial System* naturally falls, from a structural point of view, into a series of habitats corresponding to ecological succession from bare ground up to climax woodland, and it has been found convenient to adopt the term used by Tansley.[493] 'Since eco-systems developed under essentially similar (though not of course identical) conditions, and dominated by the same life forms, are often widely separated geographically and may possess entirely different floras, it is convenient to consider them as separate formations, but belonging to the same *formation-type*.' We use four commonly recognizable formation-types on dry land (Plates 3 and 10): The *Open Ground* formation-type includes bare soil and rock and any other ground in the open with vegetation not more than 6 in. high. This upper limit is a clear one for many kinds of grazed land and for the Arctic-Alpine zone. The *Field Type* in the open comprises all such habitats as meadow, closed marram dune, tall heather, low bramble and scrub – in fact any formation or seral stage in which vegetation is not above 6 ft. *Scrub* is assigned an upper limit of 15 ft (see Ch. 9, p. 172), anything much higher than this being counted as *Woodland*, though in certain instances it is convenient to take the actual top of the scrub as an approximation to that level. All four of these formation-types are well seen together in the photograph of Midsummer Hill in Plate 2. Part of the clarity of the zones there comes from the action of grazing sheep and rabbits. Tansley[493] on this subject states: 'Similarly, I regard pastured grasslands as a formation-type, again marked by distinctive life forms, though here the stabilizing factor is zoogenic and usually anthropogenic.'

The vertical limits adopted for these four formation-types correspond to well-recognized plant forms such as mosses, herb or grass mat, and alpines; taller grasses and herbs; full-grown shrubs; and trees. But some of these life forms vary so much that it is convenient for the zoologist to work also to an absolute height as far as possible. The same limits are incorporated as vertical zones within the three higher formation-types, and are most easily understood from the diagram in Fig. 2. The *Subsoil* is not assigned an absolute depth, but lies above the *Subterranean System* and includes roots of trees and the deeper burrows of more powerful animals such as the badger and fox. Mostly it corresponds to the C and D horizons of soil nomenclature, and the organic material in it is chiefly tree roots. The *Topsoil* is the layer above the Subsoil consisting of mineral and organic matter, or with the latter compacted on top of it. Typically it has a very fine texture of cover. In mull soils of scrub and woodland there is usually little difficulty in deciding where the loose

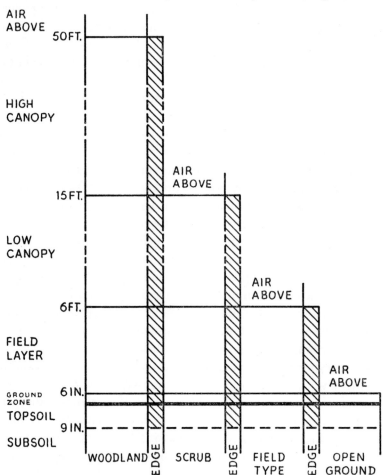

FIG. 2. Terrestrial formation-types and their edges, with their vertical layers. Field Type includes rotation arable, and Open Ground includes close-grazed pasture

litter ends and the topsail begins, at any rate in situations where the litter can be brushed away with the hand. But in acid mor soils of habitats like developed conifer woods or moorland peat and sometimes in beech woods separation is not easy, since the loose whole leaf litter, if any, may change gradually through increasingly compact layers of raw humus down to an amorphous mixture in which the mineral soil element may be either poor or abundant. Soil scientists have invented several different classifications for this layering of the soil, and their conclusions and terminology cannot all be harmonized. A perfectly good criterion of the boundary between the Topsoil and the Ground Zone is often supplied by the vegetation itself, the green stems and leaves being in the latter, and roots etc. in the former.

The *Ground Zone* is an extremely important habitat although its vertical thickness is so thin, and in many examples of the three higher formation-types undoubtedly carries the richest zonal fauna. In so far as nearly all vascular plants in this country root in the soil and many non-vascular green plants like mosses and ferns grow on the ground, it often carries also the maximum number of green plant species present in the community. The Ground Zone is important in other ways. It is the receiving platform for all manner of objects and substances falling down from above; branches and twigs, sometimes whole trees, leaves especially in the autumn, dead bracket fungi, tree fruits, insects dropping to pupate, excreta of animals (for example faeces or 'honeydew'), dead animals, and 'aeroplankton' insects and spiders brought from a distance alive or dead. This zone forms a permanent habitat for a great many species, and a great transit station or clearing-house for others that (if they are not intercepted or otherwise die on the way) pass through it to and from the soil, or into it from above for cover. The Ground Zone has a special meaning for human beings because it is what we walk on, so that it and the Field Layer are the zones we as ordinary people know best. In handling information about it we have found it convenient to follow two conventions which help in bringing together information about the same community. The first is that any object falling or lying on the ground is counted normally as being in this zone, even though it may often stick up higher than 6 in.; thus logs and stones and some of the smaller human artefacts are counted there. Secondly, in a good many Field Type habitats, especially bracken and meadows and arable land, there may be a dense summer field layer several feet high which dies down in winter below 6 in. Records from the latter are assigned to Field Type (Ground Zone), not to Open Ground. It may be noted here that the largest community lists of animals for Wytham Woods so far are from the Ground Zone of deciduous woodland, and from dying and dead deciduous wood. Since a great deal of the latter lies on the former, the remarkable richness of this whole zone can be appreciated. The cover texture is always coarser than that of the Topsoil, permitting freer movements of larger species, and the microclimate usually damper than that of the Field Layer, which in turn has a still coarser structure, and is more affected by air currents.

The *Field Layer* is here used in the same sense as by plant ecologists, with the difference that it does not include the lower 6 in. that have been assigned to the Ground Zone; that is to say, the field layer of botanists corresponds to our Field Layer plus Ground Zone. The upper limit of the vegetation is often much below 6 ft, nevertheless that is a convenient height to use, since it is not only about the height of a man, but also not many herbs and grasses in this country get above it. Animals living in this stratum of scrub or woodland do not necessarily act according to the canons of plant ecology or distinguish between what might be called the self-contained plants of the Field Layer and the woody stems and trunks and lower branches of shrubs, saplings and older trees rising up through it. Therefore another difference from botanical practice is that the Field Layer here includes *all* plant structures present in it above 6 in. and below 6 ft. (The same principle operates in the Ground Zone.) An example of how animals may use this stratum of woodland is seen in the two species of scorpion flies, *Panorpa germanica* and *P. communis*, which may be seen sitting about on nettles, elder leaves or the lower branches of oak (among other plants), occasionally dropping down to the Ground Zone to pick up a dead insect for food.[229] With the absolute height or the vertical zone of an ecological event and the species and part of plant concerned entered on the record card, it is possible to sort out situations of this kind. It is sometimes convenient to distinguish a Low Field Layer up to 3 ft and a High Field Layer from 3 to 6 ft.

Above this comes the *Canopy* in scrub and woodland; though some of it may occur below 6 ft, even in a fully developed wood, canopy of this kind is much more characteristic of Scrub and Woodland Edge, where it may actually sweep the ground. Fig. 2 shows the canopy of woodland divided into Low Canopy, corresponding to the Scrub Zone (6-15 ft) and High Canopy (above 15 ft); but this distinction has not yet been followed very much in practice and we still know very little more about the vertical heights of various species in the canopy than that there are certainly preferences, for example among feeding and nesting birds, and in some insects. We still need more arboreal ecologists! To complete the vertical zonation we add the *Air Above*, meaning not the whole column of air, but that immediately over the top of the bare ground or the vegetation of the four formation-types. It is chiefly intended to take in flying insects and birds that actually belong to the habitats beneath, not the rather 'scrambled' mixture of species from many habitats forming the 'aeroplankton' drift that exists up to several thousand feet (the High Air System), though some of this does descend into and through what is here called Air Above.

We now have to add certain *Qualifiers*, of which the first four concern *Open Ground* and *Field Type*. They are *Acid*, *Non-Acid*, *Maritime* and *Arable*. The distinction between the first two of these depends on soil and vegetation, and is derived from Tansley's classification of the British grasslands and heaths.[493] Anyone familiar with the main plant associations and soils of this country can learn to distinguish these broad classes and knows that siliceous grasslands and heaths are on base-deficient, acid soils and that chalk and limestone meadows are on base-rich soils. The former are often though not necessarily associated with peat forma-tion, while the latter come on less humus-dominated well-drained soils. The term Non-Acid is chosen in order to include what Tansley calls 'neutral grassland', one of the commonest types in England particularly on lowland clays and loams, and seen very commonly along road verges and in the grazed state in a great deal of lowland pasture and meadow. On the whole, the Acid types are decidedly less rich in numbers of species of animals than the neutral and basic, though they do carry some very interesting species that may be confined to them. Since the dominant grass species may be the same (as with *Festuca ovina*, *F. rubra* and *Agrostis tenuis*) in Acid and Non-Acid grassland, the differences, where they are not simply due to the contrast between upland and lowland, must relate to the soil differences and the more luxuriant species composition and often also fuller growth structure of the Non-Acid types. There are some classes of vegetation in the Field Type that cannot easily be assigned to one or other qualifier by inspection alone, bracken and bramble being important cases in point, since the former flourishes on a wide range of soils, and over a basic subsoil might in fact be growing in leached surface soil; and brambles also range fairly widely, and the species differences that would provide a clue are not easy for the ordinary field ecologist to determine.

By *Maritime* is meant the very important, rich and peculiar series of communi-ties that occur along the still undestroyed stretches of the 2750-mile coastline of Great Britain. It includes a series greatly dependent upon the recent and active physiographic processes of erosion and deposition at work on the coast, and ex-tends to a varying distance inland according to the history of the place. Since a great deal of our country has suffered successive glacial invasions and much con-sequent change in surface soil structures inland as well as on the coast, it would seem that the chief factors that give the Maritime series its special ecological character are the instability of some of the soils now, combined with proximity to the sea with its wind-blown salt spray, also to some extent the direct effect of wind itself upon plant and animal life. This category includes dry mud-banks, sand-dunes, shingle spits, sea-cliffs and sea-cliff tops and slopes, but not any of the zones immediately above or between tide-marks which belong to the Transition System. A further useful subdivision of the Maritime communities of Open Ground, Field Type or their mixtures, is therefore given by four subsoil Quali-fiers for *Clay*, *Mud* and *Silt*; *Sand*; *Shingle*; and *Rock*.

Arable land provides enormous areas of temporary bare ground, in fact the largest of any English habitat, especially since the impetus was given to ploughing up old pasture during the last war. But it is convenient to treat all stages of ordinary rotation Arable as belonging to a Field Type, with a one- to three-year cycle, though it is essentially a very rapid ecological succession from bare ground checked by cropping and ploughing. In the case of ley grassland, that is land ploughed up and laid down to semi-permanent grass, it has been found practical to define it as Arable during the first year, and thereafter assign the grassland to its particular type under Open Ground or Field Type, Acid or Non-Acid (though owing to the use of fertilizer or lime it is usually the latter).

For Scrub and Woodland there are three main Qualifiers: *Deciduous, Conifer* and *Mixed* (deciduous and conifer). 'Deciduous' follows the ordinary English usage in describing what are sometimes called broad-leaved trees, including the holly but omitting the introduced deciduous conifer, larch. The winter leaf-fall is such a tremendously big event in nature, and has such profound effects on animal life that it seems right to emphasize this attribute of the broad-leaved tree. Of course all trees and shrubs shed their leaves at some time, but not in the dramatic manner of our common deciduous species.

A final and most important Qualifier is the *Edge* of a formation-type, used mainly for Scrub and Woodland, but sometimes worth employing for the edge of Field Type on to Open Ground, especially with Mixtures (see below). Though it is a narrow transitional zone, sometimes just the interface between a higher and a lower formation-type, and always allocated to the higher formation-type present, it is usually richer in species of plants and animals than the heart of a closed scrub or wood. In woods it includes the actual outside edge, and also the rides and smaller glades within them. The whole of a narrow shelter belt between fields is classified as Woodland Edge, as is a hedgerow with a row of trees in it. Similarly with Scrub, there are hundreds of thousands, perhaps millions, of miles of hedge, which is counted as Scrub Edge, unless it has too many trees in it. This leads on to the difficult question of *Mixtures*, which has to be faced because these form quite a large fraction of the terrestrial habitat, even where unaffected much by man's works. For example the front zone of a sand-dune usually has a pattern of marram or other grass tussocks separated by open spaces of bare sand, and in each live certain species of animals characteristic of Field Type and Open Ground respectively. What is often called by naturalists 'rough ground' or 'waste' or 'common' may have scattered hawthorn or blackthorn shrubs and patches of bramble with areas of grazed pasture between. A regressive woodland may consist of oaks standing at intervals in tall bracken. Another instance, becoming of increasing frequency with modern forestry planting methods, is where some conifers occur in a deciduous wood or *vice versa*, and more often an equal mixture of the two kinds. The simplest solution of this problem is to adopt the botanists' system of assessing mixtures by cover-mapping, or by judging or counting the relative number of the component parts concerned. Braun-Blanquet[31] used a scale of five degrees of mixture. Obviously No. 3 represents an approximately equal mixture. We have chosen for convenience to treat this as Edge, wherever higher and lower formation-types are involved (i.e. edge of the higher type) and indeed the total amount of 'Edge' in such cases must be enormous. With deciduous and conifer trees (or scrub) of equal heights it is necessary to keep a separate *Mixed Woodland* (or *Scrub*) community. Nos. 1 and 5 are the pure types and the only problem is what to do with Nos. 2 and 4, say a few pine trees in an oak wood, or a few oak trees in a pine wood. I have chosen to group them with each end type, though it is true that even the addition of a few pine trees to an oak wood will have an influence on the fauna, not only by adding conifer insects, but for example by providing roosting sites for tawny owls that range in the whole wood. Nevertheless, in our system of habitat grouping, many equally wide variants are included in one category.

We may now take stock of the number of habitat components arrived at by this method of subdividing the Terrestrial System. The total of 172 is reached by taking the four Formation-types and their Edges, multiplying each by the number of Vertical Zones in it (the Field Layer being counted as one) and then by the number of Qualifiers (including the four subsoil types for Maritime). Although we know that there must really be an almost unlimited number of differently composed animal communities occurring within these components, our aim at this early stage is just to provide a basis for comparing the total pool of species within each component from which these variants may be derived. But even to deal with 172 communities is a large task, and they cover only one part of the whole living scene. We can if desired reduce this total by regrouping certain of the components to-

TABLE I. Habitat components in the terrestrial system

Formation-type	Vertical layers		Qualifiers	Total components	
	(a) All	(b) Recombined		(a)	(b)
Open Ground	4 (No Edge)= 4	2 (No Edge)= 2	×6	24	12
Field Type	5 + Edge 5 = 10	3 + Edge 3 = 6	×7	70	42
Scrub	6 + Edge 6 = 12	4 + Edge 4 = 8	×3	36	24
Woodland	7 + Edge 7 = 14	4 + Edge 4 = 8	×3	42	24
				172	102

gether, though this is subject to a rule that the original field records are so far as possible fully defined on the punch-cards, so that any such regrouping can always be broken down again into its components. By combining Soil and Subsoil into one layer, Low and High Canopy into one, and Air Above with whatever layer is below it, the total becomes reduced to 102 (Table 1). It is possible to make even further economy to a total of 82, by grouping together the Subsoil, Topsoil and Ground Zone of Open Ground and Field Type each into one unit. This is not an ideal proceeding, but has a certain practical value in processing the kind of information that is available, since quantitative work in these habitats is often done by making core samples through the surface and upper soil, without separating the results into layers. For one of the uncomfortable features of this whole subject is the entirely haphazard manner in which information accumulates, each having some particular value of its own, but not designed to fit any general conception of habitats. It is rather as if some taxonomists still preferred to follow the quintuplicate system devised by John Ray, others the new-fangled binomial system of Linnaeus, but most of them no system at all. How difficult it would be to get a species named! There is of course a delicate problem here involved, of the freedom of ecologists to follow their own lines without being bound to any preconceived classification. That is one of the reasons why such a classification has to be practical and reasonably real, otherwise people will not use it – why should they?

The Terrestrial System has been analysed at some length to illustrate how one sets about constructing this sort of classification and some of the working decisions that arise from using it. As the other six systems are discussed in later chapters they can be treated more briefly. The *Aquatic System*, domain of the hydrobiologist and more narrowly of the limnologist, is still rather inadequately classified as a whole. It includes a tremendous number of different kinds of water bodies, some of them scattered compact units like ponds, some forming narrow lines as with streams and rivers, while others again are so large as to be major geographical features. This system, as defined here, includes all water bodies (defined by the edge of surface water), whether natural or artificial, their margins being usually separated from dry land by a Transition belt. Although there are a great many different gradients in habitat conditions, physical, chemical or biological, that could be used to classify water bodies, it was thought that the greatest integration of these factors would be obtained by taking the commonly employed distinction between standing (lentic) and flowing (lotic) waters and expanding it in terms of *speed of flow* and *size* of water body, to provide a theoretical maximum of twenty-five *Formation-types* (not all of which actually occur in Britain). These range in size from puddles or tree-holes (not normally studied by limnologists) to lakes and oceans, and from still water to waterfalls and weirs (Fig. 3). The ordinary zonation of limnology gives a basis for eight *Vertical Layers: Bottom, Water Mass, Submerged Vegetation, Water Surface, Emergent Vegetation* (i.e. the part above the water), and the *Air Above*. The first two are again subdivided into *Light* and *Dark*, to separate the superficial zone with green plants from the lower and sometimes profundal zone without them. In practice these Vertical Zones are only fully developed in large lakes, and become reduced in number in the smaller water bodies. The main chemical *Qualifiers* are *Fresh-water, Brackish* and *Saline*. Other important ones exist within the freshwater series, but are not easily classified. *Temporary* is necessary for some smaller types of water. A fifth Qualifier is needed to show the difference between smaller water bodies like ponds in the open and those strongly influenced by scrub and woodland round the edge. This is called *Woody*, and is to be carefully distinguished from Woodland, as it includes both that and scrub. The Qualifier *Tree-Hole* explains itself. The total number of such combinations of Formation-types, Vertical Layers and Qualifiers that have much real meaning in

	A Very Small	B Small	C Medium	D Large	E Very Large
1. Still	Tree-hole	Small pond < 20 sq. yd (17 sq. m.)	Pond < 1 acre (0·4 hect.)	Large pool or tarn < 100 acres (40 hect.)	Lake or sea
2. Slow	Trickle, shallow stream	Ditch, field dyke	Canal, river back-water		
3. Medium	Trickle, shallow stream	Lowland brook or small stream	Lowland river	Lowland large river	River estuary
4. Fast	Spring	Upland small torrent stream	Large torrent stream		
5. Vertical or steep	Water drip, pipe outlet, cascade	Small weir or waterfall	Large weir or medium waterfall	Large waterfall	

FIG. 3. Water bodies classified by size and speed. (After C. S. Elton and R. S. Miller, 1954)

this country is about 87, but by certain regrouping, as was done with the land components, this can be reduced to 33.

The *Aquatic-Terrestrial System* which will be referred to here for convenience as the *Transition System*, occupies the most striking of all surface boundary zones, the belt between water and land. It includes a very large series of habitats: marshes (but not swamps), the edges of lakes and ponds, rivers and streams, various kinds of salt-marsh, and the intertidal zone of the seashore. Though it exists typically in the form of narrow strips, it can also form very extensive marshes. Its special ecological characters are derived from one or more of the following features: (1) the occurrence of waterlogged ground, (2) fluctuations in the water supply, (3) proximity to a water body. These features may occur singly or in combination.

What we call 'dry land' does not normally have waterlogged soil (though some heather moors are difficult to classify in this respect), most of the permanent water in terrestrial soils being bound in a capillary state among soil particles, leaving some air spaces between, at the level of rooting vegetation. Where there is a more or less gradual slope down to a water body, there will be a zone where the soil is usually waterlogged but there is not ordinarily any surface water, and this zone is always characterized by very obvious vegetation differences that can easily be learned. A hole dug in the ground to a depth of a foot or two would partly fill with water in a few hours, or else one would reach an existing standing water level. It has been necessary to insert various words like 'usually' and 'typically' because of the second common feature of many Transition habitats – their liability to alternate flooding and drying at the surface, and sometimes violent fluctuations in the level of the whole water table in soils. If these changes are irregular and drastic the zone can become rather sterile. Thus in the great reservoir of Liverpool's water supply at Lake Vyrnwy, there is an almost barren shore belt and a poverty of sublittoral communities, so that the brown trout living in the lake have to feed mainly on plankton crustacea.[558] Even on the seashore, partly left bare twice a day regularly, or for longer in some higher zones, the length of exposure out of the water is one of the severe limiting conditions for some species of animals. Strictly speaking, these intertidal shores are a temporal mixture of land and sea habitats, and could really be classified either as such, as the edge of the land, or as the edge of the sea. But since we are land animals ourselves, and the phase we usually see is marine animals attached to or living on the shore itself (though chiefly active only under water), it is natural to think of it in the third category, and accordingly it is included in the Transition System. This fits in with the decision, mentioned below, to classify these habitats by the kind of water body they adjoin.

The third feature arises from the great numbers of aquatic insects that have their early stages in water and then emerge to complete their development and their mating and breeding cycles on the margins of water. They include flies (Diptera), stone-flies (Plecoptera), caddis-flies (Trichoptera), mayflies (Ephemeroptera) and dragonflies (Odonata). Most of them – some of the larger dragonflies and caddis-flies being exceptions – spend most of their time not far from the water. This often massive invasion from the water on to the land gives a special character to such marginal communities, even though otherwise they may be more or less terrestrial in composition. There are quite a number of water-marginal situations that do not have waterlogged soil, and may even never be flooded, because they are on steep banks or on rocky soils, or on human constructions. But such sites usually also have certain species of birds and mammals that live or hunt or nest by water margins, whether the soil be waterlogged or not.

It has been found convenient to identify the Transition habitats (including those falling in the Domestic System) by the Formation-type of water body they adjoin, rather than by their Terrestrial components, the latter being recorded as well. This decision was based on a certain simplicity attained by so doing, and by the fact that the Transition System gets its main special characters from the invasion of water or of animals from the water. This leaves a different series, of marshy types, that do not adjoin standing surface water. We distinguish throughout this analysis between *marshes*, as having waterlogged soil but no surface water except periodically or occasionally, and *swamps* as being standing water with vegetation emerging from it. This formal description of the Transition System conceals a riotous abundance and a most complex meeting place of land and water species (rather analogous in the horizontal plane to the Ground Zone of Woodland in the vertical plane). It also has a considerable fauna confined or partly confined to it. The angler who sits quietly by the edge of water is in one of the most advantageous positions a naturalist could choose, for he may experience much of the fascinations of watching movement in this community, even though his main thoughts be under water. Any *Vertical Layers* in the Transition System conform to those of the Terrestrial habitats, and are so recorded. In addition certain Qualifiers are necessary, of which *Brackish* and *Saline* and the subsoil categories mentioned are the most important. With marshes not situated by any water body, it is also possible if desired to use the Qualifier *Woody*, since woodland marshes are so distinct from those in the open. In our own practical classification which can accommodate not more than 48 different Transition components, regrouping together of some of the water bodies reduces the total number to 17.

The *Subterranean System* is meant to include rock caves and galleries, as well as certain deeper parts of sandy soils in which a few species live in interstitial ground waters. All are dependent upon waste organic products washed in from above or brought in by bats or birds. The most highly specialized forms in these communities are aquatic, but a good many terrestrial forms live there as well, but these are mostly the same species as live above ground. It is convenient to keep the whole of the aquatic and terrestrial and transition communities of the Subterranean System together. The *High Air* takes care of the floating insects, often called 'aeroplankton', that are borne up to heights of hundreds and thousands of feet, with the swift (*Apus apus*) that feeds on them, and it is also a transit zone for many migrating birds, as well as in modern times for human beings.

The *Domestic System* is intended to comprise all those areas in which alterations by man, especially buildings and gardens, are so extreme as to change the habitat quite drastically, often impoverish it, and yet at the same time create new conditions (as in food stores) suitable to species that could not flourish in the wild. Broadly speaking the Domestic habitats are in the direction of biological deserts, or at any rate very unnatural surroundings, though this fact is a bit concealed by the multitude of exotic plant species that inhabit our gardens and parks, yet have so few animals attached to them. Smoke pollution, though perhaps likely to diminish a great deal, is another sterilizing agent. As already indicated, the Aquatic and Transition habitats are kept out by themselves, for convenience.

The *General System* includes a very diverse series of clearly defined habitats, that may be divided into (1) *Dying and Dead Wood*, (2) *Macrofungi*, (3) *Dung*, (4) *Carrion*, (5) *Animal Artefacts* – mainly burrows and nests, (6) *Human Artefacts*, and (7) certain others, including *Sap Flows* on trees. This System is not set up just as a convenient receptacle for a miscellaneous assemblage of small habitat components. These do have in common not only the feature of being relatively small in compass and scattered through the major habitats, but also of being chiefly or solely composed of decaying organic matter – at any rate having that as the main resource of the community. The second property can be expressed more exactly in this way: the main resource is not green plant matter in a healthy condition. On this point there are exceptions, as with all such classifications, for example Human Artefacts such as fence posts may be made of inorganic material like concrete and the only food resource on them lichens (a mixture of green plant and symbiotic fungus).

The first property, being small and scattered, is possessed by a great many Minor Habitats (the term employed by me in 1949[130]) that are not put in the General System. Individual green plants, clumps of plants, tussocks, and tree-trunks are all repeated units that contribute to the whole habitat pattern. Also there are some water bodies, particularly spring pools under dense canopy, and tree-holes with water in, that are not only scattered and small, but have resources of decaying matter. It is purely a matter of practical convenience to put the latter in the Aquatic and not the General System; just as it is to group all Aquatic water bodies and their Transition habitats together whether or not they occur in the Domestic System or some other one. It will also be realized that there are many habitats that consist chiefly of decaying organic matter, but are not grouped in small distinct units. Among these are litter (and in a cognate way, topsoils) and aquatic benthos. These undoubtedly show smaller patterning, and further research may prove that the component parts are more distinct than they appear at present.

The General habitats greatly enhance the complexity of interspersion, though they also add extremely interesting units to the pattern of most ecosystems. They afford many opportunities to the ecologist who wishes to study in the field replicated examples of a small compact community, with the special advantage that they can often be maintained and studied in the laboratory, and that fairly good imitations of these natural habitats can be set up with any desired number of species, and these in turn put out in the field for further experiment. This is not to say that any of the General communities are closed systems of population, as will be demonstrated later on.

CHAPTER 5

Recording Communities:
The Wytham Ecological Survey

THE FORMAL CLASSIFICATION of habitats given in the last chapter is intended to provide a kind of grammar of the subject, though a rather broad one that omits the behaviour of irregular verbs or exceptions of idiom. It defines a habitat not only by its own characteristics but by its position in relation to other components interspersed in the same ecosystem (Plate 8). The advantage of this comes from the fact that the nature of any animal community, by which is here understood any recurrent mixture of species living in the same kind of habitat, is determined not only by its own intrinsic properties but also by its setting amidst other kinds of communities, with which species may be shared and between which species may be interchanged.

The system is a hierarchy of the main structures found in nature. These structures are on very different scales. They are mainly formed of mineral matter or vegetation, but are often much modified by the activities of animals (as with grazing, burrowing and nest-making), and of course of man; while the animals themselves form structures inhabited by parasites or used for transport both by animals and plants. Without at all discounting the effects of climatic and chemical factors on the composition of communities, one can reasonably regard structure as the basic thing that determines most habitat patterns especially on land, and a great deal of the species composition of animal communities in them. This statement needs qualification in two major respects. It is obvious that the chemical differences between plants play a huge part in limiting herbivorous animal species, so that, for example, most though not all of the key-industry animals living on oak, ash and beech will actually be different. This will make the species composition of an oak or an ash wood different, and create a patterning of these species where the two trees are intermixed. In placing the emphasis upon general habitat structure there is never any intention of underestimating the differences in plant associations that may occur within one of the component habitats described in the last chapter. It is simply a question of the order in which one approaches the classification, and have found it most useful to put general structure first, and plant species com-position second. Thus one considers a deciduous wood first, and whether it is oak, ash or beech second. The reasons for this have already been partly discussed (Ch. 4), but one of them is that predators are by no means confined to one kind of plant on account of chemical factors, being more often than not quite wide-spread.

The other qualification refers to plankton communities, with their associated nekton. These communities of open water in lakes and the sea seem to form an exception to any generalization about habitat structure, since their habitat has no structure, except for some parasites of the animals themselves. In a lake it is true that the physical and chemical conditions of the water are greatly influenced by the topographical shape of the basin containing it, just as tree canopy modifies the water bodies and microclimate of the wood as a whole. But plankton has no cover structure in which predator hunts for prey, though in most other commun-ities it seems quite likely that without such cover the community would actually collapse before long. I believe that for this reason plankton is profoundly different in its organization from terrestrial and most aquatic communities. Two features can be noted, though the whole subject merits much deeper comparative attention. For one thing, plankton has rather few species of animals living together; for another, its survival seems to necessitate very intricate vertical and other move-ments. But for all terrestrial communities habitat structure is an invaluable key to classifying communities.

The woodland system offers a grand profusion of interconnected structures, and it is easy with practice to perceive that the hierarchies contained in the classi-fication used in this book actually exist in nature, and are arranged in patterns of repeated components. The ultimate aim of classifying nature is to bring into some sort of order the extraordinary cornucopia (in some sectors almost a huge scrap-book) of information jostled in books, journals, theses, indexes, museum labels and maps – and in the brains of biologists and naturalists, whose continuous know-ledge of one place may supply such a valuable background knowledge for a survey. In a scientific age that is immersed in the discovery and measurement of processes by studying small and therefore incomplete parts of nature, general classification may not seem a particularly powerful tool for opening up a new field of thought. In 1925 Whitehead wrote: 'Classification is necessary. But unless you progress from classification to mathematics, your reasoning will not take you very far.' But he must have been unaware of the relatively enormous amount of qualitative information that has to be mastered in field biology, and the absolute necessity of mastering it before setting up elaborate technical and quantitative experi-ments. In the ecology of communities, classification as I see it is simply a kind of intelligent reconnaissance to ensure that the whole does not become forgotten in the study of the parts. Without it, quantification may turn out to be inapplicable or irrelevant. The aim of employing a stratified system of habitat recording is to combine as far as possible the investigation of bits of nature small enough for study, with their progressive incorporation into the rather more real and larger framework of ideas into which they should fit. The ecologist who despises natural history soon cuts himself off from his base, and may get lost in the forest.

A grammar can only be understood by means of examples. Let us suppose that a zoologist has recorded the capture of ten female spiders as having been found 'on grass stems', or just 'on grass', and that we are able to cross-examine him in order to find out more about the spiders' habitat. The species of grass turns out to be a *Brachypodium* – the yellowish-green false-brome. But there are two species of this genus in Britain, one living in thin woodland, woodland glades and woodland edges, and the other out in open grassland, where it may often be dominant where it occurs. These spiders were taken about 150 yd away from any wood, and so the grass was almost certainly *Brachypodium pinnatum*, unless the place was a piece of regressive or recently cut-over woodland. But the difference can easily be verified by any amateur, since this species has a great deal of silica in its stems and foliage and therefore stands rather stiffly, whereas the woodland *B. sylvaticum* has lax hairy foliage. Here are two differences in habitat that obviously might matter very much to the spider: presence or absence of shelter from sun and wind, and the structure of the plant itself, which could affect the feeding and thread-weaving of the spider. These spiders were found in small, inconspicuous orb-webs, which need not be described in this instance, as they are abundantly documented for the species. But the phrase 'grassland with *Brachypodium pinnatum* dominant' is still too imprecise. It turns out that there are hawthorn and privet bushes scattered in the grassland, mostly over six and under ten feet high, and that the cover is about equally divided between the two types of vegetation. Therefore, in terms of the grammar used here, the major habitat is strictly mixed scrub and grassland, and as the mixture is in about equal parts, it amounts to a form of 'scrub edge' having a very large number of small interspaces or 'glades' between the bushes. The presence of scrub greatly modifies the microclimate, as well as the biological associates, of what would otherwise be an exposed meadow. This kind of habitat often masquerades in entomological literature under such vague and ancient headings as waste ground, common or rough ground. The spider in the grass also has to be given a vertical coordinate. It was found in the field layer at heights of 15-24 in. (or 38-61 cm.) and the web gave it, at any rate temporarily, a fixed home base. But did they spend all the time at this height or move up and down with changes in the weather or at night? Here the time of day at least adds something to fixing what Orlando Park (taking a metaphor from the physicists) has called the space-time community lattice in which the species lives. Of course it is necessary to avoid future confusion arising from changes like Summer Time, therefore one always records the natural or basic time, in Britain the Greenwich Mean Time or G.M.T. The weather is sometimes but not very often worth recording carefully for single ecological events, at least in our climate. It may help to pin-point the circumstances of feeding or mating or resting; but usually the weather conditions are best noted only in systematically organized observations over a period of time – a kind of observation that can be quite rewarding even over a few hours. Where conditions fluctuate less violently, as in a freshwater stream or in the soil, the actual temperature or other note can be of value.

There are dozens of other things that might be added to the original description 'on grass stems', among them being the composition of the grassland, the nature of the soil or subsoil, the aspect, presence of grazing by rabbits or stock, and the influence of man in mowing or trampling or burning. But to do all this for a relatively simple ecological event would completely overload the observer and his field notes and specimen labels, also the observation itself. The object of the exercise just described is not completeness but relevance, and the setting of the simple kind of event that naturalists are seeing every day into its ecological context, instead of leaving it floating entirely by itself as a fact of geographical distribution and taxonomy. It is meant to aid in building up some day a more coherent picture of how species are arranged in natural communities and how these relate to the repeated structural patterns of the habitats they use. For this sort of purpose, which has a modest and realistic attitude towards coordination of ecological information, the vague phrase 'on grass stems' can now be expanded without undue difficulty into a workmanlike and usable record, something like this: '*Singa pygmaea* Sundevall. 10 ♀♀ each in a web, 15-24 in. (or 38-61 cm.), on stems of *Brachypodium pinnatum*, dom. grass in c. equal mixture of scrub (*Crataegus* sp. dom.) 150 yd from oak wood, 3.25-4 p.m. G.M.T., 12 July 1985. Sundays Hill, Wytham Woods, Berks. W 9054. A. B. coll. Y. Z. det. 1986.' If the record is safely put in a field book or on a card-index, and the book or index held in a permanent institute, the label on the specimen need have only the essential abstract of the fuller information. But the whole simple hierarchy or facts can easily be put on to a label measuring $1 \times 1\frac{3}{4}$ in. by someone using a fine stilo pen.

'Satan', said O. Henry's gentle grafter to his friend, 'is a hard boss to work for.' The same might be said for many kinds of field ecology, and perhaps more especially in the matter of noting the habitats of animals. Some of the best collecting records on a large scale are those made by Donisthorpe[102] in his survey of the beetles of Windsor Forest over many years. They are particularly good in giving the minor habitat, that is the immediate habitat of the animal, in terms such as these: 'in deer's dung', 'in sappy decayed wood', 'on dead squirrel', 'by beating hawthorn blossoms', 'in fungus on beech', 'in the runs of *Acanthomyops fuliginosus*', 'by sweeping *Solanum dulcamara*', 'in some numbers in the topmost branches of ash tree', 'in birch-bracket fungus', etc. For what may be termed a taxonomist's natural history, these records are very good indeed, and in many respects they are uniquely valuable because the collector had found in this area something like half the British species of beetles. But at the present day we are justified in asking more than this, more than a record of the minor habitat *in vacuo*. Each of the notes quoted above could be expanded and set in a wider framework. One could ask questions like this: Was the deer's dung (obviously in the ground zone) inside a wood, or in a track or glade that would be an 'edge' habitat? Or in both? Was the dung fresh or old? What species of tree supplied the sappy decayed wood? What does 'sappy' mean here – decayed wood does not ordinarily have any sap left? The dead squirrel was presumably on the ground, but the same questions could be asked as for the deer dung, also which species of squirrel? In both instances we could ask what kind of woodland (if woodland it was), at least what dominant trees, and what kind of ground cover of vegetation (bracken? dead leaves?). The hawthorn blossoms could be in a deciduous wood, or on one of its kinds of 'edge', in scrub, or on the edge of it (perhaps along a hedge) or in mixed grassland and scrub, or for that matter in a town park or garden. At what height was beating done (it is more useful to separate collections from above and below 6 ft)? What was the beech fungus, was the beech dead or dying or apparently healthy (as could happen with the bracket-fungus *Ganoderma*)? What height? Was the fungus fresh or old, and what part of the fungus was the beetle on? What part of the tree was the fungus on? The local ant, *Acanthomyops* (*Lasius*) *brunneus*, has a rich myrmecophile fauna in Windsor Forest, discovered by Donisthorpe, and the ant makes its runways and nests inside old oak trees. It would be additionally illuminating to know at what height these myrmecophilous beetles, and indeed the ants themselves live – something that is probably quite well known to ant specialists, but not usually mentioned in the natural history literature. Similar comments could be made endlessly about other records of the kind, most of which are far less useful and penetrating than the ones that Donisthorpe fortunately made, and some of which almost amount to saying 'this species lives where it is'.

It might be expected that after one or two hundred years of steady work by naturalists, we should be well acquainted with the habitats of all our species, at any rate the commoner ones. This is often true in terms of the limited 'one-decker' kind of description so excellently made by Donisthorpe, though his observations are themselves exceptional. But there are two ways in which the usual statements about habitats given in papers and textbooks are deficient. The first is that they are satisfied with an elementary, abbreviated remark, probably in part derived from the amount of information which will go on the label of a specimen. The second is that, although there may originally have been some useful information, this gets whittled down and smoothed in the course of decades of chain-repetition, into an almost meaningless condensation. If our knowledge about separate species is ever going to be woven into a complete picture of how animals live in a patterned grouping of communities, a fuller system like the one described here is needed. It is difficult to see how the ecological pressures that species experience and their variations in space and time, and therefore the nature of evolutionary adaptation, can ever be understood unless we boldly investigate these patterns and groupings, rather than being content with standards that would astonish a mathematical physicist (who does not scatter dots about without giving them coordinates) or an organic chemist (whose whole emphasis is on connections within groups of component parts).

It is not the actual difficulty of fixing an ecological event into its lattice of reference that prevents naturalists and zoologists (and quite a number of ecologists too) from doing it, but the absence of any inclination to do so. I have found by experience that a great many of the facts needed can be obtained from any observer soon after he reports an occurrence, by a process of cross-examination like that described in the case of the spider on the grass. As observations accumulate and are handled in some such manner, the life of each species begins to emerge gradually into view, and opens out a very fascinating branch of detective work in which a sort of codified woodcraft delivers information that can be analysed by means of a cumulative index. This is itself only a stage in a long uphill research into the form and fabric of communities, and the system requires further criticism and moulding by many trained hands. One of the curious aspects of habitat recording by field taxonomists has been that we often know more about rare species than common ones. The remark made by a famous dipterist illustrates this: 'Of Anthomyids only common species were seen, so I refrain from mentioning any of them by name.' But this is at any rate more useful than the statement by another entomologist (in 1958): 'Looking back on the past season it surprises me that there is anything to write about at all!'

I have dwelt rather particularly on the reasons for making records of habitats conform to a standard method of classification, a hierarchy of components; but it will perhaps help comprehension to describe how such records are actually handled in the Wytham Ecological Survey, and how they are used to build up a picture of animal communities. The assembly lines are quite simple in principle but require considerable discipline to operate, since at every stage ecological (also sometimes taxonomic) judgements have to be made, while at the same time the methods are so designed as to make it possible not only to use data for construction, but to track back to the original records in case any doubt arises. To begin with, the information we use comes from three kinds of source. First, unpublished records may result from the field activities of the Survey itself; but these are so closely involved with other parts of the Bureau of Animal Population's work that the line between them is not distinct. For example, a student may derive his starting point from some problem thrown up by the field surveys, or he may become an expert on the identification of some group of animals. Secondly, unpublished records are given by other people. Not infrequently a research worker at Wytham makes observations that are not sufficiently complete for publication,

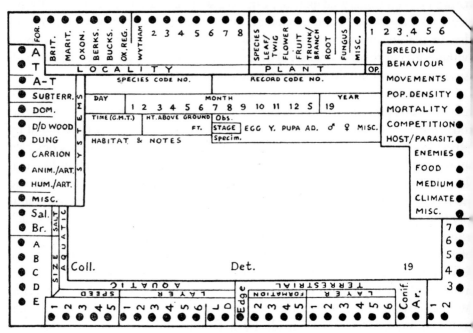

FIG. 4. Species punch-card used in the Wytham Ecological Survey. Localities and plant components on the top, habitats on the left-hand side and bottom, other biological data on the right-hand side. (Actual size 4 × 6 in.)

or decides to fill in a gap in the Ecological Survey. In this way extra raw material accumulates. It is especially the younger zoologists who grasp the notion of contributing to a common pool of information in more ways than by personal publications. Thirdly, information may become available in the ordinary scientific channels, including both printed publications and unpublished theses (the latter being available in libraries under certain technical conditions).

The chief vehicle for handling all this material is the punch-card mentioned in the previous chapter (Fig. 4). As was explained there, the present stage of ecological survey requires a reasonably large hand-sorted punch-card that gives adequate unused space in the centre and on the plain back to allow of a description of the ecological incident or other information, or else an abstract of information stored more fully elsewhere. By this means any question that arises later on can be re-assessed quite easily. Of course, the information that goes on a single punch-card for one species of animal may either be a single observation of an ecological event, or on the other hand the product of three years' study by a research student, or even a whole book on one species. In other words, each card has a different 'weight'. One of the first decisions the operator has to make is whether to admit a record at all. Doubt about a record may arise on three grounds. It may be taxonomically suspect, e.g., it may refer to a group that requires special competence for naming, or it may not be accompanied by a voucher specimen that could be referred to an expert. It might be taxonomically reliable, but ecologically unusable: it is not uncommon to receive a record that has inadequate description of the habitat, though this difficulty is usually met by a careful cross-examination, which itself has some training value. And then again, the record may be too trivial.

Having resolved any doubts about the quality of the information, which usually proves to be useful, it is entered on a punch-card. These punch-cards, of which there are now many thousands, obviously have to be kept in some permanent index, in a certain order. This is not so easy as it might sound, because the names of many genera and species, sometimes even of families, are being changed as taxonomists continue to put their vast mansion in order (or as some would say, into greater disorder). Therefore any alphabetical system of arrangement is quite impracticable, because the ecological survey would have to spend much of its time changing the names and order of the punch-cards and other material such as community lists. From the start it was therefore decided to create a system of code-numbering species that would remove much of the tyranny of purely nomenclatorial changes. This was done by taking the best available check-list for each group of animals and numbering it in the following way. A three-decker system was used, in which family, genus and species were each allotted a serial number, following the order in the check-list, the numbers being preceded by a short letter code for the larger order or comparable grouping. Thus, the seven-spotted ladybird becomes COL 51.13.1, this standing for Coleoptera (beetles), Coccinellidae, *Coccinella septempunctata* Linnaeus. Similarly the hornet is HYM 50.7.1 meaning Hymenoptera, Vespidae, *Vespa crabro* Linnaeus, the great tit is BIRD 44.1.1, meaning Aves, Paridae, *Parus major* Linnaeus. A similar system is used by the Survey for plants, based on a standard check-list. Since this list was published, two editions of a new British Flora have appeared, in which the names are in quite a different order and are sometimes changed. But there is no trouble at all in relating one to the other without altering the original code-numbers. The system works very well, and is quite essential for the compilation and analysis of ecological data of this kind and for this purpose. Those handling the coding system find it no more difficult than the Linnaean classification of which it is the arithmetical reflection.

All the check-lists that are sufficiently good and are needed at present have been coded in this way. The chief one is, of course, the monumental *Check-list of British Insects* by G. S. Kloet and W. D. Hincks, published in 1945. Without this remarkable catalogue it would really have been very difficult to start ecological survey on this scale at all. The professional taxonomist will no doubt feel that no check-list of species is permanent, and this is true. But in so far as the greater part of the taxonomic changes that are ceaselessly introduced refer to nomenclature rather than to substantive differences such as new species, it is quite feasible, at any rate for a number of years to come, to choose a good basic list and stick to it. There remain, however, some real (as distinct from name) changes to be considered. There is a constant trickle of alterations that represent real splits within species, newly discovered forms, and sometimes really incorrect placing of species in genera or families. To take care of these matters, the Survey has a series of loose-leaf books of octavo size for each of the groups that has a coded check-list. The latter is typed out and the appropriate coding numbers put opposite each name (and also the symbol for its occurrence at Wytham). Any additions to species or genera can then be added and coded quite easily. Each book also has a page for any species that requires taxonomic annotation, as an index to current changes. Every now and then it turns out that a species hitherto treated in Britain as one (e.g. the common wood-ant, *Formica rufa*, or the snail *Cochlicopa lubrica*) really consists of two or more genuinely distinct populations of species rank. In such instances all ecological records up to the time of the new splitting have to be kept separately and new pockets of punch-cards begun for the later ones. It does not follow that the general category 'wood-ant' is necessarily made useless by the fact that it contains several species, but it could be quite misleading for exact ecological work. It will be realized also that it is important to record not only the date that an observation has been made or a specimen collected, but the date it has been named. This point is considered again in connection with voucher specimens.

I think it should be understood that the use of ordinary Linnaean species as the primary ecological unit for a survey does not mean that the existence of polymorphism in natural populations is overlooked, and it may well be that future research will uncover a large number of ecotypes that are sufficiently important to be treated quite separately. My own view is that, provided this idea is recognized, it is a matter of practical convenience what level of demographic homogeneity is regarded as most relevant in the distribution and relationships of animals. For some purposes one can deal with large categories such as 'grazing animals', 'burying-beetles', 'dung-beetles' or 'oak moths'; for others one might use a genus such as *Necrophorus* or *Aphodius;* for most ordinary purposes one uses the grouped data that we treat as species, though no modern biologist regards them as homogeneous. For some ecological problems the biological race may be a vital unit – as has become clear enough with malaria mosquitoes. The trained ecologist should obviously be quick to detect any anomalies in the behaviour or habitats of what he has been treating as one species, and be prepared to find that they have some genetic basis.

I now return to the treatment of the information placed on a punch-card, which is either complete as far as it goes, or is an abstract or index to larger sources. The species code-number is entered on the card, and above it in pencil the first letter of the genus and the full name of the species, e.g. *V. crabro,* but not the species authority (though the latter is, however, put on the guide-card for the pocket holding each pack of species punch-cards). The addition of the abbreviated name greatly reduces the chance of sorting and filing errors. From the entries on the card, which can be understood from Fig. 4, it is now possible to punch the edges for the locality, whether the plant species and part of the plant are given, any of eleven brief biological categories such as 'Mortality', and finally the habitat hierarchy. The time, date, life-stage of animals, what specimens have been kept, and some other kinds of information are not punched. To do so would require an enormous card, or else one based upon complicated code-numbering. (It is a good principle to code as little as possible through unintelligible numbers.) I will not attempt to describe all the detailed procedures by which habitats are punch-carded, as these are best explained on the spot to people who really wish to employ such methods. They do require a disciplined training, particularly in order to arrive at standard decisions about border-line cases. Two examples will show the general method. Suppose a record is of wasps, *Vespula vulgaris,* visiting flowers of the water figwort, *Scrophularia aquatica,* on the river-bank of the Thames. This would be punched A-T for Transition, C for medium-sized water body, 3 for medium speed; with two holes under Plant, – Species and Flower. Suppose, again, that it is the Lucanid beetle, *Sinodendron cylindricum,* in rotting wood of a beech log, in a glade of an oak–ash–sycamore–beech wood. This would be punched T for Terrestrial, Formation (-type) 5 for Deciduous Woodland, and Edge for glade, Layer 2 for Ground Zone, and under General Habitat the hole for Dying and Dead Wood; also Species under Plant. Had it been a conifer wood, the Qualifier 'Conif.' would also be punched.

Two more stages of assembly remain. One is the storage of voucher specimens for some of the records. There are three reasons for keeping specimens as evidence for the correct identification of material. One is that however careful an ecologist may be, and however good he may be also as a taxonomist, he may make a straight-forward mistake in naming a specimen. In zoology generally this appears to be accepted quite calmly as a research hazard of unknown size. We tend just to believe that the identifications are correct, until some remarkable anomaly comes to light. The depth and number of errors that may be built into published zoological work as irrecoverable fallacies through not keeping relevant voucher specimens may be quite serious. The practical reasons why this danger is written off are usually real enough: the cost of keeping vast collections for this purpose, the tendency hitherto for even ecologists to limit themselves to small groups of species that they become quite familiar with, and for the very reasons I have mentioned, a distrust of ecological surveys on any broad basis. The next reason for backing observations with specimens is that the substance of their taxonomy may change, as when one species has been concealing a mixture of several. The third is not in quite the same category. It is the need to build up 'life-group' collections to illustrate the communities living in different habitats. This has been done with some success in the Wytham Ecological Survey, and is proving of educational value. Much remains to be done to make such life-group collections self-explanatory of the structure and organization of communities, and to make them at all complete.

The genuine dilemma of how to ensure accuracy of identifications in a continuing ecological survey without building a museum of enormous size can be solved by the following ideas, for which I am partly indebted to Prof. E. W. Fager and Prof. C. Overgaard Nielsen. It is impossible to back every punch-card record with a specimen. A large number of species are either quite certainly identifiable correctly (for example, the heron, *Ardea cinerea*, or the stag-beetle, *Sinodendron cylindricum*), or else will have been named by a recognized authority on the group. A number of others can be correctly understood if (as with the punch-card and the specimen labels concerned) the date of naming is always inserted; for this at any rate tells one how up-to-date the identification is. For the rest it is usually only necessary to keep voucher specimens for quite a few of the records, provided they are all from the one place like Wytham Woods. The reasoning here is that in case of doubt one can return to the area and collect more material for verification, and as the whole survey becomes more and more complete negative knowledge will become increasingly reliable. Thus a record of some species in a well-studied group never encountered during the previous twenty years would be given special scrutiny, and of course a specimen kept. Another point is that an ecological study, even of one event, may involve a record of a large number of individuals in the field, from which only a sample can be taken for identification. If these are herons or *Sinodendron*, of which only one easily known species of each exists in Britain, no trouble arises. But a swarm of flies in some rather obscure group is another matter. But in this instance, twenty voucher specimens have little more validity than one. The field ecologist learns to make sensible sampling decisions, which incidentally are enormously helped if the fauna of an area is already well surveyed.

Not infrequently it is necessary to bring specimens into the laboratory for close examination, or to be stored until they can be properly identified, and these can often be thrown away later on. Such temporary vouchers are always necessary if the ability of the collector to make a reliable field identification is in any doubt. This point is mentioned because it is not unusual for a person who is doing intensive work on some group of animals or community which he thoroughly knows, to bring in information about other ecological events with which he is not so familiar. In an earlier essay[130] I drew attention to the fact that we are all to some extent amateurs: 'Our subject-matter is so wide that it includes vast outer fringes with which we have only an amateur acquaintance. This is true of nearly all scientific research, but of ecology par excellence.' And I recounted the story of an Oxford professor of theology who was a brilliant 'amateur' taxonomist, to whom I took a rare local snail whose identification I was a little doubtful about; and how he remarked: 'You know, you amateurs have all the luck!' and then added, at my look of surprise: 'If you know what I mean.' I knew what he meant.

The life-group collections can and do use voucher specimens for their display material, others where necessary being kept in a separate series of storage containers. All the material is kept, not in taxonomic order, but according to the habitat components used by the Survey. This rather unusual feature of such an ecological museum is not inconvenient in practice, even for tracing material for purely taxonomic reference, for it can always be tracked down quickly by using the punch-cards – frequently indeed by direct reference from knowing the normal habitats of the species. This arrangement not only has the educational advantage already referred to, by which a student or research worker can see a series of communities (or rather samples of their main species) arranged according to an ecological, instead of a taxonomic logic; it also provides a useful short-cut in naming field material – assuming of course that the specimens are verified afterwards in the ordinary way. The habitat classification used for these purposes is not the full number of components that the system could provide, but a smaller number that includes some groupings of the components. These are summarized on a Habitat Card, forming a bridge between the Punch-card and the Community List, which is the immediate objective of the Survey.

In the previous chapter the need to reduce the total number of habitat components for working purposes was explained and some examples were given. In particular the groupings reduce the danger of making an unnecessary number of rather similar community lists of species, and also the methods by which collecting is done themselves frequently group the information from more than one habitat zone – as when a core sample is cut through grass litter and soil and the fauna extracted in a single operation. Each pocket of punch-cards for one species has in the front a corresponding Habitat Card (Fig. 5) on which the partly grouped components are summarized in an abbreviated form. The version shown here has been slightly modified since it was first printed, and we now treat Subterranean as a separate System, and High Air should be added as another. Certain further subdivisions have also been introduced, but will not be discussed here. The card has 67 defined units for the Terrestrial System, 17 for Transition, 29 for Aquatic, 8 for General, 2 for Domestic, with 1 Subterranean. These, including High Air,

TERR. /5 DECID.	EDGE	TERR. /4 DECID.	EDGE	TERR. /3 ARABLE	EDGE	AQUA—TERR. BI & CI	AQUATIC A1	AQUATIC A2—5	GENERAL UNDEF.
4—6	←	4—6	←	3 & 6	←	0—W	0—W	0—W	FUNGUS
3	-	3	-	1—2	-	W	W. TR—H	W	D/D WOOD
2	-	2	-	0	-	UNDEF.	W. 0—TR—H	UNDEF.	DECID.
1	-	1	-	ACID	←	DI & EI	UNDEF.	B4—5. C4—5	CONIF.
0	-	0	-	3 & 6	-	A2—5	BI & CI	B2—3	UNDEF.
CONIF.	←	CONIF.	←	1—2	-	0—W	0—W	C2—3 & D3	DUNG
4—6	-	4—6	-	0	-	W	5—6	5—6	CARRION
3	-	3	-	0—ACID	←	UNDEF.	4	4	AN/ART.
2	-	2	-	3 & 6	-	B4—5. C4—5	2—3	2—3	3—5
1	-	1	-	1—2	-	B2—3	1	1	1—2
0	-	0	-	0	-	C2—3. D2—3	0	0	UNDEF.
MIXED	←	MIXED	←	MARIT.	←	BR.	W	BR.	HUM/ART.
4—6	-	4—6	-	3 & 6	-	A—E1	5—6	A—E1	STACKS
3	-	3	-	1—2	-	A—E2—5	4	A—E2—5	UNDEF.
2	-	2	-	0	-	UNDEF.	2—3	UNDEF.	SUBTERR.
1	-	1	-	UNDEF.	←	SAL.	1	SAL.	
0	-	0	-	3 & 6	-	NOT BY WATER	0		DOMESTIC
UNDEF.	←	UNDEF.	←	1—2	-	0—W. 0—ACID	UNDEF.		UNDEF.
4—6	-	4—6	-	0	-	0—W. ACID	5—6		BUILDING
3	-	3	-			0—W. MARIT	4		GARDEN
2	-	2	-	TERR. /2		0—W. UNDEF.	2—3		
1	-	1	-	ACID		W	1		
0	-	0	-	0—ACID		BR.	0		
				MARIT.		UNDEF.	DI & EI		
				UNDEF.			5—6		
							4		
							3		
							2 L		
							2 D		
							1 L		
							1 D		
							0		

FIG. 5. Habitat card used by the Wytham Ecological Survey. Left to right: Woodland, Scrub, Field Types and Open Ground; Transition; Aquatic; General, and Domestic. Subterranean (with High Air, not included here) now treated as separate Systems. Top space used for publication reference in classified literature. (Actual size 4 × 6in.)

total 125. There are also a number of categories marked 'O' for 'Undefined', to take care of unclassified or not clearly separated habitat records: some of these are not used very much, others contain distinct components of which we know rather little. In each Terrestrial Formation-type, the column of numbers represents the Vertical Layers: 4-6 is Canopy and Air Above, 3 the Field Layer, 2 the Ground Zone and 1 the Topsoil and Subsoil. The Aquatic and Transition codes follow the chart for Size and Speed given in Fig. 3 (p. 75), and 'W' stands for 'Woody'. Again, the vertical columns shown under ponds, lakes and rivers represent the Vertical Layers, 5-6 stands for Emergent Vegetation and Air Above, 4 for Water

Surface, 2-3 for Water Mass and Submerged Vegetation, and 1 for Bottom (in Lakes with either L for Light or D for Dark (Profundal) zones). The Animal Artefacts (mainly nests) are divided into two zones: field layer to canopy, and soil to ground zone.

Every habitat record that goes on to a species punch-card is eligible for entry on to the habitat card, but a certain number, though retained for information about the species, are excluded and a pencil note made on the punch-card to that effect. Here again decisions have to be made, the issue being whether a species 'belongs' or does not 'belong' to a particular habitat (or community) defined by this habitat. Or rather, whether the record gives evidence that the species does, probably does or might belong there. To some extent, therefore, one is making a reasonable hypothesis about the ecological status of each record and of each species, which will eventually be re-considered carefully before final verdict in the form of publication. It is most important that it should be understood that the allotment of a species to its community is subject to a number of criteria, depending upon one's notions about the nature of communities. In this survey the main criteria are these: (1) the less mobile an animal is the more likely it is to belong to the habitat in which it is recorded; (2) it follows that larval stages of insects are better evidence in many instances than the presence of adults; (3) any proof of a biological function being performed there is important – feeding, breeding, hibernating and so on, and this can frequently be inferred from the known habits of the animal elsewhere, as when an insect is attached to only one plant; (4) in any event substantial numbers are regarded as important, whether the animal normally lives there or not, for these may effect other species, e.g. as food supply; (5) constancy of occurrence, if only at certain times or seasons. There are other criteria as well. There is no difficulty in changing the annotation if later evidence makes it desirable.

The information is now assembled under species, and analysed on to the habitat card. The final stage is to transfer it into Community Lists. These consist of a series of loose-leaf books containing 'Kalamazoo' sheets with each side carrying about twenty-seven movable slips. Each slip has the name of a species and its code-number, and in these indexes they are arranged taxonomically within each habitat grouping. It would not be possible to assemble and manage such lists without the non-alphabetical coding that is employed in the Survey. On each slip the symbol WA is pencilled for any species known in the Wytham Area. The Survey therefore enables one to find out (1) what habitats any species is thought to live in, or known to live in; (2) in any one habitat (or near group of habitats) what the associates of any species are. The system provides an index both to the ecology of individual species and to communities. Finally, under each habitat grouping, the publications dealing with that habitat or its communities

93

are also listed, on movable slips of a different colour. These references are mainly derived from systematic screening of the incoming literature in the Bureau of Animal Population's Library for several decades, and are comprehensive. From the same screening operation an enormous amount of information about individual species has also been abstracted on to species punch-cards for the Survey

All this description of indexes and the decisions and ideas for handling them may seem a little tedious, yet it is the practical expression of a great deal of hard ecological thought. A great administrator in Oxford once remarked to me that the future of civilization depends on having really good subject-indexes. The future of ecology, with its mounting slag-heaps of information, certainly need them. How far the system described here has been successful in assembling information about the large ecosystem on Wytham Hill will have to be judged from the next fourteen chapters.

CHAPTER 6

Open Ground and Meadow

BARE GROUND and open water are the classical starting points for describing ecological succession in vegetation, with its stages (often broken, delayed or diverted) towards climax that are adopted here as the main basis for formation-types in defining animal habitats. They were indeed the actual starting points for all those parts of the country's surface covered by the last ice-sheet, or destroyed by frost and flood on the periphery (cf. Plate 11). It is now quite established[192] that a good many of the plants and at least some of the animals that had widely colonized the bare and open ground of Full-glacial and Late-glacial times – that is, over 10,000 years ago – have since survived on maritime cliffs and shingle and dune, or on mountains, where conditions are still sufficiently unstable or climatic-ally extreme to maintain the right conditions. Godwin gives a list of eighty-one such species (for example the moss campion, *Silene acaulis*, and the dwarf willow, *Salix herbacea*) of open mountain or subarctic habitats that then occurred widely in the lowlands, and are now chiefly found on cliff-ledges, screes and subalpine meadows. He also has a list of forty-six 'weeds' of arable land, saying that 'The very long list of species which we now regard as ruderals or weeds indicates the prevalence of open conditions, bare soil surfaces and freedom from competition in the Full-glacial and Late-glacial periods alike.' Some of these species are really more meadow forms than weeds of arable land, e.g. the bladder campion, *Silene cucubalus*, and the greater knapweed, *Centaurea scabiosa*. He adds. 'It is, however, easy to imagine that among the communities represented there must have been some bearing the character of the "rich-herb" communities of Scandinavia, with their deep, moist, well-aerated soils of high base status and high nitrifying power, carrying a lush vegetation of tall herbs.'

During the Late-glacial period shrubs and trees of birch, aspen and willow began to form thickets, which after a temporary recession again advanced and were in turn followed by the other trees and shrubs that produced the predominating forest cover of the country. During this sequence of events we have to imagine a steady invasion by animals, and the development of a forest and forest glade eco-system over nearly all inland localities except mountains and water. The chief open ground and field types remaining there would be formed in connection with forest glade succession, brought about by falling trees, by grazing pressures slowing down regeneration, and perhaps by fire. Later on, the clearing of forests for agriculture began to re-create open arable ground, meadow-like field margins and rough pastures on a great scale, into which spread the historically surviving species now classed as 'weeds', some of them Late-glacial, others later invaders.

The chief points emerging from this history are that open ground and field types only occur at all widely now on four kinds of habitat: (1) maritime cliffs, shingle and dunes, very rich in animal life, and though often very unstable having a permanent existence as whole ecosystems; (2) natural montane habitats above the limits of grazing, more stable than the terrestrial maritime ones, but carrying a relatively impoverished fauna, though often a very fascinating one; (3) seral stages towards scrub and woodland, very rich in woodland 'edge' animals but occurring in fairly small and rather temporary sites; (4) the whole range of habitats brought into existence by man's activities, in particular grazings, arable lands with their 'meadow' margins, roadside and railway embankment 'meadows', also many special kinds of places like golf-courses, aerodromes, parks and gardens. These habitats, between them, carry an extremely large fauna only rivalled in rich variety by that of woodland (including its dying and dead wood). In quite recent years the animal communities of arable land and of habitats nearby have been gravely threatened by modern insecticides, and those of roadside meadow (through the destruction of plant species) by herbicides; but there are already interesting symptoms of the evolution of genetic resistance in some species of plants and insects, which may slow down the destruction of these communities and partly defeat the hectic ingenuity of the organic chemist. Other tendencies are also impoverishing these habitats, apart from any contraction of their total area brought about by human spread. The practice of periodic ploughing and re-seeding grass leys greatly reduces the complexity of plant associations growing in such pastures. Afforestation is another process that is swallowing up many of the more open habitats. From the point of view of conserving this great assemblage of open ground, meadow and heathland forms, probably far the most important thing is to protect roadsides from being sprayed with herbicides, or otherwise unnecessarily simplified, rationalized or tidied. It will be seen, then, that this range of communities has historically always been somewhat on the defensive after the Late-glacial period ended, and many of them are by their nature found on unstable ground or else are temporary succession stages.

It is not the intention in this chapter (or in the rest of this book) to attempt any comprehensive treatment of the communities of animals, with huge species lists, life-histories, seasonal cycles and other details that are best shunted into monographs; nor to describe productivity or complicated food-chains, since this would still be rather premature with the census methods we possess, and our rather primitive metabolic estimates and ignorance of the rhythms of animal activity in the field. I shall only be able to indicate some of the habitat and community patterns that are to be found, and sometimes how these interlock within the system. Such patterns can be studied in three different ways. First, one can explore the relations of one major habitat or zone to another, say field type to open ground or woodland. These are the external relations. Secondly, one can trace the vertical layering within one major habitat, as with the soil, ground zone, field layer and the air above them. Thirdly, one can in some instances discern characteristic small-scale patterns mostly brought about by the action of plants and animals. Patterns of habitat usually fall into two classes. On the one hand there are zones or strips, on the other scattered interspersed patches. An example of the first is a stream flowing through a wood, of the latter logs in a wood. But if a transect is taken at right angles to such a strip or strips of habitat, you get somewhat the same effect as in crossing small patches. And of course a stream or a strip of grassland will contain internal patchy patterns along its length.

Since information about animal communities is still extremely scattered in its nature, I shall draw heavily on the results of research on Wytham Hill, where there exists a fascinating range of open ground and limestone meadow communities, mostly free from grazing by stock, though still undergoing changes caused by the removal of rabbit grazing after the myxomatosis pandemic in 1954. Examples are drawn from seven of these areas.

Rough Common (Plate 12) is an old coral reef with shallow zones of clay in places, on which can be found every ecological succession stage from the nearly bare rock of an old quarry in the very hard Wheatley limestone, up to dense meadow of tor grass or false brome, *Brachypodium pinnatum*. The calciphile flora is not as varied as it is on some of the other places, but many of the smaller grasses of chalk and limestone soils occur. There are some scattered shrubs and the main woods begin at the edge. It is no longer common land, having been enclosed about 150 years ago. Quarter of a mile to the south there is a smaller and warmer slope of dense *Brachypodium* grass, flanked by elder scrub and beech woods, called The Dell (Frontispiece). Between the two lies a big field, most of which has now been re-ploughed for ley grass pasture, though at the time of the investigations mentioned below it had been abandoned for several years and carried a good limestone meadow on ground that had many loose coral stones lying on the surface. This field, of which five acres are maintained as a fenced meadow reserve, is called Upper Seeds. A little lower down the hill, with a woodland shelter belt between, is Lower Seeds, a stock-grazed field also on limestone, the upper five acres of which are fenced off and maintained as a biological reserve. This is a tall and mixed grass–herb meadow.

Below The Dell, separated by some elder scrub and trees, is Wytham Park (Plate 69), a shallow valley lying between the two main hills. Most of it is farm land now, but five acres at the head of the Park are kept as a biological reserve for the yellow ant mound and gallery system that almost covers it everywhere (Plate 56). In order to keep the conditions right for this ancient ant civilization cattle-grazing continues here. A few hundred yards beyond lies a very interesting but somewhat complex area on the edges of the woodland. The Bowling Alley (so known since at least the eighteenth century though there is no historical evidence of its sporting value) is two acres of Coral Rag ground, i.e. the surface is covered with small lumps of coral debris and the soil is very shallow. Although rather closely sheltered by pine and birch and maple and other trees, it carries mainly open ground and meadow flora including grass species characteristic of chalk grassland. Separated from it by a narrow belt of scrub is Sundays Hill, larger area of four acres, now consisting mainly of *Brachypodium* or mixed grass meadow, but formerly having also large patches of rabbit-grazed *Festuca rubra* turf or low sward. This variety of habitats within less than a square mile suggests the wealth of plant and animal life that may develop in calcareous open ground and meadow communities.

The differences in fauna of open ground and field type are shown by some measurements of grasshopper populations on Rough Common that were carried out as field class exercises by students in the years 1948-50, 1952-4 and 1956. They were partly planned by Prof. Thomas Park and myself, and were carried out by H. N. Southern and R. B. Freeman, to whom I owe the use of the information here. On this area there are eight species of Orthoptera, five of which (four ordinary grasshoppers and one 'grouse locust', *Tetrix vittata*) inhabit open ground and field type, the other three being 'long-horned' grasshoppers living on scrub and trees. The annual exercise was done by students in September, when the adult populations have developed, and it was designed to show the changes in the fauna from bare ground up to dense meadow. The information for the first year will not be used, because of doubt about the identification of one species, but otherwise the observers quickly learned to name the species and had the help of instructors as well. Each of the three or four pairs of observers tried to collect a fixed number (usually ten, but not always attained if the animals were scarce) of grasshoppers in each of the four following habitats: (1) Almost bare rocky ground with little but low mosses and lichens (Plate 14); (2) rabbit-grazed or formerly rabbit-grazed turf of *Festuca* etc. (Plate 13); (3) short rough grass, *Brachypodium pinnatum*, mainly below 6 in. (Plate 15); (4) dense growth of tall *Brachypodium* (Plates 3 and 16). The first three habitat types were interspersed in rather scattered and not always large patches, so that there was probably some accidental movement of the grasshoppers across their boundaries. The fourth was mainly one large area of tall grass containing however some anthills with shorter vegetation. The results for the six separate years need not be given, since the same kind of dispersion through this habitat zonation is shown clearly each year. The totals are given in Table 2, and it is

TABLE 2. Habitat zones of four species of grasshoppers on Wytham Hill

	Habitat zone				Total
	Bare ground	Turf	Short grass	Long grass	
Tetrix vittata	47	24	16	I	
%	*16·49*	*9·27*	*6·18*	*0·37*	
Myrmeleotettix maculatus	159	86	80	0	
%	*55·79*	*33·205*	*30·89*	*0·0*	
Chorthippus brunneus (= *bicolor*)	71	86	90	18	
%	*24·91*	*33·205*	*34·75*	*6·67*	
Chorthippus parallelus	8	63	73	251	
%	*2·81*	*24·32*	*28·19*	*92·96*	
Total	285	259	259	270	1073

important to recognize that they form only a spectrum of the relative species composition habitat by habitat, not the absolute density of the population: for a collector would stop after catching ten animals, whether the populations were abundant or not, and it will be shown below that the densities were not the same every year. The percentages are of the total in each vertical column; these percentages may be compared for species or for habitats, i.e. vertically within each habitat, or horizontally for species. One species, *Omocestus viridulus*, is omitted, since only five specimens were caught altogether during these counts: four were in zone 4 and one in zone 3. In interpreting the figures, the factor of relative conspicuousness may possibly play some part, though most of the counting was done by 'walking up' the animals and seeing them when they moved. It cannot affect the main conclusions.

The commonest species on the nearly bare ground was *Myrmeleotettix*, and this was also true in each separate year, the percentages varying between 46 and 87. This dominance falls away steadily to zero in the long grass, where *Chorthippus parallelus* formed in each separate year 84 to 98% of the catch. *Myrmeleotettix* is not confined to limestone grassland but has a very wide range of habitats in Britain as far as soil and plant associations are concerned. It can live on short limestone grass and rather bare chalk downs, also on heaths and sand-dunes.[407] Its needs, whatever they are, do not seem to be connected with details of the plant species though the grasshoppers do require grass as food, but probably with general structural features resulting from it, and concomitant microclimatic conditions. 'Open ground' as used here would include many of its known habitats, though there appear also to be some that are a mixture of open ground and field type; for this species, like the *Chorthippus*, needs some patches of bare ground in which to lay its egg pods. In the intermediate habitats on Rough Common, *Myrmeleotettix* and the two *Chorthippus* occur together in not very unequal numbers, though *C. parallelus* is the least abundant of the three. Other information suggests that *C. brunneus* is usually commonest in low vegetation or in higher field types which have bare ground between. Richards and Waloff[407] for example point out that it can tolerate the loose sand of marram dunes in a way that *C. parallelus* cannot, and that the latter can on the other hand tolerate long grass and damper conditions.

The picture given here is an 'instantaneous' one taken during the first half of September, and is only intended to show that the broad distinction between open ground and field type communities can be a useful one. It is known that these two *Chorthippus* species do not have a single fixed habitat at all stages of their life in summer, or even in different kinds of season. They may undertake short movements for egg-laying in more open patches, or slightly alter their distribution according to the density of numbers. Another point needs mention: it is obvious from Table 2 alone that when one combines the data into a 'community of open ground', one is using a grouping method that by its nature always conceals some of the internal differences in dispersion within this broad category. Even on Rough Common there will be such subdivisions as bare ground versus turf and short grass, or turf versus short grass. In fact, as was said earlier, whatever one adopts as a 'major habitat', it will have both external relations and internal relations that make up the total pattern.

On the woodland side of this transect of habitats, there are also field layer communities in the open, but they belong to the relatively narrow zone at the woodland edge, or in some instances at the edge of a wide belt of scrub in front of the wood itself. These field layers on Rough Common can be tall grassland of the wood small-reed, *Calamagrostis epigejos*, or bracken, *Pteridium aquilinum*, or bramble – mostly *Rubus vestitus* [2]. The only one of these concerned in the grasshopper sequence is bramble, which often carries a population of a large vigorous long-horned grasshopper, *Pholidoptera griseoaptera*. In the woodland canopy is a small pale green long-horned grasshopper, *Meconema thalassinum*; here also sometimes occurs another species, *Leptophyes punctatissima*, that equally turns up on scrub or low sapling growth. The eight species occupy different stages of a partly stepped vegetation succession from bare ground to the canopy of oak or sycamore.

In any one of the zones within open ground to field type, although the species composition is characteristic (apart from some minor variations from year to year in the two intermediate ones), the absolute numbers of the population may also fluctuate. This was proved by some estimates of the *Chorthippus parallelus* populations derived by H. N. Southern from another simple class exercise, which will not be described in detail here. On the area of about 5000 square yards on Rough Common dominated by long *Brachypodium pinnatum*, counts were made by parties varying in numbers from eight to twenty-two people, in the years 1948-50, 1952-4 and 1956. Each year some hundreds of these green wingless grasshoppers were marked with spots of orange paint, and then an hour or two later further recaptures made, so that from the ratio of marked to unmarked animals the total population could be calculated. The absolute population densities per square yard calculated were as follows:

1948	1·0
1949	0·5
1950	1·1
1952	0·45
1953	0·28
1954	0·20
1956	0·19

In the first four years the density varied between one and half per square yard, but thereafter fell to a fifth of the original level.

Richards and Waloff[407] measured similar fluctuations in several species of grasshoppers in an area of acid grassland mostly dominated by *Festuca rubra* and *Agrostis tenuis* on light soil at Silwood Park in south Berkshire. This was part of a very elaborate field study and analysis of the populations in which marking and recapture were used to assess the adult numbers. During the five years 1947-51 the estimated total amplitude of changes in one large colony living on one area of about 2620 square yards, or a little over half an acre, was 3·2 times for *C. brunneus* and 5·5 times for *C. parallelus*. The maximum number of the former on this part of the area was 3500, or about 1·4 per square yard, and of the latter 6000 or about 2·3 per square yard. These generalized figures do not take any account of local differences in dispersion, and it is not to be assumed that both species were randomly interspersed; but without information about the vegetation structure it is not possible to make an exact comparison with the Wytham Hill sequence. The two places are compared here mainly in order to illustrate the point that there is such a thing as 'the grasshopper community of grassland' (or of open ground and field type): four of the five species are the same in each place (the two *Chorthippus*, *Myrmeleotettix maculatus*, and *Omocestus viridulus*), the fluctuations and the population density of *C. parallelus* are of the same order of magnitude, though density rose higher at Silwood Park. But the actual vegetation is different in species composition, Rough Common having a spectrum very like chalk grass, while Silwood Park has acid grass heath.

The habitat zones on Rough Common are fairly natural ones. But the definition of open ground habitats, in which no vegetation is more than half a foot, was chosen also because of the huge areas of grazed land that exist in Britain. A recent survey by Southwood and Jepson[468] of flies whose larvae bore inside grass stems suggests that the faunal distinction between this kind of open ground and taller grass meadow is also rather sharp. The survey was also done at Silwood Park and on the same general area, though it extended beyond natural grassland on to managed land. The grassland types were classified at first into (1) uncut natural grassland, unexploited by man since at least before the second World War, and carrying mainly a *Festuca-Agrostis* meadow, (2) grazed or closely mown natural grass of the same original type, (3) re-sown ley grass with cocksfoot, *Dactylis*, and rye-grass, *Lolium*. But the authors say: 'The present studies have, however, convinced us that the most useful division is into long (uncut) and short (grazed or mown) grasslands, grazed leys being included in the latter.' In other words, once more, the structure of the vegetation was on the whole more important to the animals than its grass species composition. The main subject of the survey was the frit-fly (*Oscinella frit*), a major pest of oats that also lives on a number of grasses. With it were also fourteen other stem-boring species, chiefly of the families Chloropidae and Opomyzidae, and most of these have more than one plant 'host', some of them many. The numbers of frit-flies emerging into field traps in the short grass was about 11 per square yard, but only 0·8 in the long grass, with corresponding differences in the numbers of larvae in the stems. But population densities in any grassland are enormously lower than in panicles of oats. Although there are no details it is implied that other stem-borers show similar differences in short and long grass.

Some further aspects of the distribution of grasshopper populations will be noticed when smaller patterns within a habitat are discussed later in this chapter. The next step now is to look at vertical zonation. In open ground there are already four vertical habitat zones: subsoil, topsoil, ground zone and the air above them. There are some versions of open ground that really have the subsoil at the surface, that is to say there may be bare material with no organic matter mixed with it. This is not merely the primordial bare ground on which plant succession starts, but is often colonized by animals even before any vegetation becomes established. Some bees, wasps and ants are especially prominent among these invaders. Also quite large bare areas of subsoil are opened up by burrowing animals themselves, in particular by the rabbit, fox and badger; but in open ground outside woods it is mainly rabbits that have been responsible for this though in most places now their burrows have been destroyed or the rabbits themselves have died of epidemic. One of the classical studies of zonation from bare ground through open ground vegetation into heath of grass or heather, was done many years ago by Farrow[150] in East Anglia on ground dominated by rabbit grazing. (Even after the disappearance of rabbits, their works may live after them for some years. On The Dell, at Wytham, there was in 1950 one large rabbit bury in the midst of grass meadow, and marked by a large patch of nettles, one of the plants avoided by them as food.[150] Comparison of air photographs of Wytham Hill for 1953 and 1960 showed that the nettle patch has persisted long after the rabbits died and has actually spread slightly.) A large book could be written just about the habits of creatures that use bare ground for making burrows, and the subject has only been glanced at here. It is referred to again in the next chapter.

Of course the formal separation of lateral and vertical zonation is in a sense arbitrary, because the very nature of open ground is that it is more exposed to weather and has a different cover structure, so that it is the addition of a field layer that not only provides a new environment for field layer species, but also profoundly influences the conditions of the more sheltered ground below it. The vertical structure of meadow communities can be illustrated by some field work on the warm slope of The Dell at Wytham Hill, carried out by C. Overgaard Nielsen and A. Macfadyen between April 1950 and March 1951. They chose a square of almost pure dense *Brachypodium pinnatum* meadow and took randomized samples every fortnight by means of small cores (varying in size according to the organisms under study). Their aim was to obtain a complete census of as many of the animal groups as possible, and from this to attempt some calculations of the productivity. The task proved much more difficult than had been anticipated, because the standard large Tullgren funnels did not extract small arthropods sufficiently completely to provide a good basis for productivity estimates, and because many questions connected with the combination of population figures with metabolic rates still remained to be solved. The material was therefore handed over to me for the Ecological Survey, and has since been identified as far as practicable. But several other results did accrue from the investigation. Overgaard Nielsen[352] invented a quite new method for almost completely extracting Enchytraeid worms from soil, though here again much further work had to be done on taxonomy of this group, now comprehensively available in his European monograph (with B. Christensen[355]). Secondly, he measured the effects of the pill millipede, *Glomeris marginata*, upon conversion of grass litter. Thirdly, Macfadyen[307, 308] went on to make many improvements in the Tullgren funnel apparatus, of which the final end is still not yet reached – it is still very difficult to extract some arthropods completely from some soils, though from habitats of looser texture like leaf litter and nests it is fairly easy now.

This *Brachypodium* grass slope was chosen because it seemed a rather simple kind of habitat compared with a mixed limestone meadow. This was certainly true in two important respects though not in others. First, there was virtually nothing but this one species of green plant, a solid natural stand of pure dominant. And secondly this species carries extremely few kinds of herbivorous insects on its stems and foliage. Its tissue is known to be very tough, for example it is not generally grazed by cattle[239] and it will clog up the machines used to grind it for chemical analysis. It also contains silica to the amount of 3%, as was discovered during Overgaard Nielsen's investigation mentioned below. (Some other species of relatively unpalatable plants that have poor insect faunas also have a considerable silica content, as bracken,[152, 331] mat-grass, *Nardus stricta*,[375, 401] and horsetails (*Equisetum*), some of whose species have so much silica in their epidermis that they retain a transparent skeleton of it even when the rest of the tissue is removed.[483]) The only herbivorous invertebrates seen to be attached to the grass above ground on the sampling area were one or two examples of Chloropid flies. This may or may not be an entirely general phenomenon; but the herbivorous fauna is undoubtedly very poor both in species and numbers, compared with that of a good many other grasses. Though *Chorthippus parallelus*, as already described, can be abundant on places dominated by *Brachypodium pinnatum*, the 94 field observations of grass-eating by this species in various parts of England made by Clarke[71a] give only one instance of *B. pinnatum*. On Rough Common, as distinct from this patch of The Dell, are found all nine of the other species mentioned by Tansley[493] as characteristic of chalk grassland, and it is likely that these provide the main grasshopper food. On The Dell sampling area no grasshoppers were observed.

Brachypodium pinnatum is a native grass that has been spreading like an invader on many calcareous parts of southern Britain in recent decades.[493] According to Hope-Simpson's[444] wide survey of the South Downs, both *Bromus erectus* and *Brachypodium pinnatum* tend to come in and dominate chalk pastures that have continued under-grazing, or where grazing ceases. His careful search in 1935-6 of the areas specially studied by Tansley and Adamson in 1920-1 revealed that on the eastern half of the region, where sheep flocks had diminished, *Brachypodium* had begun to spread in some places. For example, it had newly appeared as one patch on a slope that had the following history: grazed by sheep and heavily populated by rabbits in 1910, rabbits still numerous in 1920, completely enclosed for forestry in 1932 with all rabbits killed and grazing stopped. In 1935-6 there were very young trees in the grassland. The *Brachypodium* could not have been there in 1920. Whereas the invasion by *Bromus erectus* can be fairly quickly reversed by grazing since both

11. High Arctic tundra or fjaeldmark with glacial erratic boulders, on Reindeer Peninsula, West Spitsbergen (Svalbard), suggesting the Open Ground of Britain in Late Glacial times. (Photo C. S. E. 16 Aug. 1924)

12. Open Ground and Field Type (with mixtures and scattered scrub) forming limestone grassland in an old quarry, Rough Common, Wytham Woods. (Photo D. A. K. 7 Sept. 1950)

13 & 14. Open Ground on Rough Common, Wytham Woods. In the upper photo rabbit-grazed turf, in the lower one bare ground with low tussocks of *Brachypodium pinnatum*. (Photos D. A. K. 7 Sept. 1950)

15 & 16. Field Types on Rough Common, Wytham Woods. In the upper photo tussocks of *Brachypodium pinnatum* with patches of Open Ground, forming mixed formation-types; below, solid pure stand of this grass. (Photos D. A. K. 7 Sept. 1950)

17. Mixed Open Ground and Field Type on sheep-grazed mountains in the Lake District, rising to subalpine zone on Skiddaw beyond. (Photo C. S. E. 17 Aug. 1958)

18. Montane Open Ground on Cairn Gorm, Inverness-shire, seen from *c.* 3500 ft, with *Calluna–Empetrum* mats and unclosed vegetation. (Photo C. S. E. 2 Sept. 1959)

19. Sea-cliff grassland and other Terrestrial Maritime Open Ground and Field Types (including wind-cut scrub) at Broad Haven, Pembrokeshire. (Photo C. S. E. High tide, 28 Aug. 1957)

20. 10-mile long shingle bank of Chesil Beach, Dorset, looking east, with patches of sea pea, *Lathyrus maritimus*. (Photo C. S. E. 17 July 1963)

21. Junction of sea and land, Druidston Haven, Pembrokeshire. The Terrestrial Maritime zone starts a few feet above H.W.M., with a mixture of grassland, woodland and maritime animals: among the last, the Coreid bug *Enoplops scapha* lives here. (Photo C. S. E. 15 Aug. 1959)

22 & 23. A growing sand-dune system on the R. Camel estuary, N. Cornwall. Two main ridges covered with marram grass have an embryonic fore-dune in front, shown close up in the lower photo: 10 and 20 years before, the main ridges were each like this. (Photos C. S. E. 4 Aug. 1954)

24. Sheep Drove, a high double hawthorn hedge, with chalk scrub, flanking a green trackway over the Downs at Leckford, Hampshire. (Photo C. S. E. 26 Oct. 1938)

cattle and sheep eat it readily, that of *Brachypodium* is not reversible at all easily since stock usually only eat the young shoots and reject the mature grass.[443] I have watched adult sheep completely avoiding small patches of this grass growing on close-grazed pasture of *Bromus mollis* etc. on Lower Seeds at Wytham, and only one lamb in its inexperience trying to nibble the tough material. Usually the most that can happen is that continual grazing and trampling by stock may reduce its dominance, to give a mixed plant association. Hope-Simpson[443] (writing of course before the appearance of suitable herbicides) notes that 'To all appearances *Brachypodium* invasion on an unploughable hillside is a more or less irreversible occurrence'. I suspect that the trampling may be even more important than actual nibbling, for during the early summer this grass, with its silica stiffening, is easily broken by trampling (as also is bracken when young). This effect of trampling, in this instance by human beings, can be seen on Rough Common, where orchids, gentians, bedstraw and small grasses are able to grow in patches where the dominant grass has been broken. The Dell itself has not been grazed for many years, and has had little treading by man.

In 1950-1 rabbits were still present on Wytham hilltop, and exercising a profound influence on the structure of vegetation, particularly by creating more open ground habitats. How far they eat *Brachypodium* is not directly known, but it must be relatively unpalatable to them since it existed in tall and dense stands next to grasses like *Festuca rubra* that were kept low or as turf. (Hope-Simpson[443] thought that they had greatly helped to check *Brachypodium* invasion on the downs of West Sussex and East Hampshire before the last war.) The coincidence of rabbits dying off (in 1954) and the sheep being excluded from some pasture on the lower slopes of the hill produced a striking spread of *B. pinnatum* there. The vole, *Microtus agrestis*, on the other hand is evidently more effective in grazing it and is periodically common on The Dell. This point will be dealt with in the discussion of tussock patterns, but needs mentioning now because the very large amount of dung produced by voles may be playing some role in the origin of soil humus. The interest of the community as far as vertical stratification is concerned therefore centres upon the way in which material from the grass above ground falling as winter litter, or arriving as a result of vole activity, eventually provides the resources of the topsoil communities. Below ground *B. pinnatum* supports a larger insect population in the form of root aphids which in turn may be tended by yellow ants (*Lasius flavus*) whose 'cattle' they are. Root aphids were not actually studied during the investigation in 1950-1, but there was at least one large yellow ant nest on the sampling area, and in 1957 A. J. Pontin found *Forda formicaria* on the roots of *B. pinnatum* on The Dell, in association with *Lasius flavus*. This aphid is not confined to one sort of grass, having also been taken by him at Wytham on *Festuca* and *Lolium*.

For the next part of this story, concerned with the part played by animals in the conversion cycle of dead *Brachypodium pinnatum* litter, I am greatly indebted to Professor C. Overgaard Nielsen, who has given me unpublished information about his work in 1950-1. It was ascertained that when the year's 'crop' of dead *Brachypodium* foliage on the sampling area at The Dell died in autumn, virtually all its nitrogen that had been present in July had already been withdrawn by the plants into their roots, as also largely happens with deciduous trees (a process which must certainly have some effect on the resources of root aphids and ants). Only a fifth of the nitrogen remained, and this was locked up in the lignin fraction of the litter, which was therefore deficient in nitrogenous food, and consisted mostly of structural polysaccharides (cellulose, xylan, etc.), lignin, and a small amount of silica, the only important inorganic constituent. By far the most abundant litter-feeding animal on the ground among the *Brachypodium* tussocks is the large black millipede, *Glomeris marginata*, which looks at first glance more like a woodlouse and has the ability to roll up into a ball like the litter-feeding wood-louse, *Armadillidium vulgare*, which also lives on this site. A transect of The Dell by means of jam-jar traps set in the ground, done in May 1951 and visited every day or two for about a month, caught in the six points situated in almost pure *Brachypodium* 1938 *Glomeris marginata* and 400 *Armidillidium vulgare*. Though this method is a very rough one for comparing numbers, since it depends upon the habits and movements of species, the ratio of abundance between these two eco-logically similar species is certainly reflected in the figures. The Tullgren sample extracts were not far different. The numbers of *Glomeris* were counted from the Tullgren funnel samples and also some washed out from special cores. The former are known to be less than the actual numbers present on the ground, since not all came through the extraction process (which depends for its efficiency on the behaviour of animals towards gradients in temperature and humidity, and on their ability to wend their way down through the material of soil and litter in the funnels). It was found that towards the end of the first year on the ground, the mat of grass litter had begun to acquire some nitrogen, evidently through micro-biological activity. It was during the second year of its existence that the litter was eaten by *Glomeris*, which chew it up and use presumably not only the grass material, but probably still more the bacteria and fungi that have intermingled with it. The rate of feeding was measured in the laboratory, by the ingenious method of weighing the silica excreted by the millipedes, and from it and the known percentage of silica in the grass calculating the total amount of food in-gested. The census figures suggested that not only was the *Glomeris* population consuming practically the whole crop of litter after it had first lain for about one year, but that some of the young in the following summer may have been dying from food shortage.

From all this it is concluded that *Glomeris marginata* was the main eater of

Brachypodium litter on the area sampled, also that it must facilitate the incorporation of the litter into the soil in several ways, as by breaking it up into small pieces, adding faecal pellets, and also leaving some of the animal matter in the form of moulted chitin and dead millipedes. More recently Overgaard Nielsen,[354] in the course of a study of the feeding enzymes of a number of soil and litter invertebrates, found that almost all of the ones that he tested, with the exception of slugs and snails, lack the cellulase enzyme necessary for converting cellulose for food. Among this large group that must have at least one intermediate and external bacterial link in the chain between dead litter and its own metabolism, is *Glomeris*, which has not got cellulase, xylenase or pectinase, though it can digest sugars and starches. Therefore, before *Brachypodium* can be digested by these millipedes it must be changed, or 'prepared', in at least two ways, involving chemical enrichment with nitrogen and the preliminary breaking down of cellulose. So far we have the picture of a grass meadow rather sterile of herbivorous invertebrates living on the green vegetation (though attacked at the surface by voles). The breakdown of the dead grass falling on to the ground as litter is done by a microbial community and by one species of litter-feeding millipede, with a few less abundant species in addition. From these processes is derived most of the organic matter in the topsoil.

The amount of litter in grassland and the length of time that it lies vary very much, the greatest amounts being apparently where the dominant grasses have a strong tussock habit, and where they are undisturbed by mowing, burning or heavy grazing. That is to say, dying plant material may be consumed on the ground about as fast as it is produced and dies, or it may fall in large amounts in the autumn and create a mat of litter that sometimes accumulates for several years. The conditions for life of the ground zone fauna in respect of food, cover and microclimate must be very different at the extremes. On The Dell at Wytham the period of turn-over of the litter is about two years. There do not seem to be other British observations of the kind, but Tester and Marshall[496] have measured the litter on a large area of unploughed prairie at the Lake Itaska Forestry and Biological Station in Minnesota, that had been mown regularly but not grazed or burned for thirty-six years. On places where mowing went on, the litter from the four main prairie grasses formed 35% of the ground cover, and was on the average only 5 cm. deep; whereas on plots kept unmown for six years it had risen to 51% cover and an average depth of 17 cm. In three burned plots the litter cover fell to 12%. Their general conclusion from this and some other people's research was: 'It appears . . . that on native prairie a state of equilibrium is reached two to six years after protection from burning or mowing begins; in this state the annual increment of new litter is balanced by decomposition of old litter.' We may compare with this the conditions found on the large abandoned field on the George Reserve in Michigan, which has been the centre for some comprehensive studies on plant and animal communities. This place had been relatively undisturbed for twenty-five years (except to some extent by the activities of white-tailed deer) at the time of an analysis by Evans and Dahl[144] of its vegetion structure and variation. Of the two larger and eleven minor plant associations (all of them fairly stable in character) that occupy the field, only one had extensive ground litter. This was one of the more widespread types of vegetation, however, dominated mainly by two grasses, the introduced *Poa compressa* and the native *Aristida purpurascens*. Whereas the latter community could be said to carry a 'bank balance' of litter, the others were living up to their income in this respect.

The animals other than *Glomeris* concerned with breakdown of meadow litter have been studied at Wytham. On Upper Seeds, the stony field above The Dell on part of which agriculture was abandoned for a few years, research bearing on this question was done in 1953-6 by Mr Tom Huxley,[241] who has allowed me to draw upon his results. This meadow consisted of 50 kinds of herbs, 9 grasses, 4 mosses and some bracken. Three species of woodlouse were sampled to find out their food habits: 210 *Philoscia muscorum*, 26 *Porcellio rathkei* and 67 *Armadillidium vulgare*, the foods being identified from microscopic fragments in the gut. Not every species of plant could be recognized, the grasses then being still especially difficult. Of the 63 species of plants other than bracken, 26 were eaten; of the 37 not found in the guts of one or other of these woodlice 18 were difficult or impossible to identify, but some of the remaining 9 were common species in the meadow, and it seemed likely that there had been some selection. The greatest quantity of stuff eaten was grass. The chief conclusion is that woodlice (which are abundant) were eating a large number of different plants. It was also found from experiments that they preferred decaying matter, i.e. a mixture of plant and fungus, though this preference was not absolute. It will be remembered that *Armadillidium* also lived in the *Brachypodium* litter of The Dell, where there was nothing to eat but this grass when decaying. *Glomeris marginata* also occurred on Upper Seeds, but its food was not easy to recognize since, as Huxley remarks, 'It has the habit of eating its food in strips thereby destroying valuable combinations of taxonomic characters.' But its food certainly included cocksfoot grass (*Dactylis glomerata*) and probably other grasses, six other named flowering plants together with unnamed labiate and legume material, and one kind of moss. Evidently all four of these litter operators have a wide range of food, and the woodlice must perform in a mixed meadow part of the same function that *Glomeris* has in *Brachypodium*. This must be a very widespread and effective niche, since *Porcellio rathkei* was reported by Wolcott[554] to be abundant in a hay meadow in northern New York; and *Armadillidium vulgare* in a California hill grassland dominated by *Avena barbata* and *Bromus rigidus*, investigated by Paris and Pitelka[372] who measured the spring opulation density in the litter and soil. They found a density of 500 per square metre – a minimum figure obtained in the spring, later measurements being diffi-ult because of the summer drying of the soil. Of course there are other meadow itter converters besides woodlice and millipedes, but not much is known about heir ecology.

In contrast with the relatively simple main nexus of vegetation and animals so ar described, the rest of the fauna on The Dell exhibits a remarkable wealth of pecies living in the ground zone of litter and tussock and in the topsoil. From the ampling through a year 330 identified species of invertebrates were obtained. These do not include any of the Enchytraeid worms, nor the flies and parasitic Hymenoptera, nor certain other groups such as aphids and molluscs that do not espond to Tullgren funnel treatment, nor the smallest microscopic forms such as Protozoa. It can hardly be doubted that the actual total number of species on or risiting this area of 100 square metres of meadow dominated by a single kind of plant was over 400. The largest numbers of identified species were in the following groups: nematode worms 41, mites 76, springtails (Collembola) 20-30 [3]. These 50 or so species, also the five kinds of earthworm, mostly have their headquarters or their only habitat in the topsoil; and most of them are not predators, but feed on decaying matter or the bacterial and fungal populations involved in its breakdown. There is also a large contingent from predatory groups which includes (besides ome of the nematodes and mites) about 70 species of beetles, 9 centipedes, 3 false corpions (Chelognathida), 4 harvestmen (Opiliones) and at least 27 spiders. The predatory beetles are predominantly small rovebeetles (Staphylinidae), which seem o be particularly successful in occupying dense cover with fine texture and small hannels through which their elongate narrow bodies can move. With them are ome ground-beetles (Carabidae) and the diminutive Pselaphidae that catch ninute creatures like mites. Spiders are probably under-represented in this list, ince they require special methods of extraction.

The most outstanding description of vertical stratification in grassland com-nunities is that given by Duffey[109, 110] for the spider populations on Wytham Hill which he surveyed in 1950-1. Although at that time our habitat classification had ot been finally standardized, the vertical layers he used are sufficiently in line with hose of the ecological survey to be applicable here. The chief difference lies in the pper limit used for the ground zone, which in his work was not confined to xactly 6 in., but reached about 9 in. in some instances. On a quite small area of ·8 acres he found 141 of the 570 or so British species of spiders, so that the in-estigation is a very representative one. They were living in the field layer and round zone of three rather different kinds of habitat, none of which had recently een disturbed by human use, though rabbits lived there at that time and voles xert a recurrent pressure on the grass. On Sundays Hill there were two kinds of grassland or meadow. First dense *Brachypodium pinnatum* forming nine-tenths of the vegetation cover, but differing from the sampling patch on The Dell by having a scattering of cow parsnip, *Pastinaca sativa*, with its tall stems and yellow flowers. Secondly, a low sward partly formed of rabbit-grazed turf, of *Festuca rubra*, covering three-quarters of the ground, but with more cow parsnip and other flowering plants and grasses. After the death of the rabbits in 1954 this habitat changed rapidly into a deep tangle of *Festuca* (a grass that also grew up and choked many bits of open ground at Wytham formerly covered with rock-rose and similar mat-like plants). The third place was the Bowling Alley, a beautiful flowery enclave of open ground and dry meadow set among mixed woodland and deciduous scrub, and carrying all the typical chalk grasses among eighty species of flowering plants, six bryophytes (of which one, *Camptothecium lutescens*, covered 15% of the surface) and one lichen. It was a mixture of open ground and field type on shallow limestone coral soil exposed in some spots. Here I can only mention a few facts bearing upon the vertical distribution of spiders, omitting much else about population structure, seasonal changes, dispersal, habits and so on.

The *Brachypodium* falls in winter to make a roof over the ground at about 18 in. On the ground there is litter and voles make runs between the tussocks. The *Festuca* sward was 2–10 inches high and did not form a roof, and there was little litter, though the dense ground cover supported a rich spider population. On the Bowling Alley much of the ground surface had no field layer at all. Taking the field layer of these habitats first, six of its dozen or so taller herbs were especially important as building sites for those species of spider that lived almost permanently in the upper layers: cow parsnip (*Pastinaca sativa*), teazel (*Dipsacus fullonum*), two St Johnsworts (*Hypericum perforatum* and *hirsutum*), hounds-tongue (*Cynoglossum officinale*) and ploughman's spikenard (*Inula conyza*). There were fifteen species of spider, web-spinners from four families that lived permanently in the upper layers except for occasional excursions of the young ones to the ground. Each plant structure suits certain spiders more than others, thus orb-web species avoid *Cynoglossum*, though *Dictyna arundinacea* has a silken tangle for its retreat that can be woven on the fruit of this species as well as on the flower heads of *Pastinaca* and *Hypericum* that can also be exploited by orb-web spinners. Not only were the plants necessary in summer, but dead standing stems lasting for a year or more were vital for winter survival. The 'death-rate' of such dead stems falling to the ground would therefore affect the spiders, and this 'death-rate' depends among other things upon disturbance by animals and man. Three species otherwise living on the ground climb to lay eggs in the field layer, and some other ground-livers hung up there at times. Finally, the taller vegetation provides essential launching-pad for young spiders attaining dispersal on gossamer.[108] An autumn census revealed that one in nine of these standing stems had spiders on them, and the density was a ittle over one spider per square metre. In four species (*Lycosa nigriceps, Euophrys frontalis, Tibellus oblongus* and *Zora spinimana*) belonging to different families there are convergent colour patterns that serve for concealment as they hunt in the upper layers of *Brachypodium*.

The spider fauna on the ground was much richer both in species and numbers, especially dense populations occurring in the *Festuca*, reaching in August to November over 800 per square metre. Typical of this different situation were the very small *Hahnia nava* and *Tapinocyba praecox*, living deep in the turf and together reaching densities of 180–230 per square metre. The microclimate profiles measured by Waterhouse[540] in grassland in Scotland illustrate very well the sharp contrast

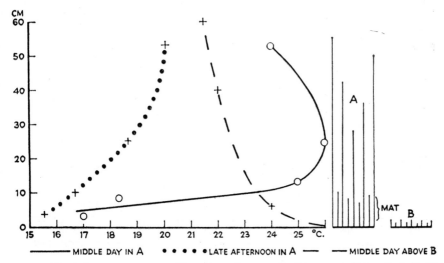

FIG. 6. Vertical temperature gradients in and over meadow grass (A) and turf (B), whose structure is shown by vertical lines. (From F. L. Waterhouse, 1955)

in conditions at different levels in it (Figs. 6 and 7). Some of the grassland was in agricultural use and some of it natural with accumulated litter. The zonation depends of course upon the degree of protection given by the vegetation. Whereas open ground (short turf) is hottest at the ground surface and cooler a foot or two above it, there can be 8° C. lower temperature at the base of meadow grass than in the air above at midday, with an intermediate maximum in the upper grass layers. Corresponding gradients exist in the humidity, which is high in the protected ground zone of meadow, and decreases upwards. Within a foot or two these gradients are quite sharp, and may be compared with the similar but broader ones within woodland. Fichter[155] cites some measurements made in the microclimate of a remnant of unbroken grassland in Nebraska dominated by prairie grasses, that illustrates the same thing and also how the seasonal change in vegetation structure affects the microclimate. In low prairie grass, the wind movement

at 5 feet (above the vegetation) was taken as 100%. The corresponding values a
14 inches, within the prairie grass, varied round the seasons from 71-76 in winter
and spring, to 60 in summer and 53 in autumn. At the ground surface it was 29-31%
in winter and spring, 13% in summer and 4% in autumn. So the gradient get
steeper as the vegetation grows and declines with its fall and decay.

This spider survey brings out a further matter that was not emphasized in the
account of The Dell communities. There it was said that *Brachypodium pinnatum*
supports few herbivores on its foliage and stems. But evidently it can carry quite a
large number of predators, of which spiders are the chief, though there are some

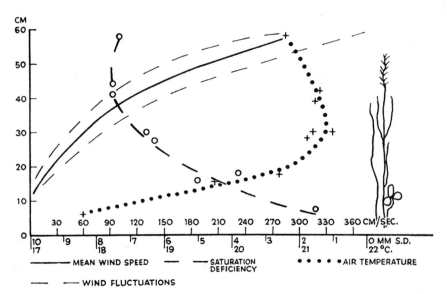

FIG. 7. Vertical gradients in temperature, wind speed and humidity in and over meadow
grass with a lower layer of clover. (From F. L. Waterhouse, 1955)

insects as well. Since there are very few herbivorous insects produced in this field
layer, the food supply of the predators must come from elsewhere, that is either
from below or from some other habitat altogether. Presumably whatever field
layer predators live on the sampling area of The Dell (of which the spider *Euophry*
frontalis is an example) must catch insects emerging from the litter and topsoil, or
drifting in from other zones like mixed meadow, scrub and woodland or even
from aeroplankton. But where additional species of plants are mixed with the
dominant grass not only are the opportunities for web-making enhanced, but the
herbivores depending upon these other plants enlarge the food supply. For example
the flowers of *Pastinaca* alone attract very large numbers of insects in summer. This
leads on naturally to the discussion of lateral patterns within a habitat, which form
the final section of this chapter.

Lateral patterns can be divided into those primarily caused by plants and those primarily caused by animals. In practice the two interact considerably, as is to be expected. Plant patterns can, for the present purpose, be again divided into those affecting the dominant plant, and those shown by the less common species. A most important structural feature often found in dominant grasses is tussock formation, and plant ecologists have done quite a large amount of work on this. Watt's essay[543] on this topic published in 1947 is particularly notable, for it treated a number of different kinds of open ground and field type vegetation, and showed how their minor patterns could be caused by micro-succession in clumps, tussocks and the like. The units of these patterns have a term of existence, and their death is followed by recolonization through several phases. Perhaps the case-history most relevant here is that of *Festuca ovina* grass–heath in the Breckland of East Anglia. Watt describes how the fescue plant begins to build up a tussock, during which time the soil accumulates there and the tussock gradually breaks up and is invaded by two stages of ground lichens.

The development of tussocks by the larger grasses, especially *Brachypodium pinnatum, Molinia caerulea, Bromus erectus* and *Dactylis glomerata*, creates a sharp pattern in grassland that deeply affects the animals living there. The vole (*Microtus agrestis*) makes runways between tussocks and frequently gives a further emphasis to the pattern. In 1949-52 Godfrey[188, 199] worked upon the vole populations living on Rough Common and The Dell at Wytham, by means of trapping, marking (including radioactive cobalt rings enabling the whereabouts of a vole to be detected by means of a geiger counter) and food analysis. It was not possible to get very accurate continuous records of the population density, but they were believed to reach maxima of under 90 per acre on Rough Common and under 120 on the Dell. As usually happens in vole populations there was a strong fluctuation in numbers, so that the pressure on vegetation was not maintained at a high level every year. By microscopic analysis of 119 groups of faecal pellets of voles, Godfrey found that on both places the leaf blades and stem bases of *Brachypodium pinnatum* were the commonest food (on The Dell they occurred in 93% of the samples). Pimentel [4] measured the food of voles and their impact upon vegetation upon Rough Common in 1961. Among other things it was ascertained that they could live and grow on a diet of this grass alone, though they did not grow so well as upon a balanced laboratory diet containing green foods. Field experiments suggested that a single vole could completely graze down as much as two square feet of grass in one day; though in practice this pressure is distributed over a wide area, and one does not generally observe any great deterioration of the vegetation. But these facts all reinforce the idea that voles play a big part in the formation and maintenance of the tussock pattern of *Brachypodium*.

In the years 1930-9 I used to visit the hills of the Scottish Border and North

H

Wales in order to measure fluctuations in the vole populations inside Forestry Commission plantings where exclusion of sheep and the stopping of burning brought about intense grass growth, which lasted in good condition for ten to fifteen years until the young planted trees grew up.[128] On one station in particular, Newcastleton in Roxburghshire, could be seen all the stages from grazed pasture of *Festuca* and *Nardus* up to a well-developed system of tussocks of the purple moor grass, *Molinia caerulea*, stretching for a mile or more over shallow acid peat. On the sheep pasture voles are mostly confined to patches of rushes which give them cover. A year or two after enclosure there is a dense sward of *Molinia*, but as yet without much tussock structure. Then voles take over rapidly, and there is time for two or three big cycles in their numbers before the grass begins to deteriorate under the growing forest. A network of vole runs interlaces between the large *Molinia* tussocks, occupied everywhere in years of abundance, but temporarily deserted when voles are scarce. In winter the dead *Molinia* forms a heavy grass litter, and it is slow to grow in the spring. But at these seasons the voles eat the basal internodes of the grass stems, which are expanded and contain a supply of starchy food: indeed, voles often erode the sides of the tussocks and may actually destroy them altogether. On a more permanent grassland it seems likely that individual tussocks of the larger grasses live for a long time and do not have the fairly short cycle of micro-succession observed by Watt in the smaller species.

Few studies have been made of the separate fauna of tussocks. Pearce[376] has pointed out what large numbers of invertebrates may be found in them, during the winter especially, a fact that has long been known to beetle collectors. He gives some examples to show that there can be hundreds of animals in a single tussock, mainly insects, spiders and woodlice. Of the insects the largest numbers are beetles and parasitic Hymenoptera, in particular Ichneumonidae. From long experience of examining nearly a thousand tussocks for beetles, in grassland and elsewhere, he says: 'The habit and situation of a tussock is in this connection of far greater importance than its actual botanical species.' The use of tussocks for winter hibernation is suggested by some of the species of beetles found in the collection from *Brachypodium* on The Dell. Among them were several that are common inhabitants of dung, and which probably came in to hibernate from the nearby cattle pasture of Wytham Park: *Sphaeridium scarabaeoides, S. lunatum, Cercyon atomarius, C. melanocephalus,* and *Megasternum obscurum.* Grass tussocks in woods are similarly used for hibernation [48].

Ford (in 1935-6) surveyed a patch of *Bromus erectus* tussocks on Headington Hill, Oxford, situated on a Coral Rag soil.[160] These tussocks were about a foot apart, and in winter the dead grass still attached blew over in the direction away from the prevailing wind. Both the dead grass and the base of the tussock received some shelter from wind and cold, as his measurements of saturation deficit and temperature showed. In February, winds from another quarter changed the tussock structure and exposed it to evaporation, and he attributed to this the sharp dip in numbers of Collembola at that time. In the tussocks he found eight species of Collembola of which one (*Pseudachorutes subcrassus*) formed over 95% of the population, and twenty-six kinds of mites. Besides these were some larger invertebrates that were not confined to the tussocks, the commonest being *Tachyporus hypnorum*, a small predatory rove-beetle that also formed about half the beetles collected on The Dell grassland at Wytham. Tussocking therefore creates a definite reticulate pattern of tussock and interspace, with some invertebrates concentrated in the former, and voles moving mainly in the latter. Voles do, of course, enter the tussocks themselves, and quite commonly construct their nests of dry grass inside them.

It is obvious that anything that helps to limit the amount of the dominant grasses automatically creates opportunities for the less common plants to exist. The exclusion cage experiments that Summerhayes[487] carried out on the Scottish Border and North Wales (see Ch. 2) proved without doubt that voles do limit the amount of *Molinia* or other dominant grasses sufficiently to allow smaller species to live between the tussocks. The heath bedstraw (*Galium hercynicum*, formerly *saxatile*) is one plant affected in this way, and it could be seen growing over patches of *Molinia* killed by voles, and became scarce in cages protected from their nibbling. I have seen the slender bedstraw (*Galium pumilum*) – its opposite number on calcareous soils – expanding in on places where voles had killed a patch of *Brachypodium pinnatum* on Rough Common. Extensive proof of the same kind of balance between rabbits, the dominant plants, and the secondary species, was given years ago by Tansley and Adamson,[493] on the chalk downland. But in many plant communities the factors that make up the composition of abundance and the pattern of arrangement of the species are scarcely known. The only thing that needs to be pointed out here is rather obvious, yet very important for animal populations: any species in grassland that is not dominant has a scattered distribution usually, or else it may have scattered local aggregations of individual plants. This means that any animal populations attached to them specially will also have a discontinuous pattern of distribution. How far this discontinuity actually matters to the animal will depend partly upon its power of movement in relation to the distance between the patches of individual plants. That is to say, the existence of this kind of pattern may or may not affect the populations concerned. But common sense indicates that, in so far as most herbivorous insects spend the greater part of their lives attached to one plant or a patch of it, dispersal being accomplished chiefly by the adults often over a much shorter period of time, the pattern of vegetation must have profound influence on the community. But one of the kinds of survey that has never yet been done, so far as I can find out, is to map a meadow and record the spacing and interspersion of plants together with the animals attached to them, and to ascertain how effectively this mosaic of different populations in the first consumer layer of the community is bound together by the wider activities of predators and parasites, many of which are highly polyphagous and mobile.

Coming to the direct effects of animals upon patterns of grassland, the importance of rabbits and voles in sometimes determining the basic vegetation patterns has already been discussed. A little should be said also about the mole (*Talpa europaea*). The influence of moles in turning over the soil has often been emphasized. In the 1930s the Bureau of Animal Population carried out an amusing survey of the distribution of moles in pastures and other kinds of field which was done from railway train windows between Oxford and Chester, once a year for several years. This proved that moles are to be seen in over four-fifths of the pastures of the west Midlands. It was also known that some four million mole skins were at that time being harvested for fur every year in England and Wales. But very little research has been done upon the micro-succession of plant life on the newly turned excavations which are scattered over the surface. According to Pigott[385] the wild thyme, *Thymus drucei* etc., often grows on molehills and hills of the yellow ant, and where the general vegetation is coarse may be confined to them. A fuller study of molehill floras was made by Urbain and Marty[513] in the pastures of Cantal, in France. The ecological succession took three years to complete. In the first year six species of plants from the pasture itself colonized the molehills: Buttercups (*Ranunculus acris*, and *R. bulbosus*), white clover (*Trifolium repens*), mouse-ear hawkweed (*Hieracium pilosella*), sheep's sorrel (*Rumex acetosella*) and soft rush (*Juncus effusus*). With them were six other species not found in the main pasture vegetation: birdsfoot trefoil (*Lotus corniculatus*), red clover (*Trifolium pratense*), stemless thistle (*Cirsium acaule*), chicory (*Cichorium intybus*), thyme-leaved speedwell (*Veronica serpyllifolia*) and bugle (*Ajuga reptans*). In the second year altogether twenty-one pasture species were present, while invaders from elsewhere included, besides three of the first-year pioneers (*L. corniculatus, T. pratense* and *C. acaule*) eight new ones: milkwort (*Polygala vulgaris*), bitter vetch (*Vicia orobus*), creeping cinquefoil (*Potentilla reptans*), lady's bedstraw (*Galium verum*), heather (*Calluna vulgaris*), ribwort plantain (*Plantago lanceolata*), the grass *Holcus mollis* and the moss *Polytrichum commune*. In the third year the molehill flora was becoming like normal pasture. This is certainly a mixture to make any British phytosociologist scratch his head in surprise. Its special interest here is a double one: there is the pattern brought about by the moles, so different from the surrounding vegetation; and the fact that they were making conditions for the temporary colonization of species from communities outside the pasture, so that as long as moles continued to turn up the soil, these invaders would be constantly present.

The impressive ground pattern made by mounds of the yellow ant, *Lasius flavus*, is still familiar to many people, though greatly diminishing under the mechanical agriculture of our times. But I shall deal with this subject again in Ch. 16 and here only mention some ways in which this subterranean peasant civilization affects the grassland ecosystem. These ants live almost entirely underground, collecting chiefly the waste products of aphids sucking the roots of plants; they bring up soil to the surface of the anthills, and rabbits visiting the mounds to defaecate add some extra organic matter to them; the vegetation there is not only different in composition from the surrounding pasture but may differ considerably in structure and composition on the north and south sides of the mound; in Denmark the soil fauna has been found to differ from that of the pasture around. Richards and Waloff,[407] in their survey on grass heath at Silwood Park, discovered that grasshoppers often have a strong preference for laying their egg pods in the soil of anthills. *Chorthippus parallelus* and *C. brunneus* both usually require bare soil for this purpose, though they do sometimes lay through vegetation as well. A sampling of the ground on one area over three years gave a ratio of egg pod numbers in the flat grassland v. the anthills as 1 : 15 for *C. parallelus* and 1 : 28 for *C. brunneus*. By making artificial mounds they were able to induce the latter to lay even more freely than on anthills, though the former did not do so, probably because of a preference for firmer soil. But on another area where few anthills existed, both species showed their preference by laying mainly in small bare soil patches. The other relationship worth mentioning here is that the green woodpecker (*Picus viridis*) attacks anthills, its beak and long tongue making it a successful anteater. These ants are a very important resource for the birds, which otherwise live and nest in woods, where they also eat invertebrates in rotting wood.

Some other relationships of open ground and meadow with other communities will be noticed in the chapters on Woodland, with which these earlier stages in ecological succession are so closely involved in lowland Britain. Many calcareous open ground and meadow communities are very rich in plant and animal species, and the brief diagnosis of some of their structural patterns given here can only begin to explain the nature and persistence of such variety. It is sometimes said that a grassland is like a miniature forest, with its dominant species, shading effects, microclimatic gradients, litter conversion and so on. But it usually differs entirely from woodland in one very marked respect: although one or two species may be dominants, nearly all the vascular plants grow to much the same height, so that the surface of a natural meadow in summer is constructed more like a tropical rain forest, with its great mixture of species, than anything like an oak or pine wood. Only in exceptional instances of total dominance, like that attained by *Brachypodium pinnatum*, does this resemblance change to one analogous to temperate woodland.

CHAPTER 7

Heath, Mountain and Croplands

FOR THE GREATER CONCENTRATION of argument, the character of open ground and field types has so far been illustrated chiefly by the communities of grassland, and among these mainly by the ones on calcareous ground at Wytham. In them the interplay between plant and animal often decides the actual structure of the habitat, with its lateral and vertical zones, and internal patterns. These communities, however, form only a small part of the whole spectrum outside scrub and woodland and their immediate edges, and not on wet soil. But although much is understood about the distribution and variety of the plant associations, our knowledge of the animal communities is still confined to small sample and usually incomplete surveys. But we can say without any doubt that meadows on calcareous or neutral soils have the richest variety of species of flowering plants and animals, far richer than heath, bracken, hill grazings, montane zones, croplands and at least some maritime habitats. Even the pure *Brachypodium pinnatum* patch at Wytham described in the last chapter – a peculiar version of grassland with only one species left and that highly unfavourable to herbivorous insects – carries probably over 400 species of animals. How much greater must be the profusion in the fauna of a mixed meadow with say 60 species of flowering plants! At the present time we only have general impressions and inferences about this matter, but I feel quite certain that there are not a few communities of calcareous meadow that have (taking all their vertical strata together) as many as a thousand or more animal species, not counting any merely stray visitors from neighbouring habitats. If this estimate is anywhere near the truth, it means that such a community would be carrying something like a thirtieth or more of the British fauna. That such an estimate is not incredible is indicated by the results of Duffey's work already cited: a quarter of the British species of spiders living on several acres of open ground and meadow on Wytham Hill.

Little has been said here so far about seasonal changes in the structure of field-type habitats, nor of mixtures of open ground and field type, which are very commonly found in this country. Both these pose some practical questions in the classification of communities. Field types that are composed of woody plants like bramble, heather, or young trees and scrub, keep much of their framework standing throughout the winter, although those of them that shed their leaves become more exposed. But the vegetation of most kinds of natural meadow collapses more or less completely in winter to early spring, except in so far as large tussocks exist and the dead flowering stems of herbs remain standing. In this period of the year such meadows often consist of open ground and tussock with some standing dead plant structures. For example, on some of the dry parts of gravel pits round Oxford, the winter picture is of a mass of fallen and partly rotting herbage, with live plant bases and rosettes, and scattered standing dead stems. In early spring an intense outburst of yellow flowering coltsfoot, *Tussilago farfara*, attracting the first flower-visiting insects, clothes the ground zone of the banks, to be followed as summer progresses by rich meadow several feet high and so dense that one cannot easily go through it. With all such habitats, and also with arable crop fields, the only possible practical convention is to classify the formation-type by its summer maximum structure, in spite of the fact that in winter and spring it is actually open ground or nearly so, or a pattern of open ground between tussocks of grass. Heathland, however, is a field type that keeps its structure permanently, unless it is burned or otherwise temporarily destroyed.

For a general idea of the animal communities of dry heath we are chiefly dependent on the ecological survey done by O. W. Richards[404] on Oxshott Heath in Surrey in the years 1922-5. This survey stands by itself, because of its intelligent yet tentative approach, the very wide taxonomic integrity of the author, and the brilliance of its natural history observations. At the same time, it was not, and could not then be, complete, being devoted only to the species ordinarily visible or detectable above ground which could be named with certainty. Richards studied the whole series of communities leading from the bare ground up to pine woods, but the parts that matter here are his lists of species from bare sand, early *Calluna* heath, old-established heather, and of insects visiting the ericaceous flowers. The first and third clearly correspond to open ground and field type, while the second must have comprised open ground vegetation (without bare sand) mixed with new heather of varying height. Of the bare sand he says: 'There are a number of animals that are characteristically found on bare sand. The most typical are the sand wasps, the fly *Anthrax*, and the tiger beetles, which often fly up as one walks across the Common . . . Few of the species live entirely on the bare areas, since most have to obtain their food from various plant communities, but many are controlled by the amount of bare sand available for nesting sites. A thick layer of humus usually makes a bare area unacceptable. . . .' This assemblage contained the surprising total of 83 species. 53 of these were Hymenoptera, comprising 18 bees (mainly *Andrena* and *Halictus*) with 5 parasite bees, 21 wasps with 8 parasite wasps (1 of which

belonged to tiger beetle burrows), and 1 kind of ant whose nests were howeve:
mainly under pine bark.

The next stage, his 'typical Callunetum', produced 104 species of animals tha
could be named – his survey did not, for instance, include the Hymenoptera Para-
sitica, the Collembola or the myriapods. Not all the species were permanent inhabitants of heather. At least seven were hibernating moths, flies and beetles
Two of the visitors were dung-flies, the green-bottle *Orthellia caesarion*, which
came to hibernate, and the yellow *Scopeuma stercorarium* which came to hunt fo1
prey. The main contingents of the fauna were flies, beetles and moths, and more
than half the moths were attached to *Calluna* or *Erica* or both. One of the digge1
wasps nesting in bare sand, *Miscophus concolor*, visited this intermediate heath tc
catch small spiders for its burrows. On the old-established thicker heather there
were 33 species of animals not found in the earlier stages of heath. The flowers o1
heather, also of *Erica cinerea*, and to a less extent of *Erica tetralix* growing in dampe1
spots, attracted a number of insect visitors, of which 28 were recorded. 11 of these
nest on bare sand areas; 2 others in rotting pine stumps; 8 kinds of bumble-bee
came from other, unspecified places; there were 2 bee parasites – a Conopid fly and
a Syrphid fly – visiting the flowers; finally the hive bee from domestic habitats, and
3 kinds of moth. One of these moths bred in the heather itself, one in other plants
perhaps not in the *Calluna* heath, while the third (the silver-Y, *Plusia gamma*) is a
seasonal migrant from abroad.

It is worth looking at some of the other communities patronized by species of
bees and wasp that nest in the bare sand, of which 10 have been noted on the
heathy flowers. 7 species of wasps visited trees as follows: 1 hunted small Homoptera on young birch, 1 weevils on oak and birch, 1 visited woodland to catch flies,
on young pines 2 wasps ate the secretions of aphids and 2 others hunted spiders
and caterpillars respectively. Sallow flowers attracted 5 species of bees and 1 digger
wasp, gorse (*Ulex europaeus*) flowers 4 kinds of bee, bramble flowers 9 digger
wasps, a parasitic wasp and 4 kinds of bees; while the rosebay willow-herb (*Chamaenerion (Epilobium) angustifolium*), attracted 8 bees and wasps from the bare sand,
out of the total of 17 visitors that included also the hive-bee and 5 other bees also
recorded from *Calluna* flowers. Not all these species visited one species of flower
exclusively, and sometimes the males alone seem to have been concerned. The
story is not at all complete. But the situation illustrates the chain-mail pattern of
activities linking communities of structurally separate habitats that is one of the
main themes of this book. At Oxshott this one habitat, bare sand, was the factory
making possible the life-histories of all these species elsewhere. Yet in botanical
surveys we are seldom told anything much about the proportion of literally bare
ground present on heathland, though sometimes estimates of the ground covered
only by lichen and moss may be provided.

I have not yet said anything about the general status of ants in heathland. The number of species concerned is small and not many of them are especially confined to heathland, but in some places at any rate (and possibly much more widely than we suppose) they are dominant animals. The leading investigation on this subject has been done by Brian at the Nature Conservancy's research station near Wareham in Dorset. 'Their importance as key animals derives from the fact that they not only tap the plant juices (with a variety of bugs) but they also eat many of the small animals that themselves feed on the living and dead heath plants. This multiple grasp which the ants have on the resources of the community is undoubtedly one of the principal means by which they produce huge populations, which, with their unceasing mining activities, have profound effects on soil structure and hence again on the vegetation itself.' [344] On Hartland Moor where this work has been done, three species have been studied specially, of which one, *Tetramorium caespitum*, is essentially a maritime species and the situation therefore not typical of inland heath communities. Interest centres on the competition between the species, in which *Lasius niger* usually wins by those methods of direct action adopted by ants. But this species does not have its optimum headquarters on dry heath, and is only able to dominate terrain that is damper at the surface or has some young trees. *Tetramorium* flourishes on the dry heath (though it also lives on cliff slopes on some coasts of Britain) and can defeat the third species, *Lasius alienus*. This fascinating pattern of interactions will not only enable us to understand the mechanics of heathland communities, but is completely conclusive instance of biotic relationships decisively affecting numbers and habitat distribution which it is now fashionable among some ecologists to deny. In this respect it ranks with Connell's intertidal investigations on barnacle populations.[79]

The fauna of dry heath living on or above the surface of the ground is evidently not very rich in species of insects and spiders. 33 kinds of insects are known to feed on *Calluna*[185] and of these Richards found 13 on Oxshott heath. Only a small proportion of the bees and wasps nesting in bare sand there were dependent on heather for pollen and nectar, most of them having different flower supplies, and some (like bumble-bees and the hive-bees) a very wide choice of these. This community at Oxshott also had few plant species living in it. The botanical survey[488] tells us that dry *Calluna* up to 18 in. high was often without associates other than *Erica cinerea*. Elsewhere there also grew dwarf gorse (*Ulex nanus*), tormentil (*Potentilla erecta*) and grass (*Deschampsia flexuosa*), also some dwarf crab-apple plants (*Malus sylvestris*) and seedlings of *Pinus sylvestris*. In addition there were bryophyte mats and lichens. But where rabbits had eaten back the heather round their burrows, a richer mixture of 18 flowering plants began to grow. The fact is that dry heathland, in spite of its tremendous charm and interest, compounded of natural beauty, the astonishing spectacle of a luxuriant low woody plant flourishing on such a poor soil, and the presence of some especially exciting species of animals, is a comparatively poor community. Tansley[493] cites an analysis of the flora of five upland dry heaths in Somerset that have between them only 59 species of flowering plants, and 4 ferns; but by contrast there is a wealth of other plants – 70 species of mosses, 37 liverworts and 76 lichens, that is three times as many bryophytes and lichens as there are flowering plants. But of chalk grassland he remarks: 'Lichens are infrequent, locally conspicuous only where the turf is short, and not always there.' Mosses also are few in species though they can be common. But live mosses, liverworts and lichens are inedible to most animals, and this must be one reason for the simplicity of the heath fauna. They do of course decay and add to the shallow litter in which, as will be described, there is an active microfauna. But a few of the animals found on heaths apparently do feed on these lower plants. The black slow-moving beetle, *Cylindronotus laevioctostriatus* (formerly, and more conveniently, *Helops striatus*), was among the insects on Oxshott Heath and on four of the south-western heaths studied by Delany.[91] It also lives in woods both deciduous and conifer. In Epping Forest it was found by Green[195] to climb the trunks in summer and feed at night on the *Pleurococcus* alga there. And since he also observed it[196] on the rocks of the island of Skokholm eating lichen (which contains *Pleurococcus*), it seems pretty certain that this is also its habit on open heaths. Another such insect is the small grouse-locust, *Tetrix vittata* (formerly *Tettix* or *Acrydium bipunctata*), living on the heather ground at Oxshott. Verdcourt[523] in Bedfordshire discovered that the faeces of this species contained practically nothing but remains of moss. But these few specialists on the cryptogams hardly enable the animal community to break into such resources.

The ornithologists who have surveyed heathland also report a general poverty of species and of populations, indeed Lack[276] who organized census operations on a number of British heaths and moors, remarked that 'heathland was chosen as being the simplest habitat in Britain', though he went on to note the difficulty of finding uniform areas of one kind of vegetation large enough for this kind of counting. Frensham Heath in Surrey, with dry *Calluna* dominant, can be taken as a good example. It had only 8 species of terrestrial birds and only 2 adult birds on the 100 acres, about half of these being meadow pipits, *Anthus pratensis*. The only species peculiar to heath was the Dartford warbler, *Sylvia undata*. Through the absence of earthworms and of Tipulid flies and many other insects, you do not see on heaths the great visiting winter flocks of rooks, starlings and lapwings, or of the thrush tribe, that are so characteristic of good grasslands. On the whole of the 10 heaths described by Lack the meadow pipit or the skylark (*Alauda arvensis*) or both were the only common birds. Apart from several interesting heath specialists among the reptiles, the other vertebrates are also few in species.

Delany's reconnaissance[91] of some dry heathlands in south-western England in

950-1 adds some information about the microfauna of heather litter lying on the ground. From five of these heaths he took a total of 60 small samples each 10 sq. cm., and extracted the fauna in the heat and moisture gradient of the Tullgren funnel. This litter was extremely thin, less than half an inch, and made chiefly of the dead leaves of *Calluna*. Only one of the heaths had vegetation much above four inches high, owing to damage done by wartime manœuvres, burning and grazing, and on most of them there was much bare ground without any higher vegetation at all. Such heaths therefore come into the category of 'open ground', the remaining one being a 'low field type' with much open ground interspersed in it. On the open ground heaths he obtained altogether about 50 species of animals in the litter, of which 38 were mites and of these again were 22 Oribatid mites that are such a strong component of the vegetation feeders in litter and soil. There were only 8 species of Collembola. The only comparative survey is that done by Murphy[340, 341] on a natural heath at Allerston Forest in Yorkshire dominated by heather and having about an inch of surface litter above an inch of raw humus. In these two layers combined, which contained practically the whole of the micro-fauna present, there were 39 species of mites (of which 23 were Oribatids), also Collembola, though in numbers of individuals the latter were seldom more than a fifth of the whole arthropod population. The actual numbers of mites extracted from this thin stratum were at least 214 per square metre in the litter, and 374 in the raw humus.

Though earthworms (Lumbricidae) are generally absent from dry heath soils, an absence that contributes to the poor structure and fertility of such places, there are a number of smaller worms of the family Enchytraeidae and also of nematode worms that live in them. From Overgaard Nielsen's work[353] in Denmark (which will be used to give a notion of what may be expected in Britain) it is now known that the Enchytraeid worms are a group especially adapted to flourish in peaty conditions, in which they reach their highest abundance. He examined a wide range of habitats in Jutland, including especially the research area of Mols Labora-tory. Among these was a series of sandy habitats with *Calluna* growing and often dominating the vegetation, ranging from almost pure sand with only about 1% of organic matter, to raw humus conditions. In the latter habitat the number of Enchytraeid worms was 12·5 times that in the former. In this investigation the number of species was not published, because of certain taxonomic problems that have since been solved; but most species ranged widely through a great many habitats, and it was noted that 'the species composition cannot well be used to characterize the habitats. This applies in particular to the abundant species.' Over-gaard Nielsen's survey[351] of the nematode worms on the same research area gave similar general conclusions: 'The distribution of the ca. 100 species met with con-firms the concept that a very large proportion of the species are eurytopic and common to all the soil types.' This conclusion is well exemplified by the fact that about half the 41 or so species of soil nematodes collected by Dr Overgaard Nielsen in the limestone grassland soil on The Dell at Wytham, are the same as on the Mols sand heath about to be mentioned. In *Calluna* heath on sand he found 800,000 per square metre, and about 40 species, of which two formed a little over half the total number of individuals. A rather similar situation occurred under isolated clumps of heather in the earlier stages of succession. These results agreed fairly closely with collections from two other places in Jutland. By comparison, *Calluna* heath with root-filled raw humus down to 10 inches, and an admixture of other heathy plants, had three times as many nematodes belonging to 32 species, of which three formed about half the total numbers, and were different from the two dominant species in sand heath. Indeed, the species, *Tylenchoaimus mirabilis*, that formed more than a third of the nematodes in the latter, was absent from the raw humus samples; and the other dominant, *Dorylaimus obtusicaudatus*, that formed about a sixth of the total population in sand heath, had sunk to about 1/130th of the total numbers in the raw humus. The highest densities of nematode populations (up to twenty million per square metre) were in some good grass fields.

From these Danish surveys it can be realized that the numbers and (for nematodes at least) the composition of the community can change dramatically between the poorer sandy soils and the raw humus stage under heather, the latter being almost an optimum habitat for Enchytraeid worms. Perhaps it would be fair to place the English heaths for which I have given the arthropod faunas somewhere between these two extremes of heath and towards the poorer end. As to the ecological functions of these litter and soil animals, whereas the Enchytraeid worms are, like the earthworms and most Collembola, feeders on the complex of dead plant and the microflora associated with them, nematodes, like the mites, include a variety of feeding niches such as microflora feeders, root feeders, predators and so on.

Lateral patterns in pure *Calluna* heath do not seem to have been very much mapped and studied, at any rate from the point of view of animal dispersion. From common natural history observation one can say that an individual well-grown plant of this evergreen woody dwarf shrub is the analogue on heathland of the large grass tussock discussed in the previous chapter, and that most heaths have some pattern of interspersed open ground on a small scale between heather plants or patches of them, which may be apparently bare but more usually is dominated by a low layer of lichens and mosses. Some of these lichens are so loosely attached as to be slightly mobile masses. The base of the heath plant, that is the ground below its canopy, usually has a mixture of mosses and lichens that aid in preserving a moister microclimate. According to Farrow's early work[150] on Breckland heath infested with rabbits, extreme grazing pressure reduced the heather plants to low

ummocks whose surface was invaded by the lichen *Cladonia coccifera* and the
moss *Leucobryum glaucum*. He considered that thereafter these increased the humid-
y round the dying heather plant, and eventually replaced the latter. By excluding
rabbits from sample patches he quickly reversed this sequence, the heather re-
overed its competitive ability, and the lichen and moss were in turn destroyed –
that is if the heather plant had not degenerated too far.

Delany's records[90] of the gradients in microclimate on dry heathland near
Exeter give a good idea of the decisive influence of heather on the temperature
and dampness at ground level. He chose an open ground formation-type with
dense *Calluna* (free from other dominant heath plants) not higher than 6 inches,
and much of it not very thick above 4 in. It follows that in a more fully developed
heath the effects of the plants on microclimate would be still greater than were
found here. In the daytime, the temperature on exposed ground surfaces or on the
surface of the heather itself, could run as much as 10° C. higher than near the
ground under the plants. At night, however, these differences tended to disappear
or even become slightly inverted. A few centimetres above the exposed ground
surface by day, the temperature begins to be cooler. The relative humidity was
highest at the base of the heather, that on exposed ground being as much as 25% less
than under protection. Evidently heathland must have a pattern of small cooler
damper patches interspersed with hotter dry ones that cannot fail to create a
corresponding pattern in animal dispersion and activity. This needs to be measured
by means of micro-transects carried out by day and night. For example, does the
woodlouse *Porcellio scaber*, found by day under heather plants, emerge at night to
feed in the open, as it does from crevices on the trunks of beeches in woods, where
grazes on algal food? Do temperatures on English heaths reach levels lethal
o animals on the ground surface, as they do for the spider *Theridion saxatile*
studied by Nørgaard[358] on a Jutland heath, and as has been observed even above
the ground on our sand-dunes, where bumble-bees sometimes drop dead while
ilying over very hot open sand? Nørgaard's spider partly keeps its nest cool
enough by hanging it clear of the ground, thereby attaining a temperature some
5° C. lower. From this safe level it has sticky 'fishing lines' that catch ants running
below. There must also be small-scale patterns in the deposition of heather litter,
with consequent effects on the soil structure; and as in all mixed plant communities
there are the dispersion patterns of the non-dominant species, and of animals
attached to them.

Dry *Calluna* heath has been chosen here to illustrate some of the patterns in open
ground and field type habitats with a permanent vegetation structure; but it is only
one of a kaleidoscopic and rather bewildering assortment of habitats in which
heather is dominant. Some of these have been summarized though not really
explained ecologically in Gimingham's monograph[185] on the biology of heather.

There are heathlands on maritime dunes, on gravels, on inland sands, on uplands mixed with open pine and birch and even oak (provided about two-fifths of the sunlight can pass the tree canopy). Again, there are deeper peaty soils in wetter climates that produce moor or bog conditions, but still with *Calluna* the dominant plant. We know little about the fauna living in most of these, or else the information is not in the form or sufficiently complete to be used in the present context. But two matters should be mentioned: the effects of grazing upon vegetation and the nature of 'grouse moors'.

Dry heathland is to a very considerable degree an artefact, a succession stage towards woodland checked by the combination of grazing by domestic stock and rabbits and of periodic burning by the farmer. It has been repeatedly observed that protection of grass pasture from these on many acid soils brings about a reversion to heather. On great areas of hill pasture heather is itself a very important source of food for sheep, especially in winter, and too heavy grazing on some of these places may kill out heather. The complicated interplay of these processes on the dry heathlands of Dorset has been analysed by Moore[333] who has also traced the historical shrinkage in the areas of heathland there, from the ecologically balanced and extensive stretches of Thomas Hardy's 'Egdon Heath' to the fragments of today embattled against all kinds of human pressure. It may well be that dry heathland in England will soon become as much a local relic as the great heaths of Jutland. The composite account I have put together for dry heath with dominant *Calluna* was chosen to give a relatively simple picture. In practice a great deal of lowland and mountain heathland consists of a very variable pattern of heather and grass, together with other species some of which can also dominate quite large areas – other heathy plants, gorse or bracken. No research on the effects of these patterns upon animal communities (other than that by Diver at Studland Heath[95]) has been done in this country; but again some valuable measurements have been made in Jutland by Schjøtz-Christensen[68] on the scientific reserve of Mols Laboratory. In using these for illustration I am indebted to Mr Schjøtz-Christensen and to Professor Overgaard Nielsen for advice and some unpublished information. At Mols Laboratory (which I have visited several times) there is a remnant of the heathland that once covered so much of northern Jutland and it has been added to by allowing certain arable fields to revert to heathland at different dates. There exists therefore a whole series of habitats ranging from bare sand or gravelly sand through increasingly denser vegetation, mostly with much grass, back to heath dominated by *Calluna*, at any rate on slopes that are not too hot. On these stages the beetle fauna was sampled, named, counted and weighed. The beetles were caught in jars sunk flush with the ground surface, and consisted almost entirely of adults running on the ground. About 65 species altogether were involved in the whole sequence (though more live in these habitats the sampling

lid not catch all of them). The total weight of beetles changed progressively
Fig. 8) and there were also great changes in the relative abundance of species.
n the first stage there were scattered tussocks of the smallish grass *Corynephorus*
anescens and several other plants, with bare ground or moss–lichen heath between.
n the second stage the vegetation was moving towards dense *Corynephorus*, with
ı few other species including *Agrostis tenuis*, the ground surface being mostly cov-
·red with lichen and moss. In the third there was even more dense grass heath or
variants of it with legumes such as rest-harrow, *Ononis*, and some other plants of
·vhich the mouse-ear hawkweed, *Hieracium pilosella*, and mosses and lichens made

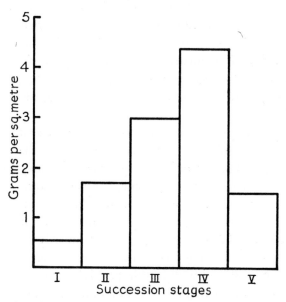

FIG. 8. Biomass of beetles in five succession stages from open ground to dense acid meadow
(the stage before *Calluna* heath), on heathland at Mols, in Jutland, Denmark. (After B.
Schjøtz-Christensen, 1957)

ı close mat on the ground. This vegetation was taller and denser than Stage 2. The
ourth stage was a very varied vegetation, mostly continuous grassland with
Corynephorus, *Agrostis tenuis* and *Anthoxanthum odoratum*, and also much moss and
ichen in the interspaces. The fifth stage was completely covered with dense 'acid
neadow' with a great deal of lichen (*Cladonia*) on the ground. At this point the
·egetation begins to change into *Calluna* heath, plants of the latter colonizing by
.eed and eventually making a fairly closed canopy.

The total amount of adult beetles is seen to increase as the initial bare ground
ets covered with field type vegetation, the maximum biomass occurring in Stage
ı. and falling off thereafter. The relative importance of different species also

changes. At first the Elaterid *Cardiophorus asellus* and some Carabid beetles dom
inate. Then, still with *Cardiophorus* important, the garden chafer, *Phylloperthe
horticola*, becomes abundant; but by the last grass stage another chafer, *Amphi
mallus solstitialis*, replaces it in importance, accompanied by an abundant herbi
vorous Carabid, *Harpalus anxius*. Exactly comparable measurements of the beetle
fauna in *Calluna* heath have not yet been made, but it is known that the chafer
and the larger Carabids disappear, with a loss of at least 1000 grams per m.^{2} o
biomass, making the heather communities as poor in quantity of beetle as the
original scattered *Corynephoretum*. If something like this picture is applicable to
British dry heathland, we should expect any mixture of grass and heather to have
quite a strong faunal pattern with the grass heath much richer than the heathe:
patches, which is another way of saying that the grazing of heathland not only
produces mutton (and if regulated to give the right herbage mixture, more
mutton), but also increases the insects living there. These points can only be
explored by making small-scale transects across the different units that make up
a heathland pattern.

The interest of grouse moors in regard to the habitat classification discussed in
this book, is that although usually dominated by *Calluna* they include not only
the relatively dry upland heaths with varying depths of relatively shallow peat that
are the chief headquarters of the red grouse, *Lagopus scoticus*, but also wet moorlands on deep peat such as those on the northern Pennine Hills. The former are
mainly terrestrial habitats, but the latter essentially a mixture of terrestrial and
transition. On either kind of place the grouse are primarily dependent on heather
for food, and they eat it through much of the year. Yet there is a profound difference between dry heathland with its thin peat layer and the waterlogged deep
peat of moorlands under a regime of heavy rainfall, with bog plants such as
Sphagnum and cotton grass (*Eriophorum*) mixed with the heather. During a discussion of the classification of habitats at Moor House National Reserve in the
Pennine Hills, I remember a botanist rushing out into the night and returning with
a large handful of 'moor' containing *Sphagnum* moss, out of which he squeezed
the water as from a bath sponge. This was done to convince me that *Calluna* moor
is not a terrestrial habitat. But as far as the red grouse is concerned, the emergent
heather forms a terrestrial structure and food resource just as effective as that on
drier heaths. For soil animals such as Enchytraeid worms or Tipulid fly larvae the
differences are decisive. But even on grouse moors that can truly be classified as
upland terrestrial heathland, there is a great deal of interspersed bog or flush habitat. The whole question of how these complex habitat patterns affect the survival
of the grouse population is at present being explored by the Unit of Grouse and
Moorland Ecology of the Nature Conservancy at Aberdeen.

It would be natural at this point to say something more about the upland habiats of Britain, since they consist predominantly of treeless land and include very large stretches of terrestrial open ground and field formation-types, or mixtures of the two (Plate 17). As Dr Johnson[248] wrote during his *Journey to the Western Islands* in 1773: 'Regions mountainous and wild, thinly inhabited, and little cultivated, make a great part of the earth, and he who has never seen them, must live unacquainted with much of the face of nature, and with one of the great scenes of human existence.' But there are two reasons why not much can be usefully canvassed here. One is that it would be almost an impertinence to try and summarize or repeat the basic description of upland systems so trenchantly given by Pearsall in his book on *Mountains and Moorlands*.[377] The other is that really very little is as yet understood about the distribution and organization of terrestrial animal communities in these regions, which he refers to as 'another Britain, to many of us the better half, a land of mountains and moorlands and of sun and cloud . . . its needs forgotten and its possibilities almost unknown'. It is symptomatic of the episodic and fragmentary state of field zoology in this country that the first attempt to give any orderly account of the animal life of our uplands was made by this plant ecologist. There is now an important exception to what I have said, which originated partly from the interest of Pearsall himself in this subject: the setting up of Moor House Research Station by the Nature Conservancy on the high moors at the head of the River Tees. Lying above the ordinary limit of trees but below the true alpine level (which is scarcely reached in the Pennines), a complex mixture of basic and non-calcareous rocks partly overlaid with glacial drift, and much of it covered with great depth of peat, in a bleak and rainy climate, with innumerable bogs and streams, this great National Nature Reserve (which I have often visited in summer) promises eventually to yield a comprehensive picture of one whole ecosystem not matched anywhere in the country except in Wytham Woods. But the information so far discovered about animal populations there mostly does not provide suitable material for analysing the patterns of interspersion of the habitats or the interrelations of their inhabitants. Research has, however, already reached the stage where some notions of the role of vegetation types and the scale of population density and biomass of some of the animal groups have been estimated. This and other aspects of the Moor House enterprise have been summarized on the botanical side by Conway;[81] and on the zoological side by Cragg,[87] under whose stimulus students from the University of Durham have carried out projects on these moors.

The chief obvious features of the lower montane region of Britain and still more of the arctic–alpine zone (such as has most fully survived on the Cairngorm Mountains between 3000 and 4000 ft; see Plate 18) is the simplicity of the habitat structure especially in the terrestrial series. There is an absence or poor development of all the 'furniture' one is accustomed to see in natural woodlands at lower levels.

There are no logs and stumps, no large bracket fungi and not many large toad stools, carrion – except for occasional bodies of sheep and deer, and these ar quickly attacked by birds – is scarce, dung is in small parcels (from sheep or deer o game-birds) not in luxuriant pats, nests are poorly developed or very scattered in deed, and human artefacts at the higher levels are mostly confined to loose ston walls and primitive bridges. The vegetation itself is simpler in structure than tha of well-developed meadows – at any rate as regards the vascular plants, and larg tussocks are not common. Though heather and bilberry provide woody growth of a sort, they cannot be said to contain roomy plant organs in which many insect can easily develop. The 'furniture' that is abundant at the levels where frost action slope, and diminution of peat expose the native rocks, is the stones of screes an frost-shattered detritus fields on the tops. Some of these display the curious stripe and polygonal differentiation so commonly found on Arctic tundra. The variet of the habitat is still further cut down as the field layer diminishes, and at th highest levels there are left only open ground formation-types, which themselve may not carry a closed vegetation but only poverty-stricken plant mats or patche or else moss and lichen heaths. The cryptogamic flora of the alpine zone of ou mountains is extraordinarily rich, as it is in the Arctic.[493] But as has already bee pointed out in the description of heathland, these have few invertebrate feeder though the introduced reindeer now established on Cairngorm occupy this niche representing, though in an almost nominal way, this great food-chain from lichen existing around northern regions. Terrestrial soils are poor, and above the zone where raw humus accumulates, very shallow. Rather locally in our mountain there are unexpected growths of meadows at heights of as much as 2400 feet wher basic rocks have permitted a more luxuriant supply of nutrients. Of course simplicity in communities does not make them uninteresting, rather the reverse as they offer hope of solutions for ecological problems, and may also be ver attractive aesthetically and historically.

The chief patterns likely to be found in montane animal communities will b interrelations between interspersed different major habitats, rather than intern patterns laterally within any one. One of the chief variants, apart from soil an aspect and height, is water. Terrestrial habitats on mountains are very frequentl interspersed in a complicated manner with damp ground, bogs, flushes, stream and sometimes pools. (At the alpine level even this kind of variety is far dimin ished.) Two examples of the effect of this interspersion upon terrestrial anima populations can be mentioned. The heather beetle, *Lochmaea suturalis*, which some times devastates the foliage of heather on grouse and sheep moors, also needs high humidity of the environment for the survival of eggs and pupae.[334] It seem pretty certain that, even allowing for the naturally high rainfall and often ver damp air in the hill regions where this species can become important, this beetl would be unable to maintain effective populations without the presence of damp or boggy areas interspersed with the relatively drier grass moors and upland heaths.

The other example comes from the work of Coulson[83, 84] at Moor House, where he carried out a general survey of the habitat distribution of craneflies (Tipulidae) and gave special attention to one very common species there, *Tipula subnodicornis*. The larvae of this fly live in a rather wide range of habitats, from permanently wet *Sphagnum* bogs, through moor zones dominated by the heath rush, *Juncus squarrosus*, to peat-moor of *Calluna* with *Sphagnum* and cotton-sedge (*Eriophorum*) and also in the slightly drier *Calluna* moor with lichen on the top of deep peat. In 1954 the highest densities of larvae were found in the soil of the *Juncus squarrosus* moor. This habitat is essentially a terrestrial formation-type in which the rush stems rise a little above the normal six-inch limit for open ground, but have leaf rosettes close to the ground. It is relatively well drained and its usual water content is about half that of the *Calluna* bog-moor. It is of course ordinarily kept moist by the tremendous rains of these hills. By contrast the fly larvae were only a fifth to a quarter as dense in *Sphagnum* bog. In 1955 there was a very severe drought which killed many invertebrates in the peat, and apparently affected the young larvae of *Tipula subnodicornis* so severely that it virtually died out everywhere except in the boggiest habitats. Dr Coulson informs me that they actually disappeared from most parts of the *Sphagnum* bogs sampled, but survived in certain local spots described as *Sphagnum* flushes, that had more water supply than the rest. Cragg[87] has summed up the significance of this story: 'We are left with the general impression that populations of *Tipula subnodicornis* on high moorland form a mosaic and that survival is dependent on the range of habitats being sufficiently great to ensure that in unfavourable seasons some at least of the isolated populations manage to survive.' The special point to be noted is that these survival centres normally carry a population much lower than those of the *Juncus squarrosus* moor. The 'best' habitat is not sufficient to support this normally common insect in all years.

At montane levels the field layer of vegetation is not inhabited by a large number of invertebrates, but there is one animal that is very widespread and which depends very directly upon the vertical layering of vegetation in order to fulfil its life-cycle. This is the sheep-tick, *Ixodes ricinus*, a carrier of virus diseases of the sheep and some other animals, and whose main areas of abundance in this country lie in hill pastures. Here the chief habitats are rough grazings – better ones usually being free from ticks. These rough grazings are distinguished by having some sort of field layer, though often low and very irregular, below which lies grass mat that may be quite dense. Ticks are also abundant in bracken, which carries a litter layer corresponding structurally to the grass mat. Heather, though having ticks, is less occupied, and has less of a litter layer. They can also be abundant in more boggy ground dominated by *Juncus*, but are scarce where there is a short sward or turf. The sheep-tick spends practically all of its life (of usually several years) in thi protected ground zone. And here it does not move sideways to any considerable extent, its movements being almost entirely vertical. During each of its three stages – larva, nymph and adult – it may climb several times up the grasses o bracken waiting for a passing sheep or other animal. If none is available, the tick goes down after a few days into the mat again, there to soak up water that it ha lost by evaporation on the grass or bracken tips (where the relative humidity may fall to 40%). Milne's work[327, 328] in Northumberland proved that these two aspects of vegetation structure – the grass mat with its high humidity (at nearly al times 100%) and the grass field layer as a station for catching the host – are all important for the sheep-tick. Without the damp mat to retreat to between activity periods the tick would not survive. Without the leaf tip to sit on it would not get . host. The survival of the engorged female after it drops from the host is also closel dependent on falling into the right kind of vegetation. Milne's closest observation were made on mat-grass (*Nardus*) grassland, mixed with a little *Molinia* and *Juncus* and the grass stems were less than a foot high. Even in this abbreviated field layer the vertical differences in microclimate were very great. And the controlling facto was not the species of plant but the physical structure of the vegetation in a region of wet climate.

In our lowlands far the greatest extent of land is occupied by crops, yet littl space can be given here to discussing them as animal habitats, except to try and place them in the context of structural classification. In this country especially little is really known about the whole communities of crops, and our general idea must at present rest upon American and European investigations. There have been studies of bare life-histories, of a few populations of major pests, and of their immediately associated parasites or predators, and of the soil fauna. They have no been reviewed as a whole, on the contrary every effort is being made by means o toxic chemicals and other methods to destroy them. Most British croplands com into the category of temporary field type, almost invariably with a field layer les than three feet high – cereals, potatoes, root crops, clover, the cabbage tribe, and lucerne. Because they are sown crops, they are all preceded by a stage of bare ploug land unless they happen to be some kind of follow-on undercrops that expand when the main crop canopy has been cut. In the typical older rotation systems o three- or four-year cycle, there were seasons of fallow stubble or other open ground conditions, carrying temporarily a great flourishing of other species – the plant that we call weeds. The term 'weed' has two connotations. One is simply that they are the competitors with crop plants, inedible to modern man unless converted (and this only happens in a very limited degree) for human food into partridge or hare or roedeer or some similar wild species of animal; also in some degree in the form of poultry gleaning stubble. Godwin[193] has noted that 'the distinction between crop and weed was formerly less obvious than now. The stomach contents of the Iron-Age man hanged and buried in the Danish bog at Tollund showed that he had eaten a meal containing beside barley and flax, seeds of such species as *Polygonum convolvulus, P. lapathifolium, Spergula arvensis*, and *Chenopodium album*.' There are other indications of this kind.

The second attribute of weeds is that the periodically disturbed and open environment afforded by arable land, as also by similar patches of waste land disturbed by other human activities like building and road-making and gravel digging, enables weed species to survive because of less intense natural plant competition, especially from established perennial species. And these weed species are in turn mainly derived from two sources: Late-glacial and other historical colonizers of Britain then occupying the incompletely vegetated soils (see p. 95); and more modern invaders from abroad. These two categories merge historically, in so far as invaders seem to have been arriving at intervals all through the Holocene Period. A good example of a fairly modern arrival is *Crepis taraxacifolia*, a large and showy yellow hawkweed several feet high which, according to Salisbury,[420] first arrived in 1713, but began its rapid spread at the end of the nineteenth century. Druce[106] first found it in Berkshire in 1881, and in Oxfordshire[105] in 1884. By 1897 in the former it was 'locally common and rapidly increasing and likely to become permanently established in the county'. Nowadays it can be seen in many fields that have not been yet too drastically denuded of their weeds. But the whole status of weeds is changing so rapidly under the impact of herbicides, that their fate is hard to foresee; the chief question-mark being whether they will evolve chemical-resistant strains that begin, like those of insects and ticks, to run ahead of the inventive destruction of the agricultural chemist. Perhaps another consideration might be added: will it always be found to be the best kind of investment to reduce the diverse plant and animal communities associated with crops to sterilized mono-cultures? As regards the historical origin of the animal species of croplands, we know practically nothing, except that some have risen to the position of pests at various times, and that some of these are invaders from other countries. My impression is that invaders of this kind are still much fewer among animals than among plants, and that there are a good many more species of foreign animals established in gardens than in arable land communities. And I do not think that at present there is a single inland animal found on croplands that could be traced as an exclusively Late-glacial survivor, though such may exist.

I have already pointed out that much of the natural field-type vegetation other than heaths reverts temporarily to an open ground condition in winter. Crops differ considerably in the length of time that they are left standing before being harvested (or in certain instances ploughed back into the ground). The great majority (wheat, oats, barley, potatoes, roots, for example) are strictly annual, as also are most species of weeds. *Brassica* crops such as cabbage and kale may stand for two years, while lucerne (usually called alfalfa in America) may be left for as long as eight years, but usually for less, and during this time it is harvested at least once a year. Still longer periods of renovation are found in ley grasslands, now one of the leading crops of this country. These start with bare ground usually sown with one or two grass species, making a sward that gradually becomes diversified with other plants arriving naturally from without. Then there are hay-meadows, cut once or twice in a season, but otherwise with their basal structure forming a permanent system. The classification of these various cropland habitats presents a few practical difficulties, which can be overcome provided it is remembered that the object of having a classification of habitats is not to enable us to erect rigid barricades between so-called communities, but rather to assemble information about interspersed components in an orderly manner. I have counted all croplands except ley grass and hay-meadow as 'Field-type arable', though recognizing that they are at intervals reduced to low structures of open ground nature, or – so far as vegetation is concerned – destroyed altogether. This reduction in vertical layering occurs at almost any season, not just in winter. They might, theoretically, equally be registered as 'Field-type, very temporary'. Ley grass is counted as an arable crop in its first year, thereafter as 'Field-type, non-acid' or 'acid' according to the soils. Lucerne has not been treated in this way, because it is a foreign crop species, and its survival and harvesting over several years do not lead to the establishment of a normal mixed grassland or meadow type. Hayfields, where on non-flooded ground or marsh, are regarded as semi-natural field types, in so far as they retain the permanent structure of stem base, minor tussock bases, and soil with roots. Also quite a rich field-layer fauna is able to develop during the spring and summer before harvesting.

The recent colossal expansion of the treatment of croplands with toxic chemicals, either to kill plant competitors or insect, mite, nematode and other pests, also to a lesser extent for fungal diseases (and it is always possible that fungicides may have side-effects upon invertebrates, as has been proved in orchards), is obviously tending to simplify any communities that are present – communities already partially reduced in variety by ordinary methods of cultivation. It remains to be seen how far this simplification is itself going to create dangers of new and unsuspected outbreaks of pest populations. One example of this kind of thing was the spread of the wild oat (*Avena fatua*) in cereal fields, when other competing weeds began to be cut back by herbicides, though newer chemical measures are said to be able to differentiate between it and the crop. In the following remarks I shall be concerned not so much with the actual cropland communities that survive at this time under intense chemical and other control, but with what *potential* they have as communities in comparison with the natural field types I have already discussed. For, in addition to its intrinsic ecological interest, knowledge of this is fundamental in understanding the balance of communities in and around croplands, whether specially controlled by man or not.

The plant and animal communities of any ordinary field crops must be derived annually from four different sources. First, from the ground zone and soil of the field itself, usually from the soil alone into which elements from the obliterated ground vegetation will get incorporated by ploughing. Of course one of the objects of rotation ploughing was to dodge these resident species, but some seeds can remain dormant for many years. Secondly, they are brought in as contaminants in the sown seed. Wellington's analysis[545] of crop seeds revealed a surprisingly large 'seed community'. Thus his samples had 9 species of weeds with the wheat seed, 11 with the barley, 12 with the oats, and 7 common to all three. Different grass species contained 12-20 species of weeds, clovers 16-18, lucerne 17. Here the still existing technological inability to make sown seed 'clean' results in the sowing of a pre-packaged plant community. There is also the question of pathogenic organisms, many of which can be carried over in seeds: it was recently reported that wheat seeds can carry the organisms of 55 bacterial and fungal diseases.[306] Thirdly, species may arrive from other crop fields either with the same or a different dominant crop. Fourthly, and possibly most effectively of all, they come in from the permanent habitats interspersed with or surrounding these fields. These habitats include verges of fields and roads, hedges, woods, gardens, marshes, ditches and so on. Patches of unmanaged rough grass at the edge of cropland may, for example, carry populations of the frit-fly (*Oscinella frit*), whence oat fields can acquire some of the population that builds up to such a high level in the oat flower panicles.[468] I have found the seven-spotted ladybird (*Coccinella septempunctata*) breeding on the stems and leaves of a standing oats crop near Oxford, and here it must have come in from the neighbouring oak and birch coppice woods or the hedgerows; for it is a prominent predator with a wide range of habitat. The winter quarters of crop animals, whether herbivore or predator, must therefore be a strong link in the continuity of the crop communities, and to understand them we would need to know much more about the whole mosaic pattern of cropland and other habitats. A species of Thysanoptera, *Limothrips cerealium*, which (among a wide range of plant hosts) attacks grasses and cereals, was studied by Lewis[291] at Silwood Park in Surrey. The seasonal peak in numbers on plants was from the end of July to early August, after which the numbers fell rapidly, and by means of water-traps it was found that the females were flying away, to hibernate eventually under the bark of pine and oak trees around the field, where they remained until the spring. The same phenomenon has been seen in Europe. They have similarly been found hibernating in rotting oak branches on trees within Wytham Woods.[284]

To me the great marvel of arable agriculture is that (in the ecological sense) the apparently shocking disturbance of the land by ploughing has been able to produce empirically such successful results in the production of crops. From our ecological standpoint, it is perhaps an equal marvel that hitherto (that is, not counting the unpredictable long-term results of toxic chemicals) crop fields are able to acquire each season a comparatively abundant and diverse fauna. Some vertebrates have actually adapted themselves successfully to the new patterns, in a changing regime of feeding round the year. Of these the common partridge, *Perdix perdix*, is the most notable, and has been well studied. Middleton and Chitty's analysis[322] of the food at different seasons, in the conditions of agriculture prevailing before the last war, was done on 429 adult birds from different parts of Britain. The seasonal picture of the crop contents (Fig. 9) was interpreted as follows. In September, stubbles left after corn-cutting provided abundant grain. By October to November about half the land was bare after ploughing, grain was scarcer and supplemented by grass, clover, sugar-beet and weed seeds. From December to February three-quarters of the food was grass, the rest beet and weed seeds; in the spring period March to May little weed seed, no grain, and except for a few flowers and buds, all grass food. The summer months show the outburst of flowers, the increase of weeds, and the use of a little animal food as well. Incidentally, all four of the weeds found in the Tollund man occur in the diet of these modern partridges!

For a notion of the scale that animal communities can attain in a crop, we can use some surveys that have been done of lucerne and cabbage fields abroad. In the course of sweep-netting on plots of alfalfa in Oklahoma, which were being used to test the results of insecticide treatments upon the fauna, Fenton[151] took 396 species of insects, 15 species of spiders as well as several kinds of mites, a total of about 415. This does not include the regular soil and surface forms. One practical significance of there being such a diverse community on this crop is brought out by his conclusion that 'the toxic effects of some of the insecticides to certain insect predators created favourable conditions for their prey which became more numerous later on in the sprayed plots than in the untreated checks'. A more elaborate survey of lucerne fields in Hungary, by Balgh and Loksa,[16] also indicates what a complex system of species exists, though it is not possible from their work to arrive at a complete list of them. Perhaps the most extensive and continued observations on crop communities have been made from the University of Kiel in Schleswig-Holstein, by Tischler and his associates, especially Heydemann. Again, the full details are not at present available in published form, but Tischler[505] (basing himself a good deal on Heydemann's surveys) points out that very often the soil type is more important than the particular species of crop in deciding the species composition of the community, at any rate in the case of ground and soil-living forms. 'The fauna of a rye field on sandy soil is therefore in many respects

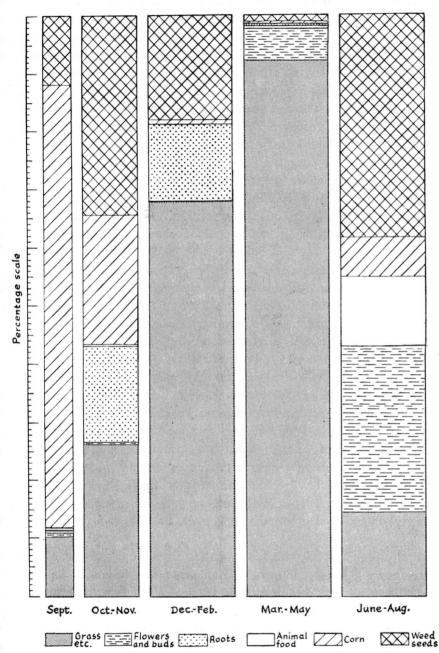

FIG. 9. The percentage composition by volume of the food of adult partridges, *Perdix perdix*, in Britain, at different seasons. (After A. D. Middleton and H. Chitty, 1937)

similar rather to that of a potato field with the same type of soil than to that of another rye field with a clay soil. . . . In respect of both weeds and animals, fields of leafy vegetables are, in general, merely variants of fields with bladed vegetation having the same soil type, even although some species of plants and animals only occur in grain fields and others in potato or beet fields.' These statements contain two large implications. One is that the basic structure of the habitat, i.e. the soil structure, with whatever microclimatic effects accompany it, dominates the picture. The other is that every crop field carries a high percentage of the fauna of any other crop field on the same soil, and is therefore a reservoir of species for recolonization.

The most interesting effort to untangle some of the processes and relationships within a whole crop community, and their dependence upon habitat patterns, has been made by Pimentel, working at Cornell University, Ithaca, in the State of New York. He used the domestic cabbage, *Brassica oleracea*, which includes several different structural forms such as ordinary cabbage, kale, broccoli and collard (a variety that does not make a heart). In his experiments the cabbage and collard were allowed to flower, and this added variety to the community of animals attracted to the crop. An ecological survey[389] of pure stands of *Brassica*, kept free from weeds, and each run for one season from planted seedlings, gave a total of 198 species of animals (chiefly insects) on or visiting the plants, without taking account of ground surface and soil organisms. Of these 48 were flower visitors (mainly flies) from elsewhere, so that the main community, which was largely based upon three species of aphids, contained 150. In detail, there were 16 species of moths and butterflies; 19 species of plant-sucking Homoptera of which 10 were aphids and 3 the dominant herbivores present; 10 species of Heteroptera, including 7 predators; 24 species of beetles of which 11 were predators (8 of them ladybirds); 17 flies; 32 Hymenoptera belonging to 11 families of which 7 are parasitic; and a residue of groups with a few species in each, that included herbivores such as grasshoppers, slugs, voles and birds, and carnivores such as lacewings and spiders. A good many of these 'resident' breeding insects also fed at the cabbage flowers when mature.

Practically all these species must have come in from outside, except possibly for a few remaining in the soil. Pimentel[388] remarks that all the animals he found on *Brassica* crops occur both on cultivated and natural crucifers in the Ithaca region. In one particular field that is described, a 15-year-old fallow field now a rich meadow, there were about 300 species of plants, including five wild crucifers of the genera *Brassica*, *Barbarea*, *Armoracium*, *Cardamine* and *Lepidium*. Of the animal species living in this field, he says: 'Considering the estimated number of 300 plant species in that planting, I would estimate at least 3000 species of heterotrophs for the mixed-species habitat' – the term heterotrophs here including also some fungi

nd other microflora. The fallow field was used for an interesting experiment to
est the effect upon the community of the *Brassica oleracea* crop itself, of placing
plants in this 'natural' meadow, and comparing the fauna with that on control
plots with only the domestic crop, kept at the same spacing in some controls, and
is an ordinary dense crop in others. It is always rather difficult to assess the results
of such pioneer experiments, because of the number of purely technical points that
are involved. One thing that was done in order to make quantitative sampling
efficient enough to throw light upon the development of the community, was
that some species had to be grouped together (for example where larvae could not
be separated). 'The methods of grouping species for counting reduced the categories of taxa in this study to one-fourth of the total noted in the initial survey.'
But in spite of this the different communities could, it was thought, be compared
in these terms. The results indicated a substantially greater number of taxa in the
pure crop than in the mixed community. That is to say, although the whole plant
and animal community of the rich meadow was richer by far, the cabbage population carried fewer of its possible species when living in it. Also, aphid, flea-beetle
and Lepidoptera populations on cabbage reached outbreak levels in the pure crop,
but never in the fallow field.

In another series of field experiments, Pimentel[387] found that when cabbages
were grown as a dense crop they carried a poorer community of 'taxa' than when
they were planted sparsely. There were other marked differences that would
require a more elaborate discussion than I can provide here. All these surveys and
experiments illustrate how much can be found out about the patterns of whole
communities by contrasting artificial with natural mixtures in an ecosystem where
the crops are chiefly colonized from the latter. They also bring out the feature that,
although acquiring quite well-developed animal communities with the usual food-
chains mostly based on rather a few kinds of abundant herbivores, these communities are nothing like so rich as natural ones with mixed plant species, and even
at the level of 150 species may be sufficiently unstable to develop outbreaks or near
outbreaks. And universal observation proves that they are often only too vulnerable to new invaders from other regions.

It is evident that although the intricate yet broad pattern of croplands and their
'interstitial tissue' of more natural habitats is part of the deep background of most
people's awareness of the countryside, and especially that of the thoughtful
naturalist, only a little has yet been done by professional ecologists (especially in
Britain) to explore its meaning and the ways in which it remains or is artificially
kept in balance. The growth of insecticides and herbicides has certainly sharpened
this awareness. A great monograph like Tansley's on *The British Islands and their
Vegetation*, published in 1939, hardly alludes to ordinary croplands, only to the
semi-natural grasslands of a permanent kind. The major works on agricultural

pests scarcely notice the natural communities, though game-managers and bee
keepers have for many years recognized the double context in which their par
tridges and hive-bees live and survive. The great question about crop fields tha
now awaits an answer is how far the scale and diversity and patterns of crop com
munities, plant and animal, is crucial in the stability of their population systems
From what I have briefly described here, it is at any rate certain that the seasona
building-up of animal populations in crops depends very largely on invasion from
surrounding communities, superimposed upon the continuum of organisms tha
live in the soil and to some extent the ground surface. These surrounding com

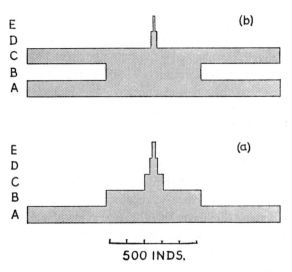

FIG. 10. Normal pyramid of numbers according to 2-mm. size classes of invertebrates in the
field layer of an old meadow in Michigan, and (above) distorted pyramid caused by immigration of spittle-bugs from nearby mown fields. (After F. C. Evans and U. N. Lanham, 1960)

munities have more permanent habitat structure and much larger species diversity
But apart from any practical considerations, this process of re-invasion of new
vegetation is ecological succession on a very extensive scale all over the country
and deserves study in its own right – a kind of research which Pimentel's field
studies show to be very productive. These invasions do not, however, take plac
only in one direction, for there is usually also a mass exodus of the animal popu
lations that develop in summer crops after harvest. One of the best known ex
amples of this is the dispersal of rats and mice from cornfields into surrounding
hedges at the time of reaping. A remarkable instance of insect movement wa
noted by Evans and Lanham[145] during their ecological survey of an old meadow
on the George Reserve in Michigan. This field lies inside a fairly complex wood
land and bog area, but there are cultivated fields outside the Reserve. They too

egular sweep-net samples of the field layer animals and sorted them into 2-mm. length size classes, and found that the size pyramid for the species normally living on the field was of the usual shape (Fig. 10a), but superimposed on it was an enormous number of adult meadow spittle-bugs, *Philaenus leucophthalmus* (a species also common in Britain), which produced an extraordinary distortion by extending the size class 4·6-6·5 mm. (Fig. 10b). These bugs had flown in from surrounding clover and alfalfa fields at the time of mowing. 'Essentially all adult *Philaenus* present in mid-July had come into the field from the outside, the small "native" populations having fallen nearly to zero by the end of June.' The diagram shows the situation in 1957, but in 1958 when the invading *Philaenus* were about ten times as numerous the distortion would have been greater still.

CHAPTER 8

The Terrestrial Maritime Zone

THE MAGNIFICENT Maritime communities around the coasts of Britain have a certain affinity with those of croplands, in as much as they are physically unstable and include some Late-glacial survivors that used to live inland. Godwin[192] says 'Of species present generally in the Late-glacial landscape, several, such as *Armeria maritima*, *Silene maritima*, *Cochlearia officinalis* and *Plantago maritima*, now grow in the sub-alpine mountain vegetation or in maritime habitats of sea-cliffs, dunes or salt-marshes.' This is of course not just an inference, since actual remains of the plants have been found in early deposits. All four of these species are abundant and often dominant ones. Some animals, including the sand-dune snails *Succinea oblonga* and *Catinella arenaria*, have a similar history.[471] The total length of coast line in England and Wales (including the larger islands but not the Isle of Man has recently been estimated by the Ministry of Housing and Local Government under the supervision of Dr E. C. Willatts, by courtesy of whom I am able to quote from the results here. By taking the coastline measured along High Water Mark of ordinary tides on one-inch to the mile Ordnance Survey maps, and using a convention about where to stop in estuaries or long inlets of the sea (e.g. the lowest bridging or ferry point), they determined a round total of 2748 miles This confirms the earlier estimate by Dr Willatts published by Steers[480] in 1944 of 2750 miles. Apparently there are no comparable measurements for Scotland or Ireland; but the total amount of maritime habitats in the complex indented shores of the British Isles must be impressive, and this zone still supports one of the most important natural 'reserves' of our flora and fauna. In so far as these communities contain a great many species also found elsewhere in the country, the preservation of the coast, like the preservation of our roadsides, becomes one of the major means of conservation. The English counties with the longest coast lines are Cornwall (272) and Devon (176), the latter closely followed by Pembrokeshire in Wales (160). If the coasts of islands like the Scillies, Lundy, Skomer etc. are added to these, the total for the three counties forms about a quarter of that for England and Wales as a whole.

The Ministry has also measured the lengths of various land types along these coasts, and these fall broadly into the habitats I am dealing with here. This was done from a manuscript map specially made on the 10-inch to the mile scale. The subdivisions were as follows: cliffs above 25 ft, 1012 miles (of which 866 was over 50 ft high); marsh (i.e. presumably mainly salt-marsh) 269; sand-dune 230; shingle 525; residue, including sand and mud, etc., 549. Of this whole coast-line 380 miles was substantially built up (about the year 1958). The distribution of these 'Domestic' occupation-sites according to the original habitat underlying them was not calculated, but common sense indicates that they do not ordinarily cover much sand-dune or marsh, though they may encroach on shingle and cliff-tops. A good deal of the shingle represents a narrow zone at and above H.W.M. that would not be in the same class of terrestrial habitats as the great shingle spits of Chesil Bank in Dorset or Orfordness in Suffolk. (In quoting these subdivision figures I have rounded off the fractions.) During the last war, J. A. Steers under-took a remarkable perambulation of much of the coastline of England and Wales, in order to weigh up its conservation value. His map (complete except for a stretch from Southampton to the Thames that was in war-time closed to such research) enables one to see the distribution of cliff, dune and salt-marsh, and the manner in which they are interspersed.[480] The parts modified or obliter-ated by industrial or other occupation are also shown, and the coast divided into three categories of scenic quality: 'exceptional', 'very good' and 'good'. It is not entirely surprising that all the coast unspoiled by man falls into one or other of these categories.

In order to show the distribution of these habitats by another method, I have borrowed several maps (Figs. 11-14) from the great *Atlas of the British Flora* compiled by the Botanical Society of the British Isles.[379] Each dot indicates the presence of a species within one square of the 10-kilometre grid that they used for mapping. The marram grass, *Ammophila* (formerly *Psamma*) *arenaria*, typifies sand-dunes, on which it is a common dominant; the spring squill, *Scilla verna*, is a cliff-top plant, though with a geographically restricted distribution; the sea-campion, *Silene maritima*, lives chiefly on cliffs and shingle, occasionally on moun-tains. But the map (not reproduced here) of the distribution of *Festuca rubra*, a most important dominant grass of the maritime zone, covers almost every part of the country, inland or coastal. I have also included the map of the common salt-marsh grass *Pucciniella* (formerly *Poa*) *maritima*. The reason for doing this is that there are not any very remarkable terrestrial communities developed from salt-marsh, though the pastures and croplands into which they are usually converted have some maritime species in them. But this salt-marsh grass does indicate the places where sea or estuarine mud has been undergoing the long and complicated stages of ecological succession towards dry land formation-types. Few terrestrial maritime animals have been - or could be - recorded so thoroughly that maps

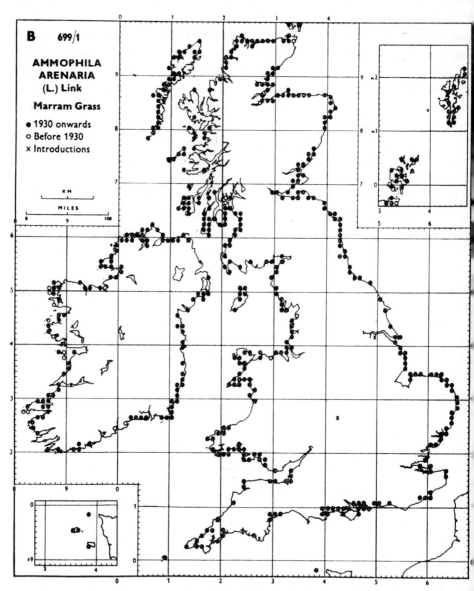

FIG. 11. Maritime distribution of marram grass, *Ammophila arenaria*, on sand-dunes. (From F. H. Perring and S. M. Walters, 1962)

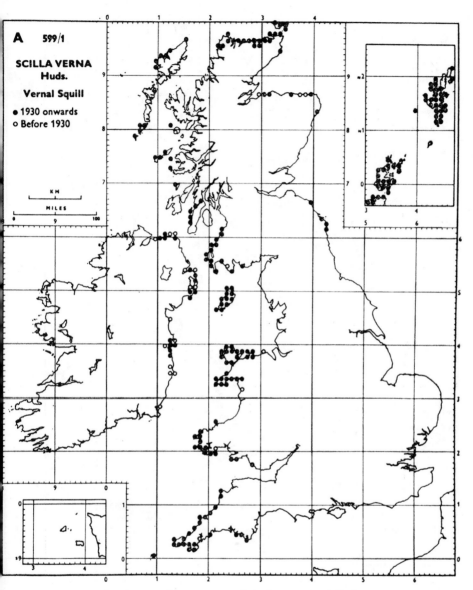

FIG. 12. Maritime distribution of the spring squill, *Scilla verna*, on cliffs. (From F. H. Perring and S. M. Walters, 1962)

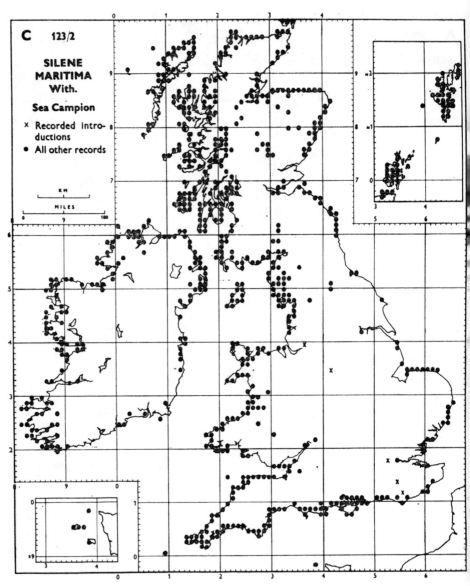

FIG. 13. Maritime (and a little mountain) distribution of the sea-campion, *Silene maritima*, on cliffs and shingle. (From F. H. Perring and S. M. Walters, 1962)

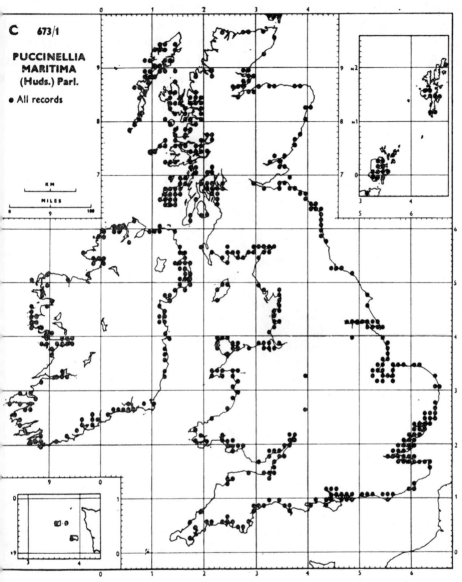

FIG. 14. Maritime distribution of the salt-marsh grass, *Puccinellia maritima*. (From F. H. Perring and S. M. Walters, 1962)

for them can be made. The non-marine molluscs have, however, been industriousl
mapped by the Conchological Society.[78] On these maps the smallest unit is
vice-county (being either a whole county or part of one), which exaggerates th
distribution detail a good deal. Although only very few land molluscs are actuall
confined to the maritime zone, the pointed snail *Cochlicella acuta*, which live
chiefly on sand-dunes in Great Britain, has a west coastal distribution (Fig. 1

FIG. 15. Maritime distribution of the pointed snail, *Cochlicella acuta* (which has also some
inland localities in Ireland). (See Note 5)

and [5]). In Ireland it extends inland as well, a characteristic noticeable in son
other species of animals, including a few sea-birds nesting by inland lochs.[62]
will already be apparent that these maritime species, both plant and anim
though important enough to give the communities a special character and in
good many instances being abundant or dominant in them, are mixed with ma
other species with much wider distribution. Hepburn, whose book *Flowers
the coast*[221] provides a very interesting modern conspectus, picks out the main
maritime terrestrial species of plants as follows: for sea-cliffs about 27 species, f
shingle about 23, for sand-dune about 32. Some of these live in more than one
these three habitats, while some also occur partly inland as well. I have omitt

great rarities. The corresponding number of animal species must be higher, though no one has compiled it.

From the structural point of view, and for understanding the distribution of animal communities, it is necessary to define the meaning of 'Maritime' as used here. The word can of course cover a great many different ideas about sea-coast, or of the sea itself. When one speaks of 'the Maritime Nations' one does not mean that they dwell on sand-dunes. For the land ecologist it means the sea-edge. But here I shall use it in an even more restricted way, to connote habitats lying within a zone above High Water Mark of sea or brackish estuary and the normal terrestrial habitats on the landward side. Tansley[493] used the word in a slightly broader sense for the convenience of including the vegetation of salt-marshes. In the present classification, all major zones at or below H.W.M. are treated as Transition to the sea, estuary or other brackish water body. Salt-marshes therefore fall into the Transition zone. It is also convenient to include there the drift-line and drifted sea-wrack. Not all the natural vegetation of the maritime zone is open ground or field type, but it is these that are really characteristic, reflecting as they do the early stages of development of vegetation on unstable terrain. (The later stages of scrub – except perhaps sea buckthorn – and woodland tend merely to be rather impoverished versions of inland communities.)

Terrestrial maritime communities really contain a minority of animal species completely confined to them, though these are fascinating to meet with and do stamp the whole system clearly with a special character. The following examples (which could be multiplied without difficulty) will serve to illustrate the peculiar amalgam of truly coastal and more widespread species that exists in maritime open ground and field-type habitats. The rock pipit (*Anthus spinoletta*) is, with some exceptions (e.g. in west Scotland and recently in the West Riding of Yorkshire[348]), confined for nesting to the maritime zone, mainly on rock cliffs, where it largely replaces the meadow pipit (*A. pratensis*).[62] The long-horned grasshopper, *Platycleis denticulata* (referred to also as *occidentalis* or *grisea*), is confined almost exclusively to coastal counties all the way round from Essex by the south and south-west coasts to south and west Wales, and again in Caernarvonshire a bit further north.[266, 267] It usually lives close to the sea, and I found it in Pembrokeshire in a low cliff meadow mixed with wind-cut privet, not far above H.W.M.[129] There is only one known inland locality, near Stratford-on-Avon in Warwickshire.[265] In southern Britain the oystercatcher (*Haematopus ostralegus*), which feeds in the intertidal zone of sea and estuary, chiefly nests along the coast on rock, shingle, sand-dune and salt-marsh, also on muddy estuary banks. In the north of the country, however, it also nests on inland river shingle, on moorland and now even in agricultural land and some open woods.[62] By contrast with these primarily maritime species, there are widespread forms such as the hedgehog (*Erinaceus europaeus*), abundant on sand-dunes, and the slow-worm lizard (*Anguis fragilis*) which can be found on sea-cliff grassland. The large woodlouse, *Oniscus asellus*, a frequent inhabitant of leaf litter in deciduous and some conifer woods, of rotting wood, and also of some domestic habitats, is not usually found in grassland; but I have found it abundantly in the ground zone of maritime cliff 'meadows' in Pembrokeshire. The buzzard (*Buteo buteo*) and the kestrel (*Falco tinnunculus*) are common and important raptors on sea-cliffs and slopes, but have wide inland ranges as well. One of their common prey, the vole, *Microtus agrestis*, has a similar distribution.

Sometimes an inland locality seems to provide a partial substitute for maritime conditions, and this seems to happen especially on sandy soils. Near Oxford, at Frilford and Tubney in Berkshire, there is a stretch of Jurassic Greensand – now partly occupied by a golf course that still retains some resemblance to the structure of heathland – where a group of maritime beetles has been found. In 1907 Walker[530] wrote: 'A very remarkable feature of the latter locality is the number of species whose usual habitat is on the coast sandhills, and which are only exceptionally met with inland; of these, *Harpalus anxius, Amara fulva, Homalota* [= *Atheta*] *caesula, Ocypus ater, Xantholinus tricolor, Orthocerus muticus, Syncalypta hirsuta, Crypticus quisquilius, Cteniopus sulphureus, Apion schönherri*, and *Cleonus sulcirostris*, may be specially mentioned in this connexion.' The last has also been recorded at thistle roots on sand at Boar's Hill, near Oxford, and many years earlier on the other side of the city, by the sandy slopes of Shotover Hill. In the London area, *Atheta caesula* has been taken at Blackheath, and *Harpalus anxius* there and also at Oxshott.[4] At least seven species of coastal dune beetles (including *Crypticus quisquilius*) live inland on the sands of the Suffolk Breckland.[103] *Ocypus*, now *Staphylinus, ater*, well exemplifies the complex nature of some of these distributions. It is or used to be primarily a coastal species that was considered very rare inland.[167, 29] It has however been found in a scatter of localities away from the coast which include Windsor Forest (where it was associated with rotting wood),[102] Epping Forest,[285] and several other places, including a few round Oxford. In the maritime zone it lives on sea-cliff tops,[131, 197] sand-dunes[29] and muddy places.[167] Some inland distributions of this sort may well be actual Late-glacial relics that have not yet been eliminated, or for some reason have found a way of surviving. But others may have spread inland subsequently from their coastal headquarters, a parallel instance among Transition communities being the farm fields near Marcham, Berkshire, where a permanent salt overflow from the Jurassic marine rocks maintains a small salt-marsh community of plants ordinarily found on the coast.[107]

The division of maritime terrestrial habitats into *Rock, Shingle, Sand* and *Mud* is convenient since it links the whole complex and often unstable series physiographically; but there are many intermediate forms and mixtures as well. Within each of these types can be found succession stages from bare surface through vegetated open ground to something resembling meadow, or sometimes heath. It is the frequency of bare ground and mixtures of the lower and higher formation-types in proximity to the sea that gives these habitats their special character. My own direct experience of them is derived chiefly from the coast of west Pembrokeshire, a little from the north of Cornwall, from the Lancashire sand-dunes, and from the Outer Hebrides. I have also seen some of the classical sites of ecological survey, such as the shingle and sand-dune island of Scolt Head in Norfolk;[481] and Studland Heath in Dorset, the scene of Diver and Good's remarkable ecological survey that was unfortunately curtailed by the last war before its faunal results could be analysed at all completely.[95] But published information about maritime animal communities is, except for the bird populations, still only in a piecemeal form, and more chaotic than it deserves to be. Here I shall only mention a few general ecological conclusions that illustrate my theme.

The photographs of *Cliff* scenery in Pembrokeshire (Plates 4, 19, 80) show the narrow uncultivated belt that characteristically fringes the crop fields on the seaward side in so many places. This is rough or steep ground that cannot be ploughed and frequently is also ungrazed by sheep. There is a tremendous range of rocks and soils and vegetation. Mixed with the later closed stages of vegetation or 'meadow' there may be a good deal of low wind-cut scrub of field-layer height, particularly privet, *Ligustrum vulgare*, and blackthorn, *Prunus spinosa*. Wind is a stiff limiting condition for animal activity too. On the west coasts where westerly winds blow for about two-fifths of the time,[25] often steadily, sometimes at gale force, and calms are not very common, insect life in the air or on exposed surfaces can be almost completely absent for hours or days at a time. The effect of a little shelter can be dramatic. I have walked in a strong breeze on Pentire Head in north Cornwall and seen nothing visibly active on the bare cliff-top grassland, and then come upon a small shallow depression in the ground that by some peculiarity of eddy-currents was completely sheltered. Here hundreds of flies and bees were busy collecting nectar from flowers of the autumn *Scilla*. In the immediate hinterland at the south end of St Bride's Bay in Pembrokeshire there are many sunken or high-banked lanes, mostly with hedgerows, that carry a great profusion of flowers and insects on the banks. I have been in one of these when a strong gale was blowing in from the sea and roaring about ten feet above my head yet in the lane itself all was calm, and butterflies such as the speckled wood, *Pararge aegeria*, were fluttering quietly. Most diurnal invertebrate life on the cliff-tops and slopes spends a great deal of its time under the cover of the stones and herbage. (I do not know what it does at night.) The activity of animal life of the field layer is consequently reduced. By contrast, insolation on these same slopes can be, especially on quieter days, so intense as to make it far too hot for a man, even on holiday. Under the mats and closed sward on the slopes facing the sea there is an extremely rich and numerous fauna. This begins a few feet above the Transition zone from the sea (Plate 21). Here there is a mixture of more or less maritime forms, others of very wide distribution in grassland or heath, and some that one ordinarily associates with woodland or woodland edge. Among the first are the large tennis-racket-shaped brown Coreid bug, *Enoplops scapha;* a small ladybird beetle, *Subcoccinella 24-punctata,* frequently met with under sea-campion mats; the very abundant ant, *Tetramorium caespitum; Platycleis occidentalis;* and the Opilionid (harvestman), *Nelima sylvatica.* Of the ordinary open ground and grassland forms there are many, including the four species of grasshoppers (other than *Myrmeleotettix maculatus*) found on Rough Common on Wytham Hill (see Ch. 6); the yellow ant, *Lasius flavus,* and another ant, *Myrmica sabuleti;* snails such as *Helicella itala* and *virgata* (mainly on turfy places) and *Helix aspersa;* and the vole, *Microtus agrestis.* 'Woodland' elements include the woodlouse *Oniscus asellus;* the small Carabid beetles, *Notiophilus hypocrita* and *N. palustris;* and the ringlet butterfly, *Aphantopus hyperantus.* More sheltered ravines leading down to the sea may have a very rich herb meadow that in midsummer is flowery and less confined by wind.

Certain mammals and sea-birds can greatly modify the ordinary rocky vegetation, the former by grazing and the latter by depositing guano or in other ways. The chief species of mammals concerned are the sheep and the rabbit; also no doubt voles, *Microtus agrestis,* do much hidden work that alters the plant life, as they do in other grasslands where there is sufficient undisturbed cover (see Ch. 6). Where sheep are present their effects on vegetation are pretty obvious in bringing more open ground or mixed ('rough') turf and tussock. There are no special studies of the effect of stock grazing upon cliff habitats and their animal communities, but the ecological survey made by Morton Boyd[37, 38] on the Inner Hebridean island of Tiree will serve to prove how great can be the changes in faunal composition that result from grazing or its removal. His survey was, however, done on a different kind of maritime grassland, growing on sand. The *machair,* as it is called in the west of Scotland, is a strip of grassland lying close to the shore, sometimes behind sand-dunes, but more or less flat or only slightly undulating. It grows on calcareous shell sand and may be used either for grazing or for arable cultivation. The place selected by Morton Boyd was a cattle-grazed machair that had never been tilled. Although there were dunes near by, it did not have an especially sand-dune type of fauna, e.g. the snail, *Cochlicella acuta,* was absent from the machair. There were no rabbits or voles. The grass turf, closely grazed from December to May only, grew to a height of about three inches in the summer[6], and was therefore a permanent open ground formation-type. It carried a dozen common pasture plants, including *Festuca rubra*, but the latter never overwhelmingly dominant. Twelve years earlier a part of the machair had been fenced off to make an airfield, which remained ungrazed. Here the *Festuca* had grown about a foot in average height, forming a thick intertwined sward of rank grass, with only local patches of the other species surviving. In order to compare the ground-running fauna, parallel lines of jam-jar traps were sunk in the ground on each side of the fence and a little way from it, and visited at intervals round a whole year. Earthworms were collected in the pitfalls, and also by laying out traps composed of cattle dung. Snails were counted on quadrats. In the whole survey 97 species of invertebrates were named, besides the seven species of birds and mammals seen on the place. This would by no means exhaust the faunal list, even at ground level, since only the beetles, ants, Opilionids (harvestman), spiders, millipedes, Homoptera, three species of Tipulid flies, and the snails and worms were dealt with. The chief result relevant here is the sharp difference in numbers, and for some species presence or absence, in the two formation-types. This can be shown clearly for certain beetles – the numbers given below being for the whole year's collection, though the differences were also very noticeable in each separate month as well:

	Grazed	Ungrazed
Carabus granulatus	28	118
Nebria brevicollis	5	86
Pterostichus vulgaris	82	1379
Longitarsus jacobaeae	11	338
Serica brunnea	9	74

The spider, *Lycosa pullata*, was almost absent from grazed, but abundant on ungrazed ground, whereas the females of *L. tarsalis* and *monticola* preferred the grazed ground. There are figures to illustrate the greater abundance of certain other species of invertebrates on the latter. Some quite important differences were also found in the earthworm populations, partly because two species, *Dendrobaena octoedra* and *Lumbricus rubellus*, are commoner where there is cattle dung. The breeding activity of earthworms went on all round the year under the thick grass, but on the pasture was limited to winter and spring. And all these differences in faunal composition and biology were controlled by the presence or absence of one kind of ungulate during half the year.

Before the advent from France of myxomatosis and the sharp decline in numbers of rabbits all over the country, it was not immediately obvious how much sea-cliff vegetation was held in equilibrium by their grazing. In particular, the beautiful mats of sea-pinks, *Armeria maritima*, on the cliff margins and tops are often unable to exist unless aided by the selective feeding pressure of a rabbit population. Gillham's extensive series of field observations on this subject in the Pembrokeshire islands are of especial value because they were begun not long before the myxomatosis pandemic of 1954. She also recorded the effects of various seabirds on the flora. On the island of Grassholm, where a very large gannetry covers part of the island in summer, there are no rabbits. On the part unoccupied by these birds there are about a dozen species of plants able to live under salt spray, the main dominant being *Festuca rubra*, and corresponding with this there is absence of *Armeria*. But on the rabbit-infested island of Skokholm this forms an extensive mat on the cliff-tops above the sea.[182] The exclusion of rabbits from this kind of turf on Skokholm resulted in increased growth and flowering of *Festuca rubra* which had suppressed most of the sea-pink and other plants within two years.[18] It will begin to be seen that this grass is an extremely widespread performer in the ecological changes in which rabbit populations are concerned. For example it has been equally aggressive in invading the mats of rock-rose, *Helianthemum chamaecistus*, at Wytham Hill. *Festuca rubra* waits in the wings, or in a subsidiary part, ready to take over the main act when other plants no longer have the benefit of the rabbit's preferential grazing – whose intensity can be imagined from the estimate of forty rabbits per acre on Skokholm. The interactions are really very complicated, and nothing but a mention of their existence is intended here. They include two different main processes. First are the preferences and dislikes of the rabbits. For example they do not eat ragwort, *Senecio jacobaea*, and they largely avoid the grass *Holcus lanatus* (often called 'Yorkshire fog'), because it is hairy and acrid. Under rabbit grazing this grass often forms large patches in places where *Festuca rubra* is suppressed, though in the exclusion cages it did not survive much. On the other hand, the kidney vetch, *Anthyllis vulneraria*, is succulent and is eaten. In June 1959 the edge of the red sandstone sea-cliffs at St Bride's Haven in Pembrokeshire had enormous patches of the kidney vetch in yellow flower, such as I had never see developed in the 1940s, and there were now no signs of rabbit there. But by 1964 much of it had become replaced by *Festuca rubra*. Here and elsewhere on the mainland cliffs, also on the island of Skomer, the invasion of sea pink dominated mats by *Festuca rubra* could be seen as well. On Skomer the situation actually fluctuates quite quickly with the ups and downs of the post-myxomatosis rabbit populations there. Gillham found that on Grassholm there was a large succulent form of the buckshorn plantain, *Plantago coronopus*, which on the rabbit-infested island of Skokholm grew only in inaccessible crevices, its place on the cliff-tops being taken by a smaller hairy form which survived in the close turf. (This island rabbit population has never developed myxomatosis, because the rabbit flea vector of the virus is absent from Skokholm.[502]) The second main process is of course the competition between the plant species themselves, whose outcome is so often decided by the tastes and numbers of the rabbit population. It is well known that ragwort is highly susceptible to plant competition, though it is avoided by rabbits. In these various ways the vegetation is deeply affected, although of course the rabbit is only one of the pattern-making factors. In the absence of ecological surveys, we can only rely on inferences about the fate of the animals living in these maritime mats and meadows. There are at any rate a certain number of species of insects directly attached to plant species that live there, whose populations must change.

The kind of open ground brought about by intense rabbit grazing, partly aided by human trampling, with its fine dense turf and absence of surface cover, would not at first glance seem likely to carry a rich animal community. On 5 September 1951 I saw the sudden emergence of ants on a cliff-top near Daymer Bay in north Cornwall, where there was a stretch of turf, smooth as a billiard table. On this warm and cloudy day, with a light steady rain, the ants appeared at the surface in the late afternoon, about 3.30-5 p.m. (Greenwich Mean Time). There were hundreds of individual aggregations emerging from underground nests, and hardly a square yard of the ground was without evidence of their subterranean work. At least two species were active, *Lasius flavus* and *L. alienus*, the former at any rate dependent upon root-aphid secretions for food. The males and females everywhere were undertaking their mating flights [7]; and scores of herring gulls (*Larus argentatus*) were strutting about feeding on them. A truly maritime scene! There was also on this same place a metallic blue Chrysomelid beetle, *Chrysolina haemoptera*, walking about and mating on the surface. According to Danish records [208] the larvae of this species feeds on *Plantago coronopus* (which is abundant in the turf here), also on *P. lanceolata*. Two days later the gulls were still catching ants on various parts of the cliff grass, as also were pied wagtails, *Motacilla alba*. De-alated queen ants were a common sight, and the emergence from the nests less intense, or finished. But the whole life of such communities is little known, and awaits research.

There are 24 species of British birds that feed at sea and are regularly dependent upon coastal habitats for nesting. They comprise 11 species of cormorants, petrels and auks, together with the gannet; 5 species of terns; 6 species of gulls; and 2 very local and northern kinds of skua.[62] There are a few others that are too scattered or uncommon to need discussion here. 21 of the 24 use rocks, either mainland cliffs or offshore rocky islands and stacks. There are about 8 found on sand-dunes or sand-banks, about 6 on shingle, and 6 or so extend also on to moorland or the edges of fresh-water inland. In the sand and shingle nesters are chiefly terns. Whereas some species like the gannet and guillemot are confined to sea rocks, others (like the herring gull) have a wider range of habitat. Then there are also a few other common birds, of which the oystercatcher is the chief, that

nest on many maritime habitats, from rock and shingle to sand, salt-marshes an
muddy estuaries. But it is with the dense and large colonies of sea-feeding bird
on cliffs and rocky islands that special interest lies here, on account of the variou
shapes and positions of the rocky structures that determine where they can safel
nest, and the great changes they cause in vegetation and soil by their activitie
including especially the transport of 'sea-guano' on to the land. These rock-nestel
are mainly concentrated for breeding on the west and northern coasts of Grea
Britain, and around Ireland. On the east coast there are very few south c
the Farne Islands in Northumberland, and few along the south coast – evidentl
owing to the scarcity of good cliffs and islands that are undisturbed. As Thoma
Pennant remarked in 1785:[378] 'Where you hear of the haunts of the Razor-bil
and Guillemots, Corvorants and Shags, you may be well assured, that the clif
soar to a distinguished height. Where those are wanting, they retire to sea-gii
rocks, as spots the less accessible to mankind.' In such places, he said, 'all the
oeconomy may be viewed with ease from the neighbouring cliffs; their love
incubation, exclusion, and nutrition'. The paucity of eastern and southern cli
colonies is clearly shown in Fisher and Lockley's maps[156] of the nesting colonie
of common guillemot (*Uria aalge*), gannet (*Sula bassana*) and puffin (*Fratercu*
arctica). In contrast to them is the map for the common tern (*Sterna hirundo*
which usually frequents low-lying sandy, shingly or turfy shores, though it als
nests on rocky islets and sometimes goes inland as well.

Although the influence of these sea-birds is rather local, the ecological atmc
sphere and results of their presence are overwhelmingly memorable. One can fee
ecological process openly in full blast, and the clamorous noise adds to the in
pression of turbulence, dynamic tension and action as does also the lack of cor
cealing colours among most of the birds. And with all this may be combined th
far-reaching activities of the rabbit. I got this impression very strongly durin
a visit to Skomer Island in Pembrokeshire in early June of 1959. The enormou
bird populations were noisy and busy under a sky of serene cirrhus and cumulu
clouds. Rabbits were recovering in numbers, and the seaward cliff-tops had exter
sive sheets of sea-pink and sea-campion in flower under which the burrows c
puffins and Manx shearwaters made the ground feel soft and upholstered. Th
inner regions had coarse vegetation and the small valleys were partly occupied b
the larger gulls, herring, lesser and greater black-backed, standing in noble pos
by their nest sites, or screaming in the air. On the steep cliffs were guillemot
razorbills, kittiwakes, and a few fulmar petrels. There was universal and tremei
dous interaction in progress which made one feel that here was unconcealed ar
intense community pressure among and within the species of plants and animal
(In August 1957 rabbits were rather scarce, and one could observe *Festuca rubi*
invading the cliff-top mat, but ragwort was scarcely flowering, whereas in 19.

(before myxomatosis) when rabbits abounded the ragwort was well grown and flowering profusely. In 1959 it was not conspicuous.) Among the birds there was endless strife, whether formal or serious it was not easy to judge. The puffins cruising into their burrows with fish in their beaks were chased by herring gulls; at the burrow mouths there were sometimes jackdaws shadowing the puffins; gulls were scrapping in the air with buzzards or ravens; curlews were chasing away herring gulls and jackdaws from their nesting areas; corpses of the Manx shearwater (*Puffinus puffinus*), which is nocturnal and lives underground by day, littered the ground.

Gillham[184] has analysed the effects of sea-birds upon the vegetation, soil conditions and microclimate in the Pembrokeshire islands, especially on Skokholm. They are, of course, complicated by the strong influence of rabbits (except on Grassholm), and the birds themselves act broadly in three different ways, by trampling, burrowing and manuring. Only a few examples of the clearer results can be mentioned. Trampling can be locally very severe, as on the cliff-top margins where puffins congregate and shuffle about or on the points chosen by gulls for watching or preening. At the time of her surveys, there were thought to be over 10,000 puffins breeding on Skokholm, and they make parts of the cliff edge actually bare. But as the occupation of these islands, intense as it is during the breeding season, lasts only for a few months in the year, some bare patches can become colonized after their departure by annuals such as the chickweeds, *Cerastium* and *Stellaria*, and meadow-grass, *Poa annua*. A minute but apparently important feature of puffin entrance holes in the ground is that the birds need a flat step for alighting, especially on steeper slopes. Although the sea-campion is worn away on the surface by this treading, it grows all right on the vertical 'microface' of the step and helps to support and stabilize it. Burrowing by puffins and Manx shearwaters (of which there were thought to be over 20,000 breeding birds on Skokholm) is mingled with that of rabbits especially on the extensive sea-pink areas. Here even when rabbits are scarce, the sea-pink can partly hold its own against *Festuca rubra*. The reason put forward is that burrowing makes the soil below the vegetation fluctuate more both in temperature and moisture, thus giving advantage to the deep-rooting sea-pink, especially during dry spells. And the relative humidity inside the burrows is about 10% higher than in the air above ground. (It is believed that the large puffin colonies that used to exist on Grassholm may have destroyed the grass turf by burrowing in it and making it too dry and so brought about their exodus.) On the burrowed areas there is a micro-pattern of dry and damper soil patches that produces a corresponding pattern in the surface vegetation mat. Gillham remarks: 'Paradoxically the presence of a burrow may lead at one and the same time to the existence of patches of both moisture-loving and unusually xerophytic vegetation in an otherwise mesophytic community. This is perhaps a logical outcome of the differential moisture content of the soil in the burrow vicinity.'[184]

It is not to be thought that all sea-bird islands are covered with low vegetation, for much of the inner parts may have very rough field types of heather or grass with coarse herbs, or mixtures of this with open ground patches. The general effect of heavy bird occupation, as by gulls, is to break down and discourage the taller plants. Little can be said about the special effects of manuring, important as they are, since they cannot easily be disentangled from other results of occupation. But whereas moderate manuring may encourage growth, heavy manuring by birds often kills some or even most species. On some parts of the cliffs where razorbills nest on Skokholm, there is a thick green mat of grass, *Agrostis stolonifera*, which can flourish under both manuring and trampling of these birds. But the rock samphire, *Crithmum maritimum*, a widespread plant of sea-sprayed cliffs, quickly succumbs to their excreta. Associated with sea-bird colonies generally there are a good many algae, lichens and mosses. The alga *Prasiola crispa* is usually dominant. This species has an extraordinarily extensive range, from the bird-islands of Spitsbergen[489] down to the penguin colonies of the Antarctic continent.[232] The moss *Ceratodon purpureus*, prominent in Pembrokeshire bird colonies, also occurs on bird colonies in Spitsbergen.[489]

Little useful can be said about the communities of maritime shingle (Plate 20), though these have received plenty of attention from plant ecologists, both for their own interest and because shingle bars are frequently the forerunners upon which sand-dunes later become based. The decrease in rabbit populations has encouraged great changes and increase in density of the vegetation, so that the extent of open ground has diminished in favour of taller growth. This has, for instance, been noticed on the four-mile shingle bar of Orfordness National Nature Reserve in Suffolk which the pandemic of myxomatosis reached by July 1958.[344] A great deal more is known about the communities and animal life of sand-dunes, although even on them there has been no comprehensive and analytical survey (with the notable exception of the Divers' on Studland Heath, of which however only a description of the grasshopper populations has been published,[95] the other available information being about the history, physiography and vegetation).

An extensive survey of sand-dune areas was done by Krogerus[272] from 1921 to 1932 on twenty-six collecting stations along the coast of Finland, at which he took numerous 1 sq. metre samples. Although his main aim was to find out about the fauna of the dunes themselves, he covered a wide range of neighbouring habitats for comparison, including some more salty, and others more marshy, or actually water. Altogether he found 1,443 species, but of these he considered that only 127 were confined ('stenotopic') to drift sand, which confirms my statement earlier in this chapter that maritime terrestrial communities consist mainly of species found, and often commonly found, elsewhere as well, though the peculiarly maritime forms – albeit in a minority – give great character to this zone. This character results no doubt partly from the peculiar charm and instability of dune areas, and one's feeling of surprise that animal life can survive here in such quantity; also from the contrasting scarcity of natural open sandy areas further inland. In Britain the most thorough collecting exercise has been done upon the animals of a sand-dune complex running along the distal four miles of the remarkable narrow tongue of Spurn Peninsula, on the Yorkshire side of the Humber estuary. This was organized by W. D. Hincks and others[225] in the Yorkshire Naturalists' Union from 1947 to 1953. The total number of species taken (which included insects and some other invertebrate groups, as well as vertebrates other than birds) was 1885, on an area equal to less than a square mile. It is remarkable that a purely maritime complex (with only some higher vegetation in patches of scrub or garden – the place is almost bare of trees) can harbour such a large number of species. The organizers of this survey remark that at first sight the landscape here looks monotonous, but 'closer investigation has revealed a wide range of environmental conditions. In addition to the sand-dune habitats, there are the damp clay conditions of the Phragmites area, the salt marsh, and the inland water habitats of various degrees of salinity. The fore-shore has a characteristic fauna, and there are cultivated fields immediately adjacent to the Warren. . . . The unravelling of the numerous interrelationships between plants, animals and physical environment is largely a task for the future.'[57] Because the habitats were not recorded in a very systematic way, it is not possible at present to extract from this survey an exact list of the sand-dune community itself, though it is evidently a large one.

The growth and zonation of sand-dunes from above High Water Mark to the final condition of fixed and closed grassland or heath have been too completely described by botanists to require a summary here; but it is worth giving some visual impression of these changes, defining how the habitat structure and micro-climate are affected, and mentioning a few of the features of the fauna in the earlier stages – the typical dune stages. In his book on *Flowers of the coast*, Hepburn[221] gives two photographs (his Plate XVIII, p. 99) of an actively developing sand-dune between the villages of Daymer Bay and Rock, inside the estuary mouth of the Camel River in north Cornwall. The first was taken in 1933 and shows a moder-ately high solid dune fronted by a much lower flattish one, at the seaward edge of which again there is much open sand with scattered plants colonizing it. The second was taken ten years later: by this time the embryonic dune on the sea-face had begun to grow into a low broad-front dune with scattered tall grass in it. The width of the new dune area produced during this time was from 80 to 100 yards, and at the same time the average level was raised about 25 feet.' My own photographs (Plates 22 and 23) were taken at exactly the same place eleven year after this, in 1954. The low fore-dune had now grown higher and from a distance appears covered with grass (a mixture of marram, *Ammophila arenaria*, and sea couch-grass, *Agropyron junceiforme*). This view from above is seen from Brea Hill, which appears as the background to Hepburn's photographs. In 1954 a new embryonic fore-dune was to be seen, with the usual scattered growth of grass and a few other plants. Thus within twenty-one years two full-scale marram dune had arisen, and a third was well on the way. But, as is so often found, a short way up this coast the dunes were being eroded quite fast, and the late Mr Hepburn sent me a photograph taken by him in 1943 of the war-time invasion defences of barbed wire being washed away by the sea, and such erosion was still to be seen in 1954.

The ecosystem of open marram dune is peculiar in that it may frequently change either forwards by increasing denseness of vegetation towards a closed stable dune with very mixed flora, or be set back again to zero by wind erosion (sometimes aided by the activities of man, rabbits or other animals). These changes take place moderately quickly, depending very much on the size, history and position of the dune. The rates of change lie somewhere between the very rapid succession to be found in a cowpat, a dead animal or a small log, and the more majestic events involved in the growth, maturity and dying of trees in a wood and the glade sequence that follows. All communities share or interchange species of animals with those around them, but perhaps nowhere so much as on dune, and other shore systems are habitats affected so deeply by the physiographical processes going on next door. Ardö's account[8] of the zonation of flies (Diptera) across the seashore and dunes in Scandinavia is an especially valuable record. Besides adding much to the biology of the animals in the maritime zone, he gives the point of view towards the whole ecosystem of a zoologist who draws also upon considerable experience of the physiography and vegetation. He worked chiefly in southern Halland (in south-west Sweden) but also visited dunes in Norway and Denmark. Many of the species also live in Britain. I shall refer to his work on several matters. Ardö measured the organic content of the sand at nine stages from the zones of sea-wrack through the dune stages finally to stable dune heath. His generalized diagram (Fig. 16) is based upon ten samples from the top 10 cm. of sand in each zone and expressed as ignition loss in percentage of the total weight. The relatively high organic content of the upper shore is of course brought about by the accumulation of seaweed wrack washed up on to the drift line; although some of this matter gets blown on to the new dunes, the organic content there is at first very low, only building up gradually again with the progress of vegetation.

If one follows the chain of reason put forward by Salisbury[419] (originally based on extensive measurements made by his students at Blakeney Point in Norfolk in 1931-2[418]) it can be realized that this low organic content, in the large-grained and mobile sand, greatly hinders the retention of water. From this it results that the conduction of heat is poor through the upper soil layers, the sand acting as a partly insulating layer. The temperature in hot sunny weather builds up during the day to a maximum on and an inch or two above the ground surface. The sand surface may rise above 60° C. (a level lethal to animals remaining long in it), and in spring the temperature may often be two or three degrees more just above the surface than it is higher up. But not uncommonly the sand surface may have

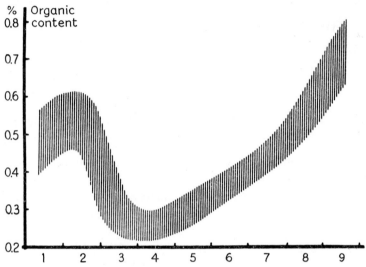

FIG. 16. Changes in the soil organic matter at 9 stations, from the drift-line (1) across unstable dune to stable dune heath (9), Halland, Sweden. (From P. Ardö, 1957)

a slightly lower value than at 2 in. above it, and this Salisbury attributes to convection currents that bring in moister sea air at surface level and cause internal dew formation in the surface sand that lowers the temperature. He also remarks: 'The uniformly lower temperature at 2 feet than at 2 inches above the surface is a striking feature, both in summer and spring, and doubtless accounts for the habit of dune mollusca to crowd to the top of the *Psamma* leaves in hot weather.'[418] Two graphs from the Blakeney Point investigations illustrate some of these gradients. In Fig. 17 a number of temperature readings from bare sand (not in hollows of the dunes, where the slightly damper conditions modify the regime somewhat) are plotted, those at 2 in. in the sand against those taken with the thermometer bulb just covered by the sand surface. In practically all instances the latter are higher than the former, and more so as the season advances and when the air is generally hotter. In Fig. 18 the temperatures at 2 in. above the sand surface are compared

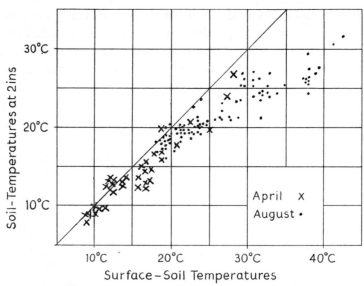

FIG. 17. The microclimate of a bare sand–dune at Blakeney Point, Norfolk. Temperatures at the sand surface are nearly always higher than at 2 in. below. (After E. J. Salisbury, 1934)

with those at 2 ft, again on bare sand and not in dune hollows. Nearly always the latter are lower than the former.

On the other hand, the same poor conductivity of the sand has the opposite effect in cold weather, by slowing down the escape of heat from the sand. Arde

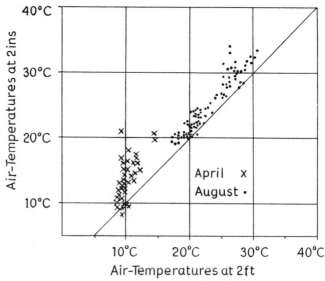

FIG. 18. The microclimate of a bare sand–dune at Blakeney Point, Norfolk. The temperatures at 2 in. above the surface are nearly always higher than at 2 ft. (After E. J. Salisbury, 1934)

describes some measurements he took when a cold snap in January lowered the air temperature at 1 m. above the Halling dunes from about 2° C. to about minus 14° within a few hours. At 2 cm. below the soil surface it fell (with a lag of a few hours) only to about 10°, while the temperatures below this showed progressively less effect, e.g. at 10 cm. only to minus 5·6°. The main upshot of all this evidence is that the dryness of the surface sand has a blanketing effect upon any fluctuations in the air conditions, and over the cycle of day and night the ground remains relatively more constant, while the air temperature may be above it by day and below it by night. It can be realized that in such an unstable, exposed and climatically rugged habitat the influence of vegetation in ameliorating conditions for animal life becomes of paramount importance. The chief agency in doing this is the marram grass.

When marram is at its best stage, well grown and flowering freely, it is not a closed vegetation (though distant photographs like that in Plate 22 might give this impression), but a pattern of tussocks often made up each of a group of plants. Greig-Smith[459] has studied this pattern of growth statistically on the dunes of Newborough Warren in Anglesey, and found that the maximum output of lateral growth (tillering) at the base of the plants falls in the middle stage of succession when flowering is also good. Apparently the groups of plants may be derived from those seedlings that survived quite early in colonization, only a few of them being successful. Within the marram tussocks or tussock groups the microclimate is sharply different from that over the bare sand. Let me describe what I found by crawling into such marram grass on the top of the front dune near Daymer Bay, on a late summer day, 4 September 1951. The weather was warm but not sunny, and there was a strong wind blowing from the south-west. In the open dune hollows the wind was much less noticeable, and some places were calm – and hot. As soon as one burrows inside the marram tussocks quite a different world is encountered. In a smaller way, it feels like going from an open ploughed field into a wood: cooler, and the sand firm and damp, held by the marram tussock bases and roots. There is not much litter apparent, but a small moss (a species of *Bryum*) carpets the sand thinly. Thousands of small fat black Collembola, *Achorutes reuteri*, are aggregated on this sand surface. This is a typically maritime springtail, also found under sea-wrack (for details about this and other species mentioned here, see [8]). There are a few small Staphylinid beetles, *Stenus ossium*, of a genus that catches springtails with chameleon tongue. But this beetle is also present on the limestone grassland of Wytham Hill. There is also another predatory Staphylinid beetle, *Tachyporus hypnorum*, which is the commonest species of beetle on this same grassland on The Dell at Wytham, together with a small Carabid beetle, *Risophilus atricapillus*, and a tiny pink-and-white spider, *Theridion bimaculatum*, also found there. There are many other animals inside these climatic refuges.

Snails such as *Helix aspersa* (a country-wide species, though not found in woods, and not on all grassland places, and on these dunes probably an important food resource of the hedgehogs whose numerous tracks can be seen), and *Cochlicella acuta*, a true maritime. Also there is the woodlouse, *Porcellio scaber*, which I have found on sea-cliff grassland in Pembrokeshire. It is known to live also under drift-line seaweed.[56] Inland it inhabits tree-trunks, rotting logs but never the woodland litter; and it occurs in heather clumps on dry heathland – the nearest analogue to its marram habitat.

Of the British spiders that occur on sand-dunes, Bristowe[46] says: 'One feature of the list of sandhill species is the number which are found elsewhere in marshy or damp surroundings. The parched surface of the sand in mid-summer is liable to mislead us as to the climate in the interior of the denser marram clumps where most of the species live. Here conditions are always humid. Several species, including *Synageles* and *Attulus*, live a part of their time in silken cells beneath the surface of the sand and deposit their eggs there. *Arctosa perita* Linn. excavates a burrow.' The Salticids *Synageles venator* and *Attulus saltator* are two of the ten species of spiders that Bristowe defines as practically confined in Britain to sandhills. He gives a list of a dozen other species that live otherwise mainly in marshy habitats, amongst them *Tetragnatha extensa*, which is not uncommon in the field layer of shady or marginal marshes inside the deciduous wood at Wytham, where it is frequently found on the tall *Carex pendula* at the edge of streams.

The extraordinary contrast between the interior of marram patches and the often blistering environment of the bare sand between them is shown by the microclimatic measurements made at Blakeney Point and on some west European dunes. At Blakeney it was found that when the surface temperatures during sunshine over bare sand and under marram are compared, the latter is often 3-6° C. lower than those outside. This difference becomes greater at higher temperatures. In cloudy or overcast weather the position is reversed in many instances, because the grass cover shelters the air within it from wind movement.[418] Van Heerdt and Mörzer Bruyns,[518] who did an excellent survey of the ground-living communities on dunes in the Netherlands, measured the temperature and relative humidity during thirty hours at the centre of a marram tussock (whose size is not mentioned) and outside it at a height of 1 m., on the early 'yellow' dunes (Fig. 19). The ameliorating influence of the tussock is clearly seen, also the high relative humidity at night within the tussock. All these facts build up a picture of a sharp patterning of the micro-habitats on marram dune, with the main concentration of life within the marram tussocks, not only because these provide the main natural resource, but because of the shelter they give against extreme fluctuations of the climate.

The microclimatic shelter afforded by plants is also sharply seen under isolated

lumps of other species scattered in the marram dune. On a warm September
day on the front main dune near Daymer Bay, I looked under a single large clump
f flowering sea-rocket, *Cakile maritima*, a rather succulent-leaved crucifer more
haracteristically found on the small embryonic dunes. The sand under it was
amp – a minute oasis in a desert. Among the animals were abundant sand-hopping
mphipod shrimps. (These ordinarily live at the drift line under seaweed, but
an Heerdt and Mörzer Bruyns[518] recorded that in one of the three years they

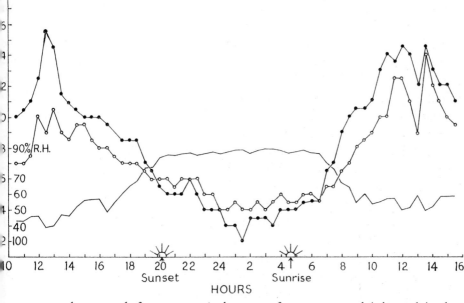

FIG. 19. 30-hour record of temperatures in the centre of a marram tussock (*white circles*) and
in air at 100 cm. (*black discs*); and mean relative humidities on N. and S. sides of the tussock
(*black line*). Yellow dune, Terschelling I., Netherlands, 9-10 Aug. 1955. (After P. F. Van
Heerdt and M. F. Mörzer Bruyns, 1960)

ere surveying the Netherlands dunes there was an invasion of *Talitrus saltator*
n to the outer couch-grass dunes, though not as far as the main marram ridge.)
here were also a few woodlice, *Porcellio scaber*, and several kinds of insects. The
tter included a ladybird, *Coccidula rufa*, often found in marshes; two small
erbivorous flea-beetles, *Psylliodes marcida* and *Phyllotreta aerea* (= *punctulata*), the
rst of which is solely attached to sea-rocket and the second associated with various
rucifers; a small weevil, *Sitona lepidus* (= *flavescens*), probably associated with
lover; and a green Mirid bug, *Calocoris norvegicus*, an enormously polyphagous
ecies on many plants, and living in many habitats [9]. Under an isolated plant
f sea-beetroot, *Beta maritima*, in the same place were again numbers of sand-

hoppers and also a good many Coreid bugs, *Enoplops scapha*, that I have mentioned as common on sea-cliff slopes in Pembrokeshire. Such scattered plants not only increase the kinds of cover for animals, but add variety in other ways, as with the flea-beetle specifically dependent on the sea-rocket, and the male bumble-bee *Bombus lapidarius*, seen visiting its flowers. These subsidiary species are harbingers of the much richer variety to be found in the plant carpet of the fixed dune association that follows later, and in which the main patterns are provided by the interspersion of different plants rather than by the mixture of open sand and tussock.

Several other aspects of this general pattern must be mentioned. They are the vertical zonation within marram patches, the fauna below ground, that on the open sand, and the relations between the open marram community and other zones in the dune succession. There is a permanent fauna living in the field layer of waving leaves and stiff flower stalks, as well as a large visiting or partly accidental fauna which probably forms much of the food supply of spiders there. Web-spinning spiders are uncommon in the marram community, though *Tetragnatha extensa* is one. Most of the field-layer spiders – the species are rather few – are long and thin in shape, and lay themselves along the leaves or stems which they clasp firmly. They tend to be camouflaged in colour as well. A similar convergent adaptation was noted in the field layer of limestone grassland at Wytham.[10] There are two separate species of *Tibellus*, one common on ordinary grassland (also coming on dunes) and the other mainly confined to dunes.[46, 525] Then there may be vertical migrations on the marram plant. The shore wainscot moth *Leucania litoralis*, feeds only on marram, and is common round the British coast except in the more northern parts of Scotland.[462] By day the caterpillars are buried in the surface sand, but at night they ascend to the tall marram spikes.[31] The moths emerge in summer. (This habit is not one particularly confined to sand-dune Lepidoptera, for the caterpillars of several species of grass-feeding butterflies common in mesophytic grassland both outside or in glades of woodland of which the meadow brown butterfly, *Maniola jurtina*, is a familiar example, also climb up on to the grass at night.) The extent of field-layer insect life in marram dunes depends very much upon the strength of the wind: in a strong breeze sweep-netting the leaves may produce hardly anything, whereas on calmer warm days there are large numbers of flies, weevils and bugs.

Animal life even by day is not of course confined to the marram tussocks, and there is great activity on the bare sand, again chiefly on warm and windless days. There are many predators that hunt in this part of the dune – Asilid flies like *Philonicus albiceps*, many hunting wasps, tiger beetles (*Cicindela hybrida*) and some spiders. Various other creatures wander on the rather loose sand, among them some of the large harvestmen (*Leiobunum*, *Opilio*) moving, with their very long legs, like camels in the desert. We need to know so much more about the behaviour of all these species by day and night, in different weathers, and throughout the season, that no useful summary can be given here. One wishes that some of the very elaborate European investigations of dune faunas had given less time to statistical abstractions and cryptic classical terminologies, and more to finding out what the animals do and where they do it, in relation to the rather obvious patterns of habitat structure and climate. We hardly know what are the basic industries that support the marram fauna! I think one must infer that they are only to a small extent attached to the superficial green parts of the plant, that some Collembola probably live on the moss layer in the surface sand, but that probably the main resource is the unlimited supply of live and dead marram roots which bind the dune together. Added to these are insects moving across from other zones.

The abundance of predators and some of their relationships have been described by Hincks[226] for the marram dunes of Spurn Peninsula. *Thereva annulata* is a fly with a predacious larva living in sandy soils. 'These flies, rare in July and absent in August, form one of the dominant features of the sandy areas, marram and otherwise, and literally swarm in mid-June. . . . The flies themselves were also noted as the prey of one of the abundant Lycosid spiders of the marram areas (*Pirata piratica* Oliv.). These and other spiders are in turn preyed upon by the spider-wasps *Pompilus plumbeus* (F.) and *Episyron rufipes* (L.). Individuals of the first species simply swarm on the sandy areas of the peninsula in June. . . . Their numbers dwindle in July and August when they are replaced by smaller populations of other spider-wasps. It seems extraordinary that the great numbers of individuals of these Pompilids and Therevids should be able to support themselves here and that their hosts should be able to survive at all.' Hincks also noted on Spurn Peninsula the great mortality to which insects are subject because of the conditions in the 'desert' parts. 'In August, 1949, after a hot dry spell earlier in the year, little drifts of insect remains were found in small depressions around the roots of the marram, resulting from the action of the wind. These mortuaries were everywhere in the marram areas, and contained many remains of ants, weevils and other arenicolous insects.' The list of eleven species from only one of these accumulations included some, like the beetle *Phylan gibbus*, commonly found walking on the bare sand.

On dunes, as elsewhere, the diminution of rabbits has had extraordinary effects upon the structure of the vegetation, and White[546] describes the following changes that have taken place on the famous maritime reserve of Blakeney Point in Norfolk. It was on this island that William Rowan made pioneer observations upon the food-plants of the rabbit in 1913. Here rabbits had been abundant for a long time, but died out through myxomatosis from February 1954 onwards. By the summer of 1959 they seemed extinct. White laid down some transects in 1955 and also studied the whole vegetation. With decline in the rabbit pressure grasses grew more densely, and *Festuca rubra* partly stabilized some of the dune surface. Pathways became grassed. Sea couch-grass, *Agropyron junceiforme*, multiplied on the foreshore and speeded up fore-dune growth there. *Agropyron pungens* became denser on shingle fringing the marshes, and flowered well. Some less common grasses (such as *Catapodium* spp.) were now able to grow and flower, and *Corynephorus canescens* to spread. The *Festuca* began to crowd out certain common dune mosses ordinarily associated with stabilization of the surface, but the fern *Polypodium vulgare* spread remarkably on the older fixed dunes. The sand sedge, *Carex arenaria*, flowered abundantly and held its own against *Festuca*, and two large mosses were also flourishing more than formerly among the sedge. In Rowan's day, ragwort, *Senecio jacobaea*, was abundant everywhere and untouched by rabbits, indeed may have derived benefit from disturbed sand round their burrows. Now it was less common, probably because the seedlings cannot compete with a closed sward of *Festuca rubra*. 'The absence of the large areas with much *Senecio jacobaea* is one of the most noticeable changes to be observed on the Point in late summer.' The sea convolvulus, *Calystegia soldanella*, had become very rare, but now reappeared in some quantity. The flowers and ovary (though not the leaves) of this plant were relished by rabbit. Much the same sort of changes have also occurred on the salt-marshes. On the dunes of Newborough Warren in Anglesey, Ranwell[400] was able to measure transects of the vegetation before and after the arrival of myxomatosis which reduced the rabbits in 1955 from some thousands to only a very few. Close-grazed turf of *Festuca rubra* and *Agrostis tenuis* grew to 5-8 cm. in a year, the grasses flowering and producing seedlings profusely, though the *Festuca* later spread somewhat at the expense of the other grass. Three and a half years after the rabbits died out there was a deep mat of grass 15-20 cm. high. Heather also grew and flowered.

I have concentrated upon an outline of the open marram grass stage of dune succession, where some of the links along the chain of climate, sand drift and stabilization, vegetation and animal life can be discerned on what is the most striking mixture of open (and mostly bare) ground and field type to be seen in Britain. Its superficial resemblance to a kind of desert margin is rather misleading because of its proximity to the sea and the resulting flow of humid air, whose moisture gets partly trapped in tussock and soil. When the dune eventually becomes fixed, and covered with a closed vegetation, the plant community becomes far more varied, and offers opportunity for more herbivorous animal to come in. Salisbury[419] says: 'Thus we find that, ignoring casuals, there occur on fixed dunes in Britain some 145 different kinds of flowering plants, compared with 70 species on the late yellow dune phases and only 26 kinds on the early yellow dunes and dune face taken together.' By the later stage the whole system begin to be more like ordinary meadow (or heath, if the soil is base-poor, as for example on Studland Heath). But even under the semi-stabilized dune, the soil only carries a very poor population of earthworms. Reynoldson[402] compared a number of north Wales habitats, in which he dug out or extracted by potassium permanganate solution samples of the earthworms. Pasture soils had high numbers and biomass of worms. The lowest numbers were, by contrast, found in the soil of semi-stabilized dune, where the population density was over 200 times less than in pasture, and the biomass around 400 times less. On fixed dune the situation was rather better, with numbers only 16-18 times less, and biomass only about 20 times less. The only two species taking any real part in the soil of these dunes were *Allolobophora chlorotica* and *Octolasium lacteum*, the former being a large constituent in pasture, the latter a very subordinate form there.

In discussing communities by means of limited examples, rather than by filling the text with the analysis of enormous lists of species, it is a little difficult to convey the full meaning of their scale and complexity. Perhaps the only way to become seized with the meaning of all this is to abandon books for a time and sit or wander slowly on a sea-cliff slope or rolling dune on a day of good weather, watching, listening and imagining for many hours. I get the impression that this is one of the things animal ecologists too seldom allow themselves to do, the conscious mind being in our university science training hypertrophied at the expense of that intuition which is needed to manœuvre the thoughts into a correct angle and position for objective studies in the field.

> Quis enim quidquam nescius optet
> aut quis valeat nescita sequi?

These lines from Boethius are broadly rendered by Helen Waddell[528] thus:

> How shall he follow the unknown?
> How shall he find it, and when found
> How shall he know it?

On sand-dunes we hardly know as yet what are the main production lines in the system, what the species require, and how they interlock. It remains for some animal ecologist to weave together properly all the components of the marram ecosystem and its fauna – open sand and protected tussock; soil, ground zone and field layer; the cooler air above; the temporal activities of animals, especially under cover of night and in different states of the weather; and their movements between this and other zones. The general surveys by Krogerus[272] in Finland and by Van Heerdt and Mörzer Bruyns[518] in the Netherlands already mentioned give some notion of the size of the dune fauna. The latter survey was done on the

West Frisian Isle of Terschelling in the years 1950-2. Patches of ground, that is their surface and the soil down to about 5 cm., were searched *in situ*, along a transect that started on sandy beach, crossed the marram belt and ended in the sea buckthorn (*Hippophae*) scrub. Each search of a quadrat took four or five hours, and although the less mobile forms could be taken, there are clearly some absentees, including Hymenoptera (other than ants) that must have escaped. The total number of species of invertebrates was 368, of which about 165 were actually recorded on the main open marram ridge. 146 of the total were beetles, and 57 spiders. But a great many of the animals caught were single or few individuals and a more realistic estimate was arrived at by excluding any species that had not been present in all three years of the survey, or had not reached a total of 10 individuals. This brought down the marram dune list to about 70 – not all of which were confined to it. From these again they picked out about 36 species as being especially characteristic of shore and dune, 12 being attached to the open marram belt. In a survey of spiders on the marram dunes of Germany Von Bochmann[525] collected 129 species, but of these again only comparatively few were special to the dunes. Ardö's very thorough survey[8] of flies (Diptera) on south Swedish dunes produced a long list of species, but he considered that only 36 were especially dune inhabitants. His transect numbers are based upon a rather sub-jective system of counting, but they do show quite well how the dominant fly species change as you go from upper seashore through fore-dune, across the main marram ridge (12 chief species) on to heath.

Still on the note of rapid colonization and change, I will now turn to the form-ation-type that comes next in succession in terrestrial communities – Scrub. Here also grazing by animals is often decisive in selecting the dominant plants, or even suppressing scrub altogether – a subject alluded to nineteen centuries ago by Virgil in the Second Book of *The Georgics*.

CHAPTER 9

Scrub and Hedgerow

SCRUB IS THE HALF-WAY HOUSE between meadow or heath and woodland, and often a rather temporary habitation because of the speed with which ecological succession moves. It is also half-way in another sense, because shrubs are mostly of little use for forage or timber – too woody for the former and not large enough for the latter. The chief reason why so much scrub exists in this country is that man has grown or retained it for shelter and as a barricade between fields and along roads. Nearly all the rest is either a temporary stage in the development of woodland (Plate 10) or else forms part of the developed woodland or glade. In the habitat classification I have been using there are four situations (other than such places as gardens) in which Terrestrial scrub may exist. It may be in substantial groves or thickets; or form the edge of these, or much more commonly, exist as an 'edge' itself in the form of hedgerow; occur on the edge of woods; or as an under-storey inside the woods. This chapter will be concerned mainly with pure scrub or its edge, growing away from the cover of trees, and not in Transition zones. Most natural scrub in Britain is deciduous.

Scrub derives its primary character as a habitat for animals from its woody structure, its dense branching on a fine scale, its low height and its ability to colonize rapidly and kill out meadow or heath, so that it is not uncommon to find it mixed with the latter temporarily in an open formation-type. From the woody structure – often very hard, as with hawthorn, box and elder – comes the enduring nature of the habitat, and this wood is seldom attacked by insects until it dies and begins to rot. Therefore not only does the living scrub last longer than a purely seasonal structure such as the stem, leaves and flower heads of a wild parsnip or an annual grass, but it also lasts longer while it is decaying. The dense, often stiff branching gives rise to thickets that are impenetrable by man, though offering excellent cover to mammals like the rabbit or fox, and good structural support for the nests of birds as well as a deterrent to their enemies. But the trunks and branches of most shrubs are too restricted or too hard to afford nesting holes for birds. An exception is the rotting touchwood of elder used by marsh and willow tits (see Ch. 14). On the trunks and branches moss may grow, but more important as a resource for invertebrates is the epiphytic layer of lichens and alga (*Pleurococcus*). On herbaceous and grassy plants there is nothing of this, except to a certain degree on semi-woody plants of low stature such as broom. But microfungal attack both on the living and dead tissues is common on meadow plants, and the mixture is a food for woodlice and other species (see Ch. 6). The dense canopy of thick scrub prevents the survival or development of a rich underflora below it, so that thickets are much poorer communities than woods, and may even be quite bare below. This is often to be seen under hawthorn and blackthorn. Tansley[493] has described a thicket of hawthorns probably over sixty years old and about 18 ft high, under which no other shrubs had survived, though dead rose bushes were still present. Herbaceous plants were confined to five species, these only here and there. The ground had a layer of dead branches and twigs, and the few mosses mostly grew on the former.

The height of scrub varies considerably, and the following procedure has been adopted for defining it as a formation-type. Originally[137] we proposed 25 ft for the normal upper limit of scrub canopy, but have since decided that 15 ft is a more convenient height to use. However, Yapp,[559, 560] in his classification of bird habitats uses 26 ft (= 8 m.). The height of most scrub growing in the open is usually not much above 15 ft, and where it exceeds this slightly there is not much difficulty in knowing what one is dealing with. The necessity for some conventional height limit arises from the frequency of trees like the birch that form a scrub layer during succession towards woodland, but eventually grow a good bit higher; and of plantations where the same thing happens. The convention used so far in our ecological survey (and it may have to be modified with further experience) is that *all* woody structures rising to between about 6 and 15 ft are 'scrub formation-type'; though some latitude is kept for slight further increase in height. But in woodland the 15-ft limit is retained for all circumstances, and anything above 15 ft is counted as 'tree canopy layer'.

In Britain there are some eleven species of shrubs that commonly contribute to the terrestrial scrub formation-type, to which may be added five species of woody or semi-woody climbing plants. It is one of the interesting features of all these shrubs and climbers, that they nearly all have flowers that are attractive to insects though not by any means always conspicuous to man (see Ch. 13). The great stretches of flowering hawthorn and elder, and lesser displays of sallow, *Viburnum*, wild roses and privet come to mind, in contrast with the unexciting flowers of the spindle, buckthorn and ivy. They are also all, except *Salix* and *Clematis*, dispersed by having their 'fruits' eaten by birds. This is in contrast with trees, which are mostly wind-pollinated and frequently also employ wind-dispersal seed mechanisms. One curious consequence of the fruit dispersal by birds is that shrubs may occur, sometimes in abundance, under the full canopy of wood-

and where they are unlikely to flower and seed successfully – a very interesting example of the relation between edge and centre.

One reason why hawthorn (*Crataegus*) is such a frequent and successful pioneer is its comparative immunity from rabbit nibbling. This it gets when young from the spines (which in turn enable more vulnerable species to grow under its protection) and when older from the very hard dense bark and wood. I noticed a dramatic illustration of its relative immunity during the last war, in a mixed deciduous woodland at Ley Park in Gloucestershire, which was being used by A. D. Middleton to show the effectiveness of gin-trapping on the open ground surface. This woodland had already been worked over with other methods of rabbit control, yet in the three weeks of March 1942 a further 527 rabbits were trapped, with another 65 in May – a *surviving* population of about three to an acre. At this time deep snow lay on the ground and rabbits were reduced to browsing on the bark of trees and shrubs. A number of scrub species were ring-barked completely and killed, yet hawthorn remained very little touched. It is perhaps more than a coincidence that the spread of field enclosures by means of hedgerows made of hawthorn ('quickset') during the last few hundred years went parallel with great increase in the abundance of free-living rabbit populations in this country. The vulnerability of some other scrub species is illustrated by the damage to spindle trees (*Euonymus europaeus*) illustrated in Plate 25. The big rabbit warren where this occurred lay on a patch of river gravel on the slopes of the River Test valley in Hampshire, at one end of a long hawthorn hedgerow system which I am about to mention, along which – because of the hard nature of the soil and of effective control – no rabbits ordinarily lived, and so various vulnerable species of scrub were abundant. The other species that is avoided by rabbits [9A] is the elder (*Sambucus nigra*), so often seen adorning the sites of warrens, or nowadays former warrens. Although the fruits are very edible to birds, the bark is violently purgative to man.[220, 300] On a good many parts of Wytham Hill large pure elder thickets still stand as witness to the period long before the last war when they became established on ground heavily occupied by rabbits. Many of these shrubs are beginning to die and fall from old age and are providing interesting rotting wood habitats. They remind us that the structure of habitats and the interrelations of species cannot be judged just from present-day ecological events.

The finest mixtures of scrub species are to be found on calcareous soils, especially on chalk and limestone, but no full surveys have been done of the animals living in them, so that I shall have to confine myself to a few examples which at any rate suggest some of the situations that exist. The first comes from my own field study of a hawthorn hedge in Hampshire. As I have explained, a hedgerow is really an extreme form of 'scrub edge', and it has many practical advantages for study because of being accessible and easy to map. And although the extent and denseness of internal cover are so much less than in solid scrub, there is a much better development of stratification and richer variety of fauna and flora. This ecological survey was begun in February 1938 and carried on, with the help of my wife and of some colleagues [10], until April 1939. The war stopped it, and since the hedges were subsequently erased to make a wartime aerodrome, no further work could be done. Nevertheless, incomplete as it is, the survey may perhaps be accorded a sort of scarcity value. Although hedges have been extolled and used as collecting grounds by naturalists, they seem to have been rather neglected as ecological systems, indeed there is no mention of the word 'hedge' in the index of Tansley's great work on British vegetation, although they are really in the same category as the semi-natural communities such as grasslands under grazing to which plant ecologists have given very great attention. And hedgerows are among the commonest and richest habitats in Britain. The survey we did was only made possible by the generous help and cooperation of the late Mr John Spedan Lewis, on whose estate at Leckford it was done and who was deeply interested in natural history. Sheep Drove was an old downland trackway bounded on each side by high hawthorn hedges (Plate 24) running for a mile across the top of a chalk hill and flanked on either side by arable fields carrying cereals, roots, flax and other crops. Inside was a wide green ride which provided the ground zone and field layer component of the scrub edge, the hawthorn itself rising above ten feet, and occasionally as high as twenty feet. Because the hedges had for some time ceased to be needed as stock-proof barrier, they had not recently been cut and laid, only trimmed back to some extent at the base. Very few trees stood in them, and these were chiefly isolated ash; but a short double cross-hedge led down from the middle of the Drove to join a large beech-mixed wood called Leckford Plantation. One reminder of the neighbour influence of this wood, which possessed a great deal of hazel coppice, was the spreading of hazel bushes along the cross-ride and the establishment of some scattered bushes in parts of the Drove itself. This could only be attributed to gradual carriage of nuts by red squirrels and birds along the hedge as highway.

The chalk scrub flanking parts of these long hedges on the inner side was rich and well representative of this kind of association on pure chalk. There were blackthorn, guelder rose, wayfaring tree, wild rose, dogwood, elder, hazel, common buckthorn, privet, spindle and sallow (*Salix caprea*) – the Latin names of these can be found in Ch. 13. Also several climbers: ivy, honeysuckle, black bryony and white bryony. Of trees there were very few indeed: one common maple (*Acer campestre*), one wild pear (*Pyrus communis*), one crab-apple (*Malus sylvestris*), one holly, one young oak, one or two young yews, and several grown ash trees with some spread of young saplings from them. The comparative isolation, the uniform chalky soil, the scarcity of trees, and the shelter inside the double hedges gave

Sheep Drove a special character, and as it ran in a slightly curved line each stretch seemed rather enclosed. Since attention was concentrated upon the hawthorn canopy, it is not necessary to describe the flanking field layer and ground zone except to mention that there was in some places a great deal of bramble. Apart from birds, the most conspicuous animals in summer were butterflies of nine species. Only one of these had its larvae on scrub – the brimstone (*Gonepteryx rhamni*) whose eggs were found on leaves of the buckthorn. The others fell into four ecological groups. The peacock (*Nymphalis io*) depends on nettles; the orange tip (*Euchloe cardamines*), the green-veined white (*Pieris napae*) and the small white (*P. rapae*), on cruciferous plants; the meadow brown (*Maniola jurtina*), gatekeeper (*M. tithonus*), and large skipper (*Ochlodes* or *Augiodes venata*) on grasses; and the common blue (*Polyommatus icarus*) on birdsfoot trefoil, *Lotus corniculatus*. How far all of these lived and bred in Sheep Drove itself was not ascertained.

Another very noticeable summer insect form was *Simulium*. These blackflies often surrounded one while walking, and especially when working near the ground. Two species were common, both of them breeders in rather slow weedy rivers, and certainly derived from the River Test below. *Simulium equinum* especially bites horses inside their ears, also to some extent cattle, but seldom man. *Simulium ornatum* mainly bites cattle, and less often horses, on their lower parts and face, but not in the ears.[115, 448] Although it is reported to bite man occasionally, Zahar[561] states that nothing would induce them to do so in his experiments and he was never attacked in the field. We were never bitten by either species. The double hedges therefore provided excellent conditions of shelter both for the patrolling of local butterflies and for the swarming of immigrant aquatic flies, though the former completed their programme more effectively than the latter. And for only a few of the eleven species concerned was the scrub itself the food supply – it acted by its influence on the microclimate.

A double hedgerow like this one, with the additional advantage of a slightly curved trackway, affords particularly quiet shelter and is really like a large glade within walls of scrub. But the influence of the hedge extends also outside for some distance into the fields on either side. A great deal of research has been done on hedges and on shelter belts of greater height, especially in countries like Russia, United States and Canada that have great stretches of farmland exposed to wind and drought and soil erosion. Perhaps the most thorough investigations of the aerodynamics of shelter belts have been done in Denmark, where the open country that was once heathland growing on light soils is now farmed and depends for the local amelioration of climate upon shelter belt planting. This is a very large and technical subject that has been studied not only by measuring wind effects in the field, but has extended to more refined though rather less naturalistic analyses of experiments in wind-tunnels. Two aspects of this work will be mentioned here.

The first is the behaviour of wind when it meets a vertical obstacle like a hedgerow. If the hedge is very solid the wind rises over it and then forms more or less violent eddy-currents on the lee side with the result that the shelter zone is fairly narrow. The effect of this is always clearly to be seen after snow blizzards. It sometime happens that the eddies on the lee side of a very solid barrier actually damage crops. If on the other hand the hedge is a fairly open one, some of the air passes through the spaces, being partly checked thereby, and there is a much more even flow of air over the top and beyond, creating a wider lee zone of slower wind. These effects are in addition to any other roughness of the ground that may also cause a frictional drag on the air. (An inclined surface hit by the wind causes even closer eddying and a narrower shelter to leeward: hence the wind-cut trees and hedge often seen near the coast are for this very reason less efficient wind-breaks.)[61]

It is generally agreed that the chief thing, other than penetrability, determining the width of the downwind zone of comparatively slow movement, that is of shelter, is the height of the barrier, and observations are usually expressed not just in actual widths, but as a ratio of the height. Jensen's[246] wind-tunnel experiments in Denmark have a great ecological interest. Among other things he placed different kinds of barriers, or as an ecologist might say textures of cover, in the tunnel. These were hurdle-like structures with bars or crossed bars or holes. He found that the percentage of the surface occupied by holes was what mattered, not their shape in detail, and concluded that the optimum hole percentage for getting shelter effects beyond was about 35-40. It has been found that the full width of the lee zone, i.e. to the point at which the wind regains its normal speed measured by more distant controls, often extends to a distance about thirty times the height of the shelter belt. But these figures vary a great deal with circumstances. A fairly representative example for an English hedgerow is that measured by Rider[409] on the edge of a sports field outside which was a field of corn stubble. The hedge at this point was about 1·7 m. high and although the bottom quarter metre was rather open in texture, above it was a very dense barrier to airflow. The wind speeds were observed when the wind was approximately at right angles to the hedge. On the exposed (upwind) side the slowing of wind already appeared about 25 m. from the hedge, even at heights of 1 and 2 m. On the lee (downwind) side the slowing of the wind was detectable as far as 100 m. from the hedge even at 2 m., and was even more marked nearer the ground. Some of Jensen's measurements indicate that the presence of summer foliage only increases the shelter effect in a 12-foot hawthorn hedge by about 40%, and proves the importance of the interlacing branches and twigs. These tend to be thickened in hedges that are regularly cut and laid, and in old hedges there is also a growth of epiphytic lichen on the branches.

The second major influence of shelter belts, or indeed of any kind of vegetation

hat increases the 'roughness' of the landscape, appears to be a general slowing
down of wind as it crosses the land. Jensen took two lines across the southern parts
of Denmark and recorded the wind's behaviour. He says: 'From the measurements
on Line 1 it appears that the wind on the passage from the sea and in across an open
and flat terrain with a roughness coefficient of 0·003, in the course of a distance
of about 10 km. will have its velocity reduced by 20% in the layers close to the
round. . . . From the measurements on Line 2 it appears that the wind on its
passage from the sea and in across a rugged terrain with many hedgerows (roughness coefficient 0·010-0·015) and large plantations and woods over a distance of
about 20-30 km. will have its velocity reduced by 50% in the layers close to the
ground. . . . The eastern part of Line 1 is very well provided with hedgerows
(roughness coefficient 0·020) and the terrain is very hilly. When the west wind had
passed this section of the line its velocity had been reduced to 55% of the velocity
at the west coast. The wind then passed across a 10 km. distance of sea and the
velocity again increased to 75% of the original value.' It is pretty certain that the
many English farmers who are cutting down or removing their hedges, especially
those in the drier region of East Anglia, are unaware that by doing so they are increasing the evaporation from the land in general, and of the edges of their fields
in particular. North German investigators[315] claim that the yields of grain and
other crops are considerably raised by the existence of hedges.

So the structure of a double hedgerow, though having a clear identity and sharp
boundaries, is only the centre or clearing house for activities of animals with
widely differing powers and distance of movement. It also exerts or combines with
other hedgerows to exert considerable influence on windflow near the ground, and
therefore on humidity, evaporation and to some extent on temperature. In these
respects the habitat structure is analogous with the living body of an animal, whose
physical identity is real enough, yet rather deflects attention from the constant
physiological exchanges going on between it and the environment – breathing,
heat loss, excretion, moulting, eating vegetation and so on. Movements and contacts within and without the species extend these influences to varying distances.
And although animals cannot be said to affect the climate, they sometimes influence the microclimate, as inside the nests of warm-blooded species, by attracting
blood-sucking insects or indirectly by being the sources of nest materials. For
Sheep Drove (or similar habitat) these radiating relationships can be arranged in a
series according to distance from the source. It was a focus for migrant birds:
summer visitors like the turtle dove and willow warbler from the south, and winter
visitors like the fieldfare from the north which feed on and may incidentally disperse the fruit of hawthorn and other shrubs. The regional 'roughness' of the
landscape comes next. Then immigrants from a mile or more, like the *Simulium*,
and a mayfly, *Baetis rhodani*, from the river. There are the local shelter belts both

M   177

within and without the Drove, the former providing shelter for insect activity, the latter probably affecting crop communities. And finally the central structure itself, whose permanent fauna I will now mention.

During the winter and early spring, the inhabitants of a hawthorn hedge are either in resting states there or on the ground and winter field layer or are confined to the lichen-covered growth on the branches. Some may remain as eggs in cracks of the bark, others may hibernate as adults in cracks or holes or under the lichen covering of the branches. These hibernators are not only species directly attached to the hawthorn itself, but also come from other zones of the system. On 4 March 1939 I brought in some dead ends of hawthorn branch from Sheep Drove, which had cracks and some holes, and some lichen, and were from the lower part of the hedge. They contained five categories of animal: first a beetle that excavates galleries in small rotting branches of trees, *Grynobius excavatus*, either endemic or from the nearby woodland; secondly, a hibernating crop-pest beetle, *Phyllotreta nemorum*, attached to crucifers; thirdly, residents among the dead wood or lichens and algae, including a mould-eating beetle, *Corticaria fuscula*, springtails (Collembola) of several species, mites, young spiders and woodlice; fourthly, a hibernating weevil, *Anthonomus pedicularis*, that feeds on the hawthorn in spring and summer; fifthly, a hibernating ladybird, *Micraspis sexdecimpunctata*, that lives in marshes [11] This small example merely illustrates the way in which species from different habitats come together in the available winter cover, subsequently to disperse again. By April (1938) the hawthorn leaf buds were partly expanded and flower buds visible, and by 25 April the leaves were fully out and the flowers nearly open, the first appearing about the 30th, flowering being over by the end of May. Collecting was done on the pure hawthorn hedge by beating the canopy over a tray. At this time I had not realized the value of exactly recording vertical zones so that the information comes from about 3-9 feet on the hedge – the upper field layer and the lower canopy combined. From the middle of May until at least the end of June there was a continuous outburst of invertebrate life in the hedge which coincided with the nesting of many passerine birds. The character of this fauna changed markedly with the months. In late April and into May there were large numbers of small moth caterpillars, while in June flying leaf-hoppers (Hemiptera) predominated. By August the main abundance had ceased.

Throughout the summer various other forms were common, including Collembola (evidently derived from the epiphytic zone of the twigs), spiders, Psocoptera, small flies, sawflies and small parasitic Hymenoptera. We kept no really detailed picture of all this variety, and it can only be illustrated by certain groups of insects. Among these adult weevils were common and were carefully collected and named. Out of thirteen species only three were species particularly dependent upon hawthorn (*Anthonomus pedicularis, Rhynchites aequatus* and *R. caeruleus*). These were abundant in April and May [12]. The others came from such plants as clovers (either in Sheep Drove or in surrounding croplands) or other shrubs or from trees.

The only other beetle actually attached to hawthorn and found here was *Lochmaea crataegi*, a close relative of the heather beetle. Apart from beetles visiting the flowers the rest were predators. These included two Cantharid beetles, *Cantharis pallida* and *Rhagonycha limbata*, that develop in the ground; two ladybirds, *Adalia decempunctata* and *Coccinella septempunctata*; two Staphylinids, *Tachyporus hypnorum* and *Stenus ossium*, undoubted strays from the ground zone; and *Risophilus atricapillus*, a small Carabid usually found also on the ground but going up on to scrub canopy as well. All these are species with a wide habitat range. Two common species of predatory ants, *Lasius alienus* and *Myrmica laevinodis*, foraging on the leaves also came up from the ground. Bugs (Hemiptera Heteroptera) were carefully collected and were often (as with *Psallus*) abundant, but again were few in species. Of the twelve encountered, *Physatocheila dumetorum* lives on lichen-covered hawthorn, whitebeam (*Sorbus aria*) and blackthorn. Of the others only five characteristically inhabit scrub or tree canopy, particularly *Psallus ambiguus* (reported from hawthorn, sallow, elder and apple) and *P. perrisi* (found on oak, hawthorn and other species). These like a good many Heteroptera eat small insects but may suck plant juices as well. *Lygus cervinus* and *Deraeocoris lutescens*, the former herbivorous and the latter carnivorous, live on various trees and shrubs.[469] Three predatory bugs of very wide range and important indifferent food-chains, including those of crops, were *Anthocoris nemorum*, *nemoralis* and *confusus*. The only other major groups of hawthorn-eating insects were sawflies and moths, but these were not studied in sufficient detail at Sheep Drove to permit of generalization, beyond the observation already made, that the caterpillars reached their main abundance early in summer. L. T. Ford's conspectus[161] of the smaller British Lepidoptera covers 1375 species or about two-thirds of the British species of moths. This gives 53 species for which hawthorn is a food-plant. Only 12 are solely attached to it, 5 being general leaf-feeders, 5 leaf-miners, and 2 berry-eaters. 26 of the rest occur mainly also on other members of the Rosaceae, especially blackthorn, or sallow. Some have rather a wide range. To this list could be added some of the larger moths as well.

The following impressions are left of this hawthorn community. First, the size of most of the invertebrates except for some Lepidoptera was small, mostly less than half a centimetre. Secondly, there was a great summer outburst of herbivores from the end of April to about August, with one group following another in abundance. Thirdly, the commonest herbivores were partly confined to hawthorn, and partly had a wider range of habitats. Fourthly, all the predators were widely distributed in various habitats (including various kinds of canopy) and polyphagous. Fifthly, the number of species actually attached to the hedge as a habitat, whether confined to hawthorn or not, was relatively small. To this central community based upon the hawthorn leaves and to a small extent also their fruits, must be added four other components: flower and fruit visitors to the hawthorn, the general fauna of associated shrubs, and the fauna living on the epiphytic growth. Enormous numbers of insects visit hawthorn flowers in May, especially beetles and bees. Most of them are in search of pollen and presumably play some part in cross-pollination and the fruiting success of the plant. The output of nectar is said to be very irregular in different places and seasons (of course the flowering itself is much greater in some years than others), and Howes writing about hive-bees states that 'the seasons when hawthorn is a good honey source only come round at long intervals. In some parts of the country 1943 was a good year as were 1911 and 1933'.[238] At such times the hives may actually have the fishy smell of hawthorn flowers, caused by the chemical triethylamine that acts as an attractant to insects[527] though not to most people. This is the only respect in which hawthorn is ever much of a food resource for man, but when it is available this nectar makes a fine honey with a nutty flavour and lacking the fishy smell that it starts with.

The fruits or haws, unlike those of the wayfaring tree to be mentioned, do not attract insects when ripe (several breed in the green berries), though they must certainly be one of the most important winter foods for many birds, specially of the thrush tribe. Hartley[217] concluded, from widespread field observations, that fieldfares (*Turdus pilaris*) and redwings (*T. musicus*) are the chief specialists in feeding upon haws in winter, the blackbird being the only other British thrush to do this to any large extent. That such a long-distance ecological relationship, between northern Scandinavia and Britain, should result in the spread of one of our dominant shrubs is worth comment, and it only needs one successful young hawthorn to start a colony, since birds stop and perch on the young shrub when it reaches a certain height, and thus start further dispersal. The numerous old nests of passerine birds left in hedges in winter time are not infrequently used by mice and voles as platforms in which to sit and eat the gathered fruits. This was noticed at Sheep Drove. In his study of the food of small rodents Miller[324] found that in captivity the wood-mouse (*Apodemus sylvaticus*) takes off the outer soft part and eats only the nut within, whereas the bank vole (*Clethrionomys glareolus*) does the opposite, eating the flesh but often leaving the nut. Oldham[360] found wood-mice taking rose-hips up into old nests of birds such as song-thrush, blackbird, hedge sparrow and greenfinch, where they extracted and ate the seeds but left a mass of flesh. He trapped mice up to 7 feet. Forrest[166] found the same habit in Shropshire hedges. No trapping was done at Sheep Drove, but in a similar hedgerow not far away trapping proved the presence of both the wood-mouse and the bank-vole, the former living not only in the hedge itself, but also out in open hawthorn scrub

hat was colonizing the grass downland. The hawthorn fruit crop fluctuates
tremendously from year to year.

At Sheep Drove the hawthorn hedge was flanked on its inner side by chalk
scrub of eleven species, and there was often a gap of a foot or two between them,
apparently caused by root competition from the old hedge. There were also four
kinds of climber, of which ivy was far the most important, and a very thin scatter
of trees of seven species. All these added to the total variety of the system, but
since we did not collect their fauna it is necessary to substitute work from elsewhere. The only non-maritime terrestrial shrub so far treated in the *Biological
Flora* is the common buckthorn, *Rhamnus cathartica*, for which a list of animals
specially attached to the plant (but omitting polyphagous species other than those
living also on the other species of buckthorn) is given.[191] There are 2 species of
aphids, 4 of Homoptera, 1 or more gall-midges, the brimstone butterfly, 9 species
of moths and some gall-mites on the leaves, a total of around 18 species – not a
very large number. For a more complete picture of what may be built up round a
British shrub there is Side's excellent survey[442] of the fauna of the wayfaring tree,
Viburnum lantana (a shrub growing usually not much more than 15 feet), on the
chalk of the North Downs in the region round Maidstone in Kent. To this I shall
add a little extra information collected by myself about the wayfaring tree on
Wytham Hill. The special value of Side's survey is that the biological links were
sufficiently well established to distinguish between species directly or indirectly
dependent on the shrub, and casual visitors.

The outstanding 'key-industries' on the leaves of the wayfaring tree in summer
were two kinds of aphid, three moths, a beetle, and two kinds of leaf-gall made by
mites and by a gall-midge. *Ceruraphis eriophori* attacks some leaves severely, curling
them partly into galls. It has a double life-history, because only the early summer
is spent increasing parthenogenetically on the shrub, the aphids flying in mid-June
on to another host plant, which may be a *Carex*, *Luzula* or *Typha* (*Eriophorum* is
also mentioned but cannot come into the chalkland picture). In autumn they fly
back and later on winter eggs are laid on the twigs. At Wytham Woods I have
found this aphid almost defoliating parts of some wayfaring trees. *Aphis lantanae*
was also common on the North Downs, but this has a simpler life-history confined to the two species of *Viburnum* (*lantana* and *opulus*). *Aphis fabae* – the bean
aphis – has also been found on *Viburnum* but is not mentioned by Side. Around
these aphid populations assembles a circle of predators: *Chrysopa carnea* adults as
also the larvae of lacewings; the larvae of hover-flies (Syrphidae) of at least two
species; the predatory bug *Anthocoris nemorum*; a small Carabid, *Risophilus atricapillus*; several species of adult ladybirds, especially *Adalia decempunctata*; several
kinds of Cantharid beetles; spiders, of which *Theridion pallens* certainly preys on
aphids; and one or two Hymenopterous parasites. This is a fair example of the

kind of assemblage of predators that may be found with aphids on a great many situations. Some of them breed on the spot, while others are visitors. None are confined either to *Viburnum* or even to scrub. At Wytham I found lacewings (*Chrysopa perla* – a rather characteristically shrub species and *Hemerobius humu linus*), *Coccinella septempunctata* and Syrphid fly larvae associated with *Ceruraphi eriophori* [13].

Of the three small moths, *Peronea schalleriana* makes web-held folds on the leaves, *Lithocolletis lantanella* mines the undersurface, and *Coleophora ahenella* make a minute case in which it lives on the surface [14]. No other moths of importance were found. The Chrysomelid beetle *Galerucella viburni* belongs to a genus that have found causing considerable damage sometimes to other plants. Its larvae can partly defoliate both this *Viburnum* and the guelder rose *V. opulus* at Wytham Woods. On one guelder rose shrub at the edge of a deciduous wood there, half had been almost defoliated and the other half only lightly attacked, and the former had not fruited. The larvae pupate in the ground and the adults return in autumn and feed on the leaves also. The female makes curious hollow nests on old stems in which the eggs pass the winter[304] and which Von Lengerken[526] takes to be evidence of incipient parental care. There are two sorts of gall on the upper surface of the thick hairy leaves, one made by an Eriophyid mite, *Eriophyes viburni*, that has another mite commensally living with it, and the other by a gall-midge, *Phlye tidobia solmsi*.

The aphids and caterpillars alter the leaf structure by curling it up, so making shelters inside which are the remains of cast skins, excreta and sucked corpses. Sid observed that these become occupied by other species – nocturnal woodlice like *Porcellio scaber* spending the day there, earwigs and spiders sheltering while they moult, and insects probably eating the refuse there or moulds. Otherwise there is a rather notable absence of extra 'furniture' on this shrub, as there is in most other scrub, the main exception being the nests of passerine birds. Omitting the visitors to flowers and fruit, and realizing that some ecological events though real enough may have been rather insignificant, one arrives at a total of roughly thirty-six species of invertebrates associated with the leaves of the wayfaring tree (and this does not include a good many spiders that were not named). This is a respectable but not an enormous community. The chief herbivores are solely attached to this shrub, or sometimes live on the guelder rose as well, whereas practically all the predators range widely through other habitats, and prey on many different species. The chief general difference from the hawthorn system is that the latter does not have a large aphid-based set of food-chains. Aphids were found sometimes on the shoot-tips at Sheep Drove, but there was never an assembly of the usual regimen of aphid-eating forms. Another great difference is that the wayfaring tree has no large epiphytic covering of lichen or alga, and correspondingly does not support

Psocid fauna. Springtails, however, are always abundant at Wytham, as they were also on the North Downs, and since they do not live on the leaves they must ordinarily inhabit the stems, though in spring they also congregate on the flowers presumably to eat pollen. A sample from Wytham proved to belong to one species *Entomobrya (Mydonius) nivalis* [15]. This lives on the bark of a great many species of trees and shrubs, as well as on wild *Clematis* and bramble. According to South[461] it is especially abundant on older branches of shrubs, where there is a considerable flora of microfungi.

The hawthorn on the other hand usually has a covering of lichens which may be very dense, that is a fungal-algal combination associated with which is always some free alga such as one can see in much larger pure culture on the branches of elder or the trunk of beech. On hawthorn the alga is often abundant on the undersides of branches. At Wychwood Forest in Oxfordshire, where old hawthorn forms a high understorey or even 'tree canopy', it can be noticed in winter that the trees are grey with lichen (including *Parmelia physodes* [16]), and this is evidently more marked in the hawthorns that are dying of old age or have recently fallen, as many are now doing. (Since the heavier lichen layer on older or dying twigs may be just due to their naturally slow growth, they do not use the tree otherwise than as a neutral substratum.) Beating the canopy of hawthorn at Sheep Drove always produced a large number of Collembola, and also (from April to August at least) numbers of winged Psocoptera. The latter live on lichen or alga, and have wingless earlier stages. They belonged to five species: *Elipsocus westwoodi*, *Mesopsocus immunis*, *M. unipunctatus*, *Graphopsocus cruciatus* and *Caecilius flavidus* [17]. Like many other Psocids these species live on a good many different trees and shrubs. Broadhead[47] mentions that larch trees in the Pennine Hills have 24 species out of the British total of about 70, though 9 of these made up 95% of the populations he counted. The first three mentioned above were important constituents of the larch twig and branch fauna and Broadhead's experiments give a good idea of their food habits. All three preferred alga to lichen, and indeed both nymphs and adults starved on a lichen diet. *Elipsocus* was found also to lay its eggs more on alga. The dead larch twigs are covered with the lichen *Leconora conizaeoides*, but rather little of the alga *Pleurococcus*, and when these Psocids were confined to such twigs they would eat some of the lichen even though it was not adequate food. It was the younger living branches and twigs that had *Pleurococcus*, together with fungal spores but only a little lichen. Grazing experiments on larch twigs proved that the two *Mesopsocus* also eat alga in preference to lichen. For *Caecilius flavidus* there are some observations from the broom survey at Silwood Park, Surrey, where their guts were found to contain alga and fungus spores.[48] It would seem likely therefore that the main food resource of these five Psocids in Sheep Drove was *Pleurococcus*, and that there was no common lichen-feeding species. Dr E.

Broadhead has kindly given me some unpublished information about the Psocids he has found on hawthorn in various parts of England. The five Sheep Drove species are among the eight most frequent or occasionally abundant on his list. Besides these he found eight others less commonly. Among the latter were *Elipsocus maclachlani* and *Reuterella helvimaculata*, both proved lichen-feeders, and abundant at higher levels on the Pennine Hills on hawthorn and larch. Much of the fauna inhabiting the twigs and branches of hawthorn is active at night, as we observed at Sheep Drove in March. Many woodlice, *Porcellio scaber* (also a keen nocturnal alga-feeder on tree trunks – see Ch. 10) were out, also earwigs, *Forficula auricularia*. Spiders were active, some of them making small webs or strands across the twigs. Some harvestmen (Opilionids) were on the move, also two species of small Carabid beetles (*Dromius quadrinotatus* and *meridionalis*) – as one might equally see on tree trunks.

It is impossible to write about the communities of scrub without becoming rather obsessed with the densely interlacing branches and devious cover that make the character of these thickets and hedges, and the reader may possibly feel that the style of this chapter has assumed something of a slow journey through thick low jungle. The main ideas that one reaches are, however, fairly plain. Scrub and its edges are the forerunners of woodland, and most wild shrubs belong primarily to the woodland edge or its earlier succession stages, during which there is intense competition in which the spread of fruits by birds plays a leading part. This historical and partly temporary role of scrub must always be in our minds. The animals that depend on scrub canopy are in four categories: those that live there permanently or have a regular alternation with nearby zones; those birds that visit it to nest in summer; the insect visitors to the flowers, of which there are a steady succession through the summer; and bird visitors to the fruits in autumn and winter. The residents can again be divided into those based on the leaves or green twigs, and those based on epiphytic growth.

The bird life of Sheep Drove remains to be mentioned in greater detail, and it illustrates what a large bird population the scrub community supports, as well as the strong dependence of birds upon habitat structure as shown not only by which species are present but also by those that are missing. Two systematic bird counts were undertaken. The first was by Mr L. S. V. Venables on 25-27 May 1938, when he made a fairly complete nest census along 500 yards of the Drove, i.e. along 1000 yards of hedge. The second was a walking count done by the late Miss Averil Morley on 10-11 March 1939 – too early for the summer migrants but a valuable survey in that it covered the whole mile of the Drove, i.e. two miles of hedge scrub. In addition I made a number of more casual notes through the season, which agreed closely so far as the nesting species were concerned and added a few extra items. The passerine birds living there in summer were as follows:

25. Spindle, *Euonymus europaeus*, ring-barked and killed by rabbits, Leckford, Hampshire. (Photo C. S. E. 2 March 1938)

26 & 27. The structure of oak canopy, Wytham Woods, in the same area as Photo 10. Above, a small bracken–bramble glade; below, collecting in the canopy at known heights. The epiphytic growth on the bark can be seen. (Photo D. A. K. 11 Sept. 1953)

28. A mouse-trapping team in Wytham Woods (l. to r. W. P. Crowcroft, H. N. Southern, R. S. Miller). (Photo D. A. K. 10 June 1950)

29. Collecting from field layer sweeping in an oak–ash–sycamore glade, with much St Johnswort, *Hypericum hirsutum*, Wytham Woods. (Photo D. A. K. 8 Sept. 1952)

30. Sample of small invertebrates extracted from one sq. metre of oak–sycamore woodland litter, Wytham Woods. (Sample by M. J. Davies; Photo D. A. K.)

31. Edge of oak–ash–maple–hawthorn woodland in a ride, with hawthorn in flower, Wychwood Forest, Oxfordshire. (Photo C. S. E. 7 June 1958)

32. Edge of oak–ash woodland with flowering rose and elder, showing vertical layering of lime
stone grass, bracken, etc., scrub and tree canopy, Wytham Woods. (Photo C. S. E. 19 June 1960

33. Flowering ivy on an old stone wall by a farmhouse, Cumnor Hill, Berkshire; also *Convolvulus sepium* leaves perforated by a beetle. (Photo C. S. E. 27 Sept. 1960)

34. Vertical layers of a glade in a pine wood by Loch Garten, Inverness-shire, with Ground Zone, Field Layer of *Vaccinium*, Scrub layer of juniper, and Tree canopy of *Pinus sylvestris*. (Photo C. S. E. 3 Sept. 1959)

Blue tit	*Parus caeruleus*	
Long-tailed tit	*Aegithalos caudatus*	
Wren	*Troglodytes troglodytes*	1
Mistle thrush	*Turdus viscivorus*	1
Song-thrush	*Turdus philomelos*	2
Blackbird	*Turdus merula*	9
Robin	*Erithacus rubecula*	
Whitethroat	*Sylvia communis*	2
Willow warbler	*Phylloscopus trochilus*	2
Hedge sparrow	*Prunella modularis*	3
Greenfinch	*Chloris chloris*	7
Linnet	*Carduelis cannabina*	4
Chaffinch	*Fringilla coelebs*	2
Yellowhammer	*Emberiza citrinella*	1

The numbers on the right are the numbers of nests or nesting pairs found in the May census, only three species being missing from this 1000 yards stretch: of these there was not more than one pair on the rest of the total 3500 yards. Besides these passerine birds there were nesting seven pairs of common partridge, *Perdix perdix*, counted by the keeper in 1938, and a few pairs of turtle doves, *Streptopelia turtur*, and wood-pigeons, *Columba palumbus*. Non-nesting visitors from a wider area included swallows, *Hirundo rustica*, hawking for flying insects; a barn owl, *Tyto alba*; and probably the sparrow-hawk, *Accipiter nisus*, and cuckoo, *Cuculus canorus*. Most of the birds were the smaller species dependent on seeds or invertebrates, the latter especially during the breeding season.

This community of passerine birds is well representative of scrub, for it is practically identical with that described by Venables[522] for open deciduous scrub on the South Downs, a formation-type described by him as mainly hawthorn and blackthorn, usually not more than 15 feet high, with some elder in places, and interspersed or undergrown with various vegetation from rabbit-grazed chalk grass to bramble, bracken or gorse. This similarity incidentally confirms the justification for treating equal mixtures of two formation types as equivalent to 'Edge' (Ch. 4). The birds at Sheep Drove were, of course, using the whole system of scrub, field layer and ground zone in varying degrees, not necessarily just the shrubs themselves, and some of them also went out on to the croplands outside. The frequent dependence of birds upon structural features of the habitat that do not seem to have much immediate ecological relevance, though they are a psychological necessity for the birds, was pointed out especially clearly by Lack[275] in 1933, in his study of the zonal colonization of pine plantations on Breck heathland; though obviously birds are only partly so limited. Three examples illustrate this point. On Sheep Drove there was only one pair of blue tits and these nested in the only shed standing along there, there being no natural holes in the scrub itself. The only pair of long-tailed tits nested in a part of the hawthorn hedge where there was much heavy growth of ivy, inside which wood-pigeons roosted in winter. They ranged along a stretch of about 300 yards. It seems likely that they were attracted by the wood-pigeon feathers, since the long-tailed tit makes a very substantial nest containing often 2000 or more feathers (and which is also covered with lichen, abundant on the hawthorn). The turtle doves lived and nested only where the hedge was at its tallest. But the species will nest from field layer up to about 14 feet[62] (one at Sheep Drove was at 11 feet), and it seems likely that the preference for taller scrub falls into the category of psychological requirements. The scarcity of trees there has already been mentioned. The small number of song-thrushes, and the absence of such species as the chiffchaff (*Phylloscopus collybita*), and tree pipit (*Anthus trivialis*) might be attributed to scarcity of song-posts. The two song-thrush nests found by Venables in his Sheep Drove census were not far from the maple tree and the wild pear tree respectively. However I sometimes saw song-thrushes singing in the hedge.

From his Breckland survey Lack[275] concluded that 'the birds were affected far more by the height of the vegetation than by its nature. . . . Selection of the ancestral habitat implies recognition, and one would therefore expect habitat selection to be correlated with the conspicuous features of the habitat. The height of the vegetation is certainly one of the most conspicuous features of the habitat on the Breckland, and the close dependence of distribution on it, irrespective of whether it was correlated with any essential avian requirements, is just what one would expect if distribution was limited through habitat selection.' Some of the common summer birds of 11-12-year-old pine plantations on the Breckland[277] (that is, scrub reaching on the average 12-15 feet) were wren, song-thrush, blackbird, whitethroat, willow warbler and chaffinch, all of which occurred in Sheep Drove. The only species in significant numbers found ordinarily in this pine scrub but not in thorn scrub are two typically conifer-haunting birds, the coal tit, *Parus ater*, and the goldcrest, *Regulus regulus*, which began to come in at about this stage of the pine succession. Therefore most of this scrub bird community is attracted by general scrub structure and height, not to deciduous or conifer scrub as such. This conclusion is additionally confirmed by the survey Venables[522] did of open yew (*Taxus baccata*) scrub on the Downs, consisting of yews up to 25 feet high, often with a short chalk grass carpet below and between. Fourteen species of passerine birds (omitting the crow family) came there, of which ten occurred in the hedgerows of Sheep Drove. There were indeed differences such as the whitethroat's absence from the yew, and the presence of goldcrests there. Both the whitethroat and the willow warbler (which was relatively scarce in yew scrub [17A]) require low dense vegetation which was not well developed in the open yew

The average number of passerine nests (or bird pairs) found by Venables or the 1000 yards of Sheep Drove hedges was about one to every 30 yards, this being possibly a slight underestimate since a few nests in very thick cover may have been missed. The influence of other species of scrub in modifying the hawthorn hedge as a total habitat was shown clearly in two ways. The east hedge had 26 nests and the west hedge only 8 nests. The reason for this was that the west hedge was mostly pure hawthorn whereas the east side had much additional chalk scrub as well as bramble, providing in the lower 6 feet a much denser and more sheltered cover. At one point in the east hedge there was a considerable concentration of nests – nine in 25 yards. This could be explained, though not entirely, by the great abundance of elder along most of this short stretch. My wife's records showed that on 2 March of that year some elders were beginning to sprout leaves when hawthorn was still wintry; on 19 March elder was in half-leaf but only one or two hawthorns had begun to open buds; even on 1 April when the elder was in full leaf, the hawthorn was only half in leaf. It seems likely that birds concentrated on that part of the hedgerow that provided early cover, though the fact that a section of this nest concentration extended a few yards beyond the main part with elder indicates that nest cover was not solely involved.

Any attempt to convey the enormously rich tapestry pattern of a whole formation-type like scrub, a pattern changing endlessly in its details and timing, must steer between pure abstraction without evidence and pure evidence without form. Much ecological work staggers rather uneasily between these two extremes, and the only method that I have ever found adequate is just to offer some of the main situations in the form of examples. In seeking a Middle Way by means of example, the picture must however still remain rather bare and much has to be omitted that people with other interests will consider equally essential. So my description of summer scrub may seem to have more the character of a leafless December hedgerow. This at any rate enables one to see the structure clearly, and it is from this structure that the habitat develops its further potentialities. The facts brought together in this chapter, and in the previous chapters about grassland, heath and the maritime zone, already begin to suggest a rather illuminating principle about the structure of communities and their relation to other different ones. This is, in fact, an annexe to the established notions about food-chains and size pyramids. It is exemplified in the communities of deciduous and coniferous woody habitats, and I shall to a certain extent anticipate the next chapter, by including both scrub and woodland here. In making this comparison for the present purpose, the climatic and historical aspects need to be excluded as far as possible. Relics of the great Boreal zone of pine forest now survive in the Highlands of Scotland, and confined to them are several species of breeding birds with only this northern distribution: of passerines the crested tit, *Parus cristatus*, and the siskin, *Carduelis spinus*. Conversely there are southern species, including some of the warblers, absent from the

Highlands.[282] There are similar instances among insects. The comparison I shall make is therefore not between the original Boreal fauna and that of the broad-leaved 'Atlantic' zone, but between conifer and deciduous woodlands where there has been equal opportunity for colonization. Most or all of these southern conifer woods were planted in historically recent times, and they are often structurally less fully stratified than those of Scotland. And yet there is a surprising amount of resemblance between the bird life of the two kinds of woodland in England. Some years ago[126] I collected evidence on this subject through an organized inquiry covering different parts of England, with one report also from North Wales. Of the 27 woods surveyed 18 were deciduous, 5 conifer (mainly pine) and 4 mixed. For each the summer birds were listed. Here I shall analyse only the passerine birds (omitting the crow family, which are not always resident or may be subject to 'vermin control'). As some of the species occurred infrequently, I include only the 31 reported from at least four woods of each kind – a procedure which actually weights the results against the conifer woods, since they are so few in number. The upshot is that deciduous woods had 31 species, conifer 27, the difference being solely due to four more species present in the former, not to a net balance. The agreement is remarkably close, as it is in scrub, though it does not imply that the density of populations was similar either in general or in detail. From this survey I concluded that 'we have in England and Wales one bird community, which shows minor variations in different types of woods, but is on the whole very constant in species, though not in densities and would appear more so if our woods were not in such small units'. Lack and Venables[282] from their later and more extensive survey of woodland birds have stressed that the presence or absence of scrub or field layers in woods is perhaps more important than the species of the dominant trees.

I have already pointed out how many of the insect predators on a hawthorn hedge live also in other habitats, and this without doubt would be found to apply also to the spiders and harvestmen. The lacewings (Neuroptera) afford good material for looking at this question, because Killington's standard monograph[270] has unusually good information about their habitats, in particular whether they live in deciduous or conifer woods and scrub. Taking those species common enough or well enough known to provide a reliable habitat picture, there are about 41 species that frequent woody vegetation. 19 of these do not live in conifers or are seldom found there, but occur in deciduous woods and their edges, or in scrub or hedgerows, the exact range through these formation-types varying some-what. 16 come only or almost only on conifers. *Semidalis aleyrodiformis* is a deciduous woodland and scrub species, but the adults (though not the larvae) also go on to conifers. There are only about 8 (i.e. about a fifth of the 43) that frequent both deciduous and conifer. Ladybirds (Coccinellidae) show a similar division nto two groups. When we come down to the herbivorous invertebrates the differentiation is almost complete: there are practically none that live on both deciduous and conifer trees or scrub, e.g. none of the herbivorous insects mentioned n the Sheep Drove survey, and none of the hawthorn moths discussed there. So, he difference in fauna between deciduous and conifer is very sharp at the base of he food-chains, still strongly marked at the insect predator level, but much less so t the passerine bird level.

This change in habitat range according to the consumer level cannot be attributed just to greater body-size giving higher powers of mobility, since many small insects such as aphids can be dispersed over great distances by air currents, though their food-plant preferences are usually limited. Winged insects can also e carried for hundreds of miles. The now well-known instance of insect drift from the conifer forests of northern Europe to Spitsbergen in 1924 illustrates not nly this point, but also the one about habitat range. The conifer aphids forming he preponderant element of this 800-mile dispersal, were accompanied also by a over-fly, *Syrphus* (or *Syrphidis*) *ribesii*, whose larvae prey on aphids.[123] But this pecies is very common also in oak–ash–sycamore woods on Wytham Hill, where s aphid preys would be totally different. This phenomenon might be termed 'The nverse Pyramid of Habitats', i.e. the higher the consumer level the fewer and arger the animals, but also the greater the habitat range. With one large exception, to be mentioned, it is a principle that probably applies throughout most ecosystems. But it remains for population research to determine what its dynamic results on the community are likely to be. For one has all the time to keep carefully distinct the energy and production lines throughout the species network, seen mpirically as a piece of working machinery, though also as a system that can be udied at this level in its own right; and any consequences that these interrelations ay have for the control of population density and structure, or the habitat istribution of animals. I think it would be safe to assume, however, that anything widespread and penetrative throughout ecosystems must have at any rate some onsiderable dynamic consequences, among which might be greater stability of he whole system. The exception mentioned above is this: mammal and bird erbivores are not necessarily confined to a narrow range of habitat, this coming ot so much from their range of movement as from their greater adaptability of ehaviour, also to some extent from the need to draw upon a great variety and nount of plant matter. Examples one immediately thinks of are the wood-pigeon, *olumba palumbus* (which nests equally in deciduous and conifer scrub, though deed the latter is mainly exotic spruces rather than native pine[77]); the rabbit, hich is not restricted to any formation-type, and deer. The principle applies iefly to food-chains based upon invertebrates, which form the great mass of imal life.

CHAPTER 10

The Forest Canopy: Herbivores

THERE IS A magnificent Polish epic poem, *Pan Tadeusz* by Adam Mickiewicz, i
which a wild forest is the background to the story. Part of it is called 'The Fore
Community' and the first seven lines of this run as follows:*

> Those woods of Lithuania – who has dared explore
> Their depths abysmal, penetrate their midmost core?
> A fisher on the beach shall scarcely sound the sea!
> The hunter can but skirt our forest-bed – and he
> Beholds its outward form and feature, these alone;
> To him its inner heart and secret are unknown.
> Only report and fable tell what there is found.

He then goes on to describe what could be termed the components of the fores
tangled weeds, stumps and logs, anthills, nests of wasp and hornet, deep pool
springs – 'those irised springs are fleckt with rust like blood', the leaves and bar
devoured, the mossy boughs – 'with loathsome fungus-beards the stems ai
huncht, and stoop'. No sensitive person can enter a forest without feeling at on
that here is the supreme development of nature on land; indeed for mass an
variety of species packed into a small compass it transcends all fresh-water an
most marine systems. Ecologists faced with the task of studying as a whole any
thing so impressively complicated might well 'fly, dash whimpering away, wit
wild distracted eye' like the hounds that entered the wild forest of the Polish poen
Our knowledge of the forest community is still vague and unformed, and tl
reader is asked to remember that one is, as it were, trying to fit together an ancie
mosaic from random fragments, or solve a jigsaw puzzle with only a thousand
of the pieces on the board.

The nature of woodland can be indicated by adopting the analogy of a house
οἶκος, in comparing it with the more lowly formation-types – once described l
A. H. Church[69] as 'a constant stream of phyletic débris of such races, which, failii
in the full arboreal habit, may nevertheless make a working-success of some alte

* Translation by Oliver Elton, 1940.[138]

ative line of existence'. This house is larger and more elaborately constructed; here are more storeys though their floors are insubstantial and partly imaginary; he rooms, doors and windows themselves are bigger and the Gothic beams are hicker; the carpets are deeper and richer, especially in winter, when they are most eeded; the new furniture deteriorates in freshness after a time but as it gets older s very popular (or populous); there is a great deal of second-hand furniture, some f which however lasts for many years; the place is draughty though less so than he fields outside, it is rather ill-lit during the summer, and the wooden walls often un with moisture; in some parts of the house there are actual slum conditions, hough remarkably little disease and an unknown extent of emigration; there are nany visitors, much social life in the higher echelons, many parties – indeed floral êtes through the summer season and harvest festivals after it; and an extraordin- rily large number of births, liaisons and deaths, which are only now beginning to e recorded systematically. Even a Eugene O'Neill might hesitate to give a con- incing account of all the ramifications within it.

The word 'furniture' already used in several places in this book is a convenient erm for the heterogeneous accessories that are extra to the basic structure of a abitat, i.e. to rock, soil, water and vegetation. It includes not only the various cattered general habitats such as logs, bracket fungi, dead bodies, collections of lung, nests and small human artefacts, but also loose stones and the litter of leaves nd twigs. The word is used here in its older sense – nowadays furniture is mostly hought of as movable objects – including both what landlords call 'fixtures' (as listinct from the main fabric) and movable furniture. Another difference between ts ordinary meaning and its application to natural habitats is that our furniture is ot edible except to a few insects like the furniture beetle (*Anobium punctatum*, vhich also lives in decaying trees), whereas many of the natural accessories are ither eaten by animals or decay rather rapidly, the decay organisms providing till further animal food. On the whole the furniture of woodland is concentrated hiefly in the ground zone. As one passes upwards the plants themselves provide nore and more of the structural variety, other than the occasional nest or rookery, racket fungi and the more frequent patches of dying and dead wood. The scrub nd tree canopy layers, conventionally assigned to levels above 6 feet but sometimes lescending below that line, especially in the edges of glades or of the wood itself, orm an intricate persistent forking system of more or less cylindrical branches oming off the larger cylinder of the trunk. The impression of interlacing that one ets when looking up from the ground is not strictly correct: the whole arrange- nent is more analogous to a river system and its tributary streams spread out in hree dimensions. The trunk and branch system is a notable highway linking round and canopy, and it is used by a host of animals (particularly the wingless orms) many of which move in an upward direction after dusk and down again

by dawn, or else have a seasonal upward march into the canopy (see Ch. 12). On
some nights this rich miscellany reminds one of the Great Trunk Road of India so
colourfully described by Rudyard Kipling in *Kim*. The surface of the trunk and
branches usually carries some kind of epiphytic growth, including mosses and
lichens that provide cover and some food for very small animals, or large pastures
of the alga *Pleurococcus* upon which woodlice, millipedes and Psocids graze, mostly
by night.

Except in the smaller terminal branches and twigs, the framework of a large
deciduous tree or of a pine is rather clumsily constructed and does not offer the
same densely grown support for birds' nests that is found in scrub or younger trees.
As a result, the number of smaller birds nesting in the higher canopy of a wood
is far less than in the scrub zone below or the scrub outside. Most of the ordinary
scrub-nesting species are left behind above the field layer and nearly all above
the 15-foot line of the scrub canopy zone. All the thirteen species of passerine
birds nesting in the hawthorn hedge and associated chalk scrub at Sheep Drove
(Ch. 9) also nest in woodland or its edges, but only four of them ordinarily nest
above the scrub zone. These are the mistle thrush and blackbird that go up quite
high, the song-thrush which does not ordinarily go much above 25 feet, and the
long-tailed tit which prefers two separate zones for nesting – either in the scrub
layer or at heights above about 25 feet in trees.[280] None of the warblers and very
few of the finches nest in tree canopy, though of course they range up into it for
feeding. Tree canopy is unsuitable for the nests of many small birds for at least
two reasons: the branching system has too coarse a texture for constructing a base
and it also provides much less effective cover against enemies. Where dense creep-
ers climb high, as with ivy and even *Clematis*, a special cover is created among the
branches that takes some birds higher. There are a good many larger birds that
manage better and commonly use the higher canopy, including some pigeons,
hawks, and members of the crow family, and locally the heron; but the outstanding feature of woodland canopy is the presence of holes for nesting, a feature almost
lacking in scrub. Some holes are made by the birds in fairly solid wood (green and
great spotted woodpeckers – another relation of size and strength to the size of the
tree) or in rotting wood or they use those that already exist through rotting or
some natural accident. For example nearly one-third of the breeding birds in the
Terrestrial habitats of Wytham Hill are hole-nesters. More is said about this in
Ch. 14. Squirrels and hornets also use such holes, the former also making its drey
at various heights in the canopy as well. These various canopy nests attract a
special fauna of invertebrates some of the species of which are widely shared between different hosts. And indeed different hosts may occupy the same site at
different times (Ch. 16).

Only the rook and one or two other larger birds are able to nest in the high twiggy canopy. Everyone must have seen how wildly such end twigs and branches thrash about in a strong wind, and anyone who has climbed a tree and tried to collect there knows how unstable they are under any conditions. There is a strong gradient in wind speed from the top of a wood down through the canopy to the ground, which is only partly diminished by the absence of summer foliage. A standard example is given by Geiger,[176] measured in an old oak wood in Germany composed of 115-year-old trees interspersed with younger beeches of 40 to 50 years. The height of the wood was 24 m. (c. 79 ft). Anemometers were set at this height, also at 27 m., i.e. just above the forest roof, and at 20, 14 and 4 m. That is to say the wind was measured at three points in the high canopy, and one in the low canopy, with one control up in the open. The gradient was measured in spring before the leaves were out and again in autumn while the leaves were still on. In the bare spring wood the average wind speed of about 4 m. per second up above the wood was about four times that at 4 m., with a gradient between. Even at 24 m. the speed was only three-quarters what it was 3 m. above in the open. With full foliage the speed at 24 m. was only half, and by 20 m. it had almost reached the low speeds of the 4-m. zone, which were below 1 m. per second. Geiger expressed these results in another way, by calculating the number of hours in which 'calm' was recorded, this being when the anemometers, which required a starting wind speed of 0·7 m. per second, were not moving. The percentage of calm hours at 4 m. was 67 before leafing and 98 with the leaves on, with the usual gradients upwards. 'Once the million leaves have unfolded, the trunk space is virtually stagnant.' The further consequences of this and other gradients for the microclimate of woodland can be imagined and will not be pursued here.

Although we ordinarily see the details of a wood from the ground, a better idea of the canopy pattern can be gained from the air, except that this does not reveal all the variations in height. Plate 9 is a view taken from about 2000 ft on 9 June of a small part of the oak–ash–sycamore woods on Wytham Hill alluded to in Ch. 3. In this mosaic the oaks show as large dark units, the ash trees as lighter ones with a more feathery look, and the sycamores as rather solid foaming masses of light foliage. Subdividing the main mass of each tree is often a minor cauliflower-like pattern formed by the separate branch systems. The ashes and sycamores are of various ages and sizes, and the photograph does not distinguish the smaller saplings pushing up in spaces between the larger trees, except where they are in family groups. But the oaks are all large mature trees (Plates 26 and 27) because there has been no effective regeneration in the present century, nor (in this area) any planting. There is no simple method of counting all the trees of different sizes from this photograph, but a ground enumeration of all trees over and under 14 in. diameter (at breast height) done by the University Department of Forestry[371] in 1949 included the 14·6-acre forest compartment of which the photograph covers about two-thirds. There were then 118 oak (*Quercus robur*), 18 ash (*Fraxinus excelsior*) and 40 sycamore (*Acer pseudo-platanus*) over 14 in., or counting in also the smaller trees, totals of 118, 22 and 81 respectively, i.e. about 12 larger trees per acre and 15 'total trees' per acre. This is not a dense population; but the trees in the lower part of the photograph are more dense than this general average. No other species of tree occurs in this compartment, except one large beech (*Fagus sylvatica*) and four common maples (*Acer campestre*), which also come into the photograph. This section of the woods, lying on a shelf and slope of the Coral Rag limestone with superficial patches of glacial clay here and there, includes a portion of the original woodland, no doubt modified by earlier handling and cutting, but essentially a semi-natural system where the canopy is reasonably dense in places. For the map in Fig. 20, derived from the photograph, I am indebted to Mr C. A. Elbourn, who identified the species of trees by a ground survey in 1963. The most important change in these woods has been the introduction of the sycamore in the nineteenth century. This European maple grows naturally among beech or ash in the mountains of central Europe, though older beech forest suppresses it. In North America large maples are a common feature of many forests. Although Britain is slightly north-west of its natural limits in Europe, the sycamore can reasonably be regarded as filling a more normal niche in our woods than some other invaders. At any rate this bit of Wytham Woods, modified and perhaps unusually simple floristically as it is, will serve as a peg on which to hang a discussion of the pattern of the canopy fauna. Its species represent most of the more influential dominant broad-leaved trees of Britain, except birches, though many of the subsidiary ones such as elms and poplars are missing. The scrub below and in gaps between trees contains some of the main British species (hazel, elder, hawthorn, spindle, sallow and others).

It is not suggested that a detailed ecological survey has been done on the actual patch of wood shown on this map, which is only intended to assist the imagination in thinking about the matter. There is, it is true, some information from there but most comes indirectly from various sources. The chief features of a tree that directly influence the animal life on it are as follows: (1) the central factory of green leaves – their structure and chemistry, with their necessary buds, bud scales and twigs; (2) the flowers; (3) the fruits; (4) the method and scale of forking branches; (5) the hardness and texture of the wood; (6) the surface structure of the bark; (7) the epiphytic growths on the living bark. The animal life found on each species of tree will be decided by all these, by the reservoirs of species in the neighbourhood – especially required to replenish the populations after severe local disasters – and indirectly also by the pattern of interspersion itself. On this particular area there is no single dominant species of tree such as can be found in many woods. This means that the individual tree canopies mostly form partly separate 'uni-

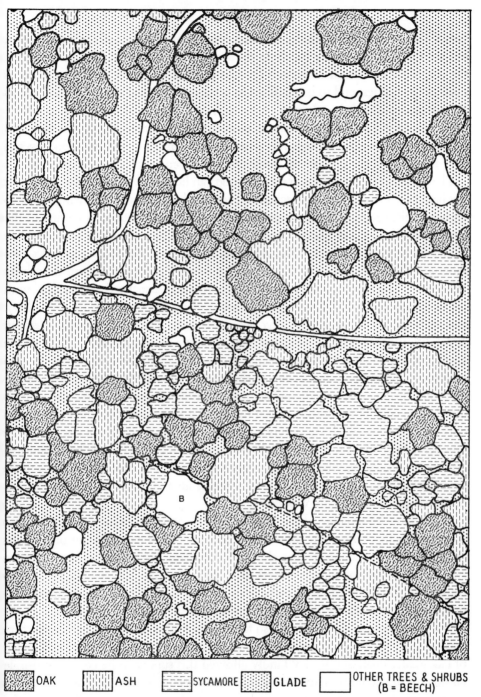

OAK   ASH   SYCAMORE   GLADE   OTHER TREES & SHRUBS
(B = BEECH)

FIG. 20. Pattern of canopy and spaces between trees in an oak–ash–sycamore wood at Wytham, derived from Plate 9. The lower section has denser tree canopy than the upper, which has large glade spaces of bracken and bramble. (Map by C. A. Elbourn, drawn by A. J. Dunford)

195

verses' that have only intermittent faunal contacts with others of the same species, but are touching or nearly touching those of different species. This is, of course, the commonest form of dispersion for herbivorous species in nature, in so far as most of the species tend to be confined to certain plants, and most species of plants are not dominants. It is only in a pure stand, or where the dominant species has a network of touching canopy, that the populations of animals have a complete and continuous dispersion, though the actual degree of individual isolation depends very much upon the power and frequency of movements leading to dispersal.

The pattern of interactions in such a wood can best be approached by starting at the base of the food-chains attached to each kind of tree and following them to higher levels, keeping attention on the tree mosaic at each stage. A picture of the herbivorous mites and insects exploiting these different trees can be pieced together from several sources. The *Biological Flora of the British Isles* includes two monographs on the oaks and the maples by Jones, [252, 250] and one on the ash by Wardle.[537] The first two have lists of the herbivores associated respectively with the two species of oak, *Quercus robur* (= *pedunculata*) and *Q. petraea* (= *sessiliflora*), and with the common maple, *Acer campestre*, and sycamore, *A. pseudo-platanus*. A definition of 'association' is rather hard to arrive at, but the lists include all the known invertebrate herbivores specific to the tree, or to the genus – for the two oaks were lumped together owing to the scarcity of reliable plant records for the mites and insects concerned, and because in authenticated instances the animals usually live equally on both oaks. Of the latter it was stated that the list 'includes only those species which are closely associated with *Quercus* and not the very large number which feed on it occasionally; many general feeders have been omitted, even though they may be very abundant on *Quercus*'. A similar remark is made about animals on the maples. There is however an additional list of polyphagous moths on oak in Wytham Woods.

So we have knowledge of the central core of specialists living upon oak – that is the species that contribute most to the primary faunal pattern – but only an incomplete idea of the insects that also feed elsewhere. Besides these lists, there are two main sources for canopy insects used here. The first is G. C. Varley's long-continued field study (done in collaboration with G. R. Gradwell) of the population dynamics of oak moths and their insect parasites in Wytham Woods. In the course of this work, which has not so far been published fully, a general collection was made by several different methods of the insects in this particular small patch of oak glade. Professor Varley kindly allowed this survey to be copied in simple fashion for the Ecological Survey index at the Bureau of Animal Population, where it has been of great value, the detailed records and a magnificent collection of the insects themselves being kept in the Hope Department of Entomology at Oxford. It is worth mentioning that the total number of species found by collecting in this small area for over 12 years is nearly 1000, though not all of them belong to the habitats there. For sycamore, I have relied upon some general field surveys done by students under my supervision and with much valuable help from Dr B. M. Hobby, in Bagley Wood, Berkshire, in the years 1941-5, and at Wytham Woods in 1946-8, together with a special survey of my own at Wytham in 1948 and some other observations at different times. The work of Dixon adds to the ecology of sycamore aphids in Wytham Woods and elsewhere. For the ash there are no full surveys, though I have done some reconnaissance at Wytham, mainly with student classes; and some rather interesting indirect conclusions about the status of its fauna can be drawn from the Edward Grey Institute of Field Ornithology's studies of the feeding habits of birds in the same wood. It will be realized that whereas the *Biological Flora* provides a consolidated list of herbivores for the whole country, the other evidence is from small areas of woodland in one district; but as I have already pointed out (Ch. 3) the fraction of a national fauna that may turn up in one quite small area is surprisingly high.

The *Biological Flora* gives the names of 227 species specially associated with *oak*, but not all confined to it. 50 of these are makers or subsidiary eaters of galls, and these will be considered further on. Another 12 live on bark or acorns, leaving 165 species dependent upon the leaves and twigs. In addition are the 31 polyphagous moths. There are other polyphagous insects and some of them can be abundant. More than half the 165 species mentioned occur in Wytham Woods. The list for the whole country, in more detail, contains 6 species of mites (5 of which are also partly predatory); 5 Thysanoptera (thrips); 19 Hemiptera Heteroptera (bugs, of which 11 are also partly predatory) and 22 Hemiptera Homoptera (including leaf-hoppers, aphids and coccids); 83 Lepidoptera (one butterfly and the rest moths of which one at any rate has a partly predatory caterpillar); 10 Diptera, gall-midges of the family Cecidomyiidae, included here because their galls are small and simple – there are some others in the galls of Cynipidae; 13 Hymenoptera Symphyta (sawflies); and 7 Coleoptera (beetles). This huge assemblage of species, together with the 50 gall forms, the general feeders not included here, the insect parasites many of which are specific or nearly so to their hosts, the predatory insects and spiders and harvestmen, the birds and squirrels, fully bear out Connold's remark[80] that 'the British oak is the abode of a vast concourse of dependents'. And this does not count the species on branch and trunk, or living semi-detached in rotting wood, fungi or nests. There is no really clear explanation as to why the oak besides being a successful tree carries such a rich fauna. Although it is historically one of the chief dominants of the climatic zone we live in, so also is the beech which has a conspicuously poor variety of fauna. There is even a further paradox in the fact that the oak leaves that fall in autumn are for many months one of the forms of litter least consumed by animals, while the ash, a soft-leaved species with a poorer fauna on its living canopy, is quickly attacked. This toughening of the oak leaves starts while they are still on the tree, so that the leaf insects (other than galls) become much less numerous towards the autumn. Probably the singularly tough, steady, enduring and rigid branching of the oak and the varied surface structure of its bark play some part in encouraging animals on it, but the reasons are probably deep historical ones.[466] Whatever the explanation, the oaks carry by a long way the richest mixture of animal life of any native tree, and of any native plant.

Moths, which form half the restricted herbivore species on oak, also dominate in the power of their numbers and size. Rather paradoxically, the oak is the only British tree to be frequently and sometimes entirely defoliated by outbreaks of moths of several kinds. The green oak moth, *Tortrix viridana*, confined to the oak canopy in early life, but able to feed on other trees later on,[240] and the winter moth *Operophtera brumata*, a more general feeder that pupates in the ground, are the chief performers in Wytham Woods, where together they are more abundant than the hundred or so other oak-eating species there.[519] They often break out elsewhere in the country. Several other species may also be abundant, including the mottled umber, *Erannis defoliaria*, the spring usher, *E. leucophaearia*, and *Eucosma isertana*.[519, 252] Although the oak counters such disasters by producing a second crop of leaves, these are often badly attacked by the oak mildew, *Microsphaera alphitoides* (an invader probably from North America early in this century), which can even lead to the death of trees. And in so far as the caterpillars destroy flowers as well as leaves, the acorn crop is reduced.[252] Varley and Gradwell[52] measured the increment of trunk wood on the oaks they were studying at Wytham, and found that although the early spring growth (dependent on nutriment stored in the previous year and taking place before the full impact of the caterpillars) was not affected by heavy moth populations, defoliation could cut down the summer growth to two-fifths of the normal amount. The most striking further result of defoliation is that the second crop of leaves appearing by July denuded of insect life often to an extraordinary extent, and there is a noticeable absence of predatory insects and spiders as well as of herbivores in the height of summer. Such influence by one or two species of moths upon the whole community is as drastic as anything that the rabbit does to a grassland or sand-dune. And yet these disasters are not necessarily universal in an oak wood, because certain individual trees are regularly resistant to oak moths, as has been found both at Wytham,[520] and in the Nature Conservancy's reserve at Roudsea Wood in north Lancashire.[426] The general opinion now seems to be that this comparative immunity is connected with the date of bud-opening in the spring, the worst attack occurring when the first young caterpillars hatch just as the buds are beginning to break open, earlier flushing of foliage giving to leaves a good start and later flushing succeeding because the young caterpillars tend to die if the buds are still closed and they cannot get into them. Whatever the details of these processes, whose exact relation to the weather is still not understood, these variations in susceptibility to defoliation influence the pattern of canopy in many ways. To begin with, the resistant trees provide reservoirs not only of healthier trees (with all that implies about growth, acorn production and survival of living branches instead of the production of many dead stag-horns), but also of the rich fauna on them, also no doubt a series of chain effects on the lower vegetation pattern of litter, and the ground and soil fauna that have not as yet been measured. Since the differences between individual trees are maintained from year to year and are probably genetic, there will be in any wood a pattern set for some time at least, that is a pattern within the oak population itself.

As several more references will be made to Varley and Gradwell's oak study at Wytham, a note is needed about the habitat. The patch of twenty-one small oak trees, mostly about sixty feet high, grows on heavy Oxford Clay and the trees are not at all large specimens as oaks go. They are scattered in a glade though some of them touch one another. Originally there was heavy scrub below, but this was cleared for research reasons and the ground is now mostly occupied by the tussock grass, *Deschampsia caespitosa*, that often enters woodland on this hill when it is thinned, or occupies the edges of glades. A map of this glade is given by Turnbull[510] in his paper on the spiders of oak. It is surrounded by dense high scrub with scattered broad-leaved trees. Most of this oak moth research has been concerned with understanding the population dynamics and processes of natural control – especially by parasites and predators. Only short summaries of it have been published. The standard population sampling was done on five particular trees, by the following method of estimation. The larvae of the winter moth falling to the ground to pupate were collected in trays, their pupal parasites similarly counted by samples trapped while emerging from the ground, and the adult female moths (which are wingless) trapped on their way up the tree-trunks in early winter. From knowledge of the 'species spectrum' of caterpillars in the tree canopy itself, the total numbers of species other than the winter moth could also be calculated. This was necessary because the green tortrix especially pupates mainly in the canopy, although Satchell has noted that when a tree is severely defoliated some larvae also go down to pupate. By this means the average population density of mature caterpillars in a square metre column of canopy could be arrived at. Varley and Gradwell have published two examples of these results. The first [521] is from two trees over a period of eight years, the total numbers fluctuating between levels of 263–912 per m². on one tree and 204–1202 per m². on the other [18]. Some other figures[519] give the averages for all five trees together over the same period for the winter moth, the green tortrix and the spring usher, i.e. the greater part of the moth population there. These varied from 152 to 712, the highest number being in 1949 which was a defoliation year, the densities for two other defoliation years in 1952 and 1954 being 519 and 562. Betts[23] made some estimates by a different method for two years in a Forest of Dean oak forest in Gloucestershire which in neither year showed any visible signs of defoliation. She measured the number of faecal pellets of caterpillars falling to the ground over the month of maximum abundance, and calculated the number of caterpillars this represented from laboratory measurements showing that they produced on the average 2 pellets an hour. Her estimates for two years in two different woods were (converting from the numbers per acre) 309, 140, 232 and 86 per m². Satchell obtained a population count by injecting a systemic insecticide into the trunks of some trees in Roudsea Wood, collecting the dead caterpillars that fell, and completing the census by sampling the foliage. His column densities varied from 156 per m.² (in a year when there was no defoliation) to 944 per m.² (in a year when there was, though this was a resistant tree). The highest number on a defoliated tree was 679 per m.² These figures from Roudsea Wood are estimated from the total numbers per tree, and the approximate areas of canopy which Dr Satchell has kindly supplied. The metre column density must vary with the size of the trees. Both at Wytham and at Roudsea the oaks, which I have myself seen, are distinctly small ones and could in no sense be described as monarchs of the woods. The total numbers of caterpillars on the Roudsea Wood oaks varied from 7600 to 55,700 in a high-density year down to 2500 to 11,000 in the following low-density year.[427] All these figures are only cited here in order to give some idea of the extraordinary abundance reached by oak moths and to show that it only takes a doubling or trebling of ordinary numbers to produce defoliation, provided that the timing of larval development in spring is of a particular sort; and that there is a pattern of defoliation that varies from year to year and from tree to tree.

In most summers, if one turns over the leaves of a *sycamore* there will be found a great abundance of aphids feeding on the undersides, and when one beats the foliage into a tray a number of insect predators and spiders many of which are well-known aphid-eaters. This great abundance of aphids, of which the two chief species – both found in Wytham Woods – are *Drepanosiphum platanoides* and *Periphyllus testudinatus*, is the chief positive characteristic of the sycamore leaf fauna [19]. The highest adult population density of the former species counted by Dixon[97] through the summer at Glasgow and also at Rossdhu in Dumbartonshire was 48-9 per leaf. The average leaf area of sycamores in Bagley Wood sampled by Jones[250] was about 59 sq. cm. Thus each aphid would perhaps have about a square centimetre to live on. Dixon in fact noticed that these aphids live spaced out in what are really mobile territories, and in his experiments three-fifths of them were more than 5 mm. apart and none were closer together than 2·5 mm. He also ascertained that the mule is not the only animal to kick in defence of its needs: 'A feeding aphid begins to kick

as soon as another aphid approaches close to it. Kicking usually results in an avoid-
ance of feeding aphids by other individuals, or, more rarely, if the intruder persists, both aphids move away from each other.' Some other species of aphids also
kick ladybird larvae, with some success,[96] but the sycamore aphid only kicks its
fellows. These high densities, clearly representing the upper limits of accommo-
dation on a leaf, are only reached in some years at the height of the season. The
other thing one notices on sycamore foliage is often a fair number, but seldom a
huge number, of moth caterpillars of various kinds. The sycamore seldom suffers
severe defoliation, and when it does get somewhat tattered by caterpillar attack
this is usually in the same year that moths are defoliating the oaks. Sometimes one
will find a sycamore next to some defoliated oaks, with damage probably resulting
from the overspill of polyphagous moths on to it. There is no second crop of leaves
such as the oak is able to muster, so the sycamore is not well adapted to the hazards
of heavy moth attack.

The *Biological Flora* list of 'closely associated' herbivores contains 29 British
species for the sycamore canopy, 16 of which are attached also to the common
maple, while 3 live on a variety of trees including maple. One of the gall-midges
assigned to sycamore alone is now known to occur also on maple, and another
species is known to live on both.[20] This raises the figures given above to 30 and 18.
The remaining 9 species include 2 seed-eating moths, so that the sycamore foliage
may have only about 7 mites and insects peculiar to it in Britain. This is a very
small fauna. The status of the sycamore as an invader is discussed in Ch. 18, and
it only need be said now that it has been in Britain for several centuries at least, and
certainly in the south of England since the seventeenth century, and at Wytham
Woods since the first part of the nineteenth. In all these years it has evidently not
acquired more than a handful of specific herbivores, and much of its present fauna
must have been derived from the common maple, which itself is not very rich –
38 closely associated mites and insects. It may have brought a few species with it
when it was introduced, but more likely they have straggled across later, either as
floating aeroplankton or by human transportation. The sycamore list runs as
follows: 7 species of aphids, 4 other Hemiptera Homoptera, only 1 Heteropteran
(a very polyphagous bug), 7 moths, 4 gall-midges, 3 sawflies and 4 gall-mites. To
these must be added various other more polyphagous herbivores, mainly moths,
that have as yet been incompletely studied. The overwhelmingly important contribution of the sycamore to the forest canopy pattern, as far as foliage is concerned,
is the aphid-based section of the community.

In spite of being an old native tree, the *ash* has a rather thin fauna, as can be
ascertained by beating its foliage in the summer. There is none of the rich variety
of the oak, nor the aphid biomass of the sycamore. The *Biological Flora*[537] mentions
about 22 species of mites and insects associated with the foliage and twigs of ash.

There are 2 gall-mites; among Hemiptera a scale insect, a leaf-hopper and an aphid; 14 moths (including the winter moth); and 3 gall-midges. Not more than 8 of these are specific or even probably specific to the ash itself, and 12 of the moths are polyphagous. The ash bud moth, *Prays curtisellus*, though a killer of young shoots, does not attack trees above 15 feet high. Another moth, *Argyotyza conwayana*, develops in the ash keys, while one of the mites makes galls in the flowers. Although Wardle[537] says that 'caterpillars make considerable inroads into the leaf surface by the end of the summer', I think this happens mostly in saplings, and I have never seen a completely defoliated mature ash tree, nor is such damage usually conspicuous; furthermore, the leaves that fall in autumn are usually whole. The extremely unstable and rather small leaflets of the ash – the poet Hopkins wrote of 'their fringe and fray of greenery' – are neither firm platforms for most invertebrates, nor easy for small birds to explore. The chief user of the ash canopy for food, the coal tit, *Parus ater*, is one of the best acrobats among titmice (see Ch. 11).

The *beech* is known for its heavy foliage and the toughness and persistence of its fallen leaves, so that in many beech woods this species is dominant or even the only kind of large tree, and the ground may be quite bare of any continuous cover of vegetation except in the glades. Where, as at Wytham, old planted beeches occur as individuals or groves among other trees, this contrast in the ground zone, field and scrub layers shows very strongly, and gives a special emphasis to the beech canopy. No concentrated survey of this community has been done in Britain, though the common canopy insects are well known. Therefore I shall describe instead a very good survey of virgin beech forest growing on Jurassic limestone and sandstone in the mountains of the Crimea done single-handed by a Russian ecologist Bukhovskii,[51] in the years 1929-34. This is not so remote and inapplicable to our own conditions as might appear, for the chief species of animals in this Crimean forest are also common in British beech woods, though no doubt they might differ in their genetic constitution. The Crimean beech belongs to the form or species *Fagus orientalis*, which is closely related to our own *Fagus sylvatica*,[50] or to a mixture of the two [20]. Also this survey illuminates the numerical relations of the canopy fauna as a whole.

In the Crimea the beeches grow in a zone of mountains between about 1500 and 4000 feet, where the climate is damper than in the oak and other forests lower down. Bukhovskii begins his monograph with a quotation from a Russian writer, Sedlachek: 'Seen from the side, a dense, dark mass; seen from above a dark green sea with still waves, and from within regular arches on strong grey supporting pillars: such is the beech forest in summer time. A picture of silence, stillness. . . .' It is almost pure beech, with no layer of scrub, and otherwise only a local field layer of coral-wort (*Dentaria quinquefolia*) and sedge (*Carex digitata*) except in the higher hills where the poorer tree-growth permits some dog's mercury (*Mercurialis perennis*), wood-spurge (*Euphorbia amygdaloides*), woodruff (*Asperula odorata*), and a grass (*Poa nemoralis*). While the last four are common in some British beech woods or their glades,[493] the *Dentaria* is not British, and the *Carex* rare with us. These forests appear to be truly virgin, there being no trace of man's activities except for the removal of a certain amount of naturally fallen timber in some parts of what is now a reserve. The ecosystem therefore consists of a truly natural pure stand of beech, with no scrub, little field layer or ground vegetation, otherwise only leaf litter, rotting wood, fungi and soil. The canopy was explored from the ground, where branches came within reach, and we have to assume that any differences at higher levels were not such as to alter the main picture that was obtained. The sample unit was about 100 leaves, and he worked in 29 different localities. To understand the moth population, caterpillars were also bred through to adults. The following community of at least 180 and probably over 200 species of invertebrates was found: 19 species of moths, at least 22 beetles, 1 snake-fly (*Raphidia*), 5 lacewings, at least 29 flies, 1 bee, 1 sawfly, over 52 parasitic Hymenoptera, at least 20 Hemiptera, 3 Psocids, a grasshopper and a cockroach, 2 springtails (Collembola), 20 spiders, also unnamed Opilionids and mites. Four of these species really belonged to the bark, and there were in addition many thrips that were attracted to the flowers.

In order to bring out the nature of the main machinery in this assemblage, Bukhovskii devised an arbitrary method that excluded all species not present in 15% of the samples (at the period of their peak seasonal development and occurring over at least a month) or forming at least 0·5% of the total population in them. The survivors of this strict examination for 'importance' were as follows: a small leaf-mining moth, *Lithocolletis faginella*; the leaf-mining weevil, *Orchestes* (now *Rhynchaenus*) *fagi*; a parasitic ichneumonid, *Stenomacrus fortipes*, whose host was not determined but may have been a fungus fly; a leaf aphid, *Phyllaphis fagi*; a leaf-hopper bug, *Typhlocyba rosae*; another bug, *Psallus varians*; and three predators – the bug *Anthocoris nemoralis*, and two spiders *Phyllodromus aureolus* and *Theridion pallens*. Several groups of animals (thrips, mites, some parasitic Hymenoptera, Opilionids) were not named to species and may have included one or two other important ones. The beech winter moth, *Operophtera fagata*, though not in the top rank individual numbers, was the most abundant moth, forming about three-quarters of the caterpillars. All moths together destroyed on average not more than 5% of the foliage, though there were some local patches where half of it was eaten. The leaf-mining weevil on the average never destroyed more than 6·5% of the leaf surface. The greater size of caterpillars made them important in their effects; but Bukhovskii never saw any important defoliation in these woods. Here is an ancient and relatively simple ecosystem whose canopy is dominated by only a few species of leaf-feeders, and which remained (over these years of the investigation) mainly in a state of balance, with the herbivores taking only a small fraction of the leaf substance. The other aspects of these forests were not fully explored and Bukhovskii remarks: 'The real state of affairs is much more complex, and individual food chains interconnect. For example *Raphidia* in the adult form preys on aphids etc., upon beech leaves, while its larvae prey on the larvae of bark-beetles under the bark; insectivorous birds can hunt both on the foliage and on the surface of the ground or in the air, and feed both on plant-eating and predatory insects; *Orchestes fagi* and the pupae of Geometridae during their sojourn in the litter may provide food for the predators living there; the roe-deer feeds both on beech twigs and on herbage.'

Most, perhaps all, of the important species mentioned above are actually found in Wytham Woods. I have never there or elsewhere in Britain seen a mature beech tree defoliated or even severely damaged by insects, though of course the actual effects of sap-sucking species like the leaf aphid cannot so easily be allowed for. One does, however, sometimes see partial defoliation in younger pure plantations of beech in this country. But the beech canopy community is evidently a very old-established, widespread and on the whole stable affair.

This basic pattern of herbivorous insects living on oak, sycamore, ash and beech is of two kinds: species confined to one kind of tree, giving a more scattered distribution, and others of wider food-habits covering more, but very seldom all of the canopy. In so far as the polyphagous range is not the same in different insects, there is to some extent a chain-mail type of pattern as between different species. There are a few insects that come on a number of trees, one of which seems to be the pale green long-horned grasshopper, *Meconema thalassina*. In Wytham Woods it has been found in the canopy of oak, sycamore and ash. Lucas mentions also lime (*Tilia*)[302] and maple,[303] and I have found it elsewhere on hornbeam (*Carpinus betulus*). It also lives on beech at Wytham, for one may see these grasshoppers in the autumn climbing up the trunks at dusk or after dark, just as they have also appeared in night traps set on oak trunks in Varley's investigations. Evidently these grasshoppers fall from the canopy and return to it by the trunk route at night.

The multiplication of billions of sap-sucking insects in the tree canopy not only sets the stage for the numerous food-links to their enemies and parasites, but also gives rise to a massive side-chain through the production of the waste product called *honeydew*. This substance has been known since antiquity as a source of food for bees, though Aristotle and Virgil, for example, believed that it fell from the skies,[415] and it was not until the eighteenth century that its production by insects was recognized by anyone, just as it was not proved until the present century that the manna eaten by the Israelites in the Sinai Desert consisted of crystallized sugar drops derived from two species of coccids living on tamarisk shrubs.[562] Aphids and (more especially on conifers) coccids are the chief sources. A few other Hemiptera also supply it sometimes in quantity, for instance Psyllids on the elm. This stuff, containing almost entirely a mixture of various sugars, is only a slight modification of the plant sap. It is to be supposed that this enormous surplus excretion is caused by the filtering out of other scarcer food substances such as those containing nitrogen. There is a broad similarity in the composition of honeydew from different insects and different host trees, in spite of some variations in detail, such as the higher amount of dextrin in honeydew from limes. In his experiments on insect longevity and fecundity Zoebelein[562] found that 'honeydew from different species of insects has different food value. Saccharose, glucose and fructose were found to be the most valuable constituents of honeydew for insects. Melezitose has a harmful effect.'

Honeydew is exploited by a very large mixed population of insect visitors, and is taken in two different ways. Ants collect it directly by tending the aphids or coccids, which they often protect. I have seen birch trees entirely bare of all invertebrate life except the wood-ant (*Formica rufa*) and its aphid flocks, over which the same ants stand sentry while the rest go back and forth to the nest.[125] This situation seems to be commoner in European woods than in our own, because in Britain the most important group of ants involved, the large wood-ants, has rather local distribution. But there is a profound difference between woods under 'ant management', and those like Wytham Woods that have no wood-ants. There almost the only ant commonly climbing trees to collect honeydew is the small *Lasius niger*, and this on no large scale. In a small open mixed wood in the New Forest in which I studied the territorial and feeding patterns of *Formica rufa*, the source of food varied with the position of each nest territory. Between them the different aphid resources were tapped on birches (the chief ones), oak (probably from aphids living on the bark), pine, hawthorn, broom (*Cytisus scoparius*) and gorse (*Ulex europaeus*). Zoebelein[562] in Bavaria estimated that wood-ants were collecting in a year approximately the following dry weight equivalents of sugar on an average individual tree by tapping aphids: 14 kg. from pine, 6 kg. from spruce, and 5-6 kg. from beech. The original honeydew would be about five times these weights.

The other and in Britain much more widespread and important channel for collection of honeydew is by a great range of insects from the foliage on to which it falls. At first it contains about four-fifths of water, but later evaporates and may end as crystallized sugar. In the sticky or gummy stage it often becomes infected with sooty mould fungi (Capnodiaceae)[21] that turn it dark – the blackened upper surfaces of birch or lime leaves in later summer are a not unfamiliar sight. It is not unlikely, I think, that the great variety and amount of leaf fungi on sycamore leaves may be aided initially by the presence of honeydew from aphids. The chief

source of information on insects taking honeydew is Zoebelein's German monograph,[562] which concerns various conifers, also oak, sycamore, maple, beech and
other broad-leaved species, but does not mention ash (though our ash insects may
produce it in quantity in certain years.[238] He found members of about fifty different families of insects visiting the foliage for honeydew. Perhaps the most extensive use of it was made by a good many parasitic Hymenoptera, among beetle
by the Cantharidae, among flies by the Syrphidae, parasitic Tachinidae and th-
Bibionidae. The last group, especially two common species *Dilophus febrilis* an-
Bibio marci, which breed in the ground, were the target for a predatory dung-fl-
Scopeuma (Scatophaga) stercoraria, which breeds commonly in cow dung. Zoebelei-
did some laboratory tests of the longevity of several parasitic Hymenoptera an-
Diptera which showed that they lived two or three times longer if fed on honey
dew than without any food; also that the reproductive rate could be increased. O-
sycamores one may see a hover-fly such as *Syrphus ribesii* feeding on honeydew o-
the upper side of one leaf, while its larvae may be eating aphids on the undersid-
of another.

   The whole complex subject of honeydew-feeders is mentioned here because th-
widespread production of a roughly similar food substance in the mixed foliage c-
a wood attracts populations of visitors that are much more generally distribute-
than are the original producers on their separate species of trees. In this way th-
primary pattern is partly blurred. Many of these feeders are visitors from othe-
zones or from other major habitats, and I think that a large number of the apparently stray insects one may see sitting on foliage have in fact come in search c-
honeydew. The subject joins on closely to the question of flower-visiting discusse-
in Ch. 13. Honey and honeydew are both solutions of sugars. Whereas the necta-
flow from most flowers is dependent on the time of day (being usually lower earl-
in the morning) and the season's weather, the supplies of honeydew, at any ra-
as they are accumulated on the leaves, are available all round the clock – so long -
the populations of insects themselves are there to produce it, for in certain yea-
there may be great scarcity of aphids on particular species of trees. Hive-bees wi-
turn to honeydew at times of day or in seasons when nectar is scarce, with resul-
that may sometimes but not always be bad for the taste of the honey, and may eve-
harm the bees themselves.

   The predominant canopy pattern is set by the leaf and twig fauna, but is vari-
gated by the other features mentioned earlier on with which I shall only de-
rather briefly. As to the *flowers*, most dominant tree species in woodland are win-
pollinated, and animals only come into connection with them in a few ways. The-
can be a source of food, as when caterpillars destroy them on the oak and affe-
the production of seed. Some bees visit such flowers for pollen. The hive-bee visi-
oak, ash and beech flowers (also those of birches and elms) though this is a ve-

unimportant part of their supply.[238] Wild bees also collect the pollen from ane-mophilous trees. Chambers[65] analysed the composition of pollen loads carried by *Andrena* in Bedfordshire. Oak pollen occurred in small amounts on *Andrena haem-orrhoea*, and beech pollen on this species (once abundantly) and on *A. armata*. The sycamore and common maple are in quite a different class, since a good many insects visit their flowers for nectar (see Ch. 13). The former is given as one of the thirteen major sources of nectar for hive-bees, and the maple would perhaps be as good if it was a commoner tree.[238] The *Biological Flora* records twenty-three dif-ferent kinds of insects – bees, flies and beetles (most of which occur in Wytham Woods), visiting sycamore flowers, and this list is not a complete one. The only other trees visited on any large scale for nectar are the lime and fruit trees. One other aspect of flowering in the sycamore is just worth mention, although the full facts about it are by no means certain. I have a little evidence suggesting that the flowers may be necessary as a habitat-stage in the life history of aphids. On the edge of a large grove of coppiced sycamores in Wytham Woods young aphids were abundant on the closed or just opening leaf buds in late March and early April 1948. There was a long spring drought that year which delayed leafing and apparently caused an almost complete failure of sycamore flowering. By 23 April aphids (including winged forms) were very abundant on the unopened leaf buds and also on the flowers which were confined to one or two small trees only. By 11 May most of the leaves had no aphids, which had disappeared quite remarkably. The only tree with any number left was one that had flowered, while one other with no flowers had kept or acquired a few. Aphids remained very scarce during the summer, as also all their predators. I then remembered having noticed that on a sycamore in my garden in Oxford (in another year) the young aphids hatching were first seen on the leaf buds, then moved on to the flowers, subsequently reappearing on the expanded leaves. I do not know which species were involved.

Fruiting of these four kinds of tree adds to the patterning in three ways. First of all, there are a few specialized insects that breed and develop in them, specific or nearly so to each kind of tree. More important is the great influence on the ground pattern below. Beech mast and acorns are a major supply of winter food for certain birds and mammals, and these animals have various preferences between the mast, acorns, and the samarae of sycamore and ash. The actual correlation between the pattern of fruit on the ground and the canopy above must be greater for heavy fruits like the acorn and beech mast, than for the helicopter-like ones of sycamore, maple and ash that may float some distance sideways. Thirdly, the enormous fluc-tuations in tree crops from year to year, with the law that normally a good year is followed by a bad year, and the fact that although there may sometimes be good or bad crops on all three species in the same year they are generally quite or partly independent, brings in complex considerations of alternate food supplies and therefore some temporary differences in the local concentrations of the birds and mammals interested in these foods.

I have already discussed the difference in scale of *branching* between shrubs and trees and its importance for birds. The less marked but still important ones between different trees have not been analysed though some of them must certainly affect the nesting of birds, and others the cover texture in relation to escape from enemies. The *texture of the wood* comes in mostly as part of the story of dying and rotting wood communities (Ch. 14). There are certainly considerable differences in hardness, texture, speed of rotting, kind of rotting, and these in turn affect the fauna, including hole-nesting birds, and also the development of bracket fungi and their animal communities (Ch. 15). Again the *bark* has most important structural differences, not only on different kinds of tree but in the same species of tree at different ages, in so far as most of them start with smooth bark, which some keep while others develop a very rough surface in middle or later life. The common maple is exceptional in sometimes having extraordinarily strong ridges on quite young stems. Of the four species discussed here, the beech remains smooth, the oaks (and especially *Quercus robur*) develop deep networks of ridge and hollow, the ash does the same but with less depth and variety of structure, while the sycamore only develops large shallow scales at maturity. The four species can therefore be ranked from smooth to rough in this order: beech, sycamore, ash, oak. The primary structure itself provides differing degrees and kinds of shelter in which insects, spiders and other small animals can hide themselves, their resting stages and their eggs.

The *epiphytic growth* on trunks and branches of trees is considerably affected by the nature of the bark surface, but this is only one of a great many features that bring about variety and sometimes clear zonation in the cryptogamic covering. It is strongly influenced by the degree of forest cover, the height within the microclimatic gradient from ground to canopy, the angle at which trunk or branch rest (Plate 27), the climatic zone, and also by proximity to town smoke and other toxic effluents into the air. The fascinating monograph by Barkman,[19] based chiefly upon the Netherlands, describes exhaustively so many aspects of epiphytic growth that are or might be vital to animals, that it is not possible here to summarize the subject without making it appear too simple. And for most species of animals dependent upon this habitat on trees we know rather little about their exact needs and even less about their vertical and small-scale distribution on the tree. A good many years ago Olsen[361] recorded the associations of mosses on the lower trunks of Danish trees, and found a broad succession with age. Very young trees have no moss at all. As soon as minute cracks develop in the bark, which is still macroscopically 'smooth', a pioneer community of acrocarpous mosses such as *Ulota* develops, and is replaced later on by the pleurocarpous species such as *Hypnum cupressiforme*. The former are able to withstand more drought than the latter, which appear earlier on trees such as oak that grow rough bark fairly soon. The vertical zonation on mature trees reflects part of the same situation, in so far as mosses like *Ulota* tend to occupy the more exposed zone of the upper canopy.

Lichens have very complex micro-distribution, partly vertical, partly by aspect, or often inversely to the moss covering – i.e. on the drier side of the trunk. Algae, of which *Pleurococcus viridis* is the most important, form extensive thin coverings that are able to withstand all but the most sooty conditions of towns, where lichens (except a few like *Lecanora conizaeoides*[264]) are absent. This alga is grazed by a variety of animals, including woodlice, millipedes, some molluscs, a few caterpillars, and a good many Psocids. Since it forms the algal portion of many lichens as well, there is a delicate balance between the two types of epiphyte. Both lichens and mosses are also the food of some invertebrates, and the former also provide the background against which a good many moths are able to camouflage themselves while at rest. Generally speaking epiphytic growths of all kinds are better developed on broad-leaved than on coniferous trees, *Pleurococcus* for example seldom colonizing conifers. According to Barkman, conifers and also birches have a strongly acid bark that is inimical to algae. But in a general way, the distribution of algae, lichens and bryophytes is less dependent upon particular plant associations, or even particular species of trees, than upon the structural conditions and the impact of climatic factors operating through these. Phillips,[384] in a study of the bark-living bryophytes of Michigan, has proved that they may occur on all species of tree in an association, except when the conditions are dry, when they may be more selective; that many species are more widely distributed in the world than the trees they may live on locally; and that a good many tree-living species also live on rocks. The epiphytic growth adds to the colour of the general landscape a great deal more variety and beauty than is usually realized, and it is most conspicuous in winter, particularly in a damp winter. The exploration of its significance to canopy animals still awaits a new wave of ecologists who have the urge to climb and explore in the forest above.

CHAPTER 11

Hunters in the Forest Canopy

THE RICH leaf-eating populations of the forest canopy support an even richer assemblage of active parasites and predators, whose influence on the level of their numbers has attracted much discussion and some serious field study, but whose exact role is still by no means understood. I shall not enter into all these questions, but only try to describe some of the situations that illustrate the ideas in this book: especially the oak galls and their small special communities, the insect and spider enemies of aphids, and the titmice and some other small insectivorous birds, about all of which there is valuable information from Wytham Woods. The leafy universe in which these animals spend much or all of their lives in summer is really a rather peculiar arrangement of cover. Although some of the insects (including leaf-miners and gall-formers) manage to dwell inside the plant tissue, most of them (such as larger caterpillars, Heteroptera, leaf-hoppers and aphids) are fully exposed on the leaves, though almost always on the undersides, a situation which presents little protection from hunting insects and spiders but perhaps a slight obstacle to small birds. The real protective system, apart from any camouflage that may deceive birds, seems simply to be the enormous number of leaves on a tree and the time and energy required to search among them separately. Professor J. D. Ovington has kindly provided me with an abstract of some estimates by Burger, of the number of leaves on representative oak[53] and beech[52, 54] trees in Switzerland. An oak with a trunk diameter of 10 cm. (at breast height) would have about 12,000 leaves; the largest tree, of 60 cm. diameter, about 100,000. The total surface area of the undersides of these leaves would be about 18·5 m.[2] for the smaller tree and 500 m.[2] for the large one. Similar figures for beech ranged from 4400 leaves on a 4-cm. diameter tree, up to 16,000 at 10 cm. 100,000 at 40 cm. and 360,000 at 60 cm. The corresponding total areas of the undersides of the beech leaves would be 9·5, 24, 245 and 700 m.[2] Considering that one oak leaf looks very like another and that some instability through wind is common, the foliage is a more effective cover than one might at first suppose.

By contrast with this horde of exposed insects are those whose early stages live inside galls produced by the chemical action of the larvae upon the plant tissue

For the present purpose the usually very small swellings made by gall-midges (Cecidomyiidae) and Eriophyid mites will be left out of account, since they do not house anything complex enough to rank as a community; but many of the larger structures induced by the larvae of gall-wasps (Cynipoidea) attract a good many competitors and parasites and add to the already great variety of habitat structure in the canopy. They form a micro-scenery on the oaks, and just as the oak fauna is partly shared by other interspersed kinds of trees and shrubs, the different gall communities often share some of the same species. These gall-wasps are preponderantly oak inhabitants – it has been estimated that 86% of the species in the world are on oaks, half the rest being attached to roses and the others divided among various other plants.[243a] The oak-gall communities (so far as gall-makers, strict inquilines, and parasites are concerned) are almost completely distinct from those in the large red gall of the rose, known as the bedeguar or robin's pin-cushion. There are in Britain over a hundred regular members of these gall communities on oaks, of which eighty-eight species have been recorded in Wytham Woods, where Askew[13] has carried out an extensive survey of the subject and constructed food-chains for each of the forty-five different kinds of gall. Besides these ordinary members there is a fair number of more casual visitors or inhabitants. The larger hard galls, like the marble gall made by *Andricus kollari* which persists after the inhabitants have left, offer refuges for various insects, for example Blair[27] found larvae of a lacewing, *Sympherobius elegans*, completing their development there, and a Sphecid wasp, *Rhopalum clavipes*, using them as nests and larders stocked with Psocids and aphids as food for the young.

A special feature of oak gall-wasps is that many of the species have alternate generations whose galls are different in structure and position and in the season of emergence. The figure of forty-five given above treats each form as a separate ecological entity, the actual number of species concerned being about two-thirds of this. Some of these complex life-histories show an alternation between old and young growth of oak. Thus, *Andricus solitarius, A. fecundator* and *A. callidoma* alternate between the flower catkins of mature oaks, and the terminal or axillary buds on twigs, the latter often being on low bush growth although also on the canopy of mature trees. In his classical monograph on oak galls (1908) Connold[80] says: 'When searching for oak galls the peculiarities of the alternation of the generations should not be forgotten, and therefore districts should be sought, and frequently visited, where the woods contain plenty of oak saplings of from three to eight years' growth, with a number of large trees there as well, or near by. ...' He also suggests searching amongst oak scrub, or in stunted growth in hedges or roadside banks. But in modern times most oak woods have ceased to produce any quantity of naturally regenerated young trees, and it is therefore only by the activities of forest planting, and by repeated coppicing or hedge-cutting that such scrub oak is perpetuated. With the diminution of rabbits since 1954, there ma[y] perhaps be a return to more natural processes. But it would seem likely that th[e] life-histories of some gall-wasps originally depended partly on the natural juxta[-] position of glade and wood, and have been assisted in modern times by the activ[-] ities of man.

Oak galls are physically very small structures, more than half the British specie[s] having a maximum diameter of under 1 cm., the largest native species livin[g] on foliage being 3-4 cm., while the introduced marble gall of *Andricus kolla[ri]* grows up to 6·5 cm. But some of the smaller ones, such as the spangle galls o[n] leaves, may be individually so numerous as to provide a very large total amoun[t] of habitat. For example the usual numbers of the common spangle gall, *Neuroter[us quercus-baccarum* forma *lenticularis*, were said by Connold to be 80-100 per lea[f] a density sometimes much exceeded. Therefore one must think of 'population[s] of habitats', in which, according to the species or alternate form of the specie[s] the number of inquiline and parasite species ranges from none to about twent[y] Three of the largest gall communities are in the marble gall, the oak-apple ga[ll] of *Biorhiza pallida*, and the red pea gall of *Cynips divisa*. The first two are larg[e] structures, the third only about 0·5 cm. across, but up to thirty-five on a leaf, an[d] according to Connold 'in some seasons they are in such profusion that their weigh[t] causes the leaves to hang down considerably'.

The remarks that follow about inquilines and parasites in oak galls are take[n] from the work of Askew[13] and will be further confined to his survey in Wytha[m] Woods, which has the advantage of giving a fairly complete story for the woo[d] on one hill [21], and also of using modern refinements in taxonomy. One of th[e] largest communities lives in the oak-apple galls formed on the end of twigs an[d] inhabited by the larvae of *Biorhiza pallida* (whose alternate generation, *B. palli[da* forma *aptera* lives just below the soil surface in root galls, from which the wingle[ss] females crawl up the trunks to the canopy in early winter). The larvae of [a] inquiline, *Synergus gallae-pomiformis*, which also feed on the gall tissue b[ut] without killing the *Biorhiza*, can also live in nine other kinds of oak gall belong[-] ing to four different genera of gall-makers. Two important Chalcid par[a] sites of *Biorhiza*, *Syntomaspis apicalis* and *Olynx skianeuros*, are specific to th[e] gall, as also are three others, *Hobbya stenonota* (a hyperparasite of *Torymus*) an[d] *Cecidostiba leucopeza* and *C. semifascia* (that attack *Olynx* and *Synergus*). But thr[ee] species of *Torymus* that attack gall-maker, inquiline and *Olynx* alike, are wide[ly] spread in other galls – *T. auratus* in 15 other kinds belonging to four gall-makin[g] genera, *T. cingulatus* and *T. nigricornis* each in 5 other kinds. 6 other Chalcid parasit[es] all live in a variety of galls ranging from 5 others in *Mesopolobus amaenus* and *[M.] xanthoceros* and *Megastigmus dorsalis*, to 9 and 10 others in *Mesopolobus jucund[us]* and *Eupelmus urozonus*, and as many as 17 others in *Eurytoma brunniventris*. So th[e] members of these minute communities only lead a sheltered life physically; they are subject to considerable attack which, from the confined space inside a gall, is often relatively indiscriminate. In this survey, every single kind of oak gall was found to have at least one inhabitant (inquiline or parasite) in common with at least one other kind of gall. Askew's summary of the known British host-galls of the Chalcid parasites, after omission of the 10 species not found at Wytham (9 of which are monospecific, and 1 bispecific), shows that 13 are specific to one gall host, 6 to 2-4 galls, 8 to 5-9 galls, 4 to 10-14 galls and two others to 16 and 19 galls. It is to this sort of relationship between centres of action within an ecosystem, or rather to 'populations' of them, that I shall apply the term 'girder system', a metaphor that contains both a fact and a hypothesis: the fact that there are strong biotic links between different gall communities, and the hypothesis that such links may give strength and stability to the whole interspersed population complex in galls. At present we only know that these biotic links exist, that mortality rates from parasites are often high, that many of the parasites are polyphagous, and that the whole gall system does remain within bounds.

There is one further aspect of Askew's conclusions that bears on the question of habitat structure. He has been able to show by many examples that taxonomic affinity of the gall-makers is less important in determining the particular assemblage of inquilines and parasites than three other things: (1) the form of the gall, especially its size, (2) the position of the gall on the tree and (3) the time of year that the gall and its gall-making larvae are present. One striking instance of the last factor is that there is not much resemblance between the communities in different generations of the same gall-making species, but often much sharing of species among galls of similar form and position growing at the same season.

Whereas the whole field of operations of these gall communities, other than dispersal from tree to tree, is confined to oaks or their younger stages, that of the ordinary insect and arachnid predators is much less restricted. Instead of being confined to one sort of tree like the gall insects and a great many other tree herbivores, they hunt over several or many or even all kinds of tree and shrub in a wood. And quite often they are found living also outside the wood, on scrub or other wild places, not to speak of orchards and gardens and arable fields. With this generous choice of habitat goes a great variety of prey, added to which some of the carnivorous adults take honeydew as well as animal food, though not many visit flowers for nectar. This wide range of habitats and of diet raises certain difficulties about interpreting the occurrence of adults on particular kinds of tree, for their general searching movements may result in greater accidental presence, while if not accidental they may sometimes be searching either for prey or for honeydew or for both. For example, there is not much information about the behaviour of Cantharid beetles such as *Cantharis nigricans*, commonly found visiting sycamore foliage in summer; though known to be partly carnivores [22] with soil-living larvae, there is good German evidence that they often feed on honeydew also.[562]

Out of the whole large assemblage of canopy predators I can only select a few for which the habitat pattern is better known. I shall first consider some lacewings of the genera *Hemerobius* and *Chrysopa*, for which especially good information exists in the monographs of Withycombe (1923)[553] and Killington (1936-7):[270] unless stated otherwise under place names, the following facts are derived from these. These two authors are unusual in recording some of the species of tree and also the major habitats frequented by the lacewings, although their information is not complete. Also such records are usually based not only on adults but on larvae, most of which can be named. Lacewings are predatory both as larvae and adults, the former sucking their prey, the latter biting them up. These preys are not dissimilar in type and always aphids greatly predominate, though other small insects such as Jassid and Psyllid bugs are also attacked. The adults fly at dusk or during the night and are attracted to lighted houses. Killington cites a list of seventeen species of lacewings caught by a light trap in Surrey, which includes all those now to be mentioned. In Wytham Woods there are three common species of *Hemerobius* in the deciduous woodland canopy: *H. humulinus, lutescens* and *micans*, small brown insects with wing-span of 1-2 cm., to be found from spring to autumn, but spending the winter in a larval cocoon near the ground. All three are the commonest *Hemerobius* in deciduous woodland, and they also live in hedge-rows. They practically never come into conifer woods, where there are six other species of *Hemerobius* that are not found in deciduous ones. They certainly breed and hunt on a variety of trees and shrubs. *H. humulinus* commonly breeds on oak and hazel, and has been seen eating two aphid species on hazel, as well as Psyllid nymphs. At Wytham Woods the adults have been found on oak and sycamore, also spindle and wayfaring tree; in Bagley Wood, a few miles away, on oak, sycamore and birch. It is common, as is the next species, in Essex orchards.[75] *H. lutescens* breeds commonly on oak, beech and hazel. Withycombe thought it more common on beech than *humuli*, and observed it eating beech aphids, *Phyllaphis fagi*, and young Psyllids; but remarked that 'other trees with other aphids are equally suitable' and that the larvae 'will accept any aphids as food'. The adults have occurred on ash and sycamore in Wytham Woods and on oak in Bagley Wood. *H. micans* breeds on oak, beech, hornbeam and hazel, also in hawthorn hedges. Withycombe found that the larvae would accept any small insects and mites offered to them, and he saw this species eating *Phyllaphis fagi*. In Wytham Woods the adults have been found on sycamore. All this makes it certain that their choice of major woody habitat, short of conifer woods, is wide; that oak, beech and sycamore, and perhaps ash as well, are inhabited by all three species, that they also come on under-scrub like hazel and on hedgerows; and that their diet is fairly indiscriminate. Much more study is needed to give this picture sharper focus – such as identification of larvae on trees like sycamore, maple, elm and so on.

The extremely beautiful green lacewings of the genus *Chrysopa* are ancient insects that still occupy a world-wide niche as carnivores, especially preying on aphids. The following seven species have been found in deciduous woods at Wytham: *carnea, albolineata, perla, ciliata, flavifrons, flava* and *vittata*. They are larger than the brown lacewings, the first five having wing-spans between 2 and 3 cm., the last two of 4 cm. All of them are known to be regular inhabitants of deciduous woodland, and all but *vittata* and *flavifrons* also live in hedges. *Chrysopa carnea, perla* and *flavifrons* inhabit conifer woods as well, the first only rather locally, the others generally; and *flavifrons* is commoner there than in deciduous woods, and has only once been certainly recorded in Wytham Woods, where there is little mature conifer. The details that follow are given in order to under-line the wide range of trees and shrubs occupied by green lacewings. *C. carnea* is much the commonest *Chrysopa* in Wytham Woods (as in Oxford gardens; also in Essex orchards[75]), adults having been taken on the canopy of oak, sycamore and ash, also on hazels growing in the open. It differs from the other species in hibernating as an adult (often temporarily turning pink while doing so). Killington found the larvae of *C. albolineata* on oak, elm, lime and hawthorn; and while we have no records of it from the canopy at Wytham, I have found adults on the trunks of large beeches infested with the bark-living coccid *Cryptococcus fagi*. Its larvae have occurred on sycamore canopy in Bagley Wood, near Oxford. In woodland *C. perla* is practically confined to the scrub layer on hazel, hawthorn and other species. Withycombe remarks that old oak and beech woods with little under-scrub seldom have it. It is common in pine woods. In Wytham Woods its habits are little known but my experience of its occurrence elsewhere confirms what is said above. The larvae of *C. ciliata* are reported from oak, beech, lime, hawthorn and hazel, and Withycombe observed them feeding on the beech leaf aphid, *Phyllaphis fagi*. In Wytham the adults have occurred occasionally on sycamore and maple. According to Killington, the large *C. flava* shows no pre-ference for particular trees or shrubs, and he found both larvae and adults on oak, beech, lime and hazel. Withycombe commonly saw it on oaks, where it was eating larvae of Jassid bugs and once ate a small beetle and once a spider. In captivity *flava* would eat almost any small insect except woolly aphids. The adults have turned up on sycamore at Wytham. Killington reports the larvae of *C. vittata* commonly on oak, lime and hazel, and at Wytham also the larvae have been taken on oak canopy.

The ladybirds (Coccinellidae) that hunt over tree foliage to feed on aphids are even less limited in their habitats than the lacewings. Their larvae also subsist on aphids. The following species are met with on deciduous tree canopy at Wytham: *Coccinella septempunctata, Adalia decempunctata, Halyzia sexdecimguttata, Calvia quatuordecimguttata,* and *Propylea quatuordecimpunctata.* The first two occurred also on the hawthorn hedge at Sheep Drove, not very near woods (see Ch. 9) and I mentioned *C. septempunctata* breeding in an oat field (see Ch. 7). Richards found both the first two in the canopy of pine woods on Oxshott Common, near London.[403] *C. septempunctata* is really famous for its tremendous geographical and habitat range in the Palaearctic Region,[34] and has also been studied quantitatively as a possible counterpest on crops. At Rothamsted in Hertfordshire, Banks[18] identified local concentrations overwintering on nettles, whence the beetles migrated in summer on to adjacent plots of beans; and he also discovered other wintering aggregations, for example in both short and long grass.[17] In Poland they have been observed wintering in a young mixed wood and moving out on to nearby potato fields in summer.[175] This species sometimes seems to collect in clusters of up to a hundred or so in the late summer, hibernating near the ground. Colquhoun[76] encountered large numbers in August on 4-ft-high spruce plantations in Norfolk, as well as in a lupin field. The beetles also hibernate singly, as is known from various records in Wytham Woods, where they have been found on a dead thistle in a woodland ride, in a pine seedling in a mixed glade, in woodland marsh litter, in logs and so on. All this means that *Coccinella septempunctata,* at one stage of its life or other, lives in all the four main terrestrial formation-types, and moves freely between them in the adult state, feeding in summer on many different kinds of aphid. Only a few remarks need be made about the last three species on the list of Wytham tree canopy ladybirds. These also have a wide habitat tolerance, extending to hedgerows,[168] and – in the case of *Propylea 14-punctata* at any rate – field types such as nettles and bean crops.[18] The vertical range is correspondingly great. I have found larvae and pupae of *Halyzia 16-guttata* on foliage of sycamore in deciduous woodland at Wytham; but it has also been found hibernating in old pine stumps on a Lancashire sand-dune.[535] Adult *Calvia 14-guttata* occur from the ground zone up into the canopy at Wytham, and have been taken there on oak, ash, hazel, wayfaring tree (*Viburnum lantana*) and sallow foliage; and on sycamore in Bagley Wood. *P. 14-punctata* has occurred at Wytham in beech litter, on the field-layer vegetation of oak–ash–sycamore woodland, and in its canopy. In fact, none of the canopy-haunting ladybirds are confined to that situation, and probably some of their populations would not be able to maintain themselves without being subsidized from other vertical zones or other formation-types.

Several more examples of the same kind of ecological distribution from other groups of animals that are common hunters in the canopy can be added. Of the very small speckled brown bug *Anthrocoris nemorum*, Butler[55] in his monograph of the Heteroptera remarks that 'this is unquestionably one of the commonest and most widely distributed Hemiptera we possess'. In summer deciduous woodland it probably comes mostly on the scrub and field layers. In Wytham Woods it certainly hunts in oak and sycamore canopy, and its young stages have been found on leaves of the latter. Butler noted that it can be found on a wide variety of trees and shrubs, and also cited a list of seventeen species of low plants on whose flowers it has been taken. These include bramble, thistles, primrose, white dead-nettle and even the salt-marsh *Aster tripolium*! Of trees visited by it, Hill[224] mentions oak, sycamore, ash, beech and birch among others, also such shrubs as hawthorn, hazel and broom. I have found it on flowers of the wild cherry and male sallow at Wytham, while Wilson[551] recorded it on apple, raspberry and currant flowers in Surrey. On the latter they were feeding on aphids, which are one of their staple foods. But Hill, in his survey of this species in Scotland, noted over forty kinds of prey, which included Collembola, aphids, Thysanoptera, mites, and less commonly other forms such as Typhlocybid bugs, the small lacewing *Conwentzia*, caterpillars, larvae and pupae of weevils, gall-midge larvae, small spiders, to name only some. They have been known also to suck plant juices, but this is not common. In addition to visiting different plants for food, *Anthocoris nemorum* lays its eggs just under the leaf epidermis of various species;[224] but there is not a list of the plants that it uses. In terms of formation-types, in summer it lives in deciduous woods, and has been found on young pines at Oxshott Heath feeding on aphids;[404] in hedgerows and scrub (thus it was common in the haw-thorn of Sheep Drove and comes on the wayfaring tree – see Ch. 9; also on broom);[423] and on nettle beds both in the open and near trees.[470] It is common in orchards,[75] occurs in hop gardens,[55] and I have even taken it on herbage by the edge of the Oxford Canal. A third aspect of its life is hibernation, which takes place chiefly in the adult state, the males mating with the females in autumn, but usually not surviving to the spring.[470, 224] Among the sites it is known to choose are under the bark of logs (e.g. taken by Professor M. Lloyd in some small beech logs in a beech wood at Wytham), under bark of trees (e.g. sycamore[7] and pine[55]) and shrubs, under stones and in leaf litter (e.g. of beech and of oak–ash–sycamore woods at Wytham). Altogether this species has a colossal penetration into the terrestrial and probably some other habitats, whether hunting for food, laying its eggs, or overwintering under shelter.

Two compact surveys that include *Anthocoris nemorum* further illustrate its large choice of habitats. Satchell and Southwood [428] collected Heteroptera in 31 woods in the Lake District, and caught this bug in 27 of them. The survey included larch, yew, pine, birch, oak and oak–ash woods, and the collecting was done in a standard manner at various levels accessible from the ground in each during the month of July. The remarkable thing was that *A. nemorum* formed nearly a third of the total number of specimens collected (4850, including a certain number from habitats outside woodland). It occurred on oak, ash, sycamore, birch hazel and sallow, once abundantly on wych elm (*Ulmus glabra*) and much less so on hawthorn, hazel and sallow. Beech did not come into the survey. Anderson's research[7] on all species of *Anthocoris* at Silwood Park, Berkshire, showed that the generation of *A. nemorum* that had overwintered went onto *Salix*, apple, hawthorn and broom, also nettle, because all these supplied aphid and Psyllid food before most trees had opened their buds. Thereafter, the summer generation was found on sycamore and lime, less abundantly on oak, ash, beech, elm and birch. Such spring to summer seasonal change adds another variant to the whole pattern of habitats this bug can exploit. Hill[224] had previously observed this spring camping on *Salix* in Scotland.

The hover-fly *Syrphus* (or *Syrphidis*) *ribesii*, as mentioned in Ch. 9, lives equally in deciduous and conifer woods. It is very common in Wytham Woods, certainly on oak and sycamore foliage, and larvae on the latter have been bred into adults for identification. It is of course the larvae that are predators on aphids, the adults hovering in the air among the canopy or in glades, eating honeydew on leaves, or visiting flowers (including those of the sycamore[250]). But this species lives in many other kinds of places as well. At Wytham it has been seen hovering four feet above the ground litter of a larch wood; also visiting teasel (*Dipsacus fullonum*) flowers in a limestone meadow, flowers of ivy on an old wall and ripe fruits of the wayfaring tree at the woodland edge. And within the woods it settles on field-layer herbs. At Wisley in Surrey Wilson[551] noted that it was a useful pollinator of hardy fruit, for example apples and raspberries, which it visited for nectar. On gooseberries it ate the pollen – some Syrphid flies triturating pollen and sucking it up. *Syrphus ribesii* and several other species have been studied in Germany by Schneider,[432] who proved that a pollen meal is indispensable for ripening of the ovaries, and that without it no eggs are laid. He noted this species breeding in diverse habitats: on woody plants (*Prunus, Euonymus*), crops (*Brassica*) and even on the reed (*Phragmites*). Within this galaxy of habitat components, we do not quite know what the exact distribution of the larvae is, though the flies certainly breed on deciduous and conifer trees. Similarly *Syrphus torvus* and *Episyrphus cinctellus*, whose adults frequent the same sycamores on which *S. ribesii* breeds at Wytham, are also recorded by Richards[403] in pine-tree canopy at Oxshott Heath.

The small spider *Theridion pallens*, the commonest species encountered by Turnbull[510] in his complete survey of the spiders in an oak glade at Wytham (and one of the common animals in the Crimean beech wood described in the previous chapter), is also abundant on sycamores there, and occurred on the pines of Oxshott

Heath.[403] It lives on the undersides of the sycamore leaves, and I have only once seen more than a single individual on the same leaf. There it makes a very recognizable tiny white egg cocoon with small projections on it and preys on the aphid, whose sucked corpses can be seen in the irregular strands of web crossing the leaf. Although relatively abundant as a spider, it is absolutely a scarce animal compared with the huge aphid populations. At the maximum abundance in August, Turnbull[508] estimated an approximate population density of 3·6-4·8 per square metre column of the whole habitat (that is, from ground up to top of canopy). The individuals were about equally distributed in the lower zones from ground to scrub canopy (for which he took a 25-ft limit), tailing off in the higher canopy. *T. pallens* also lives on scrub (as on wayfaring tree – see Ch. 9); it is common on fruit trees;[430] in gardens I have seen it on sycamore, horse-chestnut, oak and hazel. How far it lives on beech and ash in this country does not seem to be known, but it does occur on birch at Wytham, and I have seen it elsewhere on hornbeam (*Carpinus betulus*). The vertical range within a wood is very great and is partly bound up with its annual life history, which has been worked out by Nielsen[356] in Denmark. There it lives equally in the foliage of oak and Norway spruce. The spiders hatched from summer cocoons overwinter in the ground, among fallen leaves or in ground zone plants, pairing during this time, and appearing in early summer when the oak leaves are out. At this time the females are near to egg-laying. But even in summer the spider lives at all levels in our woods.[297, 508]

It has been necessary to toil through this information about some common animals that hunt in the canopy – with lacewings, ladybirds, a bug, a hoverfly and a spider for examples – in order to ram home the contrast between their comparatively unrestricted range of habitat and diet, and the usually more specific (or at any rate generic) choice of plant by so many herbivorous insects. There is also often a greater range of major habitats, and nearly always an elastic choice of vertical layers. A predator like *Anthocoris nemorum* might, if I may combine a social and a boxing term into one ecological metaphor, be justifiably called 'a good mixer'! The primary pattern of tree species so sharply outlined in a mosaic of canopy is still traceable in the habitat patterns of the monophagous herbivores, though already at this consumer level there are a good many species with wider choice of host trees, of which the winter moth is one. At the second consumer level there is considerable blurring of this primary pattern, though no doubt more precise statistical assessments would reveal many 'contours' in population density according to the kind of tree used, and indeed even such qualitative records as we have suggest some degree of choice or of survival. If there is any truth in the effectiveness of the 'girder system' which I have alluded to when discussing the overlapping communities of oak galls, these free-ranging predators must be considered an important part of it, especially if it can ever be demonstrated that they really do (as has so often been suggested speculatively in abstract discussions) search for and stay with populations of food species that are temporarily at high densities. We equally need to know how far specific parasites of insects that are polyphagous in habits follow their hosts on to each different plant and there produce the same rates of infestation. The winter moth, *Operophtera brumata*, is known best ecologically from the work of Varley and Gradwell on oak moths at Wytham Woods. Among other connections, it has a Tachinid fly enemy, *Cyzenis albicans*, that lays eggs on the leaves, these eggs being swallowed by the winter moth caterpillar in the course of ordinary feeding. When the eggs were fed to sixteen other kinds of oak moth caterpillars, they failed to develop properly, and only in a close ally of the winter moth, *O. fagata*, that lives on birch and beech, did they even get as far as forming a pupa.[520] The moth itself is known to attack various trees other than oak, also shrubs like hazel, but neither the tree-host range of the moth nor that of *C. albicans* have yet been worked out completely.

The extensive entomological literature concerned with parasites and their hosts very seldom attempts to describe or map out the ecological surroundings at all completely. It is not uncommon to know the simple chain plant–herbivore–parasite, sometimes with further parasite links as well. But the elements of this chain have no ecological coordinates by which one can determine that the plant occurs in a particular series of habitat components (lateral and vertical), the host in all or only certain components, the parasite in all or only certain components in which the host can be found; and whether such ecological contexts are of regular occurrence and how they differ in levels of numbers from one part of the eco system to another. But this comment applies equally to the published information about predators. The reader has probably noticed that in the present chapter I have not been using with any rigidity the habitat system already discussed in Chs. 4 and 5, but instead have relied on plant species to bring out the patterns in ecological distribution. The reason for this is simply that although published records sometimes mention the tree or other plant species on which a lacewing or a spider has been found, they practically never give the exact formation-type or vertical layer. Duffey's and Turnbull's surveys at Wytham are pleasant exceptions. And seldom do they distinguish between the edge of a wood and the part inside. We have a good deal of more precise information of this kind from the Wytham Ecological Survey, but not sufficient yet to give a general picture of the canopy. But the use of plant species here at any rate proves the main point, and also another one – that the habitat classification is in no way intended to replace or by implication to under-rate the importance of plant-host records or of phyto sociology generally. As remarked in Ch. 4, it is only the order of priority that is involved, and the reasons for adopting it need not be repeated. It follows from all this, that throughout the present chapter the general use of terms like 'woods or 'canopy' implies a grouping of the habitat components we use at Wytham. 'Woods' includes centre and edge, also glade and ride; 'canopy' is low and high canopy, and sometimes this foliage will have been actually down in the field layer, especially when an 'edge' is concerned.

The examples given in this chapter are of species having a wide choice both of habitat and prey, and I believe this to be a common situation, and probably the commonest, among predators both invertebrate and vertebrate. There are, however, some species with much more restricted habitat. The small lacewing *Sympherobius pygmaeus* appears to be confined to oak trees, and to those growing in isolation or at the edge. But the prey include several different kinds of insects such as aphids, smaller lacewing larvae, and probably coccids.[270] Then certain lacewings are confined to pine trees, though here the situation is somewhat artificial in so far as the Scots pine is the only ordinary native conifer we have in Britain other than the yew and the juniper, both of which are notably poor in invertebrate life. So it is interesting to find that *Hemerobius atrifrons* occurs on larch and Scots pine, *H. pini* on spruce, *Wesmaelius concinnus* mainly on Scots pine but occasionally on spruce and larch, *W. quadrifasciatus* mainly on larch and less commonly on Scots pine and spruce.[270] Evidently these species, when given the opportunity, are able to occupy more than one kind of conifer. Another instance of a very restricted habitat range is *Anthocoris sarothamni*, which is mainly confined during the breeding season to broom (*Sarothamnus* or *Cytisus scoparius*). Even the overwintering adults live in the curled pods remaining on the bushes. But Anderson found some populations on elm and on nettles in the spring, where they evidently fed, but did not necessarily breed. The diet is not restricted to one kind of prey, though it seems that on broom the bug mainly eats two kinds of Psyllids.[7] I think that such relatively restricted habitats are uncommon among predatory insects, spiders and mites, and that most of these will be found to cross repeatedly the boundaries between different communities, both laterally and vertically.

The pattern of feeding by insectivorous birds in woodland forms, changes and dissolves with the march of the seasons and the special features of each year. It differs also quite considerably in its details according to the distribution pattern of each wood. It has been especially well worked out for some of the species that depend principally on the canopy and those of its products that fall to the ground. This knowledge we owe chiefly to the field studies of the Edward Grey Institute of Field Ornithology under David Lack, in Wytham Woods and elsewhere. These have been primarily aimed at problems in population dynamics of the birds or the extent to which different species feed in the same zones of habitat. Here I shall use only some of the observations on feeding habits, especially by Hartley on titmice; by Gibb on titmice, the goldcrest and treecreeper; by Owen on the jay and magpie; and by Lockie on the rook and jackdaw. It should be remembered first of all that the warm-blooded physiology of birds imposes quite a different tempo of feeding activity to that existing among invertebrates like spiders and lacewings. Up to a point, the latter can take their time about catching and eating the life-quota of prey they need, slowing down or speeding up according to the lower or higher temperature either side of their tolerance optimum. They can and do feed quite locally and at leisure. And being cold-blooded, they need so much less energy to accomplish the same development, survival and breeding. But titmice are highly mobile and cover very long paths of search by which they find the temporarily available and abundant prey or plant products they absolutely must eat from day to day. Their feeding pattern may therefore change even from minute to minute, though usually there are (at any rate statistically speaking) longer periods of weeks or even months when they haunt one habitat zone in search of one sort of prey, or at any rate feeding upon one sort of community.

In these feeding patterns there are several features that stand out especially. Arising from what has just been said, the small insectivorous birds tap an enormous variety of natural resources, based on all the different woodland features of leaf, gall, twig, fruit, epiphytic growth on bough and trunk, fungi, dead wood, and the accumulations of some of these on the ground. They explore in the course of the year every accessible food that can be utilized, wandering restlessly and end-lessly in their minute investigations, like shoppers in an immensely varied food store. Secondly, the abundant oak moth caterpillars act as a specially powerful magnet in the early summer, and are used to feed the young, even causing some birds like the jackdaws to become partly diverted from their normal grassland feeding. Thirdly, the feeding patterns, though overlapping very greatly – especially in the oak caterpillar season – show distinct differences among the species. A fourth feature is that in winter some birds leave the wood altogether (at any rate by day),[380] while in a very severe winter the emigration may be almost complete. All these phenomena illustrate very well the three main habitat themes of movements within a formation-type and its edges, vertical movements, and external relations with habitats right outside the wood.

The fullest information about bird-feeding patterns in woodland is for the great tit (*Parus major*) and blue tit (*P. caeruleus*): and here, for continuity of treatment, I will concentrate on deciduous woods and mainly those on Wytham Hill. Hartley[216] watched these two species (as well as four others) in Wytham Woods from the early summer of 1947 until the New Year of 1950, at the same time making some parallel observations in other woods further away [22A]. He recorded the first feeding act (but not its duration) for each bird arriving at each tree under observations, accumulating his data by moving slowly through the woods. The Great Wood on the north hill, where most of his notes were made, has chiefly oak–ash–sycamore woods (with their rides and some open glades) much like those already described in Ch. 10, which also lie on the north hill; but he also included two blocks of maturing conifer plantations partly mixed with broad-leaved trees, containing mainly larch, Douglas fir (*Pseudotsuga taxifolia*) and Norway spruce (*Picea abies*). These conifers carry an extremely simplified fauna, but the micro-fauna is quite abundant, at any rate on larch and Douglas fir. Hartley did not separate the 'wood' and 'edge'; and he used 20 ft (not 15 ft) as the upper limit of scrub (or lower) canopy. His records took in not only the species of tree or shrub, and the height visited, but also the part of the tree or shrub – leaf, bough and so on. There were admitted to be various kinds of bias in the records, such as unequal visibility in different sorts of cover; but perhaps from the present point of view the only serious omission (and from the extent of ground covered and variety of courses traversed an almost inevitable one) is that the relative frequency of the various tree and shrub species, and the area covered by them was not known. For this reason the best conclusions come from differences in the order in which trees ranked, which at any rate suggest preferences, since the trees remain the same in number and size.

The combined analysis of all these results, grouped by Hartley into the four quarters of the year, showed without any doubt that in oak trees the blue tit was the predominant titmouse, in sycamores the great tit (eating leaf aphids there), while the marsh tit (*Parus palustris*) predominated in elders except in summer months when elderberries attracted blue tits in some numbers, and the coal tit (*Parus ater*) in conifers. These are only rough generalizations about a kaleidoscopic cycle of changes in behaviour. As Hartley remarks: 'Not all the species are separable all the time; but no two are identical in their feeding behaviour.' The following examples may be given of the intricacies of feeding. The average height zones visited are different in the blue and great tits. Whereas the former ranges over all levels of woodland vegetation in the winter, it does not usually feed on the ground except when there is some special quantity of tree seeds there. But the great tit spends much time in the winter months foraging on the ground, particularly where there are beeches. I have also seen scores, perhaps hundreds, doing this under old beech trees scattered in the limestone grassland in Blenheim Park a few miles from Wytham and in habitats in which the great tit would not mainly breed. On the north hill of Wytham there are few beeches, but still the great tits feed much on the ground in winter. There is not much detail about their food there, because few have been killed for examination. But the very thorough analysis by Betts[23] of the food of titmice in some Forest of Dean, Monmouthshire, oak woods (where also there were not usually many beeches) proved that the great tits in winter collected ground-living insects and spiders, amongst which were a weevil (*Strophosomus melanogramma*) that lives also in Wytham Woods, and the ground-running wolf-spiders of the genus *Lycosa*. And, although the sycamore scored the greatest number of visits by great tits on Wytham north hill, oaks were almost equally visited, and elder and ash on a lesser but not insignificant scale. Betts found that among the foods eaten by great tits in the Forest of Dean were the seeds of the wood-sorrel (*Oxalis acetosella*); that blue tits ate a good deal of oak galls, including *Andricus ostreus*, *A. collaris*, *Neuroterus lenticularis* and *N. aprilinus* (the last being collected from the litter zone) – thus taking meat with their vegetables; and that the blue tit frequently ate the fruit of a moss, *Dicranoweisia cirrata*, that grows on trunks and boughs, whose spores produced in winter are rich in oil.

Gibb's[180] survey of feeding habits, also done at Wytham but in Marley Wood, which lies on the south hill, shows the same species of titmice working round the year within a different mosaic of vegetation. Here about three-quarters of the area is covered with woody vegetation, the rest being largely open woodland marsh or bracken patches not much used by these birds. Of the woody area about 43% was tree and 56% shrub, divided up into the following proportions of canopy cover for the different trees and shrubs: trees mainly oak but only 17% cover, ash 9%, birch 8% and other species 9% (beech being only 1% and sycamore only 3%), scrub a mixture mainly of elder 20%, hazel coppice 17% hawthorn 12%, maple 4% and other species 3%. His methods were similar to those of Hartley in that the first activity of any bird seen was recorded, the record covering about 5 seconds, but a good many additional matters were analysed that will not be reviewed here. From a total of 500 hours field observation and about 12,000 observed events, those for one complete annual cycle September 1950 to August 1951 were selected for analysis. Although the results quite confirmed the two points already established, that all species feed in a great range of habitats and have a most flexible and comprehensive diet, the differences between the species also stood out. But there were also some great differences produced by the basic plant pattern at Marley Wood, in particular by the scarcity of sycamore and beech and the abundance of hazel. Visits to sycamore practically never had any high score, though there was moderate visiting by marsh tits in October and by long-tailed tits in autumn and early summer – attributed to their feeding on sycamore aphids. The great tit was only noted visiting sycamore for aphids in April and May, and not in numbers. Although beech mast was collected by several species in the first half of winter, it was hazel nuts that chiefly occupied the great tits from September to April. They are the only titmice apparently strong enough to split the nuts open, which they partly do by using the hard branch of elder as an anvil. And although ash was relatively abundant in the inadequate tree canopy of this wood it was very seldom patronized to any extent for feeding except for a fairly heavy attendance (up to 40% of visits) by coal tits in April and May, and by blue tits also in May. In the Great Wood Hartley had never found more than 13% of visits to ash trees in any quarter, and usually a good deal less, and this can be explained by the abundance of sycamore there, with its supply of aphids from spring to autumn, a feature only poorly represented in Marley Wood.

From an earlier and less elaborate survey of great and blue tits in Marley Wood in 1947-9, Gibb[179] had concluded that the great tits on the whole preferred the hazel coppice and blue tits the canopy of more open woodland, while both species 'shunned the dense elder cover in which the marsh and willow tits were breeding'. But he noted also that these distinctions became rather less precise when the populations had increased in size as a result of nest boxes being provided. This general conclusion applies both to feeding and nesting. The Forest of Dean survey by Betts[23] gives a very detailed picture of the food of great, blue, coal and marsh tits, derived from gizzard analyses; but it was not always easy to attribute the foods to their respective trees, since direct observations on feeding were not systematically done. In the two oak woods studied, sycamore and ash were scarce, but in one of the two woods beech and birch were common. Here again the great tits could not possibly depend on sycamore insects, and they seem to have spent much time on the ground in winter collecting insects, spiders and beech mast. 'Titmice shot in the oak woodland over half a mile away, feeding in oaks, were found to have gizzards distended with beech mast.' In summer the great tits had first the winter moth larvae on oak, then oak aphids and beetles, to mention a few alternative sources of food. In Marley Wood[180] the goldcrest (*Regulus regulus*) and the treecreeper (*Certhia familiaris*) ranged over practically all trees and shrubs, though the treecreeper was never recorded on spindle, which was not an uncommon shrub. The former lives mainly in the fine canopy, and the latter works the trunks, boughs and to some extent small twigs. All these feeding studies reflect the nature of the tree pattern elaborated in Ch. 10, the oak being a rich and stable source of provisions of many kinds, the beech (in some years) producing abundant nuts that are mostly sought on the ground and especially by the great tit, the sycamore aphids (when numerous enough) a strongly attractive alternative for the great tit especially though less so during the oak caterpillar season, and the ash almost always a poor source of insect food, while hazel can act as an alternative to sycamore for the great tit.

In the centre of all these changing activities lies the massive output of the oak moth population in early summer. Some of the output is supported also by the same species, such as the winter moth, breeding also on other kinds of trees and shrubs. Ornithological works not infrequently refer to these moths as 'oak defoliators', but from what has been cited in Ch. 10 it is clear enough that high populations of *Tortrix*, winter moth and one or two others occur both on oak trees that are defoliated and on those that are not. One of the interesting accidents of ecological timing is that the caterpillars that defoliate usually manage to complete their life-cycle in numbers sufficient to provide the main food for nestling birds, as well as moths for the following generation, though by the time the caterpillars are full-grown they leave some trees fairly bare. The whole question of how it comes about that two or three species of moths, living in one of the most complex and rich communities of animals we have, at intervals get temporarily 'out of control' (in the sense of eating up most of the immediately available resources and as a result disrupting the whole life of the tree and its animal community), when as a general rule we find that the richer and more complex a community the more stable it is and more resistant to invaders, is discussed in Ch. 18. The gearing of titmouse breeding to bring about synchronization of nestlings with the height of the oak caterpillar season is now well established by Lack[278, 279] and others. How this is actually regulated has not so far been explained. Besides titmice, there are some other birds that take advantage of this profusion for the same purpose. Owen[368] studied the food of jays (*Garrulus glandarius*) and magpies (*Pica pica*) in Wytham Woods, collecting it from the nestlings by the collar method. Here the birds were living in dense oak–elm–hazel woodland with lower layers of hawthorn, elder, bramble and bracken. The nests were mainly in hawthorns. Thirty samples collected in 1953 and 1955 contained mainly larvae and pupae of oak moth species (not all necessarily feeding on oak alone), even though in these two years they did not cause serious defoliation. Only 107 out of 1283 items (17%) were other kinds of food. Similar samples taken from nestlings in open oak–alder woods set in very mixed country at Virginia Water in Surrey, about forty miles away, contained fewer but still a substantial number of oak caterpillars and pupae – 341 out of 849 food items or 40%. Jays are true woodland birds, but except for the oak caterpillar season, for 'birdsnesting' in spring and summer, and the collection of acorns from trees in autumn, they normally feed on the woodland floor.

Magpies at Wytham, studied by the same method in 1953, also brought oak caterpillars and pupae to their young (but only 148 out of 357 food items or 41·5%), apparently collecting them on the ground after they had fallen from the trees, not actually in the canopy. 'In Wytham, in the breeding season, magpies feed almost exclusively on the ground, usually at the woodland edge or along rides, and also in open fields near woods. Magpies breeding outside Wytham in more open country feed much more in open fields. A common method of feeding is for a bird to start at the edge of a wood and to make slowly towards the centre of a field.'[368] In 1951–2 Lockie[298] ascertained the food of nestling jackdaws (*Corvus monedula*), which are very numerous in Wytham Woods, where they nest in tree-holes, and also roost there in winter. At ordinary times the jackdaw collects an assortment of food from the surface of open grassy places, including longer grass near the woodland edge, but practically never visits the woodland floor inside. But during the breeding season the birds went up into the canopy and collected quantities of tree caterpillars, especially on oak and elm.

Squirrels also afford an interesting illustration of the orderly exploitation of the canopy and of some seasonable changes in doing so. In the last few decades the original population of red squirrels (*Sciurus vulgaris*) at Wytham has been replaced by American grey squirrels (*S. carolinensis*) (see Ch. 18). The latter cause tremendous damage to sycamores by stripping the bark, frequently killing parts or all of the younger trees, and although their populations are kept down by man, it is not too much to assume that their taste for sycamore has a definite influence on competition among the woodland trees. In 1947-8 Shorten[440] carried out a nest survey of grey squirrels in part of Wytham Woods, which showed that in this area at any rate they nested only in oak trees during the summer. But in the winter the nests, or dreys, were found in oak, wych elm, common maple, sallow, blackthorn and hawthorn, at heights above 12 feet and mostly below 25 feet. None were found in ash (sycamore being absent in this place). 'Squirrels seem very averse to building in ash trees ... which are common at Wytham. The author has only once seen a drey in an ash tree.' They also avoid sycamore [23]. But although squirrels need woody vegetation for nesting, they range outside the woodland edge, and are able to exploit a galaxy of natural resources.

Another example, already partly implied in the feeding habits of magpie and jackdaw, helps to place the woodland itself in a wider setting of mixed landscape. Rooks (*Corvus frugilegus*) have their young in the nest too early to profit from oak caterpillar abundance, but after the breeding season they visit woods and eat caterpillars in the canopy, as also do starlings.[368] Rooks are normally open grassland feeders, obtaining earthworms from the ground and by turning over cowpats, and Lockie's analysis[299] of the food of nestlings at four rookeries in the Oxford district showed earthworms to be the predominant food. Most rookeries are placed in hedgerow trees like elms, in smaller woods, in parkland and in gardens, rather than in the middle of large woods; but in winter very large roosts may be formed in woods or their 'edges', where the rooks are accompanied by jackdaws as well. In 1931-2 a survey of rook populations around Oxford was made by the Oxford Bird Census and described by Alexander.[2] In April 1931 most nests were mapped and counted on a rectangle 35 × 26 miles (910 square miles), and in the following winter the large regional rook roosts were added. The results are shown in Fig. 21, from which some of the marginal and incompletely known rook areas are omitted. Each 'tribal area' had one immense night roost in it, to which the rooks returned at dusk. In winter the tribes overlapped quite a lot in their feeding, the boundaries shown on the map being those used in the summer, when the birds are dispersed into numerous rookeries. In this way the countryside is parcelled out. Rough estimates were made of the birds returning to roost at four places (C, E, F,

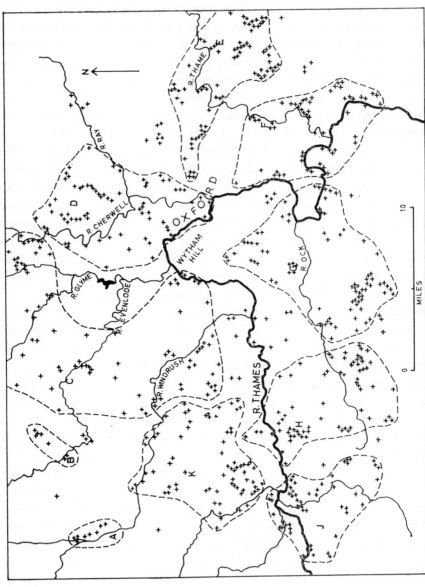

FIG. 21. Winter roosts (A–K) and associated summer feeding areas (bounded by dash lines) of rooks, *Corvus frugilegus*, in the Oxford region, 1931-2. Crosses are breeding rookeries. (After W. B. Alexander, 1933.

G) which for the counts that were fairly complete gave the enormous numbers for rooks of 12,000, 5500, 4500 and 12,500. The corresponding counts for jack-daws at these roosts were 9000, 6500, 2000 and 6500. Therefore the total number of birds in each roost was of the order of 6500 to 21,000! For some curious reason Wytham Woods seems to have been excluded from any of these large tribal areas, but Dr C. Perrins informs me that there has for some years been a regular small roost in Marley Wood at Wytham, where the birds partly use ash trees [23A]. There are no rookeries in the Woods except in part of the open parkland trees. It is well known that the huge starling roosts made in scrubby or young woods cause devastating destruction of the vegetation beneath, but I have not found any account of the effects of rook and jackdaw roosts in Britain. It is reasonable to suppose that the supply of small feathers has some influence on smaller nesting birds. But in his description of Dalby Söderskog, the Swedish woodland which is referred to more fully in the next chapter, Lindquist[293] has some interesting facts about the effects of rooks upon the flora. In one part of this mainly oak, ash, wych elm (*Ulmus glabra*) and beech wood, there was a large rook colony, the dung from which had greatly increased the phosphate content of the soil below. It was noteworthy that after the last felling, the new young woodland consisted of wych elm, although the main wood and the upper canopy were ash. The field layer contained nettles (*Urtica dioica*), goutweed (*Aegopodium podagraria*) and the grass *Poa trivialis*. This abnormal mixture he attributed to the manuring and phosphates.

In this chapter I have frequently linked the two subjects of wide habitat range and diverse diet, and to a great extent the second follows from the first. But the pyramid of numbers itself also piles on the pressure for variety of food at the higher consumer levels, in that there is seldom sufficient of one species to support the narrowing tip of the pyramid. At the top of the woodland canopy food-chain is (or was, because its numbers have become very sadly reduced by insecticides and other modern hazards) the sparrow-hawk (*Accipiter nisus*). Some careful obser-vations on its food habits were made by S. Boardman (and reported by Glegg)[186] in Epping Forest, in Essex, where a pair of these birds nested in birch or oak in the years 1923-5. There was a slaughter log near the nest, at which in 1925 the remains of the following birds were found: Song-thrush (*Turdus ericetorum*), blackbird (*Turdus merula*), mistle thrush (*Turdus viscivorus*), redstart (*Phoenicurus phoenicurus*), hawfinch (*Coccothraustes coccothraustes*), chaffinch (*Fringilla coelebs*), greenfinch (*Chloris chloris*), house sparrow (*Passer domesticus*), starling (*Sturnus vulgaris*), whitethroat (*Sylvia communis*), great tit (*Parus major*), meadow pipit (*Anthus pratensis*) (this at any rate is not a woodland form), wood-pigeon (*Columba palumbus*), lesser spotted woodpecker (*Dendrocopus minor*) and even a predator, the tawny owl (*Strix aluco*). Besides all these kinds of birds, there were mouse fur and tails in the pellets, also a good many ground beetles (*Abax*), and once a sparrow-hawk was seen to try and attack a red squirrel. In 1926 twelve of these sixteen species of birds were observed again, together with remains of cuckoo (*Cuculus canorus*) and blue tit (*Parus coeruleus*).

In this and the previous chapter I have tried to give an expanding view of the hierarchies of habitats in which woodland canopy animals live (implying also the necessity of a hierarchy of habitat components with which to round up such a varied assortment of information into a synthesis of the ecosystem). The smallest of these units are some of the animals themselves with their load of parasites – an aspect omitted from consideration here. Then there are the scattered assemblages of oak galls; leaves, twigs, flowers and fruits, epiphytic mosses, algae and lichen; larger structures such as branches and trunks; the whole individual tree; the interspersed mosaic of trees (and shrubs); vertical layering within these; the scattered furniture of dead wood, fungi and nests of varying extent and numbers (to be dealt with in later chapters); the contrast between the solid woodland and its 'edge' formation-type; different sorts of wood, e.g. deciduous and conifer; then the other terrestrial formation-types and the transition, aquatic and domestic habitats in which the woodland jewellery is set; finally the whole landscape. One can find a similar hierarchy of animal species beginning with one living in only two kinds of oak gall (*Biorhiza pallida*) and with some parasites confined to the community in only one gall-phase (*Syntomaspis apicalis* on the oak-apple phase of *Biorhiza*); or in many galls (the parasite *Eurytoma brunniventris*); on one kind of leaf (the sycamore aphid *Drepanosiphum*) or on several (the winter moth); in one vertical layer (few in the canopy, except taken very broadly, but many on the ground zone) or many (*Theridion pallens*) or in all (the winter moth); not in deciduous woods (*Hemerobius pini*), not in conifer woods (*H. humulinus*), or occurring in both (*Chrysopa perla*); in all terrestrial formation-types (*Anthocoris nemorum*); both in woods and fields (the magpie); or ranging still wider (the jackdaw, with its taste for buildings as well as vegetation). The jackdaw and rook impress us with their ecology, not only because it is complex, but because they are large species, also noisy, and their relations with man are close. In these qualities they somewhat resemble man himself, though we have still to invent a convenient way of invading the forest canopy, which is one of the reasons why it seems so wild a place, and is still one of the least explored zones on land.

CHAPTER 12

The Ground-plan of Woodlan

THERE ARE THREE major discontinuities of state in nature that affect animals: between air and water, between water and land, and between the ground and the free air above it. Whereas the first two of these are sharp boundaries (though often not staying at exactly the same level) the last is usually rather a stable interface yet not a sharp one, because – except on quite bare ground – a shallow zone of vegetable detritus, at times continuous in extent, separates the free air from the interstitially aerated soil below. The complexity of this zone is greatest in woodland (especially deciduous woodland), where the plant structures projecting up to form the canopy to a considerable extent determine the general pattern or ground-plan of the communities below. This happens in three ways. First, the canopy partly intercepts and cuts off light and rain, though it also protects the lower strata from extremes of temperature and evaporation. Secondly, it contributes a variety of dead plant materials that fall to the ground to create a number of secondary habitats there. Of these the most conspicuous are the dying and dead leaves that renew the litter zone annually, and the dying and dead wood falling at almost any time as twigs, branches or whole trees, the last often leaving decaying stumps in the ground. Thirdly, there are the vertical movements of animals, as well as whatever they contribute in waste matter and carrion. So, if we adopt a squirrel's-eye view of the woodland, the canopy pattern can be seen to determine the main outlines of the ground pattern. That it does not do so completely is because the character of the mineral soil or rock and the contours of the ground add still further elements of habitat patterning, examples of which are a sandy soil that makes it easy for rabbits or foxes to burrow, or surface sculpture that allows a small stream or pool to form. History and the numerous interactions of organisms also ensure that the result one sees and tries to survey is excessively variable and hard to analyse. But awareness of the main habitat components helps one very much in doing so.

Before analysing the Ground Zone itself in more detail, there is a principle affecting all the four formation-types of Open Ground, Field Type, Scrub and Woodland, that needs brief mention. It is not very easy to describe in interesting guage, but is most important in its effects upon the biotic links between the different zones. In the gradient from High Canopy down to the Topsoil of a wood, we can see two trends. The first really results from the nature of the four formation-types. High Canopy can only occur in Woodland; Low Canopy comes in Woodland and Scrub; the Field Layer exists in both of these and also as Field Type in the open; the Ground Zone and Soil exist in all these three as well as in Open Ground. From this rather elementary consideration, it results that there is, for example, a greater area of soil communities than of canopy. The second point is that whereas the Canopy and Field Layer are predominantly composed of green-plant-based communities, the Topsoil is predominantly composed (apart from roots) of communities based on dead matter, bacteria and fungi. The Ground Zone fluctuates between these extremes, in that it may have an important green plant element, or on the other hand (as in some beech woods) have no green vascular plants at all. Although there are a number of insects that show specific attachment to particular species of fungi, a greater number of the so-called saprophagous animals have a wide range of food and are correspondingly more likely to have (like predators within the green-plant systems) a wider habitat range. If this reasoning is correct, one would expect to find considerable sharing of species between the soil fauna in and outside woodland, rather less between woodland Ground Zone and Open Ground, and less still between the fauna living on the field layer of woodland glade and that of the meadow.

In the Ground Zone of deciduous woodland and its 'edges', taken as a whole, lives one of the richest series of animal communities we have – an extraordinarily close-packed and extensive mixture of species exploiting a zone that may often be less than the total six inches allotted to it in the present grouping, yet still very rich even within an inch or two of leaf litter (Plate 30). Its cover and food system depends on the renewal of leaf supplies from above, both from the woody canopy and from any field layer also present. In the open glades most of the surface cover is derived from plants of the field layer and the ground zone itself, apart from whatever drift of canopy leaves may come in. The Wytham Ecological Survey has assembled a great many records from the leaf-litter of deciduous woodland though these are still far from complete (for example, the Enchytraeid worms, nematode worms, a good many species of mites and springtails, and the larvae of flies, have yet to be identified). In Wytham Woods there are known at present about 335 species of invertebrates in the ground zone inside woodland with closed or fairly closed canopy. Most of these were collected from the leaf litter, the largest numbers of species being molluscs, spiders, mites and beetles. In addition there are records of 234 other species from woods elsewhere in England [24]. This incomplete list of 569 species gives some idea of the large national pool of species from which the fauna of any particular wood is drawn. There are also a number of animals that do not appear in these lists, since they pass quickly through the ground zone into the soil in order to pupate or hibernate, and upwards again later on. Then there are also very many animals attached to General habitats (especially those in dying and dead wood) or coming as flower visitors, that still further promote the variety of the ground zone inside woods. Finally, all the species that inhabit glades and other edges of woodland, as well as all the parasites in the community, make the total fauna of the Ground Zone of woodland impressive. This shallow zone is a great meeting place of woodland species – plant as well as animal, since all the green plants except some epiphytic algae and ferns grow up into or through it. There is at all times of year except perhaps in extreme cold an active litter fauna, many practically rubbing shoulders at all seasons, others having only brief encounters or none.

I have written as if the line between a wood and its glade edges is always sharp and easily recognizable. In modern Britain there are thousands of miles of abrupt woodland edge abutting on arable land or pasture. In a great many places this line is less abrupt and gives a more natural boundary passing from trees to narrow belts of scrub and field-layer plants and then a ground zone. When a mature tree falls inside the wood and makes a glade, the same sort of situation develops. But within the woods every transition can also be found between solid canopy such as is found in a mature beech wood like Burnham Beeches in Buckinghamshire and what is practically a continuous reticulum of small glades where the tree canopy is thin. The forestry practice of the present day abjures the development of thick canopy, because this does not draw up trees into the long quick-growing trunks suitable for making into planks, and it accordingly ordains a cycle of thinning that for many years keeps the canopy incomplete. This can be seen in a great many managed woods, including Wytham Woods, where a formerly rather good canopy had under it extensive sheets of the dog's mercury (*Mercurialis perennis*) that have mostly given way to a much more tangled field layer that includes a great deal of bramble. Where any true thickening of canopy occurs the bramble quite quickly dies in the shade. This kind of succession happens also in natural glades. Thus, a large dying beech that broke and fell in 1952 left a considerable open space where it has lain on the ground since then. At first it became covered with a heavy growth of strong brambles, but by 1961 young sycamore and ash saplings sprung from seed had closed over the site, grown to over scrub canopy height, and killed the bramble. This variation in canopy density in our much-managed woodlands raises practical difficulties about defining centre and 'edge', though anyone who knows the habits of their local vegetation very soon finds out formulae for meeting the problem.

The distribution of bracken in woods illustrates this point very well, and since it also has a bearing on the influence of light upon the field layer, and the differences in communities of the field and ground layers, it will be discussed with some details now. Bracken is common in oak woods, usually on lighter soils, living both on acid and calcareous soils, though apparently more commonly on the former. Tansley[493] remarks: 'In oakwoods whose canopy casts at all a deep shade the bracken fronds appear only at intervals, and are relatively feeble in development, but in many open canopy woods casting moderate shade they are more numerous', the oak and birch of Sherwood Forest near Nottingham being adduced as a place where bracken is uninhibited by the canopy, and the litter under the trees is a deep mixture of oak leaves and bracken in which few other plants are able to grow. On Wytham Hill bracken does not grow under large oaks, though it thickly fills some of the spaces between them. Again, Tansley says: 'The soil under such a *Pteridium* society is covered with a thick litter of slowly decaying fragments of the dead fronds, passing down into a peaty humus. Woodland regeneration appears impossible under such conditions.' Equally, the early seral stages of other glade vegetation are slowed or prevented, so that bracken stands are one of the most durable forms of woodland 'edge' field type, carrying the deepest natural litter layer.

A pattern of oak trees and bracken of this kind can be seen at the top of the aerial view in Plate 9. The contrast in richness of the herbivorous insects of oak and bracken is enormous – about as great as could be found anywhere in two temperate adjacent formation-types, there being only very few species attached specially to bracken, in contrast to the huge community on oak (Ch. 10). On bracken there are two Heteropterous bugs, *Monalocoris filicis* and *M. pteridis*, whose larvae feed mainly on the sporangia on the underside of the fronds. The former is widespread on bracken and some other ferns, the latter common on the male and lady ferns and some other species, but never abundant on bracken.[55, 469] Homoptera sometimes occur but their status is not clear. The caterpillars of about nine species of moths have been reported feeding on bracken, but only four are specific to it: the Gelechiid, *Paltodora cytisella*, making swellings in the stems;[161] the Selidosomid, *Lithina chlorosata* (formerly *Lozogramma petraria*); and two Hepialids, *Hepialus fusconebulosus* and *H. hectus*, living in the rhizomes. *Hepialus sylvinus* has the same habit but has also been reported on several other plants. Four other moths (*Euplexia lucipara*, *Hadena* or *Mamestra contigua*, *Diataraxia oleracea* and *Phlogophora meticulosa*) that are highly polyphagous on vascular plants, have been reported from bracken, but in circumstances that are not known to me.[433] Ten British species of sawflies (Tenthredinidae) are known to live on bracken (*Strongylogaster xanthoceros*), or on bracken and other ferns (*S. lineata*, *S. macula*, *Stromboceros delicatulus*, *Aneugmenus fürstenbergensis*, *A. coronatus*, *A. temporalis* and *A. padi*); or are polyphagous on herbs and shrubs but also occur sometimes on bracken (*Tenthredo livida* and *T. ferruginea*).[22] Finally, there is a Muscid fly, *Chirosia parvicornis*, that curls the tips of the bracken fronds.[222] Three other species of *Chirosia* are also known to mine

234

bracken fronds in Britain, though not necessarily in woodland: *C. albitarsis*, *C. crassiseta* and *C. setifemur*. They belong to a small group of rather primitive flies mainly associated with ferns, and perhaps one or two of the other species may also occur in bracken.[74a] It will be seen that, of the groups considered here, the green bracken field layer carries only about sixteen special fern or bracken insects, with the *Hepialus* (also sometimes *Chirosia crassiseta*[442a]) coming in the rhizomes. Three of the restricted species, *M. filicis*, *L. chlorosata* and *H. hectus*, occur in Wytham Woods, and the leaf-curl of presumably *C. parvicornis* is also to be seen there. Since practically all the bracken on the hill is in woodland or scrub interspaces or edges, these species may be assumed to belong to the community discussed here. Bracken does, of course, also occupy large parts of Britain as a field type on its own. Three at least of the polyphagous species, *E. lucipara*, *D. oleracea* and *P. meticulosa*, also occur on Wytham Hill, though it is unknown if they attack bracken there.

But the fauna of the decaying bracken litter is another matter. In March 1951 Professor C. Overgaard Nielsen examined a bracken patch at the edge between oak–ash–sycamore woodland and *Brachypodium pinnatum* grassland on Wytham Hill, where the limestone is close to the surface. In the litter he found abundant populations of the pill millipede *Glomeris marginata*, two kinds of woodlice, *Philoscia muscorum* and *Trichoniscus* (*pusillus* group), the small Staphylinid beetle *Tachyporus hypnorum* and the spire snail *Clausilia rugosa* (now *bidentata*). All these are also found in the ground zone of limestone grassland at Wytham, as well as in deciduous woodland litter. It may be recalled that *Glomeris* was proved by Overgaard Nielsen to be the chief consumer of partly decomposed *Brachypodium pinnatum* litter (Ch. 6), and he informs me from observations he has made in Denmark, that it is also an important consumer of bracken. Frankland[346, 347] has studied the decomposition of bracken and found a number of microfungi colonizing it, though their various roles are not yet understood, nor exactly what *Glomeris* extracts from the bracken litter it eats. Van Der Drift[515] in the Netherlands found that *Glomeris* would eat new fallen tree litter offered to them, but concluded that since they did not occur commonly in the upper layers of litter this is not their usual food, and it seems likely that (as in grassland) they depend upon the material being altered by micro-organisms before any large proportion can be actually assimilated. They do however mechanically comminute the leaves and aid the further breakdown of the whole litter, their faecal pellets containing small particles with a surface of about $0 \cdot 01$ mm.^{2}. Bocock and Heath[347] have also made measurements with this millipede at Merlewood Research Station in north Lancashire, and calculated that its populations, ranging from 10 to 100 per m^2., consume 3% of the annual leaf litter in an oak-dominated wood. This does not, of course, mean that they assimilate that amount of matter.

Here, then, is the same species of millipede, a considerable operator in the breaking down of coarse litter to fine humus, living in the Ground Zone of three adjacent formation-types. The dominant plants of two of these (*Brachypodium pinnatum* and bracken) are inedible to most animals in the green state and therefore carry poor communities in their field layers, while the deciduous canopy is extravagantly rich. To etch the contrast further, in February 1964, I took large bags of bracken litter from two of the interstitial areas shown in the photo in Plate 9, and for comparison some litter underneath the bare canopy of a large oak tree, where the only plants growing were a few stems of rosebay willow-herb (*Chamaenerion angustifolium*). There had been no rain for almost a month or more, indeed the winter of 1963-4 has ranked as one of the driest for a hundred years, and the oak leaves were still lying dry and crisp and uneaten, the litter being very thin and otherwise composed only of twigs and empty acorn cups. The bracken litter, on the other hand, amongst which were only sporadic specimens of moss or young ground ivy (*Glechoma hederacea*) plants, was several inches deep, dry on the surface, although quite damp in the lower layers above a clearly defined topsoil surface, this dampness clearly being caused by the metabolic activity of microfungal decay. A good many of the brown broken stems of bracken lying below had been almost decomposed inside, and in two of them I found a centipede and a millipede sheltering. Whereas the oak litter, on direct examination, showed very little fauna at all, except small woodlice (*Trichoniscus pusillus*), the bracken litter had much greater numbers of *Trichoniscus*, as well as a few *Tachyporus hypnorum*. The rest of the bracken fauna consisted of small numbers of the animal groups or species commonly found in beech or oak–ash–sycamore litter in Wytham Woods – Enchytraeid worms, mites, false scorpions, small spiders, centipedes (*Lithobius*), millipedes, springtails, beetles, etc. The conclusion from all this is that bracken litter in the spaces of woodland may have a flourishing litter fauna, and that many species are similar to, and probably most are actually the same as under the woodland canopy.

It is evident from all this that the resident communities of various ground zones have more in common with one another than with the faunas of the greenery above them, and that the latter on the other hand differ sharply from one another. This means to say that the chemical and physical characteristics of the green plants, limiting as they do the kind of animals (insects particularly) that will be attracted to and can survive on them, begin to be lost as decay proceeds towards something that – whatever it may look like superficially – has many common properties in cover, texture and microclimate, and food resources composed of various combinations of the basic plant materials with bacteria and microscopic fungi. This does not imply that *Trichoniscus*, say, eats the same food whether it is living in ash-sycamore litter, beech litter, bracken or grass litter, only that there are in all these places some resources in decaying matter that are suitable. This situation is quite distinct from that on green leaves, where the dog's mercury beetle, *Hermaeophaga mercurialis*, does not and presumably cannot live on the nettle, while the nettle weevil, *Cidnorhinus quadrimaculatus*, is not found on the dog's mercury, though the plants may be closely adjacent. And even polyphagous herbivores are often restricted in their main habitat.

A good many of the predators found in the Ground Zone also live in several formation-types. This was well proven in the very thorough quantitative survey of harvestmen (Opiliones) done by Todd[507] at Wytham Woods monthly from May 1946 to April 1947. 17 out of the British total of 21 species were recorded by major habitat and also in their vertical layers, the only terrestrial formation-type omitted being Open Ground, which almost certainly has very few harvestmen. Bracken was sampled in two kinds of place, both on the ground and in the field layer, though it is not surprising that the latter had a very low score of attendance by any species. The first bracken area had a few scattered sycamore saplings but was otherwise a dominant field stand of bracken glade, mixed with a few other species such as bramble, dog's mercury, rosebay willow-herb and the prevernal *Anemone nemorosa*, and some ground mosses. The second place had scattered young ash saplings and spindle shrubs, fewer herbs and only one kind of moss. Both sites were in structure and position woodland 'edge'. Among other species of harvestmen in the bracken litter were four that are confined to the Ground Zone: *Anelasmocephalus cambridgei*, *Nemastoma lugubre*, *Odiellus palpinalis* and *Lacinius ephippiatus*. All these were also found living in *Brachypodium pinnatum* grassland, mixed deciduous scrub, hawthorn hedge (scrub edge), and oak–ash–sycamore wood, the first two also in beech wood, and the last three also in woodland marsh (glades with waterlogged soil). The same wide dispersion existed also in some other common species not confined, at any rate in all stages of their lives, to the ground. A parallel case is that of the beetle *Tachyporus hypnorum* (which Dr A. Macfadyen has proved by some unpublished experiments to take a varied range of small prey such as springtails). This lives in limestone grassland (Ch. 6), *Calluna* heath (Ch. 7), marram dune (Ch. 8), and the Wytham Ecological Survey has records also for calcareous Open Ground, elder scrub, and many for deciduous woodland litter besides more sporadic ones from higher layers in the wood. I have even found it among relict Late-glacial limestone vegetation high in the Pennines, that is in montane Open Ground.

Leaving now the sharp differences between the composition of interior woodland and bracken glade litter as materials, with their considerable affinity as faunas, I shall next mention some equally big differences that exist among fallen leaves from different kinds of trees, and that do crucially influence the litter animals within a wood. I will first give some figures for leaf-fall recorded by Mr D. H.

s part of a study of the fauna of a stream in Wytham Woods in 1956 and which he has given me. This stream, under heavy shade at that time, carried na almost entirely dependent upon leaf litter as a food resource, and Mr es' survey of it is mentioned again in Ch. 17. Twelve trays each of 7 ft², i.e. totalling 84 ft², were placed along the stream edge over a distance of 160 yd in early autumn before leaf-fall had begun. Here the canopy was mainly oak, ash and sycamore, with a little beech in the offing though not overhead, and there were then also one or two black Italian poplars and sweet chestnut. The leaves were dried and weighed [25]. The main fall lasted from the second half of September to the second or third week in December, and the total air-dried weights were 2854 g. in 1956 and 3437 g. in 1957, an average of 3146 g., i.e. 405 g. per m.². This figure is not far from the range of 325-350 g. per m.² measured by Van Der Drift and Witkamp[516] in an oak coppice wood at Arnhem in the Netherlands.

This total leaf-fall, spread over two or three months, is distributed in two ways spatially, and varies several ways in time. In calm weather, particularly during sudden frosts in November, there can be an almost vertical fall, with little lateral drift. But in so far as strong winds are the other external factor that hastens the fall there will also be a considerable amount of lateral mixing. But that there really is some reticulate pattern of the different kinds of leaves depending on the distribution of the parent trees can easily be observed in any mixed deciduous wood, especially if there is good shelter from wind. In more exposed places such as hill shelter belts there will be enough drift to conceal much of the original tree pattern. The local pattern is clearly visible where large scattered beeches occur, because their bright-coloured dead leaves are present and conspicuous all round the year.

Different species of trees do not shed their leaves simultaneously, ash tending to be the earliest and oak the latest, while sycamore is more variable – for example young sycamore saplings and coppiced stems heavily infected with leaf fungi already began to fall at the end of August 1963. This succession of species can be discerned in the subjective records kept by Eccles of the commonest leaf type in each sample, and from one's own experience. A third point is that the weight of leaves falling was 24% greater in 1957 than in the previous year, a variation that was almost certainly natural here, though it would be accentuated by any of the ordinary forest thinning cycles that are practised. This means that the food supply and cover of the litter animals varies.

Both this primary pattern and any seasonal succession in kinds of leaf have considerable importance for the litter fauna, as the work of the Swedish ecologist Lindquist has proved. He surveyed and analysed the history and composition of a ninety-acre mixed deciduous wood called Söderskog, near Dalby in south Sweden which had undergone a good deal of timber exploitation in earlier years but had been a nature reserve since 1918 (his work[293] being published in 1938). Its surviving large oaks were 220 years old, but were now strongly mixed with younger trees, many of them about 120 years old, of beech, ash, wych elm (*Ulmus glabra*) and a few other species. The weight of litter collected in November was 283 g. per m.[2] – perhaps a little less than its value at the start of the fall. Lindquist mapped the density of different species of leaf on 74 metre-square quadrats over the whole wood, repeating the counts at about the same points in the following May and August. The results can be seen in Table 3 and Fig. 22. The trees selected here for

TABLE 3. Leaf litter in deciduous wood, Dalby Söderskog, Sweden.
(Lindquist, 1938)

Average of 71 1-m.[2] quadrats expressed as dry weights, grams per m.[2]

The figures for ash in brackets exclude the leaf stalks and midribs. The total of all species found includes 890 g. composed of alder, aspen, hawthorn, Norway maple and crab-apple. The 103% for beech in May is caused by the sample procedure on neighbouring quadrats.

	Beech	Oak	Ash	Wych elm	Hazel	Sallow	Total (All species found)
November 1955	3326	5206	4381	5556	1622	342	20973
%	100	100	100	100	100	100	100
May 1956	3423	4280	1959	169	492	116	10578
%	103	82	45 (19)	3	31	34	50
August 1956	2385	1668	1379	41	55	4	5629
%	72	32	31 (6)	1	3	1	27

the table are the commoner ones – beech, oak, ash, elm, hazel and sallow. There was a striking difference in the rate of disappearance. Ash, elm, hazel and sallow had all practically gone by August, though some stalks and midribs of ash remained. Oak had gone down to about a third, but beech only to two-thirds of the November amount. The combined result of this mixture of species was, as it happened, to leave 27% by weight of what had been on the ground nine months before, and most of this was beech and oak. This was not, of course, evenly dispersed. Such differential disappearance corresponds quite closely with what anyone can see for themselves in English woods: there is a large group of 'soft' leaves that go quickly, and to the list above can be added sycamore and poplar; and a small group, mainly beech and sweet chestnut, that disappears slowly and therefore accumulates a permanent litter habitat. The oak comes between these two groups. At this point,

239

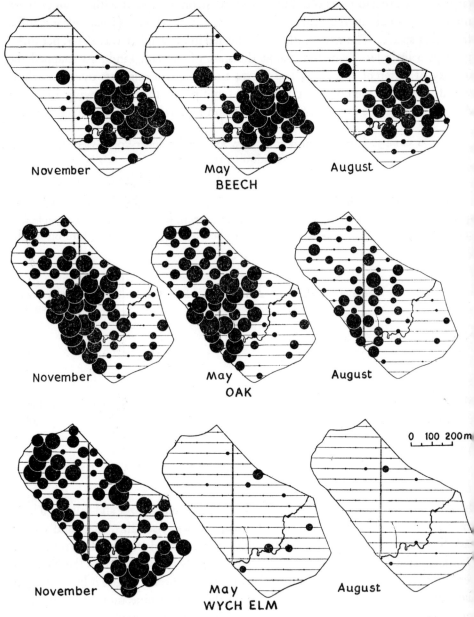

FIG. 22. Weights of leaf litter (dry, grams per m.²) of beech, oak and wych elm in November, May and August, in deciduous woodland at Dalby Söderskog, Sweden. (After B. Lindquist, 1938)

it should be mentioned that trees and shrubs are not the only contributors to the litter, for herbs, and in thinner woods grasses also, contribute as well and are mostly 'soft'. Bramble in woodland is unusual in keeping on much of its foliage during the winter so that whatever it contributes to litter comes in the spring.

Lindquist later[294] devised some experiments to find whether the rate of disappearance of leaves was connected with the food preferences of earthworms. Not all the eight species of earthworms he used are in fact commonly or ever feeders on leaf litter at the surface of forest soils. For example *Allolobophora caliginosa* is very abundant in mull soils but probably lives mainly on roots, possibly also fungal mycelia and other things in the soil,[425] seldom being seen at the surface; in the experiments it ate three kinds of soft leaves – ash, wych elm and dog's mercury – but refused the others. I will here only cite the tests on *Lumbricus terrestris*, by far the most important remover of surface litter, and a smaller species *L. rubellus* which can live both in soil and in permanent surface litter. Small lots of worms were kept in containers and offered separately the fresh-fallen autumn leaves of a number of deciduous trees and some shrubs, sometimes also dog's mercury. Some leaves they started to eat at once, others were neglected for days or weeks before a start was made, and sometimes hardly touched at all. The amounts eaten were judged by eye. *L. terrestris* completely consumed alder, wych elm, ash, birch, hawthorn, lime, rowan and to a lesser extent aspen and sallow, but avoided beech, oak and Norway maple. *L. rubellus* accepted completely the same series as *L. terrestris*, except that birch and lime were less regularly consumed, and Norway maple partly taken; crab-apple and dog's mercury offered to *L. rubellus* were rapidly and completely eaten; beech and oak were far less acceptable, though apparently more so than to the larger species. Conifer needles were not accepted by earthworms. These tests have some limitations since the replicates were few or none, and the worms had no alternative food choice. But the times taken to attack the leaves are interesting – thus ten *L. rubellus* finished off half a gram of ash leaves in three days, but another lot offered the same amount of oak ate nothing for six days, only 2% by the 28th day, and only 40% by the 54th day. The experiments clearly prove that the rate of disappearance of different kinds of litter at Dalby Söderskog corresponds closely with the degree of acceptability of various trees to litter-eating worms. All the species of tree and shrub except rowan (uncommon in southern English woods) and both species of worms are to be found in Wytham Woods.

When leaf litter is enclosed in very fine mesh nylon netting its rate of disappearance is greatly slowed down, but if it is exposed to earthworms and other larger invertebrates that live in or visit the litter, it mostly disappears within a year, unless it is beech leaves. The finest mesh (e.g. 0·003 mm.) keeps out all but micro-organisms. This is evidence that the mechanical breaking up of leaf litter is chiefly done by animals, though it by no means proves that it is mainly consumed and metabolized by them – after all, if it was there could not really be the huge complex community of soil animals and other organisms that depends on the residual humus derived largely from the excreta and leaf fragments left by these same litter feeders. A report on work done at Merlewood Research Station of the Nature Conservancy in north Lancashire[345] in 1960 says of the nylon net method: 'This technique has been used for the leaves of 26 species of common woodland trees and herbs on two pairs of sites near Merlewood. The species showed great differences in their rates of disappearance from the nets. For example, on a mull site, 9 months after the experiment was set up, oak and beech leaves had lost respectively 52 and 34 per cent of their initial dry-weight whereas weights of ash and cherry leaves had fallen by more than 99 per cent. All but four of the 26 species disappeared more rapidly on the mull sites than on mor and evidence that this resulted from greater activity by litter-feeding animals was obtained in a further experiment with ash on mull. In this experiment the weight loss in 6 months from leaves enclosed in nets which excluded large invertebrates was only half that from coarse nets.' In a forest at Oak Ridge, Tennessee, Shanks and Olson[437] did similar experiments with litter in nylon bags which had, however, a mesh-size that excluded large earthworms. Although all the actual species of tree tested were different from ours, the same order of disappearance was found, beech remaining unfragmented after a year, mulberry losing two-thirds, and oaks and sugar maple coming between these.

Edwards and Heath[113] at Rothamsted in Hertfordshire, took freshly fallen oak leaves from an oak-dominated wood with mull soil, cut standard-sized discs from them, and laid these in December on the soil surface, covering them with fine nylon and then with a layer of leaves. There was a high earthworm population here, of seven species, including *Lumbricus terrestris* and *L. rubellus* as dominants. By March four-fifths of the discs had been broken up, and by October the same proportion had completely disappeared, most of the change being caused by the feeding of earthworms. In a second experiment, oak and beech leaf discs were buried in nylon bags with four different mesh-sizes about an inch down in recently cultivated old pasture soil, and examined at intervals. In the bags with 0·003-mm mesh the discs remained intact but gradually turned brown, and it was found later that beech leaves that turn brown would not be touched by soil animals even after nine months. In the bags exposed to comminution by animals the beech discs appeared more slowly than the oak, so that whereas over nine-tenths of the oak had gone between January and August, only seven-tenths of the beech had disappeared. This farm field had a good population of earthworms, again with *L. terrestris* and *L. rubellus*.

All this work agrees about the tremendous differences in the rate at which different kinds of forest leaves disappear, and about the overwhelming part played by earthworms in breaking them down and their preferences for the softer leaves. Gilbert and Bocock[181] at Merlewood Research Station discovered that oak litter, which at the start of the season has a lower nitrogen content than ash-tree litter, gradually increases its nitrogen content during ensuing months. Since this must have come from outside, they measured the nematode populations living in the water film of the leaves but found they had only a fraction of the total nitrogen. Other sources of nitrogen were also considered. Later work by Bocock has estimated that 'the frass from the caterpillars of the oak leaf-roller moth, *Tortrix viridana*, and uneaten fragments of leaves supply more than 50 per cent of the nitrogen added to the litter in years when defoliation by this insect is severe'.[346] This is a reminder of the continual relationship between canopy and ground, not only in the main leaf-fall season. Lindquist's experiments[295] on the food choice by molluscs add other pieces to the game. He repeated the kind of experiments done with earthworms on nine species of woodland snails and four of slugs collected from Dalby. Four of the snails (*Arianta arbustorum, Marpessa laminata, Goniodiscus rotundatus* and *Trichia hispida*) and all the slugs occur in Wytham Woods, though *Arianta* there is chiefly found in woodland marshes rather than terrestrial litter. Although the results were more complex than those from the earthworm experiments, he found many examples of the same choice of leaf species as by worms. Thus *Arianta arbustorum* preferred alder, elm and ash, but would not touch beech leaves unless they had been first boiled, dipped in glucose solution and dried – a change he attributed to the removal of tannin. But molluscs have a much more varied range of food, and some of the slugs prefer fungi to leaves, live or dead.

Through this flow of details it is necessary to keep a bearing on the main argument, and avoid getting side-tracked into any attempt to analyse the current confusion about chemical changes in litter, the physiology of nutrition, the place of endoparasitic micro-organisms in providing digestive enzymes, or the exact role and dominance of this or that species. So far, the downward changes in the original tree canopy pattern stand thus: the leaves of each species have fallen vertically, but with a good deal of lateral swirl and drift that does not, however, in a mature wood (which creates its own microclimate of shelter in the lower strata) obscure the primary pattern of interspersion so easily observed in the late autumn and early winter; the leaves on the ground have been attacked by a good many of the larger litter-living animals, and even more by earthworms coming up at night from the soil; there is also much fungal and bacterial activity, at any rate in the lower litter layers, but this does not by itself account for the breaking up of the litter in the first year; beech disappears slowly or not at all in the first year, oak a good deal faster but still more slowly than the softer leaves from most trees and shrubs and many field-layer and ground zone herbs; within the range of softer dead leaves, the diet is unrestricted; the range of diet of some litter-eaters is wide and not confined to dead leaves – this is so in some snails; only a fraction of the materia ingested is assimilated, so that the excretory pellets of all these litter-eaters provide the starting point for further long food-chains going down into the soil and in these microbial action plays a very large role. In the absence of a well-developed litter-eating community, especially of the larger earthworms, the formation of a rich mull soil is prevented and raw humus accumulates at the surface and below it.

During this sequence of changes several different processes are combining to blur the original pattern of a mosaic canopy in which each component carries a recognizably distinct herbivore community. First there is the existence of non-specific herbivores like the winter moth. Secondly, the much less restricted habit of both invertebrate and vertebrate predators. Third comes the lateral drift of stil recognizably distinct species of leaf. Fourth is the gradual loss of this distinction a live chemistry turns into dead chemistry, the living structure into small fragments later into small excretory pellets which in turn tend to consist of aggregations o very small particles, often of similar size in different litter animals.[515] Fifthly ther are the lateral movements of litter and soil animals, living in what has progressivel become a habitat of common character, at any rate organically considered. I think the important trend to notice is that the litter and soil communities, based as the are on dead matter and a great microfloral complex of bacteria and fungi, an therefore to a considerable extent released from the limitations imposed on herbi vores by the structure, chemistry and seasonal timing of the live plant, have th same kind of wider diet and habitat range that has already been described for mos predators and many insect parasites. This, by creating unistratal links or girder between major habitats, is another main situation that integrates the whole eco system. This sequence will be seen again in dying and dead wood (Ch. 14). T what extent the separate species of microfungi and bacteria have qualities tha restrict them as food for one animal species or another, is yet to be discovered. Th kind of restriction, operating in somewhat the same manner as in green plants, certainly encountered in macrofungi (Ch. 15) though even in these usually mor than one species of fungus is attacked by the same animal.

The broad result of these differences in the rates of disappearance of woodlan litter at a place like Wytham Woods is to produce two kinds of situation on th ground. In the first, soft leaves like ash and sycamore are broken down before oal though the latter has nearly all gone after a year. In the second, beech litte accumulates for at least two years, and although the top layers remain rather dr and untouched by animals, in the lower layers an intense fungal growth develop and here there is a large and well-developed permanent litter fauna, includin earthworms. Exactly the same difference in habitat has already been noticed i grassland (Ch. 6) where softer grasses and herbs are mostly broken down quickl whereas *Brachypodium pinnatum* litter lasts longer and maintains a permanent litt layer. Both beech and *Brachypodium* litter, as also that under dense bracken, can blanket the ground and prevent growth of other species of green plants, but fungi are encouraged – beech litter is a well-known hunting-ground for mycologists in search of toadstools and other fungi. It would be natural at this point to give a comparison of the faunas of oak–ash–sycamore litter and beech litter on alkaline or mull soils. But for the reasons explained in [24] it is not possible to do so at present, although two important studies are on the way. But enough is known from less rigidly planned field observations at Wytham, to show that there is much more resemblance in the faunas than might have been expected from the apparent difference in habitats, especially in the summer, when many parts of the woodland floor under oak–ash–sycamore canopy can be bare of tree leaves other than the residual ones of oak. The explanation of this resemblance can only be that beech leaves after suitable 'preparation' by micro-organisms become as good a food or more correctly mixture of foods (leaf–fungus–bacteria) as the softer leaves without such long 'preparation'. In fact, an animal such as *Glomeris marginata* can exist at Wytham in the soft-grass ground zone, in *Brachypodium pinnatum* litter (here as a dominant species), in bracken litter, in oak–ash–sycamore wood, and in beech litter.

It is only too easy to be misleading and give the impression that the distribution of litter animals is simple – either widespread in a great many major habitat types or plant associations, or else restricted by the boundaries of the structural lines used in this book. A large number of species do have these types of distribution. Thus although the litter-living Staphylinid beetle *Gyrohypnus myrmecophilus* lives in deciduous woodland under various dominant trees at Wytham and also in *Brachypodium pinnatum* grassland, its ally *G. punctulatus* is confined to woodland. Of two snail-eating Silphid beetles there, *Phosphuga atrata* is primarily a woodland species, and *Ablattaria laevigata* is confined to stony grassland. The woodlouse *Philoscia muscorum* is found on both sides of the woodland edge, but *Porcellio rathkei* at Wytham is a meadow animal. But two provisos have always to be remembered in making such statements. The first is that they may only apply to one locality: thus, *Glomeris marginata* was found by Van der Drift[515] to be common in oakwood litter at a place in the Netherlands, whereas it was absent from adjacent patches of beech litter. On Wytham Hill it is found in beech litter, as well as elsewhere. The second proviso is that presence, in sufficient numbers or under circumstances that cannot be accidental, is proof enough; but absence may be caused by lack of dispersal, by the existence of a completely unrevealed physical condition of the habitat, some biotic relationship to do with competing species or other network influences such as fungal food and so on, aggregated distribution that is missed by the sampling system, or to historical fluctuations leading to temporary or permanent absence. The detailed analysis of litter communities is therefore going to be a long task for which we have as yet not enough material. Here I am only trying to trace the downward process of blurring and mixing of the original canopy patterns by which the machinery of a wood is kept in being.

The wide unistratal distribution of the soil and ground zone communities is very clearly to be seen in the earthworms, also in many litter-feeding and some soil predators, both invertebrate and vertebrate. Out of the immense literature about earthworms only a few examples are selected here, for comparison with what is known about them in the Oxford region. The local information comes from two sources. At Wytham the records consist of a number of collections (recorded in the Ecological Survey) made during field classes in the woodland by means of potassium permanganate as a vermifuge, together with worms encountered in the course of the grassland study on the pure *Brachypodium pinnatum* community ('The Dell') mentioned in Ch. 6. These were all named by Professor A. J. Cain. In addition I have the advantage of unpublished notes on earthworms in the Oxford neighbourhood obtained by Mr H. Sassoon while working in the Department of Geology. For the present purpose I shall not attempt a quantitative expression because all the methods in use for counting earthworms have some drawbacks – thus under some conditions deeper-living species like *Lumbricus terrestris* might be 'scarcer' by day than by night when they feed at the surface. In one drought summer, the permanganate method failed entirely on calcareous mull soil of the Wytham woodland, though digging into the rubble and soil several feet down disclosed a worm population. I shall take three species with different habits: *L. terrestris* that burrows deeply though it is not always living far below the surface, and which is the chief earthworm consumer of surface litter, with other sources of food in the soil as well; *Allolobophora terrestris* (= *longa*) which is an important source of surface castings from its excreta (Gerard[177] estimated that it may eat its own weight of earth a day), but feeds mainly underground; and *A. caliginosa* which feeds in the upper topsoil, partly on roots, and does not normally frequent the surface. The following notes refer to occurrence in soil or litter or both. At Wytham all three species live under oak–ash–sycamore and under beech wood, and under the *Brachypodium* tussock grassland. (No one here or elsewhere in Britain appears yet to have properly investigated the earthworms of scrub.) Sassoon found all three in pasture round Oxford, and *A. caliginosa* and *L. terrestris* in arable fields. Evans and Guild[142] recorded them at Rothamsted in Hertfordshire, living in pasture and arable fields. Reynoldson,[402] who with a team of students in north Wales searched samples of the top 9-10 in. of soil by hand, reported all three species from pasture and arable land (both with cereals and root crops), and from a mixed wood of oak, sycamore, sweet chestnut and conifers with a good flora below that included bramble and dog's mercury. In the Carse of Stirling in Scotland, Guild,[198] using permanganate extraction, obtained the same three species often abundantly in pasture soils that varied from clay through loams to gravelly sand and alluvium. In Danish woodlands, Bornebusch[35] found them in mully beech woods and in mull under oaks [26]. There are plenty of other European records of the kind.

So these three top performers in the litter and soil are common to these three terrestrial formation-types. The only comparable habitat range of an ecologically dominant primary consumer seems to be the rabbit. Both *Lumbricus terrestris* and *Oryctolagus cuniculus*, considered as species in Britain, must consume hundreds of different sorts of plants, and by their preferences affect the ultimate nature of the habitats they live in. There is a classical passage by Bornebusch,[35] in his wonderful monograph on the litter and soil communities of Danish woodland, in which he compares the maximum live weight of earthworms he found in Danish woodland soils (1800-2000 kg. per hectare) with that of the similar weights of domestic stock on a first-rate farm. Reynoldson,[402] for north Wales, has made a similar rough comparison of about 1140 kg. of earthworms per hectare as against a live weight of sheep of about half that amount. There are no reliable figures for the biomass of wild rabbits in an English pasture, partly because their foraging range is complex and census not easy. But it seems likely that the weight per hectare is considerably less than that of farm stock, and so less than the earthworm biomass. This great quantity of worms must be borne in mind when predators are considered, and from the census methods employed, the estimates quoted above must, if anything, be below the mark. A final example comes from a field survey done by Stegman[482] at the Tully Forest in New York State, of earthworms belonging to nine species that also come in Britain and of which all but *Octolasium lacteum* have been collected on Wytham Hill. These were collected by sieving the top 6 in. of soil samples, and although such collections probably did not get a complete count of the deeper-living species like *Lumbricus terrestris*, and the samples were rather few, the results again prove the capacity of some species to live in different kinds of place. The habitats, all of which had acid soils, included (1) abandoned old fields in various stages up to scrub, (2) hardwood plantations and mature stands, (3) red or white pine plantations of various ages, (4) pond edges, (5) stream edges. *Allolobophora caliginosa*, *Eisenia rosea* and *Octolasium lacteum* were found in all five of these, and *Lumbricus terrestris* in the first two and the last. But in the conifer plantations worms were scarce or absent in pure pine-needle litter, only appearing (and then in rather low numbers) where there was a locally good herb cover and the soil not too dry.

The intricate patterns of the litter itself and its fauna are further embroidered as it were by all manner of other structures, some of them being green plants, with which I will not try to deal, and others fallen from above. The chief of these falling objects are dying and dead wood, and the fruits and sometimes the galls from trees and shrubs. To a great extent these fall vertically and therefore make patches characteristic of each woody species – a beech-tree bough, a mass of acorns or crab-apples, spangle galls (*Neuroterus*) on the leaves of oak, and so on. As has been already noted, the heavier or wingless fruits like acorns and beech mast do not drift laterally very much, and so at first follow the pattern of the canopy; but those of ash and sycamore and maple are equipped to glide or twirl to some distance side-ways. They are also carried away by animals, and sometimes buried, with further effects upon woodland regeneration. However, it will usually be observed that even the offspring of a large ash or sycamore tree are grouped in a zone round it, perhaps also in the space it left if it has fallen, and in this manner the original component of the tree pattern survives though larger in extent. In Wytham Woods, this arrangement is often to be seen with ash, sycamore and wych elm. Since the reduction of the rabbit population by myxomatosis and subsequent control, beech also begins to show this, oak still only slightly. The fact is that mortality in seeds and seedlings is so high that it is usually the denser populations of young nearest the parent tree that survive, if space permits. Such large patches have a clear individuality in the woodland system.

The whole subject of dying and dead wood is dealt with in Ch. 14, and I will only mention two preliminary points now: bark-beetle communities, and the sharing and interchange of rotting wood fauna with the litter on which it lies. As will be shown in that chapter, bark-beetles do not occur commonly on all species of trees, so that in a place like Wytham Woods only the ash and elm (in the deciduous realm) are important in this respect. These bark-beetle populations essentially belong to the green-plant phase of the tree and indeed often occur on dying portions of a live tree, as well as on some of the recent fallen timber. They therefore follow the restricted pattern found in many other tree herbivores. But some of their predators and parasites are shared in common. By the time real decay sets in in the logs, a considerable resemblance of the communities begins to develop, which applies even between deciduous and conifer logs.

If you roll a log over, even a small one six inches or so in diameter, a good many of the larger litter animals may be found underneath its curving sides. Here for example are snails, *Cepaea nemoralis*, the large spotted slug *Limax maximus* and many other forms. If you take samples of the litter not near such logs, you will often find no *Cepaea* or *Limax maximus*, and the inference must be that they use the logs as day shelters, or at any rate day shelters unless it is raining. These conclusions are not absolutely proven, I think because ecologists tend not to work at night or in pouring rain. They rest upon observations I have made during several annual field-classes held in September. This subject has been explored in another way by both European and American ecologists, who have put out cover boards or similar structures on the woodland floor in order to ascertain which species go

35. Pack-horses of Carruthers' expedition to Mongolia in 1910 forcing their way through dense pine taiga in the Syansk Mountains. The ground is covered with rotting wood. (From D. Carruthers, 1910)

36. Large English elm in an old hedgerow on Wytham Hill, from which a branch has fallen on to open pasture and become heat-sterilized. The place where the branch broke off provided a nesting site for a kestrel (*Falco tinnunculus*). (Photo C. S. E. 19 June 1960)

37. Glade in oak–ash–sycamore woodland at Wytham, produced by felling an oak tree, with field layer of young ash and bracken. Dead grey squirrel hanging up to attract carrion insects. (Photo D. A. K. 8 Sept. 1952)

38. Stump of felled oak in this glade, with honey-fungus, *Armillaria mellea*, on dead stump and roots, and young ash seedlings. (Photo D. A. K. 8 Sept. 1952)

39. Dead branch of English elm with bracket of *Polyporus squamosus*, and holes in bark and gallery on wood of elm bark-beetles, *Scolytus scolytus*. Wytham Woods. (Photo D. A. K. 13 Sept. 1954)

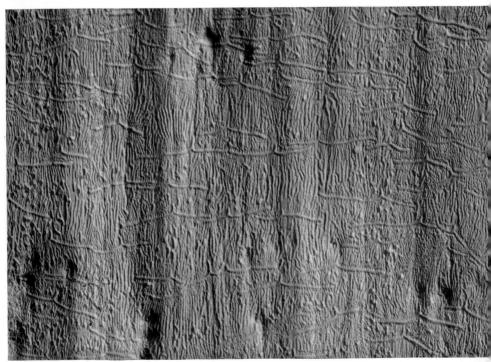

40. Galleries made by a moderately dense population of ash bark-beetles, *Hylesinus fraxini*, on the sapwood surface (the bark has been removed to show the engravings). (Photo D. A. K. from material obtained by C. S. E. at Wytham)

41. A fallen beech branch in Wytham Woods a year or two old, with heart-rot, and the bark cracked and loosened by other fungal growth, but not by bark-beetles. (Photo C. S. E. 12 Oct. 1961)

42. Remains of an old rotting beech log in a glade with bramble field layer, Wytham Woods. (Photo D. A. K. 4 Sept. 1950)

43 & 44. Beetles common in rotting deciduous logs and dying trees in Wytham Woods. Above, larvae and adult of Elaterid *Melanotus rufipes*; below, pupa of Lucanid *Dorcus parallelipipedus*, in a beech log. (Photos D. A. K. Sept. 1952 & 1950)

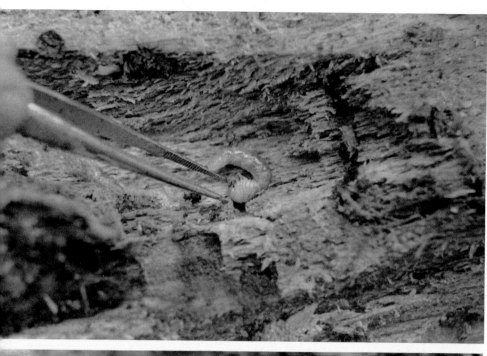

45 & 46. Larva and adult male of Lucanid beetle, *Sinodendron cylindricum*, in a beech log. Common in many kinds of rotting wood in Wytham Woods. (Photos D. A. K. Sept. 1950)

47. Broken bole and fallen top of old beech tree hollowed by heart-rot, in deciduous woodland at Wytham. (Photo C. S. E. 22 May 1960)

under them for shelter. But none of this work has been done in such conditions or in such a way to have much application to an undisturbed English wood.

Many of the species that shelter under logs also enter underneath the loose bark produced by bark-beetle invasion or the attacks of fungal mycelia. When the logs rot further, they also enter the decaying wood and the galleries made by larger insects. While there is no species of mollusc that lives entirely in logs and not in litter, a good many litter molluscs go into logs, though there are also many that do not, or do so very seldom. Good instances of species that are frequently found in both habitats are the pointed snail *Marpessa laminata* (which does not much occur outside woodland) and *Clausilia rugosa* (now *bidentata*), also the small 'ammonite-patterned' *Goniodiscus rotundatus* and the garlic-smelling *Oxychilus alliarius*. Similarly the large centipede *Lithobius variegatus* and the woodlouse *Oniscus asellus* are found in both. In Wytham Woods there is a grove of large old beeches with a rich litter layer beneath, in which Professor M. Lloyd has made a number of measurements of population dispersion of various litter animals. The part so far published[296] concerns some experiments on the question of movements between logs and litter. These were organized in the following way, and given a rather rigid statistical treatment: they are valuable as much for their methods as for their results. This beech grove, though having small amounts of young sycamore growing under minor gaps in the trees, is primarily a beech habitat both as to litter and fallen boughs. The first experiment was done during a cold spell in winter when the ground was almost freezing and a little snow had fallen. Eleven small branches, around 2 inches diameter, were each divided into two parts, one lot being brought in and the other exposed for four days, when the ground temperature had risen by about 10° C. The animals under bark and in decaying wood were counted, and most of them (with the exception of the less mobile forms such as Enchytraeid worms and fly larvae) were much more abundant in the logs brought in after the air had got warmer than when it was at zero. Lloyd concluded that 'the consistency of the pattern makes the evidence fairly convincing that many of the centipedes, woodlice, snails, slugs and even earthworms tended to come into the fallen branches as the weather warmed up and hence by implication, go into the litter during cold weather'.

The species identified in Lloyd's experiment were the earthworms *Bimastus riseni* and *B. tenuis* and *Dendrobaena mammalis*; the centipedes *Lithobius crassipes* and *L. variegatus* (the results for *Schendyla nemorensis* were too small to be significant); the woodlice *Oniscus asellus* and *Trichoniscus pusillus provisorius*; and the snails *Marpessa laminata*, *Clausilia rugosa* and *Goniodiscus rotundatus*. In most instances there were at least a few individuals even in the 'cold logs'. That there is a persistent population of such species through the winter both in small logs and larger ones is proved by the other evidence from Wytham Woods. The community analysis by

E. W. Fager[148] of small natural oak logs, only a little larger than the beech logs used by Lloyd, but lying in a damper part of the woods, is described in Ch. 14. Samples of natural logs collected by him in August, October, November, February, March and April all included individuals of the two *Bimastus* species, the two *Lithobius*, the *Oniscus* and *Trichoniscus*, and (except in November) *Goniodiscus*. *Clausilia rugosa* was absent from October to February. The other species in Lloyd's experiment did not turn up in Fager's survey of natural logs. In any case, I think such movements, even if of regular occurrence, must apply to quite small logs. All these species have been found in winter months under bark or in decaying wood of larger logs, under circumstances that do not fit the idea of frequent interchange.

The collection of logs in the first experiment was done by day. A second experiment was designed to find out whether there are day and night movements between logs and litter. At the end of March some small lengths of log were laid out in groups and left for a week, and isolated by being in turn placed in plastic bags at four-hour intervals around the clock. They were then brought in and the animals counted. The temperature did not vary much over this period of twenty-four hours, and the air was saturated with moisture. No significant differences were found in the numbers of animals at different times, and it was concluded that no important movements were taking place, and that under these temperature conditions at any rate no inherent rhythm of activity between logs and litter was operating. Under other conditions matters might be different. It should not be thought that the sharing of species between logs and litter applies to more than a fairly small part of the fauna, although the species involved are some of them important operators. One would hardly ever find, for example, the small snail *Acanthinula aculeata* in a log, or the woodlouse *Porcellio scaber* in the litter. The scattered furniture of dead wood is in fact only used by some of the inhabitants of the house, and even so it seems that for the larger and mobile species this cover is not always in a suitable microclimatic state, at any rate unless it is large.

Something now needs to be said about the fate of tree-fruit and scrub-fruit crops. In a place like Wytham Woods the most important of these crops are acorns from the oak, mast from the beech, samaras or keys from the ash and sycamore, nuts from hazel, and berries from the hawthorn and elder. There are some others. The composition of the woodland and therefore of its tree fruits considered as resources for animals makes a difference to the communities, as I have already mentioned in regard to the great tit (Ch. 11). The events that happen to these fruits are bound up with the scale of their size, for on the one hand they may be entered by insects which consume the seed and thereafter are followed by a tiny community – what Winston[552] in his study of the red oak in Illinois called a 'microsere'; or they may be consumed outright by vertebrates, with or without the micro-community as well. In this respect they resemble oak galls although the complexity of the inner communities is never anything like as specific or – in this country at any rate – probably anything like so complex as in galls. One finds the same distinction in other small centres of action such as dead bodies, cow-pats, or small logs, which may have rich seral communities of invertebrates, or may be attacked by vertebrates, either for the resource directly (a carrion crow picking the bones of a dead body) or the insect community developing in it (rooks eating cow-pat beetles).

The fate of acorns affords a good example, especially as acorns in present-day Britain, and even more before rabbits decreased from disease, have been so much sought by animals that regeneration of oak woods had almost come to a halt. But here I am more concerned with the acorn crops as magnets that draw animals to particular patches of a wood. In Britain they are attacked by insects while still on the tree, indeed before they are ripe for birds and squirrels to eat, and especially by two weevils *Curculio* (or *Balaninus*) *venosus* and *C. glandium* whose grubs are still there when the acorns fall, but leave them in order to pupate in the soil. Sometimes a Tortricid moth *Enarmonia splendana* also attacks them.[252] In the United States this matter has been studied much more thoroughly.[342, 552] There acorns on oaks different from ours are attacked by other species of *Curculio*, and by a moth *Milissopus latiferraneus* – a close ally of the apple codling moth – although it seems that the American red oak (*Quercus rubra*, now *Q. borealis* var. *maxima*) when planted in Europe is not attacked by our own *Curculio* and *Enarmonia*.[252] In America another moth, *Valentinia glanduella*, enters the acorn husks vacated by weevils, spins a web over the entrance to keep out other animals, and proceeds to eat up the remains of the acorn together with the dung of the weevils. Winston, studying acorn communities in a red oak and sugar maple forest in Illinois, found a whole minuscule world of organisms taking part in the decay cycle of acorns on the ground – including (1) the first stage of weevil and moth, also microfungi and two kinds of flies, progress being aided by grey squirrels that opened but did not eat some of the nuts; (2) the second moth, more fungi, mites and flies; (3) much of the original softer tissues gone, more fungi, with springtails and mites; (4) then animals coming in to the hollow shell for shelter; (5) eventually its incorporation into the humus. But in Britain I think the disappearance of acorns would be too rapid to allow any considerable micro-community to develop over a period as long as a year; furthermore the red oak has larger acorns than ours. A good many birds and mammals feed on acorns, among them notably wood-pigeons, jays, rooks, rabbits and grey squirrels. But I shall confine attention to the voles and mice that are so especially dependent on these and other tree and shrub fruits, because they form a link with further events that have been well studied at Wytham.

There the two commonest small mammals living on and in the woodland are the wood-mouse, *Apodemus sylvaticus*, and the bank vole, *Clethrionomys glareolus*. A very long chain of investigations on these animals has been in progress at Oxford since 1925 (from 1932 in the Bureau of Animal Population), first in Bagley Wood and from 1947 at Wytham Woods by H. N. Southern and his associates (Plate 28). Very slowly, a clear picture is beginning to appear, seen through the somewhat distorting medium of live-trapping systems, of the true population structure, changes, movements and interrelationships, though there is still no agreement as to the relative decisiveness of different natural controlling tendencies in the populations and their environment. I shall refer only to a few points that concern the habitat mosaics over which these mice and voles rove, and the extent to which they are limited by some of them. Chitty's pioneer work[66] with ringed live mice laid the basis for understanding movements, among other things. It is certain that the wood-mouse has a much wider capacity for movement than the bank vole, but Kikkawa's analysis[268] of this matter at Wytham has suggested that the normal home range is much the same for both species, only the wood-mouse not infrequently undertakes much wider movements before settling again on to a smaller area. My own earlier trapping experience in Bagley Wood, and most of the later work by others, agrees about the general activity rhythm in these two species: the wood-mouse is almost entirely nocturnal (if we include all or part of the dusk and dawn periods in this term), whereas the bank vole is out a great deal by day as well as by night. But the details of activity rhythms are complex, as Miller[325] has shown in laboratory tests, for example changing with the relative length of day and night. And at Silwood Park in Surrey, Brown[49] showed by two-hourly trapping that in this area the bank voles were predominantly nocturnal, though they were less so when wood-mice were abundant. At any rate, so far as Wytham Woods are concerned, there is the broad contrast that wood-mice, being active by night, are less dependent on the protection of cover and move on a larger scale, whereas bank voles are partly diurnal and are more sedentary.

The restriction of bank voles to thicker ground cover is illustrated by the maps in Figs. 23 and 24 taken from an unpublished thesis by Miller.[323] His field work was done in two separate parts of Wytham Woods. The Chalet Woods, to which these maps refer, contain oak, ash, sycamore and a few other species such as beech together with patches of hawthorn and elder scrub interspersed with bracken or bramble and bracken, the whole growing on an old limestone coral reef. Trapping round a whole year caught wood-mice everywhere, but bank voles were chiefly restricted to the brackeny parts. The Pasticks[326] is an isolated planted copse grown to maturity and – from the ecologist's point of view – nicely neglected. It has a dense canopy of oak, ash, sycamore, lime and wych elm, slight under-scrub of hawthorn, elder, young sycamore and elm, and in summer a dense covering of dog's mercury (*Mercurialis perennis*) and nettle (*Urtica dioica*). Here the bank vole

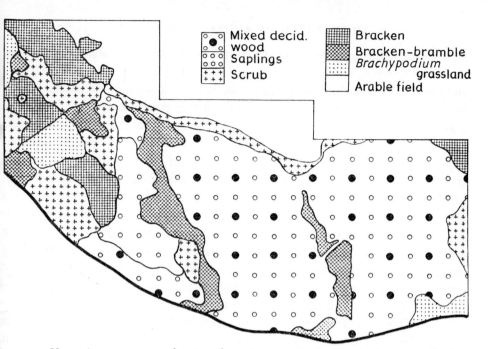

FIG. 23. Vegetation cover map of various formation-types leading to deciduous woodland, Chalet Woods, Wytham. (From R. S. Miller, 1951)

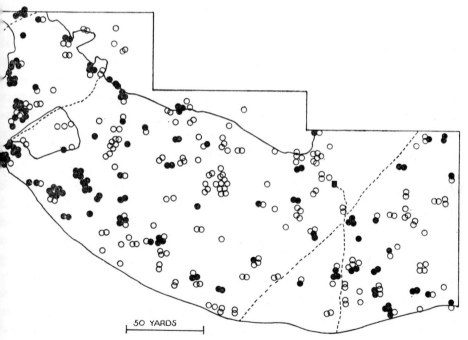

FIG. 24. Trapping record of bank voles, *Clethrionomys glareolus* (●), and wood-mice, *Apodemus sylvaticus* (○), in the area shown in Fig. 23. The former tend to be confined to thicker cover. (From R. S. Miller, 1951)

were found all through the wood in summer, but when the vegetation of the field layer died down in winter, they retreated to the residual cover provided by logs and the like. Exactly the same phenomenon was worked out in the Pasticks wood later on, by Kikkawa,[268] who also confirmed that the bank voles seldom went outside the wood into the surrounding wheat field, except for short distances, though wood-mice frequently travelled far into it. Miller's mapping[323] of some larger-scale trapping records from the unpublished work of Southern revealed also broad seasonal expansion and contraction of this kind. Bracken appears to be especially effective as a habitat for the bank vole, a conclusion reached earlier also by Evans[143] in his population survey in Bagley Wood. It must be remembered, however, that a wide trapping catch such as *Apodemus* yields does not necessarily mean that the mice are 'inhabiting' all the places at which they are caught – they may have been in rapid transit. But it does mean that they have a much greater opportunity of finding and tapping resources scattered over the whole ground-pattern of the woodland floor than do bank voles.

It is well known from general observation and from experiments on forest regeneration that both species collect and store tree fruits such as acorns. In captivity they will usually start by storing any food surplus to their immediate needs, at any rate under artificial conditions simulating a twelve- or sixteen-hour night.[323] I have kept *Apodemus sylvaticus* that stored surplus wheat grains in the nest box to such an extent that some of them were driven to sleep in the open cage. This storing habit would seem likely to give them a valuable and perhaps essential start in the intense scramble by various species to collect these seeds after they fall in autumn and winter. Miller[324] analysed the stomach contents of 69 wood-mice and 71 bank voles caught in Wytham Woods, from March 1950 to February 1951 over a period when beech mast crops were not very high, acorns and sweet chest-nuts sometimes good, and the seeds of sycamore and ash and fruits of hawthorn very abundant in both winters. Seeds and fruits occurred in about 85% of the wood-mice and 80% of the bank voles, and, although analysis of such partly broken down foods is difficult, he concluded that tree seeds were the chief food. Apart from small amounts of green plant (especially in bank voles), and roots, and occasional galls and fungi, the other main item was insects – both adults and larvae – which in the wood-mice occurred in about 30% and 48% of the stomachs respectively, and in the bank vole about 34% and 32%. There was no strong difference between the two species, at any rate in this woodland area, and the chief point is that both are largely dependent on tree and shrub seeds and fruits especially in winter, supplemented by insects all round the year. I think that the varied litter fauna of bracken, mentioned earlier in this chapter, may be of some importance to a species like the bank vole that also uses bracken for cover, where it is available. The actual habitats of the insects, which included various caterpillars and beetles, could not usually be traced, but in the laboratory mice and voles willingly ate almost any offered to them.

The chief consumer of wood-mice and bank voles in Wytham Woods is the tawny owl, *Strix aluco*, which in turn is highly dependent upon sufficient numbers of these and other small mammal preys for its successful breeding. Of Wytham Woods, Southern,[463, 464] whose long-continued and successful study of owl and mouse populations there stands unrivalled, says that 'the area can definitely be classed as "optimum" habitat for the owls because thirty pairs can maintain themselves on 1000 acres, a remarkable density for a predator living mainly on vertebrates'.[464] In addition to catching mice and voles (which include also *Microtus agrestis*, whose main headquarters is in grassland or woodland edge) and shrews, the tawny owl has a remarkable range of diet, in spite of which it is unable to produce a normal-sized family in certain years when rodents are scarce. Large numbers of pellets (that is, the rejected parts of the food eaten) were examined for all seasons and from twenty different owl territories. Within the vertebrates important subsidiary foods were moles, young rabbits and birds, the last being mainly passerine birds among which chaffinches and other finches formed nearly 70% of the identifiable birds in the pellets. The other important foods were earthworms and insects, the former detectable by chaetae in fibrous pellets containing remains of leaves. In the less heavily wooded or open areas such pellets were as numerous as the ones containing vertebrates. Of the insects beetles were dominant: half were cockchafers, *Melolontha vulgaris*, whose larvae live underground eating the roots of trees; over a quarter were dor-beetles, species of *Geotrupes*, that breed in cow-dung; 19% were predacious ground-beetles, mainly *Carabus nemoralis*; and there were a few burying-beetles, *Necrophorus*, and odd specimens of other forms.

Although the tawny owl feeds chiefly from a perch at field layer or scrub height, and collects most of its food from the ground, it is really getting its calories indirectly from every layer of the forest, and from both the forest and its edges. The wood-mice and bank voles are converted tree and scrub seeds and fruits, supplemented by insects from the ground zone and probably the field layer as well. Earthworms living in the soil but exposed at night on the surface (and that means chiefly *Lumbricus terrestris*) derive their food in the forest itself partly from dead leaves of trees and shrubs as well as from soil, though in open grassy places like Wytham Park they probably eat other decaying plants as well, and are therefore more herbivorous and less saprophagous. Earthworms may also be taken indirectly *via* the mole [27] and perhaps also shrews. In woodland edge and on grassland the voles and rabbits are herbivorous on grass and herbs. To these three main primary production channels leading eventually into the owl – green plant seeds and fruits plus green vegetation on the ground plus dead leaves – are added minor ones from the roots of trees (cockchafers); slugs, worms and beetles

(*Carabus*) on the woodland floor; cow-dung on pasture (dor-beetles); and *dead* small mammals (burying-beetles). The exploitation of this pattern of different channels, each not only having a specific origin but also a component place in the area and vertical zonation of the woodland pattern to which we can still only assign co-ordinates in rather general terms, varies with the seasons that change the cover and the numbers and activity of animals, and with the years that often see violent changes in the numbers of prey, and would no doubt also differ in another kind of woodland. The owl is, in fine, the conductor of an orchestra that draws its performers from every kind of place and rank, and changes the combinations as one player or another is absent from a particular performance. But there are limits of time and territory and skill to the degree to which each individual owl (or bank vole or earthworm or shrew) can successfully exploit all these resources, and it is not surprising to find both flexibility in the diet and individual characteristics or even idiosyncrasy contributing to survival.

The badger (*Meles meles*) is perhaps an even more remarkable assembler of calories than the tawny owl. On Wytham Hill a considerable population of badgers dig their headquarters in a sandy belt round the middle zone of the hill, and a map of these colonies is given by Southern and Linn[465] in *The Handbook of British Mammals*. From these colonies the animals hunt over all parts of the hill. Neal[349] says: 'Badgers are capable of travelling long distances in a night, but it would appear that if food is plentiful they will remain within a mile or so of their sets during most of the year. This does not apply to unmated animals, especially males during the breeding season.' Knowledge of the food of badgers in Britain is of a rather episodic nature, but nevertheless shows the quite extraordinary variety of items eaten, a variety that defies any comparatively simple reference to main food-chains such as I have just indicated for the tawny owl. A very thorough analysis has been done in Denmark by Andersen,[6] who identified the foods in 190 badger stomachs from different parts of that country. The food comprised an enormous number of items, but it was clear that oats formed about a quarter of the bulk, earthworms another quarter, toads and frogs and insects between them a little over a quarter, the rest consisting of mammals and birds, birds' eggs, berries, etc. In Britain Amphibia cannot be important because they are not abundant where badgers live, and on Wytham Hill they are almost absent. Earthworms, young rabbits and roots are among the many items known to be eaten in Britain, and also (as at Wytham) nests of wasps and of bumble-bees where these are available. They also eat *Geotrupes* both in Britain and Denmark. The chief point relevant here is that the food of the badger comes from a score of habitat components and reaches it both through the green-plant food-chains and through those that start from dead matter.

Most of the primary processes described so far in this chapter can be seen to

depend on the force of gravity bringing down objects of all kinds from the forest
canopy on to the woodland floor, especially in the autumn months. But there is
also considerable interchange between the different layers of the forest brought
about by the movements of animals, and much of this movement is in an upward
direction. A good deal of field survey on vertical movements has been done in
America, but for the sake of compactness and focus I will confine myself in the
end of this chapter to some of the examples that have been worked out in Wytham
Woods. They include the spiders, the harvestmen, and an alga-feeding woodlouse.
There is still much to do in this subject, but it often requires an amount of night-
watching and also a continuity that makes considerable demands on the observer.
Turnbull's very thorough survey[510] of the spiders living in an oak-wood glade has
already been mentioned in connection with the vertical stratification of *Theridion
pallens*, the commonest spider there (Ch. 11). This survey was done quantitatively
by taking quadrat samples of the ground zone and extracting the spiders in a
Tullgren funnel, by sweeping an approximate volume of the field layer with its
vegetation, and by beating approximate volumes of both low and high canopy
into a tray. Perhaps all these methods were a little rough and gave numbers rather
below the true ones, but they are good enough for comparisons. Turnbull used the
same vertical layers as in the Ecological Survey (Ch. 4) except for a scrub canopy
limit of 25 ft instead of 15 ft as now used in the latter. He gives a list of 96 species
of spiders, which may be compared with the 141 found by Duffey on limestone
grassland on top of the hill (Ch. 6). These two lists of species have only 55 in
common, and the differences are still greater if only the common ones are compared. Turnbull concluded that 'the field layer is the richest in species, and repre-
sentatives of practically all species present in the environment were found there.
The field layer constitutes the zone of demarcation between typically ground-
inhabiting species and typically canopy-inhabiting species.' *Theridion pallens*, however, comes in all layers of the forest. 'The high canopy is the poorest in species,
and constitutes a marginal upward extension of the low canopy.' In Fig. 25 the
population density in different months and layers is represented in the rather
abstract form of 'numbers per m.³', though of course the ground zone is only
15 cm. high, and in any case the spiders are living in different cover textures. In
the dead of winter relatively few spiders are to be found at any height. Towards
the spring there is an increase that is derived from overwintering eggs. Both in the
field layer and the canopy part of the increase is brought about by upward
movements.

There is some very good information about vertical movements in Todd's
survey[509] of the harvestmen (Opiliones) in Wytham Woods, which ranks as one
of the most satisfactory done for any group of animals there, since it extended the
interpretation of habitat choice by measuring also humidity and then testing the

conclusions by means of preferendum experiments in the laboratory. I wish now only to mention the evidence about movements, seasonally and by day and night. Twelve species of harvestmen live in this deciduous woodland and its glades. Most of the species lay their eggs in the ground zone and pass the winter in this stage.

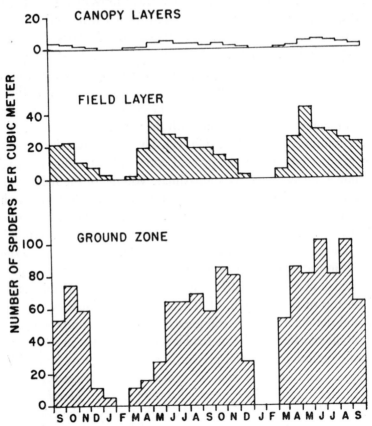

FIG. 25. Approximate biomass of spiders through the seasons in different vertical layers of a deciduous woodland glade at Wytham. (From A. L. Turnbull, 1960)

Megabunus diadema, however, lives only in the canopy where it passes the winter in the immature state, as does *Platybunus triangularis* in the ground zone. *Nemastome lugubre* can be found in the ground zone all round the year. (That there may be a certain number of overwintering harvestman eggs laid above ground level is proved by the fact that I have several times had harvestmen hatch out in the laboratory from rotting wood taken at heights up to 15 ft, but the evidence about to be cited suggests that this must be a minor contribution.) The charts by Todd (Fig. 26) illustrate how the colonization of the field layer, and also often of tree trunks and sometimes the canopy by species that have overwintered as eggs proceeds progressively through the spring and summer, the animals gradually moving upwards as they develop. The meaning of these zones needs explaining. The ground zone was sampled by 1 m.² quadrats of litter or moss extracted in Tullgren funnels; the field layer – here defined in the general botanical sense, and

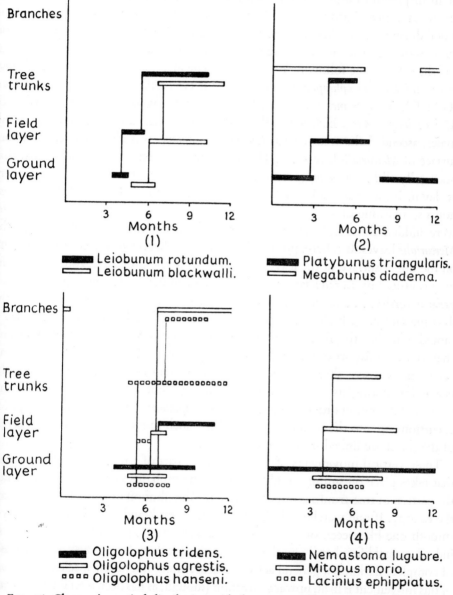

FIG. 26. Changes in vertical distribution with the seasons, of harvestmen (Opiliones) in deciduous woodland at Wytham, with *Nemastoma lugubre* remaining always in the ground zone. (From V. Todd, 1949)

usually a low rather than a high field layer – was swept in a standard manner; the trunks were searched up to 6 ft and therefore fall into the field layer as defined by the Survey but generally must have ranged higher than the plant field layer sampled; the branches accessible from the ground, and presumably at about 6–9 ft or in the scrub canopy, were beaten into a tray. These zones therefore did not extend as high as Turnbull's and they omit the high canopy. Todd also visited the wood during four nights between 19 July and 17 August, making observations on 60 trees of oak, ash and sycamore every two hours from before dusk until dawn, and she came to the following conclusions: 'The greatest number of active *Mitopus morio* and *Lacinius ephippiatus* was observed between the hours 9 p.m. and 1 a.m (G.M.T.). *Mitopus morio* was seen most frequently walking over the surface of *Mercurialis perennis* which forms the field layer, though a few animals, nearly all males, ascended the tree trunks. *Lacinius ephippiatus* was also seen on the upper surface of *Mercurialis* leaves. . . . The total numbers seen on tree-trunks show that practically all *L. rotundum* leave the trees for the field layer at dusk and return there at dawn. Now nearly all *L. rotundum* observed on the field layer between these hours were eating other animals. Further, it was discovered that many *L. rotundum* were hidden from sight as they made their way along the underside of the *Mercurialis* leaves. It is here, presumably, that these harvestmen hunt for food, and on the upper surface of the leaves that they bring the prey to devour it. . . . The prey captured by *L. rotundum* and *Mitopus morio* in the field layer at night showed great diversity. . . . *Lacinius ephippiatus* was consistently found in the litter in the daytime sampling. It also appears to migrate to the field layer to feed at night.' I should add that the field layer of dog's mercury is less than a foot high and characterizes this sort of woodland when the canopy is fairly closed, when it may occur in extensive sheets. In such a system *L. rotundum* gradually ascends the vegetation during its growth to the adult stage, but at the same time has this nocturnal descent in order to hunt. *Lacinius ephippiatus* stays in the litter except for excursions up into the field layer at night. By such movements the vertical layers of the forest are linked in overlapping ways.

These vertical movements of harvestmen are part of a regular surge of animals that takes place on summer nights, and which emphasizes another way in which the pattern of tree-trunks is imposed upon the distribution of animals living below the canopy. If one watches a large tree-trunk at dusk and after dark, especially a smooth one like beech or a youngish sycamore, very little is to be seen at first; indeed animal life is hardly on the move at all. But then during dusk and the onset of complete darkness a general activity starts among nocturnal species, and much of this movement is in an upward direction (though, as has been seen for *Leiobunum rotundum*, some is in the reverse direction). Large beech trees in a thick wood were watched on a September evening in Wytham Woods by field classes of students in three successive years, and the chief events and performers were much the same each year. Among the animals taking part, and usually beginning their upward movement rather suddenly at the approach of complete dark, were large slugs, *Limax marginatus* and *L. maximus*; snails, *Marpessa laminata* and *Clausilia rugosa*; millipedes, *Tachypodiulus niger*, seen grazing on alga or lichen; centipedes, *Lithobius variegatus*; the tree grasshopper, *Meconema thalassina*, returning home; earwigs, *Forficula auricularia*; ground-beetles, including *Nebria brevicollis*; but very few woodlice. The main migrants had come up from crevices in the surface roots of the trees, or else from surrounding litter. I do not know how high they go. Besides these animals, most of which could clearly be seen to move upwards, a good many others appeared, probably out of cracks *in situ* (as *Porcellio* does in winter), and among them were Collembola and the small Carabid *Dromius quadrimaculatus*.

In the winter months there are also the extraordinary upward marches of several species of woodland moths that breed in the tree canopy but pupate in the ground and turn into winged males but wingless females. These migrations have formed part of Varley's comprehensive research on the moths of oak trees in Wytham Woods (see Ch. 10). The traps he has used for catching these moths are situated at about $3\frac{1}{2}$-4 ft on the trunk, though not covering its whole circumference. They have caught a considerable number of other species of invertebrates, of which a list is on record but has not been published. The wingless female moths concerned are the winter moth (*Operophtera brumata*), the spring usher (*Erannis* – formerly *Hybernia* – *leucophaearia*), the scarce umber (*E. aurantia*), the mottled umber (*E. defoliaria*) and the dotted border (*E. progemmaria* – formerly *marginaria*), and the pale brindled beauty (*Phigalia pilosaria*). None of these is confined to the oak.[252]

I have described interchange in both directions between the canopy and the ground, both by day and night and annually. The amount and timing of both kinds of movement will be found to depend greatly upon conditions of weather, though I do not know of any systematic research on this aspect. I will finish by mentioning a species, the woodlouse *Porcellio scaber*, that has considerable up and down movements during the year on the trunks and branches of trees apparently without actually coming down on to the ground. This species, which was very carefully studied in the field by Brereton,[39] has a rather peculiar habitat distribution in Britain. In Wytham Woods (and apparently in other woods as well) it is confined to two main kinds of habitat: dying and dead wood both on trees and in logs on the ground, and the live trunks of trees where it feeds on the surface by night but retires into crevices by day. It is found in similar places on scrub of hawthorn and the like, and was taken actively at night on the hawthorn hedge at Sheep Drove described in Ch. 8. Elsewhere it lives also in dry *Calluna* heath (Ch. 7), under marram dune tussocks (Ch. 8) and is known to live at the seashore drift-line.[503] At Wytham it is absent from grassland and virtually absent from woodland litter. Brereton only found eleven *P. scaber* in tree litter samples in two years; a number of field exercises by zoology classes in June and September have given similar paucity; and the ecological survey done by Roberts[411] in a beech–oak–chestnut wood in the New Forest, Hampshire, did not record it at all in the litter. Brereton therefore concluded that each tree has a more or less distinct population of these woodlice. Their presence in logs on the ground must therefore either be brought about by falling down with the logs themselves, or near them, or by very occasional dispersal from near the tree.

Brereton's field work was of two kinds. The first was a general survey, the second a more concentrated population study. He did habitat surveys of the trunks of different kinds of trees, collecting for a stated time at the base and at eye level, i.e. in the ground zone and bottom of the field layer, and at the top of the field layer. This was done on two trees each of oak, ash, sycamore, birch, larch and Scots pine, in two winters (between January and March) and two summers (between June and August). A summary of the populations seen is given in Table 4. The virtual absence of these woodlice from the trunks of birch, larch and pine is easily explained by their food habits. *Porcellio* – in this habitat – lives upon the epiphytic alga *Pleurococcus* on which it grazes at night. Laboratory tests showed that the woodlice quickly removed the alga from pieces of bark, and they were also watched eating it on beech trunks after dark. Barkman (cited in Ch. 10) explains the absence of *Pleurococcus* from birch and conifers by the acid nature of their bark, which therefore provides no pasture for woodlice. *Porcellio* is, however, not absent from dying and dead wood under birches, and Miss K. Paviour Smith (Mrs Southern) tells me that she has found them in rotting wood of birch trees above the ground. Incidentally, the absence of *Pleurococcus* from birch is one of the reasons why birch bark remains so brilliantly white, even in winter when *Pleurococcus* on other trees is multiplying greatly. By contrast, *Porcellio* is common on oak, ash, sycamore, and also on beech. Brereton's analysis of populations on oak and beech trunks proved that *Porcellio* become scarcer at the base of the trees in summer than in winter, when the numbers rather rapidly increased to something like ten times as much. Inferences from the breeding and population structure suggested that such increase could not be accounted for by any sudden breeding outburst, and that the growth rates of young woodlice were not fast enough to provide the increase from normal breeding. It was concluded that there was an upward migration into the upper parts of the trees in summer, and this was clinched by going up into the canopy and finding woodlice there, and also by putting traps on the lower trunks that measured the arrival of animals descending from above.

There is no satisfactory explanation of this seasonal migration, but I might

TABLE 4. Comparative counts of *Porcellio scaber* on trees in Wytham Woods (Brereton, 1957)

	Winter		Summer	
	Base	Eye level	Base	Eye level
Oak	306	0	20	4
Ash	72	9	13	0
Sycamore	204	218	27	25
Birch	18	0	0	1
Conifer	0	2	4	1

suggest two possibilities. As the summer progresses, the thickening of tree canopy cuts off more and more light from the lower parts of the wood. It might be that there is overgrazing of *Pleurococcus* at the lower levels, and that it remains more abundant up aloft. One certainly has the impression that *Pleurococcus* bursts into great activity in the leafless winter months, to an extent that makes this alga a major colour in the landscape. Another explanation might be that, as *Porcellio scaber* does not frequent the litter, its dispersal from tree to tree is done over the interlacing boughs.

CHAPTER 13

Natural Fuel Stations: Concourses on Flowers and Fruits

A HUNDRED YEARS AGO a naturalist[449] described a lane by the coast at Ilfracombe in north Devonshire where there were 50 yd of hedgerow covered with ivy in full bloom. Here on 9 October the ivy was 'almost hidden from sight by a countless multitude of butterflies and moths', the former consisting of hundreds of red admirals, *Vanessa atalanta*, scores of painted ladies, *Vanessa cardui*, and a single Camberwell beauty, *Nymphalis antiopa*, the moths not being further identified. These three species of butterflies are all strong migrants – for example the painted lady flies over from North Africa – and without these immigrants no British populations of any of them would be found. Although the first regularly and the second occasionally breeds here in summer, there cannot be much doubt that the swarms on ivy flowers were autumn contingents from abroad that were pausing to replenish their stores of fuel. Most flying insects move much shorter distances than this, though even the ones that do not move far in a straight line may expend a great deal of energy in flight, while some undertake hard physical work when they arrive in a new bit of habitat: as in digging, or mating activities or escaping parasites and enemies. A great many of these species stop to gather nectar from flowers. A very similar habit is the eating or gathering of honeydew on the leaves of forest trees, discussed in Ch. 10. There are other sources of sugar fuel also, such as rotting fruit and the sap flow from trees; and sometimes it is evidently water alone that is sought for. The red admiral uses all these kinds of liquid resource, except perhaps honeydew.[421] Nectar is a solution of sugars, mainly glucose, and contains less than 0·2% of protein.[238] It is therefore strictly a fuel and not by itself a body-building or germ-cell ripening food. To accomplish the latter insects either carry over sufficient protein from their larval stage, or else generally feed on plants or their pollen or on animals. Although in very broad terms all sources of food are sources of fuel, I am in this chapter concerned with the users of fuel sources that do not destroy the species that produces them, and particularly with nectar and pollen from flowers and the often large concourses of insects that assemble to collect them.

264

The common meaning of the word 'concourse' in the dictionary is 'an assemblage of people or things; a crowd, throng'. It can also be an assemblage of animals. We need a term that distinguishes between the community, or a centre of action within a community, whether rather permanent (as in a beech wood) or relatively ephemeral (as in a toadstool), and the quite local mass assembly of a mixture of species or perhaps of one species in search of a single resource that I am calling a concourse, a mixture that has few or no interactions between its members and does not last long enough to cover a major part of the breeding or life-cycle. Many of the concourses on flowers or fruits happen regularly once a year for a few days or perhaps weeks, and are fairly predictable events though not highly organized ecologically; others are unique or occasional and less predictable. There are also other kinds of concourses such as birds roosting or feeding on plants or animals (see Ch. 11).

Williams, Barness and Sawyer[548] in 1943 reported some experiments they had done with the fruit-fly *Drosophila funebris*, in which each fly was held immobile by its tail-end but allowed the free use of its wings until it became exhausted. In this manner, much as physiologists time the endurance and activity of small rodents upon an exercise wheel, the capacity for long flight could be measured. Week-old flies survived for 110 minutes, but young and old flies only for about twenty minutes. When they died at the end of these periods all the glycogen stores in the body had been used up. Later calculations have been made by Weis-Fogh[159] and others about the fuel loads in locusts and some other insects, and their efficiency compared with petrol in aircraft combustion engines. A recent monograph by Hocking[230] on the energy requirements and flight of blood-sucking flies has given some very remarkable conclusions. This work was done on the northern edge of forest adjoining the tundra in northern Manitoba and was focused on ten species of blood-sucking flies – 2 *Tabanus*, 2 *Chrysops*, 4 *Aedes* and 2 *Simulium*. By elaborate experiments and calculations it was discovered that 'northern biting flies obtain the energy for flight almost exclusively from floral nectar, of which some flies may carry in their crops quantities ranging up to 217% of their basic weight' (that is, their weight when exhausted of fuel stores). It seemed probable that after first feeding on the nectar of tundra or forest glade flowers, the flies swarmed and departed on their dispersal flights, and only after that began to take blood meals as well. It was calculated that the mosquito *Aedes punctor* would be able to fly for 12 hours, the black flies *Simulium venustum* and *S. vittatum* for 19 and 25 hours respectively. In Minnesota Sandholm[422] collected between twilight and midnight 1981 specimens of mosquitoes seen feeding on flowers from June to September: 10 species belonging to 4 genera, the commonest, *Aedes vexans*, visiting 39 species of flowers. Feeding was very heavy on nights after the mosquitoes had been swarming. Hocking remarks also: 'It is not generally realized what a large proportion of adult insects are almost entirely dependent on this plant secretion. These include probably most of the Diptera, Hymenoptera and Lepidoptera, a considerable number of Coleoptera, and a few smaller groups from several other orders. Nectar must have tremendous significance in the dispersal of these species.' But even he was thinking mostly of longer dispersal movements. I think it has to be borne in mind that the mosaic interspersion of habitat units itself imposes searching or random dispersal movements on a large scale but not necessarily far afield – an immediate consideration that has to be added to the usual notions about searching for mates, and the long-term genetic and geographical advantages of dispersal as such. Some of the small lighter insects, however, do undertake long-distance aerial drift as a normal seasonal activity. Thus Taylor[494] found that most of the aeroplanktonic insects caught between 1000 and 5000 ft at Cardington in Bedfordshire were alive and undamaged after five hours in the net, and perhaps twice as long altogether in the air, and some of them (aphids and small flies) were induced to breed afterwards.

A great deal of the local movement and flower-visiting done by insects has rather been taken for granted by ecologists, except in so far as they have been related to the pollination of the flowers themselves, or to the activities that build up and maintain colonies of social bees and wasps, and also solitary bees. The flower-visiting records for an ordinary common fly, such as *Empis tessellata* or *Pollenia rudis*, show that they patronize a considerable range of different flowers and that this is a more common situation than those that attract attention by their unusual or even bizarre adaptations. If we only study the beautiful or queer pollination of the honeysuckle or the bee-orchid or the arum, it is as if a sociologist were to base conclusions about the drinking habits of the human population on samples taken at the Ritz or the Dorchester Hotels, overlooking the very large population of ordinary people that go to drink at their local inns. Harper and Wood,[213] in their monograph on the common ragwort, *Senecio jacobaea*, in the *Biological Flora of the British Isles*, print a list of nearly 200 insects recorded visiting the flowers. Prof. Harper has informed me that these are all records of British events. This list comprises 9 species of moths, 6 butterflies, 5 beetles, 1 ant, 18 wasps, 47 bees (mainly *Halictus*, *Andrena*, *Nomada* and *Bombus*), and 87 flies (of which 35 species were hover-flies, Syrphidae), besides which there were some thrips, bugs and Ichneumonid parasites not fully named. This kind of visiting, as one would expect, is to the many flowers that either have the nectar exposed at the surface, or only hidden in rather short corolla tubes as in many composites.

Involved in such visiting is often also a search for pollen, though this is mainly by bees, wasps, Thysanoptera and certain beetles and flies. Pollen unlike nectar has a high protein value, though the value varies very much in different species of plants. In reference to the resources of the hive-bee – which visits a larger range of flowers than any other species of insect – Howes[238] cites values of dry protein weight in pollen ranging from 14% in fir (*Abies*) to 46% in hazel (*Corylus avellana*). Pollen is gathered in three different ways: by bees adapted to carry it off in bulk for storage in the nest, by beetles that chew it up in their jaws, and thirdly by certain sucking insects, especially Syrphid flies, that are able to triturate the pollen by means of their palpi and imbibe the resulting 'porridge'. There is one very small Ceratopogonid midge, *Atrichopogon pollinivorus*, that sucks individual pollen grains, whereas others in the same genus suck the blood of beetles.[104] Conversely, the common mosquito *Culex pipiens*, which normally sucks the blood of birds, sometimes alights on creamy milk indoors and sucks the milk through this 'skin'.[317, 134] But the great host of flies and moths are chiefly nectar feeders, and they come to replenish fuel. Most of the flies come by day and most of the moths by night.

Flower sources in the field can be divided for convenience into three broad classes. Forest trees are mostly wind-pollinated and do not much attract insects to their flowers, though there are exceptions like the maples and cherry; on the other hand the oak, beech and elm are strongly attractive centres of honeydew (Ch. 10). All our shrubs and climbers have flowers attractive to insects, though the roses have no nectar supply. Only the honeysuckle is a specialist in its insect visitors, which have very long tongues. Then comes a host of herbaceous plants or low woody plants of the bramble and heather sort, and it is among the former that are found many of the special devices for pollination that restrict the kinds of insect visitors. Some grasses, though anemophilous, are also used as sources of pollen. Therefore most of the natural fuel stations in the form of flowers occur below 15-20 ft. Although such a wide choice is open in the summer months, supplies are more restricted in the spring and autumn. Richards[406] collecting bumble-bees in the Oxford District noted that the white dead-nettle, *Lamium album*, common in the edges of cultivation though not in more natural plant communities in Britain,[133] and starting to flower very early in the year, is visited by eleven species of bumble-bee queens. These were queens that had hibernated and were now preparing to found new colonies. Sallows, especially *Salix caprea* and *S. atrocinerea*, the former common in the slightly damper terrestrial woodland and the latter in woodland marshes at Wytham, are another important early source of pollen and nectar for insects. With them or a little later comes the blackthorn, *Prunus spinosa*.

By the autumn all the tree and scrub flowers are over, as well as most of the herbs, but in September – often quite late in the month – the ivy, *Hedera helix*, is just coming into bloom which will last through October and even to November. On to it assembles a tremendous concourse of insects, of which I will now describe a sample studied in and near Wytham Hill in late September 1960, after which I shall analyse the habitat origins of some of the visitors, their behaviour, and what implications there are for the later life of the insects. The example is selected for two special reasons because it happened at a time of year when, as explained, other nectar resources outside garden flowers are scarce; and because the abundant records of the Wytham Ecological Survey make it possible to place some of the species in the ecological context in which they belong. Most of the observations were made by Professor Monte Lloyd while living at an old farmhouse in Cumnor Hill about a mile from the centre of Wytham Woods, but separated from it by a stretch of farm fields and gardens. The ivy (Plate 33) was growing thickly on an old farm wall, and was in full bloom, though flowers were in all stages – in bud, with ripe anthers and honey flow, and with no anthers left. The great swarms of bees, wasps and flies were nearly all visiting the anthered stage of flowers, and several collections of these were made between heights of 4 and 6 ft, both by day and night. The ivy flower has a yellowish green dome or cushion around the style, and inside the ring of anthers, that secretes the nectar, which according to Howes[23] is very concentrated, and if insects are excluded will accumulate and remain as a sugary crust after the flowers are over. Hive-bees are well known to visit the ivy, both for nectar and pollen, one of the oldest records – some 2300 years ago – being given by Aristotle in his *Historia Animalium* [28]. Most of the insects to be described were visiting the ivy flowers for nectar, though possibly some of the Syrphid flies were also collecting pollen. A certain amount of day and night observation in which I took part was also done on an old wall in a lane leading from Wytham village, a few hundred yards from the nearest woodland.

I will first refer to the moths, which were only taken after dark. From 27 to 29 September the following species were found on ivy flowers at Cumnor: *Phlogophora meticulosa, Anchoscelis litura, Citria lutea, Cirrhia fulvago (icteritia), Agrochola circellaris* (also on ivy flowers in Wytham lane), *A. lychnidis, A. lota,* and *Hypena proboscidalis.* Holloway[234] gives a cumulative list of moths taken by him on ivy blossom during three successive autumns in a Hampshire garden, from the end of September until late in October. He caught 31 species of moths, including 6 of the 8 taken at Cumnor. By day he also saw painted lady and red admiral butterflies visiting the flowers. A notable thing about the 33 species of moths concerned here is that 15 of them (45%) are in one sub-family Dasypolinae of the Caradrinidae. Many of them are well-known ivy visitors, and the list is of course not exhaustive. They are species that have become adult late in the summer and either going to lay overwintering eggs or else hibernate and breed in the spring. Nearly all are polyphagous as to larval food-plants. Thus *Citria lutea* develops on sallow catkins and later on other plants; *Agrochola circellaris* on flowers, seeds and leaves of wych elm, as well as on sallow and aspen buds; *A. lychnidis* on various grasses and herbs.[462] So little has been recorded by lepidopterists about the true habitat contexts of moths, although their food-plants are usually known, that it is not possible at present to assign these species to their Wytham habitat components. But they clearly must be derived from a good many different sources. Incidentally, British floras[71] attribute the pollination of ivy to flies and wasps, but it is evident that hive-bees and moths, and sometimes butterflies as well, play a part. The omission of moths can be explained by the largely diurnal habits of botanists, whereas moth-collectors are strongly nocturnal, in the past offering liquid sugar as a counter-attractant to moths, although now they more often trap them with ultra-violet light. The botanical statement about ivy flowers is probably derived from the rather limited information given about ivy in Müller's classical book[338] about the fertilization of flowers. Some of the ivy-visiting moths also go to ripe elderberries, as is illustrated by a list given by Goater[187] in Hertfordshire. Among his 11 species 6 were on the Cumnor ivy flowers as well; while of the other 5 only one, *Tiliacea citrago*, was not included either in the Cumnor or Hampshire lists. This moth is known to visit lime trees for honeydew.[462]

By far the greatest concourse is that of wasps and flies visiting the ivy flowers by day, especially when it is sunny. The Cumnor Hill day collections were made at various times between 9 a.m. and 2 p.m. (G.M.T.) and at shade temperatures of 56-57° F. There was tremendous activity, nearly all the insects being rather toughly built, brightly coloured or metallic species. Wasps were abundant at both places, workers of the ground-nesting *Vespula germanica* and *vulgaris*, with an occasional male of the former. A few hive-bees (*Apis mellifera*) occurred at Cumnor Hill. The 27 species of flies are given in Table 5, among the most abundant being drone-flies (*Tubifera*), blue-bottles (*Calliphora*), cluster-flies (*Pollenia rudis*), *Musca autumnalis* and the two green-bottles, *Orthellia*. They were mostly named by Mr K. G. V. Smith, the rest by myself. (I shall omit a few insects of other orders.) I do not think anyone has ever tried to analyse the habitats from which such a concourse is derived, except Wilson[550] for orchard blossom at Wisley. Of course, to do so is partly a theoretical exercise, in so far as we do not actually know the exact locali-ties or distances from which they have come. Nevertheless, even within these limitations, it is worth looking at what we know about their habitats, and in par-ticular any that have been found on Wytham Hill, not far away. It would take too long to explore the life patterns of the two wasps, because these are complicated by the different facets of their elaborate lives: nesting and searching for nesting material, hunting and other feeding – as on flowers or fruits – drinking water, hibernating and so on. Both species certainly nest in gardens and both are common throughout Wytham Woods, where the queens hibernate partly in rotten logs. Recorded ground-nesting sites there for *Vespula vulgaris* include field type lime-stone grassland, the edge of deciduous scrub and grassland, and inside a beech wood. Among insects they have something of the ecological ubiquity and appe-tites of the great tit, the tawny owl and the badger.

TABLE 5. Flies visiting ivy flowers by day, Cumnor Hill (25-27 Sept. 1960) and Wytham (27 September)

Those marked ★ have been recorded from the Wytham Woods area, those marked † by Parmenter (1952) on ivy flowers in Britain (these two symbols in the left-hand column do not distinguish between sexes).

			Cumnor	Wytham
Chironomidae		*Hydrobaenus (Spaniotoma) rectus*	+	—
Scatopsidae	†★	*Scatopse notata*	♂	—
Syrphidae	†★	*Tubifera (Eristalis) pertinax*	♂	♀
		Neoascia podagrica	♀	—
		Orthoneura splendens	♀	—
	†★	*Episyrphus balteatus*	♂	—
	†★	*Syrphus ribesii*	♀	♀
	★	*S. vitripennis*	—	♀
Lonchaeidae	★	*Lonchaea lauta*	—	♂
Sepsidae	★	*Sepsis fulgens*	♂	—
		S. sp.	♀	—
Cordiluridae	†★	*Scopeuma stercorarium*	♂	—
Calliphoridae	†★	*Sarcophaga carnaria*	♀	—
	†★	*Calliphora erythrocephala*	♂ ♀	♂
	†★	*C. vomitoria*	♂ ♀	♂
		Lucilia illustris	♂	—
	†★	*Pollenia rudis*	♂ ♀	♂ ♀
Muscidae	†★	*Musca autumnalis*	♂ ♀	♂ ♀
	★	*Orthellia caesarion*	♂ ♀	♂
	★	*O. cornicina*	♂ ♀	—
	★	*Graphomyia maculata*	♂ ♀	—
	†★	*Mesembrina meridiana*	♀	+
		Morellia hortorum	♂	—
	†★	*M.* sp.	—	♀
		Fannia maculata	♂	—
	★	*Hebecnema umbratica*	♂	—
		Nupedia dissecta	♀	—
		Egle radicum	♀	—
	★	*Opsolasia roederi*	—	♂

Not surprisingly, there is a group of cow dung breeders from pasture or farm-yard, that includes certainly *Scopeuma stercorarium*, *Musca autumnalis*, the two *Orthellia*, *Mesembrina meridiana*, *Morellia hortorum* and *Hebecnema umbratica* (see Ch. 16). The *Scopeuma*, however, might have been hunting prey, though Wilson[551] recorded it sucking nectar and eating pollen. Among carrion flies are *Sarcophaga carnaria*, the two *Calliphora* and *Lucilia lllustris* (see also Ch. 16). *Pollenia rudis* is common in the deciduous woodland edge field layer of Wytham Woods and has also occurred at female *Salix caprea* flowers in the same habitat but at scrub height. The life-history of this species is known from work in Europe[257] and the United States:[202] the eggs are laid in the soil, the larva penetrates an earth-worm, e.g. *Allolobophora chlorotica*, in which it remains as a parasite, eventually pupating in the soil again. In autumn the flies tend to congregate and often hiber-nate in houses, hence their name 'cluster-fly'.[512] *Scatopse notata* has been bred from two tawny owl nests and from the nest of a hornet (*Vespa crabro*) in Wytham Woods, and from *Vespula* nests in Britain and Belgium.[374] *Tubifera pertinax* is a common drone-fly in Wytham Woods, hovering in the field layer or above it, and is noticeable in the spring, though it can be seen also until the autumn, visiting various flowers. The larvae of this genus, the rat-tailed maggots, live in very organic or dirty small water bodies or farm ponds. The exact habitat of *T. pertinax* is not known in Wytham, but it may turn out to be one of the inhabitants of tree-holes (see Ch. 17). *Syrphus ribesii* and *Episyrphus balteatus* are canopy-bred flies that have a rather wide range (see Ch. 11). *Sepsis fulgens* has been bred from cow dung,[286] but must also live in deciduous woodland glades: vast swarms of hun-dreds or thousands have been found congregated on herbage in Bagley Wood in September,[228] and in Wytham Woods on clumps of *Juncus inflexus* in a woodland ride in early September in two separate years.

At dusk this horde of flashing diurnal insects has gone, and after dark not only do moths come to the ivy flowers but also a small concourse of quite different flies, unspectacular and delicately built, and rather sedentary on the flowers. Obser-vations were made in the early part of four nights, and the species are given in Table 6. At Cumnor the air temperature at the time of collection varied between 46-54° F. The 13 species belong to 10 different families, and only one, the predator *Scopeuma stercorarium*, was also noted by day, and it was scarce at either time. Mus-cids were extremely few, so there was a switch-over not only in species but in families of flies. What these nocturnal species mostly have in common is larvae with saprophagous habits, that is living on decaying matter, though in many dif-ferent habitats. *Calliope aeneum* is, however, said from European evidence to mine the leaves of clover.[436] Although most of the species are known from the Wytham area, their exact range of habitat is usually less known, since flies are one of the insect groups (like the moths and sawflies) that have not yet been ecologically sur-

veyed there except in a few instances. The following remarks are therefore incomplete evidence for the possible origin of these species. Adult *Limonia maculata*
occur by a shaded woodland stream in Wytham Woods, but its larvae are not in
the stream; this agrees with its general habits elsewhere, in Britain, of living in
damp woods and by streams. *Cheilotrichia cinerascens* also lives in woods.[44] Hollo-

TABLE 6. Flies visiting ivy flowers at night, 25 and 27 Sept., 4 Oct. 1960 at
Cumnor Hill, and 27 Sept. in Wytham lane

Those marked ★ are recorded from the Wytham Woods area; (★) means that the
genus is known to both places.

			Cumnor	Wytham
Tipulidae	★	*Limonia maculata*	♀	—
		Cheilotrichia cinerascens	♀	—
Anisopidae	★	*Anisopus forestralis*	♂	—
	★	*A. punctatus*	♂ ♀	♂ ♀
Culicidae	★	*Theobaldia annulata*	♂	♂
	★	*Culex pipiens*	♂	♂
Bibionidae	★	*Bibio lepidus*	♂	—
Mycetophilidae	(★)	*Sciara* sp.	♀	—
Phoridae	(★)	*Megaselia* sp.	+	—
Lauxaniidae	★	*Calliope aeneum*	♀	—
Helomyzidae	★	*Tephrochlamys tarsalis*	♂	—
Cordiluridae	★	*Scopeuma stercorarium*	♀	—
Muscidae		*Delia cilicrura*	♂	—

way[234] had another crane-fly, *Tipula oleracea*, visiting ivy flowers at night. This
is a well-known pasture soil crane-fly, which, together with some other Tipulids,
has been caught throughout the night in a light-trap at Rothamsted.[412] The larvae
of *Anisopus* are well known, indeed Réamur in 1740 first described them living in
cow dung. *Anisopus fenestralis* larvae were found by Keilin[258, 259] at Cambridge in
slime fluxes on common elm and horse-chestnut and cites it as occurring in an oak
tree water-hole in Epping Forest; while Brindle[45] states that it comes in decaying
fungi in woods. It commonly enters houses as an adult, and it has in Europe bred in
rotting potatoes in a cellar.[261] *A. punctatus* appears to have been bred from dung
commonly.[45] *Theobaldia annulata*, of which 9 males but no females were caught, is

a large man-biting species of mosquito that breeds in smaller stagnant waters,[317] and often near houses. It is not common in Wytham Woods, but I have found the larvae in a shallow marsh pool at the edge of deciduous woodland. Those visiting ivy most likely came from a domestic setting. I have bred it from larvae in a very small shaded concrete pond in my Oxford garden. Female *Culex pipiens* bite birds, not man, but the species is common in houses both in summer and hibernating (often in cellars or outhouses) in winter. It breeds mostly in smaller, sometimes very small water bodies, Marshall[317] mentioning its occurrence in water butts, garden tanks, wells, puddles, ditches, pond-shallows but only rarely tree-holes. I have found its larvae in a very small basin in a tree-stump made by felling a large black poplar, in the woodland edge of Wytham. Professor G. C. Varley has found adult *Bibio lepidus* in the ground zone of the oak glade studied by him there. Some species of *Megaselia* and *Sciara* are extremely abundant in rotting beech wood, etc., at Wytham, and breed in the galleries in it or under bark. *Tephrochlamys tarsalis* is a nest inhabitant. It has been bred from an old hornet (*Vespa crabro*) nest in a tawny owl nest-box in Wytham Woods, and has been similarly bred elsewhere from nests of blue tit and sparrow-hawk and wasps.[445] Buxton[60] also bred it from eight very different kinds of fungi, including such species as *Polyporus giganteus*, *Armillaria mellea* and *Lycoperdon pyriforme* that grow on rotting stumps or logs, and others like *Tricholoma nudum* that grow on the ground, the fungi mostly but not all being characteristic of woodland.[398] *Delia cilicrura* feeds on vegetable refuse of field crops, also on the roots of some live plants; Buxton[59] bred it from plasmodium (described as resembling yellow custard) of the myxomycete *Fuligo septica* growing on coffee grounds used as a garden mulch at Kew Gardens.

I spoke of this as a partly theoretical exercise, yet in it there have been involved – and only on a small sample of a few days' local observation – 27 species of flies and 3 bees and wasps by day, and 13 flies and 8 moths by night, with a total of about 47 species of insects. And they are seen to come from a great many different parts of the local ecosystem. Since most flowering plants visited by insects have a fairly permanent position in the landscape, though changing slowly with the years, it would be possible in any locality to plot these fuelling centres on a map and work out their usage by insects derived from different habitats, and do this with regard to the changing seasons. Even in the late summer and autumn, apart from garden flowers there are certain other sources of fuel besides ivy. The visits of moths to elderberries have already been mentioned. Some other fruits are also a source of sugar for butterflies, wasps, parasitic Hymenoptera, and flies. Two quite small surveys at Wytham will illustrate this. One was of insects visiting the ripe and bursting fruits of the wayfaring tree, *Viburnum lantana*, between 2 and 10 ft in the edge of deciduous woodland at the top of the Hill, at about 2.45 p.m. (G.M.T.) on 9 September 1951 [29]. The other was at a large wild blackberry patch in a deciduous ride edge on another part of the Hill, at field-layer height, on the afternoon of 15 September 1954 [30]. Among insects on the *Viburnum* fruits were the comma butterfly, *Polygonia c-album*, which often can be seen on blackberries; workers of *Vespula vulgaris*; females of another wasp, *Mellinus arvensis*; several parasitic Hymenoptera, including a male of *Cratichneumon culex*, known as the most important pupal para-site of the winter moth on Wytham oaks; of flies, *Tubifera pertinax*, *Episyrphus balteatus*, *Syrphus ribesii*, *Calliphora erythrocephala*, *Scopeuma stercoraria*, and *Mesembrina meridiana*. The wasps (except *Mellinus*) and flies were also on the ivy flowers described already. On the ripe blackberries were also many *Vespula vulgaris* workers, which seemed to be aiding the feeding of some of the flies by opening up the fruits; and *Sarcophaga carnaria*, *Calliphora vomitoria* and *Orthellia cornicina*, also recorded on the ivy. With them were a carrion-fly, *Lucilia ampullacea*, and also a Muscid, *Muscina assimilis*, reported by Keilin[259] to have a carnivorous larva living in a variety of decomposing animal and vegetable matter. In Europe it has been bred from ground and tree fungi, but Buxton[60] only had it once from fungi in Britain. Sometimes there are also sap-flows on trees, honeydew continues to some extent, and some of the carrion-flies are drawn to the stink of that astonishing *lusus naturae*, the fungus *Phallus impudicus*, which occurs in later summer and autumn in woods, but is rare at Wytham.

At the concourses on ivy flowers I have not noticed any obvious interaction between the attendant insects, indeed the wasps seem not to make any attempt to attack the flies, and the flies seem to feed undisturbed by each other. But in Japan Kikuchi[269] noticed that there was not only interaction between Syrphids, blow-flies and Muscid (Anthomyiid) flies visiting *Chrysanthemum* flowers, but reports that he found a dominance order among them, and that this was related to size. It was uncommon for more than one fly to occupy each flower head. He recognized seven ranks of dominance among thirteen species of flies, that included among others a *Tubifera*, a *Syrphus* and a *Lucilia*. It would seem not unlikely that any such competition for supplies of food from flowers that exists would vary with the shortage or abundance of nectar, and the ivy has an extremely strong flow of concentrated nectar. This question, of some interest in itself, also has a bearing upon what one means by a concourse as distinct from a community. At present I can see a distinct line between any such temporary concourse, whether it has any predatory or competitive interactions or not, and a community with more highly developed biotic interrelations and with some of its species breeding in the same habitat.

No one is going to deny that some or large part of the flower-visits by insects do have a decisive influence upon fertilization, although it is reasonable to assume that a great deal of it may also be unnecessary in so far as some flowers may be able to use self-pollination or the plants may spread vegetatively. It is also usually admitted that exogamy is of long-term value to species. These are really botanical matters except in so far as the plants have become structurally adapted or have special timing devices and so on, in relation to particular insect groups. But there is far less known about the adaptive value of the collection of nectar or pollen to all these insects that do it. With social insects like the hive-bee and *Vespula* the importance is proven by direct observation of the results, just as it is much easier to measure the food brought by birds to their young than to understand what the food supply does to the parents themselves. Therefore, for the present, we must realize that most of the evidence about the function of nectar for insect dispersal or for survival or breeding, is based on circumstantial rather than experimental evidence. I do not share the commonly held view that circumstantial evidence is bad evidence, but there is clearly a very large field for more precise research, since if it is true that these thousands of species concerned are dependent on natural fuel stations for completing their various ecological missions, it becomes necessary to take more notice of the nature, position and seasonal timing of the stations and the habits of their visitors. One can perhaps visualize what may be involved, and probably is involved, by imagining a monospecific plant community such as a very old and solid beech forest of the kind that Bukhovskii surveyed in the Crimea (Ch. 10), with virtually no nectar-carrying flowers, no tree pollen after the early summer, perhaps no honeydew in the autumn, no scrub or bramble fruits, and let us suppose no *Phallus impudicus* or slime fluxes. Would one not expect this to bring about impoverishment of the visiting insects, and perhaps of the resident species as well? Thus many parasitic Hymenoptera depend largely on the flowers of umbellifers for collecting nectar and pollen, and there is some evidence for supposing that this feeding is necessary for them.[288] One could similarly think of a pure stand of *Brachypodium pinnatum* grassland (Ch. 6) in comparison with a flowery meadow, the former having only some pollen to offer those species flexible enough in habits to use it (the Cantharid beetle *Rhagonycha fulva*, so common on umbellifer flowers, has been observed to do so at Wytham, by Professor C. Overgaard Nielsen; and I have found the beetle, *Anaspis frontalis*, on anthers of cocksfoot grass, *Dactylis glomerata*, there: but these are quite exceptions). Whatever their exact significance for the physiological performance of the insects, fuelling and refuelling stations certainly form a very big part of the interspersed habitat components except in the winter when most of them are shut down. We need to know how far their removal would bring some populations to a halt, thus altering the composition of communities, also how far at any one place and season one kind of source can be substituted for another.

A good many of the autumn visitors to ivy spend the winter hibernating as adults and appear once more on the early flowers in the following year. The first eloquent reference to this comes in the *Georgics* of Virgil in his account of the habits of honey-bees, of which as Royds[415] remarks in his *Beasts, birds and bees of Virgil*, there are echoes in later poets, as in Gray's 'Ode on the Spring' in the lines:

> The insect youth are on the wing,
> Eager to taste the honied spring
> And float amid the liquid noon:

Only they are not all youths but veterans of many missions in the previous year! *Culex pipiens* does not feed on blood before going into hibernation, but fills up on nectar or other plant juices and lays down a deposit of fat and glycogen, of which six-sevenths may be used up before the spring,[58] when the mosquitoes emerge from hibernation and seek a blood meal before ripening the eggs.[72] There is a genetically distinct strain named var. *molestus* that can mature eggs without any blood meal at all. This capacity for what is called 'autogeny' exists in some genera of mosquitoes and in parts of the populations of some others. In all these instances the nectar meal is one of the necessary resources. Their earlier fuelling perhaps enables them to overwinter with success.

In conclusion I shall, while omitting much reference to the very large but at present inchoate mass of information that exists about insects that go to herbaceous flowers during the summer months, say something about the role of shrubs, climbers other than ivy, and some trees. Most of the shrubs are monoecious, but the willows and sallows have the male and female catkins on separate trees, so that with the latter there is no difficulty in knowing whether an insect is searching for nectar or pollen. On most of the others this is not necessarily easy to determine without close observation, at any rate among the Hymenoptera and some of the flies and beetles. Wilson[550, 551] in his list of insects visiting orchard and garden fruit flowers at Wisley (which is the best survey of its kind done in this country) classified visitors carefully in the following categories: collecting pollen, feeding on pollen, crawling over the blossom, eating floral organs, licking nectar, sucking nectar, and also those predacious on aphids in the flowers or laying eggs in the blossom. At Wytham I have observed a small weevil *Phyllobius parvulus* visiting dog rose (*Rosa canina*) flowers in order to bite the petals. But among shrubs and climbers, the roses, which have no nectaries, are otherwise only visited for pollen. Hazel catkins – primarily wind-pollinated – are certainly visited by hive-bees for the protein-rich pollen.[238] The traveller's joy, *Clematis vitalba*, produces large amounts of pollen, and is peculiar in that although there are no ordinary nectaries it does produce drops of nectar from the filaments or stems of the anthers.[238] The special feature of many shrubs in flower is their attraction not only especially to Thysanoptera, bees, wasps and flies, but to beetles which are mainly in search of pollen.

In summarizing the broad seasonal march of flowering shrubs, climbers and trees with which insect visitors are concerned I shall confine myself to those that are important at Wytham Woods, where most of the shrubs and climbers characteristic of calcareous soils grow, though there lack many of the smaller willows and some more local species such as the box (*Buxus sempervirens*) and the alder buckthorn (*Frangula alnus*). Being mainly concerned with the central features of natural communities, I shall not give details about 'domestic' orchard and garden fruit trees, though realizing that this is a rather artificial proceeding in a countryside like ours. I mean, the survival of some species inside Wytham Woods may, for all we know, be dependent upon the existence of domestic habitats at the periphery, as is suggested in another connection by the work of Perrins[380] on great tits, and might also operate in regard to supplies of fuel for insects in the spring season. The ivy flowers already discussed are part of the domestic system of habitats, though ivy also commonly grows and flowers on trees at woodland edges.

The broad seasonal sequence of flowering can be got from Druce's *Flora of Berkshire*.[106] I have cross-checked this with information from Church's wonderful seasonal description[70] of the vegetation round Oxford, also notes accumulated by myself in the Wytham Ecological Survey, and the fields records made by my wife in the Hampshire hedge survey discussed in Ch. 9. Hazel (*Corylus avellana*) comes earliest, flowering from January or February until April. Next comes a small group of shrubs, the two sallows (*Salix caprea* and *S. atrocinerea*) and the blackthorn (*Prunus spinosa*) that flower in March and April and are very valuable sources for the early insects. Then the orchard fruit trees begin in April and last into May, also the wild cherry, *Prunus avium*, the crack willow, *Salix fragilis* (in riverine situations), and the introduced cherry-laurel, *Prunus laurocerasus* (which has extra-floral nectaries on the leaves). An abstract of Wilson's records for any or all of the four earlier fruit trees, apple, pear, plum and cherry, gives a total list of at least 111 species of insects (really a larger figure because some groups were not named to species), of which bees comprised 24, flies 40 and beetles 24. In May and June comes the great outburst of scrub and some tree flowers, with holly (*Ilex aquifolium*), spindle (*Euonymus europaeus*), buckthorn (*Rhamnus cathartica*), wayfaring tree (*Viburnum lantana*), guelder rose (*V. opulus*), crab apple (*Malus sylvestris*), sycamore (*Acer pseudoplatanus*), common maple (*A. campestre*) and above all hawthorn (*Crataegus oxyacanthoides* and *monogyna*). Some climbing shrubs are also in flower: black bryony (*Tamus communis*) and white bryony (*Bryonia dioica*). A little later, in June and July, come wild roses such as *Rosa canina*, dogwood (*Cornus sanguinea*), elder (*Sambucus nigra*) and privet (*Ligustrum vulgare*) – see Plates 32 and 56. By July lime trees (such as *Tilia vulgaris*) and *Clematis vitalba* are in flower, but most of the earlier shrubs and trees are now past flowering (though holly in particular goes on rather long) and are ripening the fruit that will become so abundant in late summer and autumn. Among weaker woody plants of lower stature are the very early flowering gorse (*Ulex europaeus*), and several kinds of bramble (including *Rubus vestitus* and *R. fuscus*) whose flowers appear from May onwards and last often into September. Finally comes ivy in the autumn. The dates I have given vary somewhat according to the season in different years, but the general sequence is fairly constant.

The main force of flower-visiting beetles is out between May and July, and is not found in spring or autumn. They are not confined to tree and scrub flowers, for some of them turn up also commonly on herbs like buttercups and umbellifers. Members of several families turn up regularly. Among the Nitidulidae are *Meligethes aeneus*, whose early stages live on cruciferous plants, and species of *Epuraea* that develop under bark, in fungi or other General habitats. About half the British species of longicorns (Cerambycidae) visit blossom.[169] In Wytham Woods this group is poorly represented, but one small species, *Grammoptera ruficornis*, has been taken commonly on flowers that include cherry, sycamore, wild rose, hawthorn and dogwood. Its early life stages have not yet been discovered there, but it is known to live in slender dead twigs and branches of many trees and shrubs in Britain and Europe. Cantharidae are also commonly seen. Space prevents me from recording further details here.

Part of the special interest of shrubs in the animal ecology of woodland is that so many of them are part of the succession stages that lead towards forest (Plates 10 and 31), and this is especially true of their flowering state, since much scrub that survives or germinates from fruits carried in by birds does not flower profusely or at all under the tree canopy. And their success is closely bound up with the fact that birds eat their fruits and disseminate them. All the species mentioned already except the hard tree fruits like maple, and the plumed wind-drifted seeds of *Clematis*, are sought by some species of bird, though the sloe or blackthorn fruit seems to be seldom eaten. Encyclopaedic information on this subject is available in Ridley's book on *The Dispersal of Plants*.[410] The successful production of seeds by shrubs and climbers and some trees is therefore a two-stage affair so far as animals are concerned: the summer pollination and the autumn and winter dissemination. Conversely, the shrubs afford fixed and lavish fuelling stations for insects in summer, and partly (as with some moths) in autumn, as well as being a major source of food for birds and small mammals.

CHAPTER 14

Dying and Dead Wood

WHEN ONE WALKS through the rather dull and tidy woodlands – say in the managed portions of the New Forest in Hampshire – that result from modern forestry practices, it is difficult to believe that dying and dead wood provides one of the two or three greatest resources for animal species in a natural forest, and that if fallen timber and slightly decayed trees are removed the whole system is gravely impoverished of perhaps more than a fifth of its fauna. The indexes of the Ecological Survey contain 456 species of animals at Wytham living in wood or under bark where decay has begun or already gone far. Another 518 species are known to occur in this habitat elsewhere in Britain, and perhaps some of these will also turn up in Wytham Woods. Neither list is complete, though well advanced towards completion. The fact that about half the British species living wholly or partly in this habitat have survived in the 1000 acres or so of deciduous woodland at Wytham is no doubt explained by its history and its present condition, recounted in Ch. 3. During the last decade a method that I devised, of preserving and marking individual dying and dead trees and logs, groups of fallen logs and branches, and even large stumps, has greatly increased the amount of this kind of habitat in all stages of change, and provided opportunities at Wytham for research not only on decaying wood but on the bracket fungi that often develop on it (Ch. 15).

Natural forests that have not been subjected to logging or to more sophisticated forestry treatment have immense amounts of dead wood standing and lying beneath the canopy or in glades produced by large trees falling down. There seems to be a gradient in the quantity of dead timber lying in undisturbed forests (which may or not be 'virgin' in the long historical sense), from the colder sub-boreal, montane or continental climates in the north, through temperate woodland such as we know in Britain, down into tropical rain forest. As the following descriptions will indicate, colder conifer or mixed forests may have dense layers of fallen timber accumulated; in a place like Wytham the larger beech trees may certainly lie for a quarter of a century or more, though small items sometimes disappear in a year or two. In Savely's study[429] of ecological succession of animals in pine and oak logs in North Carolina – a warm temperate climate – much of the main faunal succession had occurred in three years, especially in the pine. In tropical rain forest the breakdown of fallen wood may be very rapid[408] except in some trees resistant to fungal decay.

Douglas Carruthers[63] has described the Siberian taiga along the Amil River on the north side of the Syansk Mountains, through which he took a pack-train of horses in 1910 (Plate 35): 'With a feeling of vague uncertainty, even of repulsion, we plunged almost blindly into this vast sea of choking vegetation, this turmoil of taiga. . . . With us was the almost overpowering sense of Nature being too strong for us. . . . It was a strange and weird experience. The endless forest, damp and dripping with the rot of ages, silent, sombre, and sodden, hemmed us in on every side. All that we saw was the tangle of growth, the young living forest springing up above the dead fallen timber which lay crosswise on the ground, trunk piled on trunk – three generations deep – all overgrown with moss, and treacherous to walk over. Around us hung the murky atmosphere of the jungle, above us festoons of lichen, showing hoary white against the dark pines. . . .' No tidiness here! So with other ancient forests, about which Jones[249] has assembled a valuable picture of structure and regeneration. For example, in the great forest of Kubany Wald at Schattawa in central Europe, that has been a reserve for over a hundred years, though said to have been at times damaged by overstocking with game animals, the volume of standing and fallen dead timber is about equal to that alive. In the 13,000-acre Swiss National Forest, composed chiefly of conifers and known in extraordinary detail from a quantitative air and ground survey,[273] about a quarter of the twenty million trees (that is, trees over about 4 ft high) and about a third of the estimated volume of standing timber is dying and dead. This forest has been strictly preserved without exploitation since its regeneration in the last century after much cutting. On the Front Range of Colorado there are completely untouched stands of Englemann spruce (*Picea engelmanni*) and subalpine fir (*Abies lasiocarpa*) dominant at heights of 10,000–11,000 ft. 'Many generations of trees have lived, died, and fallen over in these long-persisting stands, and wind-throw of both living and dead trees is common. The resulting tangle of stumps and fallen logs in all stages of decay, often with no systematic orientation, makes passage through these stands a tedious and tiresome activity. The old spruce-fir stands are relatively stable in character, changing very little from century to century.' Prof. J. C. Marr, from whose published survey[316] of the region these remarks are quoted, has allowed me to add that Mr R. C. Mills, working with him there, found that there were about 8·7 blown-down tree trunks per 100 m.², in a stand at least 500 years old in this magnificent subalpine forest, and that the logs were in all stages of decay down to those that had gone so completely that only differences in the ground cover of plants revealed that a log had once been present.

The general stages by which standing timber becomes invaded by insects and fungi are well known from the extremely extensive work of forest entomologists and mycologists. The outline I shall give here is, however, based chiefly upon knowledge accumulated for Wytham Woods, supplemented by information from elsewhere, particularly in regard to conifers of which rotting material is scarce at Wytham. In this way it may be easier for the reader to follow the development of animal communities in dying and dead wood from each of the dominant trees, and the way in which these variegate the pattern of minor communities not only on the ground but at all levels in the canopy. Death in a tree, indeed in any substantially constructed plant, is a different matter from death of an animal. A tree can survive for decades, leafing and flowering and fruiting while carrying a considerable amount of wood that may be not only structurally non-living skeletal or epidermal tissue, but actually in an advanced state of decay and inhabited by a fauna partly indistinguishable from that of a detached log on the ground. There are only minor parallels to this among animals, as for instance in sheep that suffer myiasis from blow-fly larvae living in their tissues, or in certain slow stages of parasitism and disease. Many fungi and insects appear to attack trees that are weak and in some way (usually little understood) have lessened resistance. But I will not try to define the exact point of no return beyond which there really is dying or dead wood.

If a tree or a branch falls right out in the open, as often happens in parklands or isolated trees in fields, the exposure to drying and insolation usually results in a heat-sterilization of the timber almost as effective as kiln-drying, so that in effect it becomes a fossil log with little decay or insect fauna in it. One is shown in Plate 36. Such logs, if not cleared away, may last for a great many years. Macfadyen[309] has published some graphs (of which the original figures are with the Wytham Ecological Survey) of round-the-clock temperatures in logs exposed to full summer sun and those protected by plant cover, on the top of Wytham Hill. The exposed log was of beech, about 15 in. diameter, placed in an open grassy area though partly protected from wind by trees and scrub around, and the other was a 6-in. diameter oak log under complete shade of a beech tree right inside the woodland margin. In the former the early afternoon temperature under the bark rose to about 28° C., whereas in the shaded log it only rose to slightly above 17° C. Although neither temperature would be lethal, the figures show the sort of difference that would if continued and accumulated lead to comparative sterility in the exposed log.

It follows from this that the main story of log communities is concerned with woodland and its edges (and to a much lesser extent with scrub and its edges) provided the edges have sufficient lower vegetation to keep the microclimate right. But there do seem to be conditions sometimes under which some isolated dead trees standing out in the open may have bracket fungus populations, and in them certain insects; also, as will be shown, there are some species of insects that frequent dry standing boles or trees, though usually not out in the open. I think that this subject needs much closer investigation, and that the production of water by the normal metabolism of fungi may sometimes outweigh the evaporation from the dead wood as a whole. One curiosity that I have found is that dead elder branches, even when fairly strongly exposed, sometimes have a good many invertebrates in them. This happens because the elder has a soft-centred kind of wood that easily becomes hollow (a characteristic from which the Anglo-Saxon name of the shrub is said to be derived) and this maintains a damp microclimate even when the outside is very dry.

The main ecological succession in dying and dead wood does not follow the same course in different kinds of trees and shrubs, though there is a strong tendency for the faunas to become more and more similar in the later stages. Nor does it always take the same course even in the same species of tree. There are two ways in which invasion can start. The first is by the arrival of bark-beetles that make their breeding galleries under the bark (sometimes also of other early colonists such as longicorn beetles that may do this or also go straight into the sapwood), the second is by direct fungal decay under the bark. Bark-beetles, for example, attack ash, common and wych elms, and oak at Wytham, but not beech, birch, maple or sycamore. The beech certainly has no common bark-beetle attacking it there, though *Dryocoetes villosus* found on oak has been reported elsewhere from beech, as have also *D. alni* and *Ernoporus fagi* not so far known from Wytham.[111] But the tendency to combine British and European records into one statement, makes the information in standard monographs a little difficult to use. There is at Wytham an ambrosia beetle of the bark-beetle family, *Trypodendron domesticum*, that bores through the bark into the wood below; the birch has a bark-beetle at present confined to the north of Scotland.[111] The genus *Acer* does not have any ordinary bark-beetle in Britain. Again not all trees subject to attack by bark-beetles are actually invaded. I have carried out four summers' investigation into the population ecology of ash bark-beetles, mainly *Hylesinus fraxini*, in Wytham Woods. These beetles emerge in March and April from winter hibernation in the live bark of ash trees and attack dying wood (Plate 40) – in my work, billets of ash exposed at about 2-3 feet from the ground in the deciduous woodland glades. If they found fresh-cut wood they would colonize at once. But if wood cut several months previously was offered, they would not do so. This means that the development of bark-beetle communities depends not only on the time of year that the beetles are active, but on the time of year that a tree or branch has died or fallen. Something is known of the biochemistry of this invasion, for Hopf[236] proved that *H. fraxini* does not have effective enzymes for breaking down starch, but can handle sugars and he suggested that 'death' in the ash is accompanied by a breakdown of starches into sugars which the beetles can exploit.

But even if bark-beetles are locally active, they may fail to discover a perfectly favourable site, as I noticed in the spring of 1950, when persistent cold east winds limited the dispersal of the emergent beetles, which stayed and bred on a fallen tree in which they had over-wintered, and made no migration to the billets exposed 50 yards away that had been heavily colonized in previous years. *Hylesinus fraxini* here has annual populations that finish their main work in a log by the late summer, after which, especially if the population has been dense (the 'economic density' of emergent beetles is about 1 per 0·5 cm.^{2} irrespective of the number of parents originally entering), the bark becomes loose and subject to further eco- logical succession. Even on an occupied log (or dying branch on a live tree) there are usually parts in which bark-beetle larvae cannot live successfully, because of heavily lignified areas in the surface wood; and if the invasion is small, there will also be unoccupied areas that are favourable but not exploited. It follows from all this that bark-beetle colonization accelerates the breakdown of a log. The beech, with no surface bark-beetle invasion of this kind underneath the bark, may take two years or more to reach the stage of cracking and loose bark with microfungi and fungus-eating insects beneath it (Plate 41). Just as with leaf litter, the material would eventually be broken down by the microflora even in the absence of animals, but at a slower rate.

In Wytham Woods the ash and the elms have the richest communities of bark- beetles and their associated species. On the ash there are four species of *Hylesinus*: *H. crenatus* that lives in rather thick bark of the trunk, *H. fraxini* the main colonizer of fallen trunks and of boughs on the tree or fallen from it, *H. orni* that overlaps the last but prefers smaller branches, and *H. oleiperda* that goes into twigs. The first three certainly and the last almost certainly occur at Wytham. (*H. orni* is considered to be a rare British species, but this may be because its adults are difficult to dis- tinguish from those of *fraxini*, though the galleries and pupal chambers in the wood look quite different.) Thus the four species share out the tree, with some direct competition at any rate between the two middle ones. On elms at Wytham occur *Scolytus scolytus* (Plate 39), *S. multistriatus* and *Pteleobius vittatus*, again with a gradient in the size of habitat preferred. There is also a weevil, *Magdalis armigera*. The English elm *Scolytus* and *Pteleobius*, with their parasites and predators, have been the subject of a very thorough investigation in 1961–4 in Wytham Woods, by Dr R. Beaver, who has supplied me with several facts noted below. Some work done by Mr S. W. Hurry at Wytham Woods in 1960, which he has left with me, shows that the bark-beetle community on wych elm (*Ulmus glabra*) is similar to that on the English elm (*U. procera*). The communities that develop with the common pine bark-beetle (*Myelophilus piniperda*) on dying Scot's pine (*Pinus*

283

sylvestris) have been fully described for Britain generally by Hanson.[209, 210] This bark-beetle does live in some of the planted parts of Wytham Woods and I have made a preliminary trapping study of some of the species that occur with it. From these sources of material it is possible to draw useful comparisons.

The sharp distinction at this stage of dying and dead wood succession between the bark-beetles of deciduous and coniferous trees is shown by the following analysis of the British species. There are 28 species of Scolytidae on deciduous trees, shrubs and climbers. For the present purpose some of these may be omitted: 1 on gorse (*Ulex europaeus*) and broom (*Sarothamnus* or *Cytisus scoparius*), 6 ambrosia beetles that bore into wood and live on fungi growing in these tunnels, of which 1 can also live on pine. Of the rest there is 1 on ivy, 1 on wild *Clematis*, 1 on hazel, while the rest are in trees. On conifers 32 species have been recorded. At least 24 are known (here and abroad) to attack pines either alone or as alternatives to other conifers. Two of these are ambrosia beetles (including the one mentioned above). Of the rest 1 is on juniper, 1 on larch, and 4 on spruce with or without other non-native species such as silver fir. Since Scots pine, yew and juniper are our only native conifers, some of the latter must have been accidentally introduced in recent times, and this seems to be true also of some of those on pine since Hanson[210] has recorded recent introductions as well as continued spread of some species already known in this country. Only one ordinary bark-beetle in the whole series of 52 occurs both on deciduous and coniferous trees, that is *Hylastes opacus* which lives chiefly on pine but is recorded (either here or abroad) also from elm and ash. [111]

The scale, structure and cross-relations of the communities of species that assemble around each kind of bark-beetle, or genus of bark-beetles, is reminiscent of the situation among oak gall communities discussed in Ch. 10. Each host insect is specific to or at any rate mainly found on one kind of tree, and each carries a constellation of parasites and predators, and sometimes is also involved in competition between species (and often also in some competition for resources between individuals of the same species). The food-chain attachments may be specific, or in practice quantitatively so, or they may be unrestricted. The former help to keep the characteristic community, the latter afford links between the different kinds of community. I collected large numbers of parasites in my earlier experiments with *Hylesinus fraxini* [31], but have not made a special study of these because the immediate aim of the work was to obtain parasite-free pure cultures of the one species of bark-beetle in order to measure the force of intraspecific competition. This aim was successfully attained by bringing in the exposed logs of ash into the laboratory in May before the main force of parasites was on the wing. Only a minute egg parasite, *Trichogramma evanescens*, appeared in small numbers, this being an accidental colonist that has numerous hosts, especially among Lepidoptera. Some material that was exposed to parasites produced eight other species of Hymen-

optera, a predatory beetle, and an abundant Uropodid mite that arrived hanging
on to the parent beetles, bred in the galleries, whence the offspring departed later
on hanging on to the recently emerged bark-beetles, which would then seek winter
quarters. Beaver's elm bark-beetle study at Wytham has revealed something like
50 species, though not all of these may have been ecologically regular or important.
Hanson[209] in the New Forest, recorded over 45 species in the community around
pine bark-beetles there. Some more turned up in his later surveys in other parts of
Britain.[210] These communities, operating rather intensely in restricted centres of
action, considerably amplify the patterned components of the forest.

The interrelations with other parts of the forest system are shown in two ways,
apart from the preparation of conditions favourable to later seral stages in the
dead wood. The adult beetles alternate in their habitats. *Hylesinus fraxini* makes
short blind hibernation galleries in the crotches of live ash trees, where it is associated with a bacterial disease of the ash known as 'ash rose canker'.[537] The two
Scolytus on elm feed on bark of the top twigs of elm after emerging from the
thicker bark. This habit brings about the spread of the elm disease, since the beetles
accidentally carry spores of the fungus *Cerastomella ulmi* growing in their galleries
and may infect the small live twigs they gnaw.[164] The *Myelophilus* on pine also
feed on shoots at the top of live trees.[210]

The second outside connection is through polyphagous parasites and predators.
Of the former the Chalcid *Cheiropachus colon* is a good instance. I have bred it
abundantly from *Hylesinus fraxini* logs, and it was also commonly found by Beaver
in his *Scolytus* colonies. It was also bred from *Scolytus intricatus* (which breeds in
dying oak at Wytham) by Hurry. It is apparently a regular parasite of the ash
bark-beetle, for Richards[405] got it in material from rotten ash fence-posts containing this species near Oxford, and Blair[30] from similar material with the same bark-
beetle in the Isle of Wight. But judging from its European records[504] and the fact
that Hanson did not record it in his pine surveys, it is confined to bark-beetles of
some deciduous trees. *Eurytoma morio* was abundant on *H. fraxini* colonies but only
occurred very rarely in elm bark-beetles on the same hill. It probably does not
come on conifers at all. The Braconid parasites of the genus *Coeloides* chiefly
parasitize bark-beetles, and I have watched them in summer ovipositing through
the ash bark under which larvae are growing. They have a well-developed
specificity to their hosts. I bred *Coeloides melanotus* and *C. filiformis* from *Hylesinus
fraxini*, Beaver got *C. scolyticida* on the elm bark-beetles and Hanson *C. abdominalis*,
on pine bark-beetles (*Myelophilus piniperda*) in the New Forest and elsewhere in
this country. Among predators, the pink larvae and variegated adults of the
Clerid beetle *Thanasimus formicarius* prey chiefly on bark-beetles, though they also
attack other beetles present.[209] Its larvae have occurred sometimes in *Hylesinus
fraxini* galleries at Wytham and adults were also seen; they have also been found

commonly among Beaver's elm bark-beetles, and they can be extremely abundant among pine bark-beetles, Hanson[210] remarking that 'under natural forest conditions *Thanasimus* is extremely numerous and is a very formidable enemy of *Myelophilus*'. The larvae developed in a trap-log of Scots pine exposed in Wytham Woods and colonized by *Myelophilus piniperda*.

When bark has been partly loosened by bark-beetles eating away its inner tissue and the cambium, or more slowly by the operation of fungi, it is colonized by a rich community of animals nearly all of quite different species from those of the earlier bark-beetle stage. A dead beech branch in Wytham Woods, less than two years after its fall, lying in deciduous woodland with a few scattered conifers, and looking very like the one in Plate 41 which fell not far away in the same woodland belt, had the following conditions beneath the cracking bark. Some of the bark was still fast to the wood. The thin spaces under the rest were partly filled with microfungal growth, including a mycelial mat of yellow filaments. The branch was mostly not in contact with the ground and therefore drier than ordinary logs. The animals comprised woodlice (*Oniscus asellus* and *Porcellio scaber*), millipedes and centipedes, spiders, pseudoscorpions, earwigs, Collembola, the larvae of Mycetophilid flies, and nine species of small beetles, some of which are certainly fungus eaters. A good many of the animals that live in this kind of situation, whether under the old bark of logs and fallen branches, or on the trunks of dead standing trees or boles, are almost confined to this habitat. Among them may be mentioned the paper-thin bug *Aneurus laevis*, the black tubular thrips *Phlaeothrips* (*Hoplothrips*) *ulmi*,[451] the tiny millipede *Polyxenus lagurus*, the false-scorpion *Chernes cimicoides*,[514] and various small beetles such as *Cerylon ferrugineum*, *Rhinosimus ruficornis* and *R. viridipennis*, and *Micromalus flavicornis*, all found in Wytham Woods. The beetles are nearly all very small, below about half a centimetre in length, in contrast to the much larger size of the dominant beetles and flies that make burrows in the rotting wood itself. And although we know only too little precisely about the real as opposed to the supposed food habits of most of these animals, it is pretty clear that in the early stages under loose bark the primary source of food is microfungi, together with any remains of the inner bark or cambium that have not been already exploited by bark-beetles or by the fungi. As time goes on – and this stage can last for several years, sometimes well over ten years – there is a large and characteristic community of animals living there, the largest being the spotted slug *Limax maximus* which at any rate uses the place as a refuge. To what extent some of the molluscs and woodlice and centipedes and so on roam outside the bark at night or in damper weather has seldom been studied systematically, though I have already referred to the exchanges between litter and logs studied in Wytham Woods by Lloyd (Ch. 12).

Once the dead wood has got to this stage with loose bark, the animals living in this exiguous but apparently rich habitat are no longer restricted by the particular kind of tree or shrub concerned. Thus *Aneurus laevis* has been found in Wytham Woods under bark of ash, sycamore, beech and hawthorn; *Cerylon ferrugineum* under bark of oak, ash and beech, while Donisthorpe's beetle surveys[102] in Windsor Park also recorded it under bark of oak and beech; *Rhinosimus ruficollis* under bark of beech and common elm, Donisthorpe getting it under bark of beech and maple; *Micromalus flavicornis* under bark of ash, beech, sweet chestnut and pine. The small millipede *Polyxenus lagurus* occurs there equally under bark of deciduous trees and those of pine. Snails and slugs are possibly even more wide in their choice – they also live in rotting wood and litter and other places. At Wytham Woods *Goniodiscus rotundatus* has been taken under loose bark of oak, ash, sycamore, beech, common elm, black poplar, elder and hawthorn, and *Oxychilus alliarius* under all these except elder. There is also little difference in the occurrence of most of the species under loose bark in the edge or the inside of woodland, provided the edges are not very exposed – and even so the metabolic water produced by fungi often keeps an apparently dry bark damp underneath. The explanation of this widening of the habitat range is that these animals are dependent not on the green tissues of the trees but directly or indirectly on the microfungal growth (or also on temporary shelter, moving in from outside). This microfungal growth must either be composed of one or more generally distributed forms that occur under any decaying bark, or else the invertebrates that feed on them find many forms equally edible. The present stage of mycology does not seem to give an answer to this question. But it is possible to explain a few other general points that have a profound influence on the development of these and further communities on dying and dead wood.

We are now at the stage in log succession where the superficial tissues of the inner bark and the cambial growth zone, and to a limited extent also the superficial layer of the sapwood have been attacked or even removed by animals and the remaining surfaces are being penetrated by the hyphae of fungi. Following the explanation provided by Cartwright and Findlay,[64] it seems clear that invasion of dying wood advances on two separate fronts. There is superficial invasion of the outer part of the timber, the living sapwood zone, by more than one group of fungi, whose entry depends upon the breaching in some way of the protecting bark; and an invasion inside the heart of the tree, into the central and already 'dead' tissues that form the tree's main skeleton. The latter takes place through roots or deep rabbit damage at the base of the tree or through broken stubs after a branch has fallen, and any similar wound that opens the wood to invasion and the subsequent spread of heart rot. It is interesting that trees growing without close competition, as in parks or the old-fashioned widely spaced oak woods, are more likely to lose their spreading branches by accident and become infected. The surface invaders include some fungal groups other than the Basidiomycetes – moulds for example, but the heart-rot is caused by Basidiomycetes only. Cartwright and Findlay remark: 'It is an interesting and hitherto incompletely explained fact that comparatively few of the fungi which occur in standing trees are important as causes of decay in felled timber. Since most of the fungi which cause heart rot in growing trees grow only in the heartwood of the tree which contains no living cells, it might be expected that they would find equally favourable conditions for their development in felled timber, provided the moisture content remained the same, but this is not generally the case. Some species, such as *Polyporus sulphureus*, are able to continue their development in felled logs or converted timber, but they rarely infect afresh any converted timber. . . .' But of course most of the rotting wood with which I am concerned is not healthy timber that has been felled and left, but what a forester would call diseased trees or bits of them that are already full of various fungal infections, and these do not all stop growing, indeed they may come into damper conditions in which growth can increase.

There is this attack both from without and from within. It follows that when one is opening up a rotting log to look for animals, the distribution of the rotting wood may be extremely complex and puzzling. Sometimes there is a superficial inch or two of softened wood with very firm hard wood below, but further down other decayed parts. This is especially noticeable at the exposed ends of a fallen log. In a very complicated progress, whose rate and distribution varies with many factors, the outer decay and the inner decay are moving towards one another, until they become intervolved (for each can enter the zone of the other). During all this the mycelial networks that have penetrated the cells of the tree have built up enough nutriment to produce, under the right outer conditions, the magnificent fruiting bodies that form the subject of the next chapter. Some of these, like *Polyporus betulinus*, have come from heart rot mycelia, others, like the much smaller but very densely colonial *Polystictus versicolor*, initially from the sapwood. It is also necessary to understand that although wood may be firm and may in fact be quite impenetrable by many animals, it can already have become widely infected by fungi. This is visible most readily in wood that has coloured stain resulting from such invasion.

The animal community under loosening bark is therefore living partly among and upon the mycelia of species that are able to produce fruiting bodies above the bark, just as the later invading insects in rotting wood live among and upon fungal threads that are also able to produce outside macrofungal fruiting bodies. There are two great differences between the communities under bark and in rotting wood on the one hand, and those in the various macrofungi on the other. The first is that the actual species concerned are very largely different, and the second is that

288

whereas, as I have mentioned, the species under loose bark (and as will be shown, also largely those in rotting wood) are seldom limited to one kind of tree, the insects in bracket fungi are much more restricted, as are their host fungi. In other words, part of the primary community pattern which was seen to dissolve gradually as decay proceeds, is partially restored again, before going on to become a further common substratum in the finally decayed tissues of rotting fungi themselves.

The bark-beetle invasion stage may last several months of the spring and summer, as with *Hylesinus fraxini*, or go on right round a year or more, as with the large *Scolytus* in elm, or be intermediate between these, as in the pine bark-beetle *Myelophilus piniperda* that finishes in one summer but whose parasites may partly overwinter before completing development. But the next stage under loosened bark may last for a number of years, according to the solidity of the bark, the wear and tear on it, and the species of tree. It follows that this second stage is often present while the deeper invasion of communities in the wood itself is developing, and that the communities under old loose bark are therefore in a position analogous to that of the woodland ground zone or the edge of water: a number of animals not resident regularly there have to pass in or out through this thin habitat zone, so adding to its general complexity. Therefore when you lift the bark from an old log or standing bole, you may find freshly emerged adults of log-boring species like *Sinodendron cylindricum* that are on their way out, or conversely breeding adults that are starting a new cycle of egg-laying. Any general list of the species found under loose bark will be very large, if one includes these transients as well, though a good many of them actually live in both zones, for example larvae of the scarlet beetle *Pyrochroa serraticornis*. The following figures will give a rough idea of the scale of the mesofauna (omitting those not genuinely belonging to the under-bark communities). In a series of collections by field classes from large rotting logs at Wytham Woods in September of six different years about sixty species were found under loose bark, not counting any that were just sheltering there. These include only the mesofauna and exclude the microfauna of small worms, mites and Collembola. But the total number of residents in this habitat at Wytham is certainly two or three times this number.

The situations in which rotting wood may develop are extremely varied and we have only begun to touch the fringe of all the possible variants that exist. Entomological records of the habitats of animals living in such places are almost unbelievably unsophisticated, and even the very large body of records from Wytham Woods (most of which remains to be published in detail) only represents an attempt to explore a hidden world of mostly unknown structural, chemical and fungal conditions. There are four main situations: on the live or partly dying and standing tree, on dead standing trees or the boles remaining after the tops have broken off (Plate 47), in lying logs of various sizes (Plate 42), and in the residual stumps when these die and do not grow again into coppice stems (Plate 38). Within these four types there are very obvious variants (whatever their ecological significance to the animals may be) of tree species, species of fungal mycelium or mixtures, position inside dense woodland or in thinner woods or at edges (including glades), and the natural (as distinct from the fungal metabolic) dampness or dryness of the medium. Some examples from Wytham Woods will give some idea of the fauna of these places.

On 16 January 1949 I partly dissected an old 20-foot beech log lying in dense oak–ash–sycamore woodland at Wytham. It had lost practically all its bark and had been there long enough to acquire some well-established patches of moss. The wood was red-rotted and very damp. In half an hour I found the following animals in it. Three of the four main large insect tunnellers in rotting wood on this hill were present. *Sinodendron cylindricum* (Plates 45 and 46) is the smallest of the three British Lucanidae or stag-beetles, whose male has only a minute trace of a horn. Its soft white larvae live for at least two years, burrowing diffusely and sometimes being found in quite hard wood. There was also an Elaterid beetle *Melanotus rufipes* (Plate 43) that has narrow shining brown larvae usually in red-rotted wood. The large white diaphanous larvae of a crane-fly *Tipula flavolineata*, here in soft rotting wood, are also able to live in quite hard white-rotted logs. The fourth large tunneller, the medium-sized stag-beetle *Dorcus parallelipipedus* (Plate 44), was not present. Other active beetles included larvae of a smaller Elaterid *Denticollis lineatus* that is an active gallery-maker. Living also in the rotting wood, temporarily or continuously, were at least twenty other kinds of animals [32]: smaller Tipulid fly larvae and the pupae of some other fly; four pupae from a family of Crabronid wasps, *Coelocrabro leucostomoides*, that had used a gallery to store food for its larvae; a ♀ earwig, *Forficula auricularia*; a small Staphylinid beetle, *Conosomus testaceus*; Collembola; centipedes (*Lithobius*); woodlice, *Oniscus asellus* and *Porcellio scaber*; a large spider, *Amaurobius atropos*; and earthworms. Besides these were a group of hibernating insects: three Carabid beetles, *Carabus violaceus*, *C. nemoralis* and *Cychrus caraboides*; a snail-eating Silphid beetle *Phosphuga atrata*; and a large Ichneumonid parasite, a ♀ *Ichneumon gracilentus*. All these hibernators are commonly found in logs here. This list is only the preliminary searching during half an hour. I also knocked to pieces a very soft rotten sycamore log of the same length but rather thinner, in the same bit of woodland. Apart from old holes of the dry wood-borer beetle *Ptilinus pectinicornis*, evidently made before the tree fell, and a few woodlice, this log was almost uninhabited by animals visible to ordinary field searching. This contrast is mentioned because it is quite common to find one piece of rotting wood very rich in animals and another quite poor, yet I have found all three of the main operators mentioned above, *Sinodendron*

Melanotus and *Tipula flavolineata*, in sycamore logs at Wytham, albeit much less commonly than in some other trees.

The next example is from 15 ft up on a very large old live ash tree in oak–ash–sycamore woodland at the edge of a track in Wytham Woods. From this a bit of dead branch a foot in diameter had recently fallen to the ground from a height of 15 ft and I collected a piece about 1½ ft long on 22 March 1960, and kept the animals as they emerged from it indoors. The wood was damp and red-rotted and partly protected still by thick bark (which I removed). The chief tunneller was *Sinodendron cylindricum*, with larvae of two age-classes, but *Melanotus rufipes* larvae were also there. Another twenty-four species of animals were obtained, which will not be completely recounted here. They included woodlice, centipedes, millipedes, pseudoscorpions, very young Opiliones, Collembola, various beetles (including the flower-visiting *Anaspis frontalis*), and some flies. A family of Crabronid wasps, this time *Coelocrabro ambiguus* [33], emerged, and there were also small Heteropterous bugs from the canopy, *Camptobrochis lutescens*, hibernating. The whole picture was one of intense activity and close occupation, and a good many of the species have been found also in logs lying on the ground. In both instances the fauna actually noted, some two dozen species, is below the real number, which would be augmented, perhaps even doubled if one had determined some of the unknown larvae of beetles and flies, and extracted the microfauna of mites and Collembola.

When a large tree becomes weakened internally by heart rot (often signalized already by the appearance of bracket fungi) it is not uncommon for its crown to break right off, leaving a standing bole anything from 12 ft or more in height (Plate 47). The fallen material of canopy follows the various pathways of succession already described, and to some extent the standing bole carries the same species of animals in it, with the difference that under dry conditions certain ones may be common that do not normally go into lying logs. One of these, very frequent in Wytham Woods, is the small pinhole borer beetle, *Ptilinus pectinicornis* (Plate 50), which can form very large populations. I found such a dead standing beech bole in the open edge of woodland in Blenheim Park, Oxfordshire, on 13 June 1948, in which the bare wood swarmed with *Ptilinus*, the males running actively about vibrating their extraordinary pectinate antennae as if picking up signals from the galleries within. With them was a Clerid beetle predator *Tillus elongatus*, these two species being commonly associated on dead beech.[255] The trunk was also galleried by *Sinodendron*, as was a nearby dead bole of Scots pine (*Pinus sylvestris*), which, however, had no *Ptilinus* holes. In the last week of May in 1949 and 1950, Dr B. M. Hobby and I, with the help of a class of students, examined a dead standing beech bole in the edge of a deciduous woodland glade in Wytham Woods. Among a great number of other invertebrates on it, under its bark, in bracket fungi and in the rotting wood, were the tunnellers *Sinodendron*, *Dorcus*, *Melanotus* and *Denticollis*; but *Tipula flavolineata* was only found in the rotting logs lying under the dampness of field-layer vegetation below. Another tunnelling beetle, *Melandrya caraboides*, a flattish metallic blue insect, was also found in the standing bole. This species I have not found in logs, and only occasionally at all at Wytham, yet in one very white-rotted birch branch it had galleried all through the wood and was very abundant.

In searching for the animals of dying and dead wood generally, one almost always encounters a tremendous variability from tree to tree, or log to log, and even when to the ordinary eye the conditions might appear the same, the composition and numbers of the populations are unpredictable. This subject is referred to in a more formal manner, when I come to the field experiments of Fager at Wytham. And yet the capabilities of at any rate the commoner species in rotting wood are remarkably wide. At Wytham alone, *Sinodendron cylindricum* occurs in the woods and the forest glades and edges, from ground level up to at least 15 ft (and the activities of woodpeckers up to greater heights on dead or partly dead trees show that considerable populations of insect larvae worth digging out occur up aloft as well). It has been found there in the following species of trees and shrubs: oak, ash, sycamore, beech, birch, hawthorn and elder. In Wychwood Forest, Oxfordshire, I have taken it in ash, beech and hawthorn; and in Scotland from dead alder (*Alnus glutinosa*) in very thin timber on the banks of the River Feshie, Inverness-shire. At Wytham, *Dorcus parallelipipedus* has been collected from ash, beech, common elm and wych elm, and in Windsor Forest Donisthorpe[102] also recorded it from ash, beech and elm. At Wytham, *Melanotus rufipes* has occurred in oak, ash, sycamore, beech, birch, common elm, wych elm, hawthorn and Scots pine. (Both Richards[404] at Oxshott Heath, Surrey, woodlands and Wallace[535] in sand-dune pine woods in Lancashire, found it in pine.) In Wychwood Forest I took it in ash, beech and hazel. Van Emden[517] cites it among other records of the kind from apple, cherry and willow, while I found it in the Glen Feshie dead alders. A similar sort of range is evident for *Denticollis linearis*, including for Wytham oak, beech, birch and pine, and for Wychwood Forest oak, ash and hawthorn. *Tipula flavolineata* at Wytham has been bred out from oak, sycamore, beech and hazel. *Ptilinus pectinicornis* does not have such a wide range in dead trees but is common both on beech and sycamore in Wytham Woods, which corresponds with Fisher's[157] generalization about its attacks on timber, though he says it occasionally comes in oak as well. All the species just mentioned live both inside the forest and at its edges.

These catalogues of the habitats of the chief gallery-makers in rotting wood in our area resemble those already given for some of the animals that live under loose bark. The originally distinctive interspersion of the green plant based communities on separate trees and shrubs has now been dissolved and replaced by a different pattern. This pattern takes little account of the original species of wood though it is still spaced out in separate centres of action – the log, the bole, the stump and many smaller units, scattered through the forest. Although the original primeval forest may have had a much more closely accumulated layer of dying and dead wood, modern ones at any rate still have their dead wood rather in such scattered units. Some of these animals of rotting wood are confined to broad-leaved timber, others can also colonize rotting conifers as well. Still others seem to be confined to the latter. I think that rotting pine in the south of England, which has not retained any original boreal conifer forest, has a poorer community of animals, whereas rotting broad-leaved timber has a rich inheritance from oak and beech forests coming in before the island broke from Europe. Probably the north of Scotland has a richer rotting pine community, though this has never been studied ecologically. The only British investigation of the kind is that by Wallace[535] on the fauna of pine stumps in planted woods on the Lancashire sand-dune, but the conditions are so different from those in a matured woodland that it is not very easy to compare them with ours. Savely,[429] who followed the ecological succession in dead oak and pine logs in the Duke Forest in North Carolina, found that even after the early stages of colonization by bark-beetles and the like, there remained a considerable difference in the species coming into rotting oak and rotting pine. But in spite of the more restricted habits of some invertebrates that go into rotting wood, there can be no doubt that most of the important ones are able to build up populations on a very large number of different mixtures of wood species and the mycelia of fungus species.

It will be evident enough, even if we did not have the wealth of previous information from forest and other entomologists to confirm it – a wealth whose rather chaotic presentation resembles perhaps more a plethora – that we have here one of the richest series of animal communities in the country. It is on a level of scale in variety, interest and ecological power with the communities of canopy, of field layers, of the ground zone and the topsoil, and far beyond any section of any aquatic system in these islands. It can be studied by several methods that come well within the compass of the ordinary naturalist, or the school or student group, or as a variant in the life of the too intense ecologist. Many of the wood-living animals take months to develop, but the material in which they live can be easily kept indoors and watched, the results can be obtained fairly slowly over a long period, and so can be fitted into a busy life. There are some very difficult taxonomic groups, but others that are very easy to master. Three methods for finding what is present in a piece of rotting wood are to be recommended. The first is straightforward dissection or breaking up and searching. The second is to keep intact bits in tins with an exit tube, and allow those species that are immature to complete their development over the weeks or months. The third, necessary for study of any microfauna, is to put the broken material into some kind of heat-extractor such as a Tullgren funnel. For these three methods, parallel samples are usually but not always needed. But there remains a fourth method, which is perhaps not for the busy man, yet very productive of information that may otherwise never be caught, and that is patient field watching. Of this, I shall cite the observations made by C. Morley,[335] a very talented entomologist who in June and July 1934 recorded what he saw happening at an ancient 20-ft standing beech bole in the New Forest, Hampshire. It was in Denny Wood, now a National Nature Reserve, and in a general area famous for the richness of its insects. His survey is unusual for its time, in giving subdivisions for the communities of bare rotting wood, with the burrowing forms and those sitting outside, others flying round, others under bark, walking among moss living in or flying round small bracket fungi, and finally the wasps nesting at different heights in the wood. Altogether he recorded about 70 species of which 20 were parasites (chiefly Hymenoptera) whose known habits linked them with some of the other inhabitants. About 15 kinds of insects belonged to the bracket fungi, while 2 were moths resting by day. The wood-borers included *Ptilinus pectinicornis* (with its enemy *Tillus elongatus*), *Melandrya caraboides*, 3 kinds of longicorn beetles, and several wood-boring flies; and there were 3 species of nesting Crabronid wasps, as well as a large colony of *Vespula rufa* at the top of the bole.

It can be imagined that any quantitative analysis of the animals living in rotting tree stumps (Plates 37 and 38) is even more difficult than for large boles or logs, and so far we do not know much about them at Wytham, or even, so far as populations go, in any part of Britain, except for a few specially serious pests of conifers like the pine-beetle *Hylobius abietis*, and the pine-stump survey by Wallace[535] in Lancashire. But Derksen[93] in 1936-8 surveyed the fauna living in stumps of felled beech trees near Rostock in north Germany, obtaining information that has a bearing on British communities. He trapped the emerging insects in the field, dissected stumps as well, and brought some of the smaller ones bodily into the laboratory in order to follow life-histories. I will not attempt to present his full picture of ecological succession in these one- to ten-year old stumps, as there are some rather difficult statistical conundrums. The grand total of insect species (for what it is worth, many being extremely low numbers) was 217. They included, among the more frequent rotting-wood eaters, *Sinodendron cylindricum*, *Dorcus parallelipipedus*, *Melanotus rufipes* and *Tipula flavolineata*, to mention only several that live in logs and trees at Wytham Woods. I have records, though few (because they have not been looked for much) of these also from tree-stumps in Britain, some in Wytham Woods. But stumps also have their own special inhabitants, with apparently special requirements for their micro-habitats in different parts of the stump. These have been studied in Europe, but not much in Britain. Stumps also have a rich toadstool and bracket fungus community, and altogether add a distinctive and long-lasting component to the woodland floor. Another variant in the rotting complex is the wood-mould or frass that accumulates inside holes and hollow tree-trunks, which I will not pursue here.

So far I have (except for some of the bark-beetle surveys) been describing the larger bodies of dying and dead wood. But there are many small branches and fallen bits that are extremely numerous in the forest, partly because the forester does not even nowadays trouble to remove them all, and partly because there is a continuous and large supply coming to the ground. The lower parts of trees in woodland also have a great many small branches less than, say, 3 or 4 in. in diameter, that die but remain attached for a long time. In these some insects develop that are not usually found in the larger branches or trunk scars. On 2 February 1960 I broke off a length of dead beech branch of 3 in. diameter growing straight out of the trunk of an old tree at a height of 8 ft inside a beech grove. The branch had lost all its bark and was covered with green alga. The inside was quite hard but of a cheesey texture and entirely riddled with small galleries less than a fifth of an inch in diameter. These were made by *Grynobius excavatus* (a relative of the furniture beetle) whose larvae were still there. This branch had become a limited microcosm for some other insects, partly sheltering there (the beech leaf-mining weevil, *Rhynchaenus fagi*, hibernating) and partly eating fungi in the galleries (*Phlaeothrips ulmi* [34]). Such a microcosm differs greatly from that in the larger branches and it is pretty certain that there is a whole spectrum of communities in rotting wood bodies of different sizes, just as with the four species of ash bark-beetles mentioned earlier.

When small rotting boughs, say less than 3-4 in. diameter, fall to the ground they develop quite a rich community of animals most of which might not at ordinary glance in the field or even in the laboratory be recognized because so many of them are microscopic in size, consisting of mites and Collembola. Most of the larger tunnelling insects like *Sinodendron* are correspondingly absent. The small volume and partly friable condition of the wood make it possible to extract the animals rather completely in an apparatus with heat and humidity gradients, which as has been explained is not at all easy and usually impossible to do with any accuracy for the larger bodies of rotting wood like boles, large logs and stumps. Such smaller material has been the subject of a chain of experimental studies by ecologists at the Bureau of Animal Population, starting with E. W. Fager in 1953, which will now be described. They provide a quantitative and analytical development in the study of dying and dead wood at Wytham only otherwise applied so far to bark-beetle communities. Although in certain respects the animal communities in such small logs are less generally characteristic of rotting wood communities in general than those that I have already mentioned, because they have closer affinities to leaf litter and lack many of the most prominent insect species that attack rotting wood, yet the comparative ease with which they can be manipulated and artificially simulated, and the possibility of getting fairly complete censuses, have made them invaluable for discovering the nature of community structure and variation in scattered small units on the forest floor. Fager's experimental approach has since been applied also to the study of leaf litter communities in Wytham Woods by Lloyd and Ghelardi, working also at the Bureau of Animal Population [24]. The possibility of eventually attaining a really good quantitative knowledge of the whole series of communities from the soil, through the litter, and logs lying on the ground upwards into the numerous variants of dying wood on standing trees, is attractive, and has never before been attempted, and is not conceivable without a continuity of records and the backing of survey collections over a good many decades.

In 1954 a quantitative survey of rotting oak branches less than 3 in. diameter lying on the forest floor in Wytham Woods was set up by Fager, who brought to this research the great assets of a previous brilliant record in experimental biochemistry and a mastery of mathematical techniques that are seldom combined with the outlook of an ecological naturalist. His full results have not so far been published, only a summary[149] of the statistical methods that he applied to the analysis of communities; but Prof. Fager has allowed me to draw upon his thesis at Oxford.[148] His investigation is one of the swiftest, most precise and highly concentrated attacks on community ecology yet done anywhere. The logs were within an area of about 3 acres in Marleywood Plantation, a stretch of mature deciduous woodland planted in the nineteenth century that has already been alluded to in Chs. 3 and 13, and whose streams will be mentioned in Ch. 17. Composed chiefly of beech, oak, ash and sycamore, the wood had not at that time received any drastic forestry treatment, though it has since been considerably altered. The details about its scrub and field-layer cover scarcely matter in so far as no marked connection could be found between the various sites in which logs were laid and the fauna entering them – perhaps in part because of the tremendously variable nature of the invasions themselves. But there was a dense field layer in summer, with locally very deep shade from young sycamore, that ensured a good microclimate for decay. All the 29 logs were of oak, mostly white-rotted except for a few that had acquired red-rotted wood probably after they fell, and with a hard undecayed core of wood. They were collected on various dates between August 1954 and April 1955 and their faunas extracted.

Fager also constructed some artificial 'logs' in the form of thin oak boxes a foot long and with 2-in. sides perforated with holes, filled with natural oak sawdust enriched in some cases by the addition of 10% bone flour and maize meal, and (to

48. Dead birch tree with live and dead brackets of *Polyporus betulinus*, deciduous woodland glade, Wytham Woods. (Photo D. A. K. 27 Nov. 1956)

49. *Tetratoma fungorum* feeding at night on the under surface of the hymenium of *Polyporus betulinus*, Wytham Woods. The larvae of this beetle burrow inside the tissue. (Photo D. A. K. 28 Oct. 1957)

50. *Polystictus versicolor* colony on the trunk of a partly rotted large beech, edge of beech grove, Wytham Woods. The pinholes in the hard wood were made by a wood-boring beetle, *Ptilinus pectinicornis*. (Photo D. A. K. 21 March 1956; from K. Paviour-Smith[454])

51. Brackets of a fungus, *Trametes rubescens*, on a dead beech branch in a deciduous shelter belt, Wytham Woods. This fungus is too tough for insects to inhabit. (Photo D. A. K. 13 Sept. 1954)

52. Underground brood-chamber of a burying-beetle, *Necrophorus vespillo*, with processed corpse of a small vertebrate. The female is chasing another beetle out of the crypt. (Photo in Germany, from E. Pukowski, 1933)

53. Corpses of various small animals after being buried and processed by burying-beetles, *Necrophorus vespillo*: (*a*) frog, (*b* & *c*) half frogs, (*d*) sparrow, (*e*) lizard, (*f*) mole. (Photo in Germany, from E. Pukowski, 1933)

54. Cow-pats in a pasture field on Wytham Hill, very recently attacked by rooks, *Corvus frugilegus*. (Photo C. S. E. 20 Sept. 1961)

55. Sheep dung among grazed grass tussocks and Coral Rag stones, Wytham Hill. (Photo D. A. K. 10 June 1954)

56. Pasture with mounds of yellow ants *Lasius flavus*, at the head of Wytham Park. Behind, scrub with flowering elder, woods and grassland. (Photo C. S. E. 26 June 1958)

57. Nest of wood-ants, *Formica aquilonia*, 5 ft in diameter, in old pine wood with *Calluna* and *Vaccinium*, Glen Derry, Aberdeenshire. (Photo C. S. E. 12 July 1954)

58. Molehills on pasture near R. Thames, Godstow, Oxfordshire. In front centre is a territory of one mole with main nest mound (*c.* 100 litres of earth), which contained two grass nests. (Photo D. A. K. 12 March 1964)

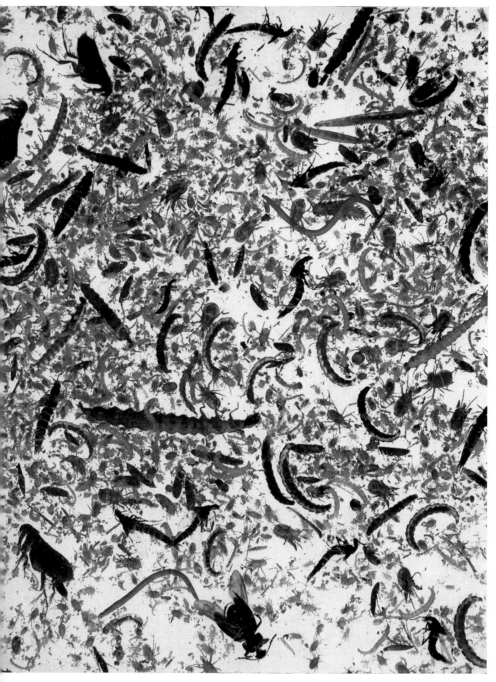

59. Part of the fauna extracted from a mole's nest in the general area of Photo 58. Three large mole fleas, *Hystrichopsylla talpae*, flea larvae, Staphylinid and other beetles and larvae, fly larvae, mites, springtails, etc. (Photo D. A. K. 1964)

60. Tawny owl, *Strix aluco*, bringing a large earthworm to its young at night in a tree nest-box in Wytham Woods. (Photo H. N. Southern)

61. Massive excavation of sand by badgers, and (in front) a pathway through dog's mercury and sycamore saplings, Wytham Woods. (Photo D. A. K. 11 Sept. 1960)

promote fungal invasion) all were inoculated with ground-up decayed oak. With various sampling precautions, variations in position and so on, 24 boxes were set out on the forest floor on 29 May 1954, partly in parallel with the natural logs. After four months 12 were brought in and extracted, refilled and put out again on 16 October and left for five months. These, together with the rest of the original boxes were recovered in March 1955. From the results of all this a number of clear-cut conclusions emerged, of which I shall only deal with some of the main ones.

Altogether 231 species were named or assigned to specific 'taxa'. 134 were found in 5 or more logs or boxes [35] and these consisted of the following: 3 species of earthworms (Enchytraeid worms were also present but not dealt with because of extraction and taxonomic obstacles); 6 snails and slugs; 2 woodlice, 3 millipedes, 4 centipedes, 1 pseudoscorpion, 52 mites (of which 27 were Oribatids, 23 Meso-stigmata and 2 Trombidiformes); and of insects 26 Collembola, 17 beetles, 1 thrip and 19 flies. These include both adults and larvae, and a certain number, especially flies, were assessed as separate species though only assignable to genus or family. The overwhelming predominance of mites and Collembola, 60% of the whole, stands out, and this was to be seen also in the numbers of individuals. In relative abundance the Collembola were first. It follows that the larger forms were relatively few in numbers [36]. In order to find out how far this situation in small logs might partly be caused by their intimate contact with the woodland litter and other habitats, I have made some comparisons with the lists of species for such communities available in the Wytham Ecological Survey. A complete and homogeneous comparison is not possible because collection has not been even. The analysis refers to the 134 species found in 5 or more samples. Of the 17 named species that are not mites or insects, 12 or 70% occur in the woodland litter zone at Wytham. Full lists of Oribatid mites are not yet available for Wytham litter, yet 7 of the 24 identified species are known from there plus 1 from woodland soil, with 7 more from oak–beech litter in Hampshire studied by Roberts,[411] a total of 14 or 58%. No adequate comparison can be made for the Mesostigmata. Of the 26 Collembola species, still incompletely recorded for Wytham woodland soil or ground zone, 11 are known from there, therefore nearly half occur outside rotting wood [36A]. Of the 11 named beetles 4 or 5 are certainly characteristic of rotting wood, but at least 5 others range much more widely, one into Transition marsh, another commonly in dung, and so on. The 3 named flies live in rotting wood. The general picture is of a high degree of association with the litter fauna, which further work will certainly amplify.

There was considerable resemblance between the species in natural and in artificial logs: of the 'over five' group of species, only 7 present in the natural were absent from the artificial ones. The resemblance applies much more to these commoner species than to the 'under five' group, which is to be expected. Fager worked out some elaborate statistical procedures for separating out recurrent groups of species within the general community, using a mixture of ranking and association methods, but I will not attempt to describe this side of his survey, because of my own inability to judge a mathematical discussion in a field that is highly technical and in a rapid state of development. But the value of being able to detect any signs of regular associations in communities that, as in rotting wood, are based on animals eating apparently one kind of food mixture – wood and fungi – would be great, because the complexities of the microfloral ecology and chemistry and taxonomy alone make it extremely difficult to find out what is going on by the ordinary direct natural history methods of the ecologist. The chief recurrent association was one of 21 species, with some minor ones as well. Fager summarized some of his main conclusions as follows: 'The total number of individuals per sample was relatively constant in the set of samples taken and within this total there was repeated a pattern of distribution of individuals per species in which a few species contributed most of the individuals and a nearly constant per cent of species were represented by one individual. The specific components of the pattern changed from log to log, but the pattern remained.'

The most remarkable feature of these communities was the variation in the order of dominance in population size among the species in different logs or boxes. 'In over 80% of the 29 natural logs 1 to 4 species contributed 50% of the total individuals and 5 to 10 additional species were needed to make this up to 75%. In over 80% of the 36 "synthetic logs" 1 to 3 species contributed 50% of the total individuals and 3 to 8 additional species were needed to make this up to 75%. The species in these classes were not usually the same in different samples; 31 species were in the 50% class and 53 species in the 75% class at least once whereas 4 and 10 respectively would have been expected if the same species had always been involved.'[148] This highly unpredictable arrangement in what appeared to be similar habitat units drawing upon a common pool of species is quite different from that among bark-beetles in ash, where only one species can be dominant in boughs of a certain size.

Whatever variety there may be within the fauna of logs at Wytham can almost be matched within a different scale by the diversity of experience brought to its study there. The next stage in experiments upon rotting wood was undertaken in 1961 by a Canadian limnologist, P. A. Larkin, and completed after his departure by C. A. Elbourn, whose previous work had been on pond Entomostraca.[284] This second series of experiments included a survey of the fauna of 27 small natural oak branches at heights of 3-20 ft from the ground in various parts of Wytham Woods and its 'edges'. These samples of branch, averaging about 2-3 in. diameter and 18 in. in length, were taken from living trees, where they formed part of the familiar 'staghorns' so often seen on oaks as they become mature. For brevity I will refer to these as 'aerial logs', in contrast to the 'ground logs' studied by Fager. One of their features is the apparent absence of heart rot, for decay starts in the outer parts, especially while the bark remains to conserve moisture, and a hard core of wood remains that may support the branch for some time. Experiments were also done with 72 artificial boxes filled with oak sawdust, also set on oaks, at heights of 4 ft and 13 ft. These will be referred to as the 'aerial boxes', as distinct from Fager's 'ground boxes', with which they were identical in construction and size, though without fungal inoculation or mineral enrichment, and lacking some minor variants in features that he used. They were left out for periods of 8, 16, 24 and 32 weeks at various dates between 20 September 1961 and 1 November 1962. The area in which they were placed lies about $1\frac{3}{4}$ miles from Marleywood Plantation, and on soils drier than the rather damp clay of the latter. It is a thin wood of oak, ash and sycamore, forming really a series of interconnected glades, and classifiable as woodland 'edge'. Although the two surveys and sets of experiments by Fager and by Larkin and Elbourn are not entirely comparable, in that they were done at different times and in different kinds of place, and not by quite the same methods, they bring up some remarkable points about the nature of the communities on the trees as compared with those on the ground. Further experiments, to bring the comparisons closer, have been continued by Elbourn within the framework of the Ecological Survey.

The animals in the aerial logs were separated from their cover by the three methods I have mentioned: direct sorting, extraction (this time in a new kind of apparatus invented and tested in the Bureau of Animal Population by Kempson, Ghelardi and Lloyd[262]), while a few additional logs were kept to allow for the natural development and emergence of immature animals. None of these 27 bits of branch had moss or bracket fungi on the outside. Altogether about 4500 animals were found in them (not a complete census, because certain groups such as Enchytraeid worms, fly larvae and spiders are not obtained as efficiently as the others). Some total counts of mites in certain logs give an additional estimate of 1500 mites for the whole, bringing the total counted fauna to about 6000. These mites were not identified further. Of the 4500 animals about 85% were Collembola, and these consisted of not more than 7 species, whereas Fager had recorded 26 in ground logs. In the aerial boxes two Collembola, *Mydonius albocinctus* and *Orchesella cincta*, were overwhelmingly abundant, though in aerial logs species of *Isotoma* (of which *I. cinerea* and *I. westerlundi* were present) were often more abundant than *Mydonius*. *Isotoma westerlundi* is one of the few species of animals that had any considerable dominance in the ground logs, in which they had the top numbers in 11 out of 22 logs in which any species reached a population of over 100. It is a winter form, and it appeared suddenly in the ground logs in November and was present until sampling ended in April. But in these ground logs *Mydonius albocinctus* and *Orchesella cincta* were quite rare. But in both, the named fauna other than mites was springtail-dominated.

The whole non-mite faunal list of named species from aerial logs contains only 13 in common with Fager's communities in ground logs; but many of them are common to the communities that live under bark and in rotting wood of large logs or standing trees. This difference can be ascribed mainly to the interchange that I have pointed out between small ground logs and litter. Some other differences stand out. The aerial logs produced about 83 species from 27 units, whereas there were about 160 species (mites omitted) in 29 small ground logs. The dominant forms in the former were far fewer in species than the very changeable ones in the latter. Then the aerial logs had on the average much smaller total populations (omitting the mites) than the ground logs. But in both investigations the numbers of animal per unit log or box tended to reach ceilings in their numbers that were sufficiently regular to suggest some kind of limitation, and this limitation did not seem to be changed by longer periods of exposure in the field, though it varied somewhat with seasons. To sum up: *small* ground logs owe much of their richness to the surrounding ground zone, and both the variety and numbers of species are probably less off the ground, though there the true community of decaying wood contributes most of the species.

Two final aspects of the log habitat emphasize the relations between dying and dead wood and other communities in the system. This is their use by animals for resting, especially in winter, and for making nests. At the later stages of rot in large logs, though seldom in the small ones just discussed, certain insects find their way in late summer and autumn into old beetle or fly galleries and crevices and holes formed by the breakdown of the structure through wear and tear. They especially favour the exposed butt ends. In Wytham Woods the hibernators are beetles, wasps, bumble-bees and Ichneumonid parasites. There are three kinds of large Carabid beetle, the violet-black *Carabus violaceus*, the coppery *C. nemoralis*, and the black snail-eating *Cychrus caraboides*; also commonly another snail-eater, the Silphid *Phosphuga atrata*. It is likely that all these also often shelter by day in logs during their active season. A good many other beetles occur occasionally in winter, including a Chrysomelid *Chrysolina polita* from the Transition zone. Recent research by W. Murdoch[339] in Wytham Woods has proved that small marsh-living Carabid beetles such as *Agonum fuliginosum* migrate a short distance above the marsh line and winter under the bark of logs, in tussocks and the like. Queens of the hornet, *Vespa crabro* – now temporarily extinct in Wytham Woods – and of four other wasps, *Vespula germanica*, *V. vulgaris*, *V. rufa* and *V. sylvestris*, are also commonly found sluggishly hibernating. The first three *Vespula* nest in the ground both in and outside woods, but *V. sylvestris* makes a hanging nest in the canopy.

Five kinds of queen bumble-bee have also been found: *Bombus terrestris*, *B. lucorum*, *B. pratorum*, *B. hortorum* and *B. agrorum*. These are usually ground-nesters, except that *B. pratorum* is reputed sometimes to use birds' nests in ivy on trees.[447] Lastly comes an interesting group of rather large Ichneumonid parasites, often elegantly coloured in red and black, others all black[37]. These are polyphagous parasites of largely polyphagous Lepidoptera. At Wytham 7 species have been found hibernating in rotting wood: *Stenichneumon culpator*★, *Ichneumon molitorius*★, *I. gracilentus*★, *I. confusorius*, *I. albiger*, *I. deliratorius* and *Spilichneumon septem-guttatus*★, while in addition *Ichneumon suspiciosus*★ and *I. minutorius* have been found doing this in Wychwood Forest. These parasites also hibernate under loose bark of dead wood, the species so far found doing so in Wytham Woods being those marked above with an asterisk, also *Ichneumon extensorius* and *Chasmius motatorius*. The largest cache of hibernating ichneumons was discovered by R. S. Miller and B. Macpherson on 16 January 1952. There were 33 specimens belonging to 8 species under the bark of two pine logs inside the edge of a mixed wood at Wytham. But logs are not necessarily the chief or the only wintering place of such insects. Thus *Ichneumon gracilentus*, recorded by the Ecological Survey in 12 different dead wood sites, has also been found hibernating in open turf and in *Deschampsia caespitosa* tussocks in the woods, and by Roberts[411] in oak–beech litter in Hampshire. *I. suspiciosus* has a rather similar range of winter habitats. And this consideration may apply to some of the other insects like bumble-bees and ground-wasps.

A good many small wasps and a few bees are dependent upon logs for nesting, finding an empty gallery in the rotted wood and stocking it with food for their larvae to feed upon. I will not give any details about these species for Wytham Woods, because they have by no means been completely investigated. So far only 7 species of hunting wasps of the family Sphecidae (= Crabronidae) and one leaf-cutting bee have been recorded, some in ground logs, others in standing dead wood. The remarkable accumulation of material about the habitats and prey of Crabronid wasps analysed by Hamm and Richards[204] forty years ago, includes a great deal from the Oxford district, but none from Wytham. I will take only one example, *Metacrabro quadricinctus* (that also nests in rotting wood at Wytham). 147 insect preys stored in nest galleries were named, mostly from colonies near Newbury, Berkshire, and the New Forest, Hampshire. All the prey were flies, the 39 species belonging mainly to the families Calliphoridae and Muscidae and many of them breeding in dung or carrion, though there were others such as Syrphid flies from the canopy. This situation connects the fauna of rotting wood with several other communities both inside and outside woodland.

Hamm, a genius in field observation of insects far beyond the capacity of the ordinary ecologist, formed the simple notion of boring holes of different sizes in two old willow posts used as clothes-props in his garden in Oxford, in order to attract Hymenoptera, and he placed one in the sun and the other in the shade. He remarks: 'On a bright sunny day in June it is no unusual sight to see 12 to 20 species on or about the posts at one time.' Altogether he recorded from them over 43 species, mostly nesting in the holes or parasitic on insects in them.[203] This is extraordinary proof of the attraction of old wood, whether tunnelled by wood-boring insects or by an ingenious entomologist!

The logs in Wytham Woods give considerable nesting cover to ants that make their headquarters in them but forage outside. In large logs and stumps the dominant species is *Myrmica ruginodis*, which finds its food in the surrounding ground zone. Sometimes a very old large beech log that has run through many years of habitation by earlier communities in the succession is entirely occupied by a colony of this ant. Whether the ants have driven out other occupiers, or whether the log reached a stage in which for some reason its remaining substance can no longer be exploited by fungi and animals is not clear. But it does seem to be a fact that a good deal of old rotted wood can reach this derelict stage without being inhabited by ants, and this happens both in red-rotted and white-rotted large logs. This is to say that a large residue of lignin and cellulose becomes almost fossilized and may only be broken down further by mechanical action of weather and so on. This might perhaps be connected with the nitrification process, of which little is known though one assumes it to be essential in the life of the system; and it is also possible that at a certain stage of skeletonization a log may simply have whatever free nutrients accrue leached out of it by rain. Smaller colonies of *M. ruginodis* are not infrequently found in earlier stages of the rotting log. Altogether it has been seen there in the dead wood of oak, ash, sycamore, beech, birch and even larch. Much less common are *M. laevinodis* and *M. scabrinodis*, which Dr A. J. Pontin (who has named many of our specimens) has informed me are less dependent upon woodland and its edges. On one rotten beech there is a colony of the rare *Lasius brunneus*, about whose myrmecophiles Donisthorpe discovered so much in the ancient oaks of Windsor Forest. *Lasius flavus*, really a grassland ant, has three times been found in rotten wood at Wytham, but in every instance in the soft wood of elder. There is also a small rather slow-moving ant, *Leptothorax acervorum*, that has colonies on the limestone reef that caps Wytham Hill. It inhabits quite small dry fallen branches, usually 2-3 in. diameter, in the margin of deciduous wood. This habitat may depend on lack of interference from larger ants. In Scotland Brian[40] surveyed the relationships between ants in a cut-over pinewood and noticed that *L. acervorum* was only living in some hard tree stumps in which the galleries were too small to admit its active competitor *Formica fusca*. The small logs it inhabits at Wytham are soft and friable and would offer no such protection; but there *Formica fusca* is extremely rare and local.[137]

Of the 60 or so species of birds that do or may sometimes breed wild in the Terrestrial habitats of the Wytham area, 18 – nearly a third – are wholly or partly dependent upon dying and dead wood for their nest sites [38]. The figure of 60 omits Aquatic and Transition species, also a few like the house-martin dependent entirely on Domestic structures. These dead-wood nesters are as follows: the stock-dove (*Columba oenas*); the barn-owl (*Tyto alba*), the little owl (*Athene noctua*) and the tawny owl (*Strix aluco*); the woodpeckers, green (*Picus viridis*), great spotted (*Dendrocopus major*) and lesser spotted (*D. minor*); among crows, the jackdaw (*Corvus monedula*); of titmice, the great (*Parus major*), blue (*P. caeruleus*), coal (*P. ater*), marsh (*P. palustris*) and willow (*P. atricapillus*); the nuthatch (*Sitta europaea*); the tree-creeper (*Certhia familiaris*); in the thrush family the redstart (*Phoenicurus phoenicurus*); the starling (*Sturnus vulgaris*); and the tree sparrow (*Passer montanus*). The last is included in the list because although it predominantly frequents riverine tracts in the Oxford region, and often nests in pollard willows, it also penetrates the terrestrial system and has invaded tit nest-boxes in Wytham Woods recently.[381] The only other regular hole-nesters in British woods are the wryneck (*Jynx torquilla*), which is now rare; the crested tit (*Parus cristatus*), confined to the Highlands of Scotland; and the pied flycatcher (*Muscicapa hypoleuca*), a western and northern species. Wytham Woods therefore has all the generally distributed British nesters in rotting wood. There are still other species to which the structure of decaying trees affords open nest sites, such as the kestrel's illustrated in Plate 36.

Some of these species can nest outside woodland, with alternatives in domestic structures (church towers, houses, ruins, walls or thatch, sometimes quite eccentric choices as well), or in rocks or cliffs, or rabbit burrows, and even in old nests or below the occupied nests of larger birds. Others, like the woodpeckers and nuthatch, are dependent on trees. Most of the species find an existing hole and make use of it. The woodpeckers peck out their own. Mr Bruce Campbell has given me the following interesting summary from his cornucopia of nest-finding knowledge: 'The green woodpecker is able to tell when a superficially sound tree has a rotten heart and can drive through about 5 cm. horizontally to reach it, but I think the shaft is always sunk in rotten wood. The green also often bores into obviously rotten trees. The great spotted usually chooses fairly rotten trees, but can certainly go through about 2 cm of soundish wood when making the entrance.' The lesser spotted woodpecker digs only in decayed branches or trunks. Some of the hole-nesting species in turn often use old woodpecker holes, for example the nuthatch, the redstart and the pied flycatcher. The tree-creeper usually goes behind loose bark on a bole or behind ivy on a trunk. The marsh tit finds a hole in an old stump or the like; but the willow tit makes its own excavation in soft rotting wood in a willow, alder, birch or elder. There are many variations and interconnections to be properly systematized by ecologists, and some of the alternative habitats may be vital for the survival of a good many of the species in our increasingly tidy and tailored woodlands.

I have now sketched, though only in charcoal outline, the progress and some of the protean richness and variability of animal communities that exploit the weakened or dying tree or parts of it, the microcosms under loose bark, the fungal and animal invasions of rotting sapwood and heartwood, and the outsiders that use or enlarge this cover for resting or nesting. Succession often takes alternative paths, but they all lead eventually to a great loosening and penetration of the originally sound wood in which fungal hyphae and tunnelling insects are intervolved. While bark-beetles are strongly dependent upon the kind of tree, shrub or climber, the inhabitants of the later fungus-dominated cover are much less so or hardly at all. Every stage and turn and side-loop in this gradual destruction of the cellulose and lignin structure bristles with problems which are still only about as little digested as the mixture of fungus and wood that passes through the beetle and fly larvae themselves. Undoubtedly the greatest technical obstacle is simply the identification of fungal mycelia of which there is such a host of species, for even the mycologist usually finds this a formidable task dependent upon methods of cultural isolation. And the zoologist usually knows nothing about fungi anyway, though he may with assiduity acquire a working knowledge of the easier macrofungal fruiting bodies discussed in the next chapter.

A central question is, whence does this massive contingent of fungi and animals in a tree or log obtain its nitrogen? The heartwood of sound beech contains 0·12% of protein, the major structure being about 49% cellulose, 20% hexosan, xylan and methylpentosan, 23% lignin, with less than 2% water-soluble sugars.[427] What does each animal extract from the mixture of fungus and wood that it ingests, and how? Are its digestive enzymes its own or secreted by commensal micro-organisms? Who exploits the excreta and cast skins of whom? How much partial cannibalism or other predatory or parasitic activity goes on? Do fungal mycelia of different species compete, for example with chemical weapons? How effectively does the metabolic output of water by fungi preserve the microclimate for animals? Why is food, apparently so solidly abundant, only slowly used up and eroded, often only at certain interfaces between rotten and sound wood? Why do some logs last longer than others, and remnants of some become almost derelict of animal life? What decides the composition of species in a particular log? How can fifty or more species of animals live together in a log the size of a man's arm, and do they compete for a common food mixture or have subtly different niches? What limits the population size of the species or the whole community? Are some of these matters determined, albeit in a manner at present unpredictable, by accidents of dispersal, first arrival, initial numbers, population structure, habitat tolerances, season, and under all this the corresponding complexities of fungal invasion by different species?

These and scores of similar leading questions, to which we have at present only got hints of the beginnings of answers, not only concern the elucidation of a particular massive field phenomenon. They also offer opportunities for setting up fundamental experiments that might be of general implication as well, particularly in the field of competition and of stochastic processes generally in populations of semi-isolated small habitat components. Some of the work described in this chapter, in which the natural habitat has been imitated and re-introduced into the field in a standard fashion, has shown what can be started in this direction. But probably many of the final answers will only be found by growing pure cultures of fungal species in different standard (if possible semi-natural) media, and introducing into them single species of animals, and later on modest mixtures of species, under laboratory controls, with at the same time parallel but inevitably rougher experiments in the field. I believe that it is in such community research upon General habitats that one of the chief meeting places in the future of field surveys and experiments, laboratory cultures, and mathematical models may lie.

CHAPTER 15

Bracket Fungi and Toadstools

WOODLANDS, both deciduous and conifer, are the chief home of the fungi that have fruiting bodies large enough to support communities of animals, thereby inserting still more side-chains into an already rich system. Passing from mature woods through scrub into meadow, heath, open ground and the various terrestrial maritime communities, and in marshes, one encounters fewer and fewer 'macrofungi' – which for brevity I shall call MFB (Macrofungus Fruiting Body). Some of those that live outside woodland and scrub certainly are inhabited by breeding insects, usually flies, but it is in woods and to a lesser extent scrub and their edges that there is not only a large and constantly renewed supply of cellulose and other materials that would not easily be disposed of by organisms other than fungi, but also a protected climate; though once fungal growth has got established the metabolism of the fungi themselves produces a continual excess of water. It is rather a paradox, though certainly a convenience for distinguishing the edible from the poisonous, that the species of mushroom we in Britain most commonly eat ourselves grows in open pastures. When toadstools are themselves in the later stages of decomposition by bacteria and perhaps moulds, they are usually occupied by many insects, but in this stage the assemblage is more of a concourse than a community, since many of the species are visitors from other habitats that do not have a complete breeding cycle in the fungus. To avoid misconception I should add that some trees that support MFB occur in the Transition zone – for example willows and the alder; but the terrestrial woods are the chief places where these highly successful parasites or scavengers are concentrated and where they provide food and cover for some hundreds of species of animals, many of which breed nowhere else.

It has already been explained in the last chapter that the MFB is the culmination of a considerable hidden growth of mycelia which are themselves the chief resource for a larger series of animal communities. The greater part of the species with whose MFB we are concerned here belong to the Class Basidiomycetes, of which we have some 2700 species altogether,[60] though hundreds of them are not in fact in the MFB scale or if they are do not necessarily support animal communities or even animal populations. There are also other MFB but not very many of them are inhabited by insects, and even fewer by communities of more than one or two species. The Basidiomycetes involved fall into two main groups: the bracket fungi, mostly Polyporaceae; and the mushroom-like fungi (in this chapter referred to as 'toadstools') of the families Agaricaceae and Boletaceae, though in both groups there are various strange shapes that cannot really be described either as brackets or as toadstools. Broadly speaking the former live on dying and dead wood, and the latter on the ground, though several agarics provide substantial animal habitats on trees as well, and more particularly on dead stumps (Plate 38). Again in very general terms, the bracket fungus communities contain most of the MFB beetles, and the ground toadstools most of the MFB flies, though some of the latter are also common in certain brackets.

The proper study of MFB communities enjoins particularly great care in the identification of the fungi, and the true communities involved also require a close study of the early stages of the insects in order to distinguish between residents and non-breeding visitors. For these reasons some of the past recording of fungus animals has been streaked with errors of identification and of interpretation. In the present chapter I shall lean chiefly on four modern sources of information that are above such criticisms, since they have in turn sifted out the good from the less good earlier work. Apart from the usual textbooks about MFB in general, Cartwright and Findlay's monograph on *Decay of timber and its prevention*[64] gives a realistic appreciation of many things an animal ecologist will want to know, with the minimum amount of jargon, about the MFB that grow on standing, fallen and felled trees. Scheerpeltz and Höflers' *Käfer und Pilze*[431] combines in a fortunate way the results of a cooperative survey in Austrian woods by an entomologist and a mycologist conducted with impeccable precision and much interesting scholarship on special topics, and it is taxonomically valuable for studying beetles. For Britain there are two modern sources that are complementary to one another. The late P. A. Buxton's remarkable leisure-time survey[60] (for leisure can promote thoroughness and reflection) of the Diptera in MFB mainly in the south of England gives a conspectus of 98 species of flies bred from a great range of fungi. He made 447 collections of 154 species of fungi, of which nearly half had flies breeding in them, though not all the fungi were in the MFB scale. For fungus insects, especially beetles, in bracket species growing on trees and shrubs, the work of Miss K. Paviour-Smith (Mrs Southern) at the Bureau of Animal Population is not only based on sound identification of the fungi and of the insects, but has added a new dimension to the subject by applying to it ecological ideas about the choice of habitats and the implications of life in small scattered communities of this kind. The background of this work is a survey of MFB communities, especially based on the Wytham area but also sweeping in a great deal of information from elsewhere in Britain chiefly obtained at first hand. Not all this work has yet been published. In trying to present simplified conclusions about a very technical subject that is opening out very fast I have relied very heavily upon Mrs Southern for help and advice and for some unpublished information from Wytham Woods.

In the present chapter I intend only to map out some of the main kinds of pattern that develop among MFB communities, using as illustrations chiefly some of the beetle population in Wytham Woods. The insects that live in MFB are nearly all small in size, indeed a 'life-group' collection of them much resembles in size those of insects that live in and under rotting bark, or in stored products like wheat and flour. This resemblance seems to be connected with the texture of the cover in which these animals live. The MFB insects feed either in the main fungus tissue, that is on the hyphae that make up these solid pieces of living textile, or upon the spores that they produce. A very important further division of the first category is that in the more enduring MFB on trees and scrub one set of insects feeds on the live fungus tissue, and later set on the dead brackets. In this ecological succession the beetle family Ciidae is prominent in the dead MFB. In MFB that do not turn hard, whether on trees or on the ground, there ensues a stage in which the fungus, by then often much eroded by the larvae of insects or by the attacks of slugs, turns to a squashy decaying mass being decomposed by bacteria and to some extent by moulds. (This also happens to hard MFB that are so wet or so much eaten that they fall to the ground.) At this stage the MFB is visited by quite a large assembly of insects and invertebrates that usually occur also in other habitats such as litter, and even dung and carrion; whereas those that breed in the fresher fungi (or in dead hard brackets) are highly adapted to this niche. To sum up: there are four chief resources formed by MFB: (1) the spores, (2) the living fungus tissue, (3) the hard dead bracket, (4) the soft decaying fungi – either brackets or else toadstools on trees or scrub or on the ground. Within these divisions there are further variants some of which will be noticed.

In the general classification of habitats we have treated MFB as one kind of General habitat, on account of many fundamental features that they have in common with the latter, such as their dependence on dying and dead plant matter, their relatively small size, their structure and successional histories, and their generally rather unpredictable and often sudden appearance. But as already described, they occupy two very different main kinds of habitat – appearing either in the ground zone of terrestrial formation-types and marshes, or on dying and dead wood. Dung is the only other natural or semi-natural resource on which toadstools are common and these are mostly small and delicate, though there are a few that support internal animal populations. The spores in dung are apparently derived usually from the food eaten by the animal that deposits it and not from direct dispersal afterwards.[399] MFB on dying and dead wood and on dung therefore form a General habitat growing on two other General habitats, though the precise parasitological status of the food-chains thus set up I will leave to ecological lexographers to decide. The completely edible MFB can provide, as I have explained, four main resources for animals: spores, the body while fresh, and the body while ageing or dead, which can be soft or hard. There are some MFB that offer a rich supply of spores but nothing else. One such is the greyish bracket fungus *Daedalea quercina* which grows on old oak stumps. I found large populations of this fungus in the winter of 1955-6 on oak stumps in Waterperry Wood, Oxfordshire, in and at the ride edges of ancient oak coppice mixed with birch and many shrubs, that had been cut about twelve years earlier. The MFB were well established and had evidently grown for several years, but whether fresh or dormant they had no insects inside the tissue, which is so tough and rubbery that it cannot be torn by hand. It is well known to be generally inedible to beetles, though the dead MFB has once been found with extensive burrowings by an Oribatid mite.[454] By contrast with this general barrennness, if one bangs the fresh fungus on to a tray, very large numbers of small animals come out of the folds on the underside of the hymen- ium. In this instance there were hundreds of a very small Staphylinid beetle, *Gyrophaena strictula*, and also many mites, *Aceosejus muricatus* [39], also other invertebrates, some of which were evidently predators visiting the oak stump from the ground zone. The Staphylinid is confined, or nearly so, to this species of MFB.[101] There are 15 British species of *Gyrophaena*, all of which live on fungus spores, and have larvae that are adapted to hang on at the base of the tubes by means of a process at the end of the body.

Gyrophaena and a few of its allies are unusual among Staphylinid beetles in both feeding and breeding by their supply base of spores. There is a large number of beetles, especially small Staphylinidae, that regularly visit MFB, especially the slit- gilled kinds, in order to graze on the spores, but breed elsewhere. Thus MFB can be regarded partly as fuelling stations directly analogous with flower pollen, which they resemble in their high protein content. The period during which spores are produced by an MFB ranges from a few days or weeks to several months in dif- ferent species. The stinkhorn, *Phallus impudicus*, that strange ground toadstool (a Gasteromycete) of woods and scrub whose terrific smell leads one to over-estimate its actual abundance, attracts a large concourse of flies, also slugs, to consume the green mucilage that covers the spore-bearing surface of the tip, and in this manner the spores are dispersed.[399] The smell is caused by three amines that attract both dung and carrion flies, also a few carrion-beetles such as *Oeceoptoma thoracicum;* while in Austria dung-beetles (*Geotrupes*) and small beetles (*Anaspis*) that ordinarily visit flowers have also been recorded.[431] One may sometimes see the tip of a stink- horn completely covered with a layer of flies such as blue-bottles (*Calliphora*) and carrion flies (*Lucilia*). This unusual arrangement goes with the fact that the spores are on the outer surface of the MFB and not hidden in folds or tubes in the hymenium. In August and September 1954 Smith[450] collected the flies from a large colony of stinkhorns in the grounds of a house in Staffordshire, partly by a hedge and partly under rhododendrons; and he also made other notes on the whole community. The MFB were visited by 14 species of flies, and 11 species also settled on old rotting remains, only one of these species being the same in both. 4 species of flies were also found inside a broken stem of the fungus, and 4 on its young "egg" stage. 3 of these 8 were not found on other parts. 5 other flies were bred out from the MFB, young and old, that were different from the spore-seeking visitors. Of other kinds of animals, he noted on the MFB 5 kinds of thrips (Thysanoptera), a dusk-visiting moth, *Conistra vaccinii*, that also goes to flowers; a slug; and a wasp that drove off the flies temporarily but did not settle. There were 4 kinds of small beetle inside the base of the stem. So this one MFB colony had about 45 kinds of animals in attendance or breeding in it.

We are here faced with a good deal of difficulty in estimating the number of species that regularly visit fungi to feed on them, since – as has already been indicated for honeydew, flowers and fruits – any general largesse of widely scattered sources of food that can be picked up without difficulty not only comes to be exploited by a very large number of different animals, especially flying ones, but the concourses that do arrive are subject to tremendous local and temporal variations. The Wytham Ecological Survey's community list for MFB is composed of records from a large number of British sources that have been mined for ore. The trouble comes in assaying the quality of this ore. But the list undoubtedly includes an unknown number of more or less accidental visitors from other habitats and also a certain number of built-in taxonomic queries because some of the Staphylinid beetles in particular are in highly critical groups. However, with these reservations, the list may be summarized: about 366 species of beetles, of which about 81 have been recorded in the Wytham area; 227 species of Diptera (only 12 so far from Wytham, where Diptera have so far been little studied); 60 in other groups (of which 17 have been recorded at Wytham); a total of 653 (158 of which are recorded from Wytham). With much the same reservations, Paviour-Smith[454] in 1960 estimated that there were 346 species of beetles and 182 species of flies recorded from British MFB. Forming the core of this assembly are the species that are actually known to breed in them, some exclusively, others not. Of these there are 12 micro-lepidoptera (of which 11 are Tinaeidae); 152 flies (of which 79 are Mycetophilidae); and 52 beetles (of which 25 are Ciidae), to which may be added 71 more that are regularly or only found associated with fungi, but whose earlier life-history is not properly known.[452] The real total number of species in the whole series of MFB communities therefore lies between 216 and about 653. But on any estimate the MFB fauna contributes a very substantial item to the pattern of communities, and it must be assumed that a great part at least of the fungus-visiting by animals from other habitats is of ecological importance not only to some of the fungi but also to some of the animals. This is clearly seen in the extreme case of *Phallus*.

The primary tree and shrub pattern in a wood controls the secondary pattern of MFB in three different ways, and this in turn partly but only partly determines the further pattern of animals depending upon the MFB. The first relationship is that described in the previous chapter, through fungal mycelia causing heart-rot and sapwood rot. But although the mycelia and their MFB are mainly characteristic of certain species of trees and shrubs, they usually occur on several kinds, not just on one, though one may be the most common headquarters. The second relationship is through MFB whose mycelia are associated with the roots of particular trees – forming part of the rhizosphere – as a mycorrhiza that sends up toadstools and other fungi above the ground under the canopy of the host tree. But these also frequently occur on the roots of more than one species of tree, though some are monospecific. The third relationship is rather less precise in that the MFB appear on the ground but are supported from mycelial systems in dead leaves or humus. Even here, as with the great abundance of MFB on beech litter, the species are often bound to the species of tree or at any rate their abundance makes that tree its headquarters. But many in this third category are only loosely associated with plant species, though they may be characteristic of a plant association. Others again can live in many habitats.

The insects that inhabit MFB, as distinct from the non-breeding visitors, are sometimes specific to one kind of MFB or almost so but usually occur in more than one. It can therefore be realized that the primary tree and shrub pattern of interspersion in a wood sets the stage for many of the MFB communities; but that because of the largely polyphagous habits of the fungi and of their insects, this pattern becomes overlaid and complicated, though not necessarily blurred; that is, with sufficient knowledge part of the pattern or the potential pattern can be predicted. In order to give a bit more reality to these rather general remarks I shall again take for a chessboard four common trees in Wytham Woods, the oak, ash, sycamore and beech, and try to show how the pieces are able to move about on the board. For this assembly of facts I am entirely indebted to Mrs Southern who has taken great trouble to prepare it at my request.

The choice of oak, ash, sycamore and beech for this exercise has advantages for compactness of comparison with diagnosis in previous chapters, nevertheless it should be borne in mind that many of the MFB species and therefore some of the beetles concerned can live on other species of trees and shrubs. For example the chief habitat of *Tetratoma fungorum* and *Cis bilamellatus* is the birch-bracket, *Polyporus betulinus,* common on dying and dead birches (Plate 48); that of *Dacne bipustulata* and *Mycetophagus quadripustulatus* is *Pleurotus sapidus* growing on elms;

and that of *Ennearthron cornutum* is *Fomes pomaceus* growing on rosaceous shrubs. The birch-bracket fungus beetles will be referred to again in this chapter, to illustrate ecological succession and the structural conditions of MFB that limit their choice of habitat; and also in Ch. 18, where the status of *Cis bilamellatus* as an invader from Australia is discussed. In selecting any examples among these MFB one encounters what I have called the chain-mail pattern of such scattered communities, and especially the difficulty of formally proving the absence of a particular species from any part of it. That is why the Wytham area affords such good material, in so far as its MFB communities have been surveyed and analysed with a thoroughness so far accomplished nowhere else in the world. Here, to a considerable extent, the negative records are substantially true, though there are two provisos to be made. The first is that a particular MFB may be present but not common enough to afford adequate habitats for some beetle, though an increase in the abundance of the fungus might change this. Thus the MFB of *Polyporus sulphureus*, though one of the most important heart-rot fungi of old standing oaks, have only five times been seen in the Wytham area, although common in Blenheim Park, not far away. Secondly, the mycelia of the fungus may be widely distributed yet unidentifiable, but conditions may not be such as to call forth the MFB itself. Even among the common species like *Polystictus versicolor* there can be astonishing changes in abundance of the MFB from one year to the next. In the winter of 1953-4, which was unusually damp, there was a conspicuous outburst of small bracket fungi of this type, sometimes running in broad streaks up decayed parts of old trees right up into the crown. In the following winter they were comparatively scarce.

The main facts about the occurrence of the chief species of beetles that actually breed in the MFB commonly found on oak, ash, sycamore and beech are assembled in Table 7, which needs a rather careful explanation. It does not provide a complete index either of the habitat range of each MFB mentioned, or of all the beetle species, though it does account for some of the more specialized ones. That is to say, it takes four of the commoner trees at Wytham and looks at their known British and Wytham occupation by (usually polyphagous) MFB and by (often polyphagous) beetles. The Table is assembled from two sources. All the Wytham records have been collected together by Mrs Southern, who also has a great deal of information from other places. The crucial point here is that these records comprise not only the species of MFB but the host tree (also, but not given here, the major habitats, heights from the ground and so on, that in turn will fit these minor habitat situations into the general pattern of communities); and also whether the beetles were found breeding or not. On the last issue, negative evidence about a particular sample of MFB examined can never be quite conclusively applied to the whole MFB population, because for one thing they might have been examined

... characters of fauna of oak, ash, sycamore and beech, mostly living in

□ breeds; ✱ breeding HQ; ( ) non-Wytham record; + adult found; Do recorded by Donisthorpe (all other records collected by K. Paviour-Smith).
Left-hand column: S spore-feeder; L breeds in live fungus; D breeds in dead fungus; ? succession stages not certain. † On all 4 trees, except *Reticularia
lycoperdon* (oak and beech)

		OAK					ASH			SYCAMORE		BEECH										GENERAL†			
		Polyporus sulphureus	*Daedalea quercina*	*Polyporus dryadeus*	*Collybia velutipes*	*Daedalea* sp.	*Polyporus hispidus*	*Daldinia concentrica*	*Fomes ignarius*	*Polyporus squamosus*	*Daedalea unicolor*	*Ganoderma applanatum*	*Pleurotus ostreatus*	*Pleurotus corticatus*	*Pholiota spectabilis*	*Lycoperdon pyriforme*	*Ustulina deusta*	*Trametes rubescens*	*Trametes gibbosa*	*Lenzites betulina*	*Irpex* sp.	*Polysticus versicolor*	*Polyporus adustus*	*Reticularia lycoperdon*	*Armillaria mellea*
D	*Eledona agricola*	(✱)																							
S	*Gyrophaena strictula*						✱			+															
L	*Triplax russica*			Do			✱																		
D	*Orchesia micans*			□			✱					Do													
D	*Dorcatoma serra*									✱															
?	*Biphyllus lunatus*							✱		✱															
D	*Dacne rufifrons*	Do								+					+										
D	*Mycetophagus multipunctatus*	+								+			+												
L	*Tetratoma fungorum*	□					+			Do			□	□								+	+		
D	*Dacne bipustulata*									+			□									□	+		
D	*Mycetophagus quadripustulatus*			Do						Do		✱											+		
S	*Pocadius ferrugineus*											□			+	(✱)						+			
?	*Cicones variegatus*											+										□	+		
S	*Agaricochara laevicollis*											□					✱					+	□	✱	
S	*Anisotona humeralis*											+						✱				+	+	✱	+
S	*Enicmus testaceus*	+								+			□						□		□	+	+		
D	*Cis nitidus*	□		□					□	□									Do			□	□		
D	*Cis bilamellatus*	□								□									+	(□)	+	✱	+		
D	*Cis bidentatus*	□								□									□	(+)		✱			
D	*Ennearthron cornutum*		+	+						Do									□			✱	+		Do
D	*Octotemnus glabriculus*		+								(+)	Do							□			+			
D	*Cis boleti*	Do		+		+													(□)						
D	*Rhopalodontus fronticornis*					+													+	(□)		+	+		
D	*Ennearthron affine*					□						Do							Do			+			
D	*Cis hispidus*			Do																		□			

at the wrong stage or the wrong season for a particular kind of beetle to be present. But it is the best negative evidence that exists and is of high quality. The second source is the earlier collecting of fungus beetles in Britain generally (though not at Wytham) by Donisthorpe, whose main paper on this subject appeared in 1935,[101] and who in 1939 also included a great many details in his survey of the beetles of Windsor Forest,[102] about 40 miles from Wytham. Windsor Forest is famous for its ancient parkland oaks, which provide the right conditions for such species as *Polyporus sulphureus*. Donisthorpe was in advance of both contemporary and later entomologists in seeking to get the correct identification of MFB containing beetles, though he did not give the species of tree or the major habitat, nor determine whether the beetles were breeding or not. His records have only been put in the Table where no other British source of information exists: in many instances his work also confirms other combinations shown there. Later mycological work has decided that the bracket named by him as *Fomes fomentarius* is *Ganoderma applanatum*,[454] and it is treated as the latter species here.

The Table contains 25 species of fungus beetles 'played against' 24 species of MFB, with therefore theoretically 600 possibilities of combination. Two species of MFB at Wytham are omitted because no beetles have so far been found breeding in them in Britain: *Oxyporus populinus* (= *Fomes connatus*), occasionally on sycamore, and *Armillaria mucida*, a short-lived soft agaric on beech. A few of the combinations are printed inside brackets, these being records from outside the Wytham area. Of the MFB only *Lenzites betulina*, and of the beetles only *Gyrophaena strictula*, have not so far been taken at Wytham. (*Eledona agricola* has so far only been found there in *Polyporus sulphureus* growing on *Populus canescens*.) Of the 600 theoretical combinations 89 have actually been discovered in Britain, and of these 44, or 7% of the 600, consist of breeding populations of beetles. The corresponding figures for the Wytham area, 529, 71 and 39, give about the same percentage. The MFB that has the most species of beetles associated with it (this analysis takes no account of other beetles casually visiting, or other animals visiting or breeding) is the soft and relatively short-lived but often very large *Polyporus squamosus*, which in Britain is commonest on sycamore and elms – in Wytham Woods commoner on the latter (Plate 39). In its later stages if it becomes dry and hard it is suitable for *Dacne rufifrons* and Ciid beetles. Other MFB with 6-9 species are *Polyporus dryadeus*, attached to oaks; *Ganoderma applanatum*, living on a number of British trees, but in Wytham at any rate growing mainly on beech; *Trametes gibbosa*, most frequent on beech; and *Polystictus versicolor* and *Polyporus adustus*, dead sapwood species with small individual brackets often occurring in immense colonies (Plate 50), both of them found not only on these four trees but on many others, and commonly attacking felled timber as well as dead standing wood or dead parts of live trees. But about a third of the MFB have only one or two breeding fungus beetles, 8 or 9 of them specialists in one fungus. Among them is *Reticularia lycoperdon*, a Myxomycete, housing the two beetles *Anisotoma humeralis* and *Enicmus testaceus*. Taking the four trees separately, oak has 5 MFB with 22 combinations; ash 3 with only 6 combinations; sycamore only 2 with (because of *Polyporus squamosus*) 12 combinations; beech 10 with 30 combinations; and the 4 more generally common MFB occurring in 2 or more of the 4 trees, 19 combinations.

This rather intricate parade of beetle habitats, resulting from the double chess-board combinations of MFB on tree, and beetle on MFB, can be looked at also in another way that is shown by the asterisks on the Table, representing the breeding combinations, and not just the presence of adult beetles, which may be accidental or related to adult feeding or even represent an intention to breed but is not in itself proof of a firm connection between the insect and the fungus. The concept of 'headquarters' (which I will abbreviate to HQ) has been discussed by Paviour-Smith.[454] By this term, suggested by myself during discussions, is meant the main centre or centres of biological activity, and with insects it nearly always includes the habitat they use in the larval stages. But even within this broader definition, which distinguishes the habitat or habitats necessary for the life-cycle and survival of the species, the concept of HQ is intended to convey something more: the habitat in which the highest average populations are maintained, and whose removal would probably alter the status of the species considerably, perhaps even making it extinct, as would obviously happen if a monospecific fungus beetle had its MFB removed. Paviour-Smith therefore distinguishes between the 'breeding-places' which may be a broad category, and the HQ. The combinations that appear to satisfy the concept of HQ in Table 7 are separately marked, and they total 17. Comparing the trees once more, the number of HQ combinations is as follows: oak 2, ash 4, sycamore 2, beech 4, and the general category 5. Thus the 5 categories are seen to be much more equal in potentiality if the HQ method is used than if all records are brought in. As already mentioned, at least 5 of the beetle species have HQ on trees not shown in the Table. But since some of the beetles with HQ shown in the Table have HQ also on *other* trees not included here, the removal of say oak or ash might or might not result in their extinction on Wytham Hill. Thus *Triplax russica* requires an MFB that grows almost entirely on ash; but *Cis bilamellatus* has a more important alternative in the birch. HQ is a useful notion, a working tool, but strictly speaking, except among monophagous species, it can only be proved to apply in a given instance by the close study of natural experiments, or making of controlled ones.

Tetratoma fungorum particularly well illustrates the concept of the HQ habitat. Its habits and life-history in Britain have been given much study by Paviour-Smith.[457, 458, 458a] Although the birch-bracket, *Polyporus betulinus*, is the MFB from which it has been most commonly reported, both in Britain and Europe, and nearly all the localities from which it has been recorded are within the Palearctic distribution range of *Betula pendula* and *B. pubescens*, it can also live and breed in some other MFB, including British records in *Polyporus sulphureus*, *Pleurotus ostreatus* (on beech and holly), *P. corticatus* (on beech), *P. sapidus* (on wych elm) and *Collybia velutipes* (on oak). On birch-brackets it lives chiefly between 3 and 15 feet up on the trees. Its major habitats seem to be deciduous and mixed deciduous and conifer woods or their edges.

The symbols by each species of fungus beetles in Table 7 show that 16 are known to live in the dead body of the fungus, and only 7 in the live, 5 of the latter being spore-feeders and 2 having larvae that inhabit the living MFB tissue. The habits of the remaining 2 species are not yet quite clear. This predominance of beetles in the later rather than the earlier stages of the fungi is connected with the length of time that the MFB remains on the tree in a dead state – much longer than the living stage – for most of these beetles do not develop very rapidly. Both the species breeding in fresh brackets are in larger *Polyporus*: *Triplax russica* in *Polyporus hispidus* on ash, and *Tetratoma fungorum* with its HQ on *Polyporus betulinus* on birches (Plates 48 and 49). For the last Paviour-Smith [455] has made a quantitative study of insect succession in ten separate birch-brackets in Wytham Woods produced in the autumn of 1956 and sampled until the summer of 1958. This was done by taking sliced samples and freezing them to prevent movement of the animals, after which the latter was killed and counted in a known volume of fungus. From November 1956 until March 1957 *Tetratoma fungorum* larvae were abundant, as were also larvae of Mycetophilid flies ('fungus gnats'), but May saw the last few of each of these. Meanwhile in March the first few *Cis bilamellatus* appeared in the now dying fungi and by April were breeding throughout the dead brackets. About the same time small numbers of the larvae of a paedogenetic Cecidomyiid fly also appeared, and these continued intermittently until early 1958. During this later period a few other kinds of fly larvae were also present. In between the autumn and spring of 1957-8 three other Ciid beetles, *Cis bidentatus*, *Cis fagi* and *Ennearthron cornutum*, were found in very small numbers. As far as beetles were concerned the dominant species were *Tetratoma fungorum*, the larvae burrowing in the fungus tissue and the adults feeding on the undersides at night,[456] and *Cis bilamellatus* in the dead brackets. Observations in other colonies of this fungus show that the latter remain abundant for at least two years or until the bracket is destroyed. The timing of this succession explains the fact that while *T. fungorum* only has one generation, *C. bilamellatus* has several annually.

This kind of ecological succession, with its concentration in very small centres of action, is characteristic of General communities, and the length of time needed to run the whole sequence in MFB varies from a few weeks to several years, the short softer fungi being on the time-scale of dung or carrion (often even faster than these), while the true fungi reach the age of small logs but are far more short-lived than large logs, stumps or standing dead trees. Those in the middle range must be about the same age-class as birds' nests. But just as with oak galls, it is necessary to think not only of individual MFB (or other General units) but 'populations' of them. This is not always very easy because they frequently grow in colonies overlapping for long periods of time, and furthermore the individual MFB may be as awkward to define as the individual grass plant in an interwoven mat of vege-tation. With bracket fungi the individual tree or shrub is a clearer ecological unit for recording long-continued changes.

We know something of the ecological distribution of the species of MFB on species of tree or shrub, and the species of insect on species of MFB. Little can be as yet explained about the reasons for the former, but something is known about the limiting factors in the latter, which seems to be partly linked with the struc-tural texture of the MFB concerned. Paviour-Smith[454] has assembled much in-formation showing that (among those species of Ciid beetles that are sufficiently known for conclusions to be valid) there are two main groups of species in southern Britain. The first consists of *Cis bidentatus, Cis nitidus, Cis fagi, Cis bilamellatus* and *Ennearthron cornutum*. As a group they are almost confined to breeding within (though not individually in all species of) the following MFB: *Pleurotus sapidus, Polyporus squamosus, P. sulphureus, P. betulinus, P. dryadeus, P. adustus, Fomes ulmarius, F. pomaceus, Ganoderma applanatum* and *Irpex* sp. The second group is *Cis boleti, Cis hispidus, Rhopalodontus fronticornis, Ennearthron affine* and *Octotemnus glabriculus*. These are confined for breeding within the following group of MFB: *Polystictus versicolor, P. hirsutus, Trametes gibbosa, Daedalea* sp. (not *quercina*) and *Lenzites betulina*. Paviour-Smith explains these two groupings by the nature of the MFB microscopic texture, which has been classified by mycologists. It appears that these MFB may have up to three different kinds of hyphae interwoven to make tissue: generative hyphae, skeletal hyphae and binding hyphae. *Polyporus aductus* has only the first, its structure being termed monomitic; *Polyporus sulphureus, P. betulinus* and *Ganoderma applanatum* have the first two and are called dimitic; while the MFB in the second group mentioned above are all trimitic. In addition there are some excessively tough MFB such as *Daedalea quercina* (which is trimitic) and *Trametes rubescens* (Plate 51) that virtually never have populations of Ciid beetles in them at all. It is to be noted that the MFB comprising the first habitat group with *Cis nitidus* etc. include an agaric, one of the Hydnaceae (*Irpex*), together with 7 Polyporaceae of which all but one are heart-rot species, the other being *Polyporus adustus* that is a sapwood liver. The second group of MFB with *Cis boleti* etc. are all sapwood Polyporaceae. Evidently the structural characters are not characteristic of one taxonomic group of MFB, but cut across them. Some further species have more recently been assigned to these two groups of beetle habitats by Paviour-Smith, but I have confined myself here to what she has already published.

Finally, in this attempt to present simply a very complicated tapestry of insects and fungi and host-trees, there is the relation between MFB communities and other habitats in woodland. Again, *Tetratoma fungorum* very well illustrates the manner in which the necessary interspersion of habitats in woodland can become built in to the life-history of a fungus insect.[457] First of all, the beetle lays its eggs, not in *Polyporus betulinus* MFB but in small crevices in the bark of the birch tree. The adults also shelter by day in various crevices on the tree. The larvae wander on to the bracket and burrow into it, the adults only feeding on the surface of the hymenium. When the larvae are full grown they drop down to the ground and pupate, usually in the soil. Thus the tree, the MFB and the soil are all used by the beetles at different stages, and the adults alternate between the tree and the MFB by day and night. Apart from such fixed life-histories, perhaps the most impressive outside influence upon fungus communities is the feeding by slugs which not only eat the softer parts of toadstools and other fresh fungi, but also assault the upper surface, destroying the skin that is too tough for most insects to penetrate.

Enough has been described in this chapter to show that macrofungus fruiting bodies are extremely active centres of action, and that their communities, at first appearance so ephemeral and varied, can be made into an orderly and not artificial arrangement by using structural criteria and other tools of modern ecological survey.

CHAPTER 16

Carrion, Dung and Nests

THE CONCOURSES and communities that result from the death, the secretions and the reproduction of plants have now been mentioned. The variegated pattern of minor communities has to be completed by describing those resulting from the death, excretions and breeding of animals. These communities are mostly based upon vertebrates because of the larger size of the latter, though of course the three biological phenomena are universal, and are frequently exploited by single species or by too few to merit the term community. If all these minor communities are added to the others that inhabit the less discontinuous and more permanent zones of terrestrial and transition litter and soil, and the bottoms of water bodies, also caves and some domestic habitats, it can be realized that dying and dead organic matter provides habitats for some thousands of animal species. This is one reason why habitat classification based purely upon associations of green plants is inadequate for the study and recording of animal communities. There is a very short poem by Ogden Nash,[343] entitled 'Goodbye Bugs', that pithily expresses this fundamental dichotomy within ecosystems:

> Some insects feed on rosebuds,
> And others feed on carrion.
> Between them they devour the earth
> Bugs are totalitarian.

But there is a further dichotomy in the dying and dead matter, since in all habitats formed by it there is some kind of race between animals on the one hand and micro-organisms on the other, to exploit the rich resources left unfinished by the communities based directly upon green plants. Where the bacteria or fungi or both are dominant in biomass or energy turnover there are numerous chains of animals depending on them for food. However, as mentioned in Ch. 13, there are not yet many instances in which the parts played by micro-organisms in providing food or in making inedible food edible to animals in such situations are really well known.

Dead bodies have a central place in animal ecology, for two reasons especially – that is, apart from the enormous biological fact of death itself. The first requires a slight digression. Death-rates in animal populations and the statistical tables that can be built from them open one of the doors to understanding the rates and nature of population turnover, and therefore the rates of utilization of resources. There are a good many different ways in which this turnover can be studied and expressed (by numbers, by biomass, by energy consumption, and also by their effects on other species and so on). At the present time most efforts towards integrating these aspects into expressions of productivity in populations are likely to be held up by two features especially difficult to measure in the field: absolute population density, and metabolic rates *in nature*, as distinct from risky extrapolations from laboratory experiments. By comparison, such matters as reproduction, range of food, age-structure, movements and general life-cycles are much less difficult to ascertain, though none are easy. In particular, metabolic calculations depend upon knowing enough about the variable rates of activity and behaviour patterns, and affecting these the variations in climate and often enough, microclimate, all extremely hard to obtain, so that any other way of approaching the problem is worth considering. There is, in theory, another method of approach that is not so dependent upon the metabolic histories shown by oxygen consumption or by loss of carbon dioxide or heat. Imagine (and here there reappears the danger of arguing from treacherous abstractions) a herbivorous insect eaten only by one species of insectivorous bird and no other enemy, and the bird hunted only by one species of raptorial bird. The insectivorous bird has only this one source of food and the insect has no other enemies or proximate method of dying. If you could obtain a death-table for the insect and analyse the calorie value of the bodies eaten you would know what potential energy the insectivorous bird population was taking in. If you did the same for the death-table and chemical content of bodies for the insectivorous bird (assuming death from enemies was the only proximate cause) you would know what was being lost to its population in this fashion. There would remain to estimate the amount of unused or discarded material passing through the population and appearing as excreta or any other waste products such as moulted skins. There may be reason to hope that this is easier to estimate reliably than might be supposed, but the point of doing so would be to avoid having incidentally to go back to direct metabolic measurements and so on. But there is here a possible method of finding out the consumption of energy in a species over a given time by using demographic methods combined with straight analyses of dead bodies and excreta, instead of depending upon metabolic rates. Something along these lines has already been explored by Teal[495] in his study of community metabolism in a cold spring in Massachusetts.

It will be obvious at once that any use that could be made of this approach depends very greatly upon the extent to which food-chains are more complicated than in this imaginary model of the insect, the bird and its enemy. Although one of the main themes of this book is that so many animals have a wide range of diet, this does not necessarily imply that all species in the diet are important. Therefore by dealing with the more important food-links the problem might not always be intractable. But this leads on to the second main point about bodies, which is their fate in nature, and the extent to which they are exploited by carrion communities as distinct from being totally consumed by predators. Carrion differs from the other General habitats in that it is itself a rich direct source of high-protein food for some mammals and birds before it has developed any insect community at all. Logs and macrofungi and dung are only attacked when they begin to produce invertebrates that have colonized and often converted some of the material. It has long been observed that dead bodies vanish rather quickly, and that one does not ordinarily see them very much except during some major catastrophe to a species such as myxomatosis in the rabbit. But little ecological attention has been given to the channels down which the material goes, at any rate in a comprehensive statistical sense. The feasibility of any demographic method of tracing the transmission of energy in organic form from species to species along the food-chains depends upon the degree to which such channels can be measured and predicted regularly, and then upon whether they are of a sufficiently definable nature, and can be sufficiently simplified by ranking orders of importance among the carrion feeders to be handled at all for this purpose. The complications most likely to occur are in the carrion insect communities which will now be described; but in our present knowledge I would not try to say how formidable an obstacle they are. But they have, of course, their own intrinsic interest as highly specialized and mobile communities, about which a fair amount is already known.

In the balance sheet of nature, *Carrion* therefore occupies an entirely special position, but it is not a popular subject for ecological research, for two obvious reasons: it is neither pleasant to think about nor to handle or be near. I think the physical as distinct from the more remote statistical or chemical ideas of death and corruption in a population must necessarily repel many people because they affect very deep layers of the mind, with fears, superstitions and history intermingled. As to handling the stuff, Fabre,[146] when he was making his wonderful study of burying-beetles at his home in Provence, found that none of the family would help him except one young grandson. Even Fabre remarked of the larval life of *Necrophorus* 'Je serai bref sur l'aride sujet'. Nevertheless, at the statistical end of the subject, population studies are steadily bringing us near the point where the output (if that is the right word) of dead bodies of some species of animals could be fairly well estimated in a scientifically well-studied area like Wytham Woods. There has so far been little effort towards expressing the death-tables of wild animals in calorie terms.

I will not attempt to discuss the many interwoven factors that lead to death, only divide the subject broadly into two: death from enemies that usually consume all or most of the body, and death from other causes. An enemy may either eat its prey alive or kill and then eat it. This is in one sense the clear-cut ecological event we think of in the predator–prey interactions of populations. In another way it is complicated, because most enemies of vertebrates do not completely consume the body of their prey, taking only accessible flesh and often leaving other parts, and especially the bones. Even when a tawny owl catches a mouse which it swallows whole, several hours later a digestive pellet of the rejected bones and fur and some other tissues is thrown up, in such a relatively fresh state that it ranks as carrion and not as dung. Raptorial birds generally produce such pellets, as do gulls and some other birds, and the pellets may be colonized by carrion insects. These include rather specialized forms able to digest fur and feathers, and the units are so small there may only be one or two species present. Chitty[67] in a cage experiment on a young short-eared owl (*Asio flammeus*) estimated that about 7% (dry weight) of a dead vole eaten is returned into circulation as pellet, and that such pellets still contain 45% (dry weight) of crude protein. I have recorded two species of small Tinaeid moths, *Monopis weaverella* and *M. rusticella*, from a great mass of pellets dropped by long-eared owls (*Asio otus*) below their roost in a grove of young larches in Argyll; and *M. rusticella* from pellets of the tawny owl and the heron (*Ardea cinerea*) from Wytham Woods [40]. Aubrook[14] bred out three kinds of flies (*Scatophaga squalida*, *Hydrotaea occulta* and *Fannia aerea*) and a parasitic Braconid wasp (*Phaenocarpa ruficeps*) from pellets of an owl taken in North Wales. So even the apparently simple event of catching and eating a prey starts up some carrion succession.

After this first stage there begins a sort of race for resources between birds and mammals (crows, gulls, foxes, badgers and so on) hunting for carrion, i.e. for bodies killed by some other species or individual and usually not quite fresh; insects and in particular beetles and flies; and the bacteria of decomposition. The insects are eating a mixture of tissues and bacteria, or else preying on other insects. Then there may be a third stage in which a vertebrate enemy, say the badger or shrew, attacks what is now a mixture of carrion, bacteria and insects. In many instances, of course, either the bacteria and the insects, or the bacteria alone, occupy and consume a corpse without any hi-jacking by vertebrates. All these are elementary considerations that require no proof other than casual observations. There is very little quantitative information about the early stages, the only systematic attempt to study them being by a Soviet worker Akopyan.[1] He followed the history of 296 dead bodies of ground squirrels or susliks (*Citellus pygmaeus*) on the steppe in south-east U.S.S.R. over a period of three years. The chief conclusion was that about two-thirds of the bodies were removed before decomposition had set in (though this would still allow for some secondary carrion from the remains left at the places to which they were removed). Those that were not removed by vertebrates underwent invasion by carrion insects, amongst which was *Necrophorus germanicus*, able to bury a suslik to a depth of 6–16 in. in the steppe soil.

Carrion communities occur wherever there are animals large enough to support them, the smaller bodies having fewer species. I am only dealing especially with terrestrial carrion, but there is a great deal also at the shore-lines of sea and fresh-water, as well as under water. But the under-water carrion probably never has any insects peculiar to it: I do not know to what extent any aquatic animal breeds only in carrion, though many attack it. Shelford,[439] in his famous ecological survey, relates how storms used to wash ashore large numbers of dead bodies along Lake Michigan, these including fish, muskrats, cats and dogs and birds. 'On one occasion, birds, chiefly young downy woodpeckers, were so numerous that one could almost step from one to the other, had they been equally spaced over the half-mile of beach upon which they were strewn. . . . Flesh-flies detect the presence of the food very quickly, and often come to dead fish inside of ten or fifteen minutes. . . . The flies are in competition with a large number of scavenger beetles. . . . Preying upon these and upon the insects that come ashore are the tiger-beetles (*Cicindela hirticollis* and *cuprascens*) . . . which pick up the flies that they often are able to seize while alighting on the ground. They also capture the maggots of the flies as they leave the carrion. . . . The spotted sandpiper picks maggots from the bodies of dead fishes. . . . Skunks visit the beach in the night and feed upon the drift.'

The carrion community consists of highly mobile species, with extremely efficient sense organs for finding their habitat. Sometimes however insects are confused by the fact that similar chemicals may be given off by several different habitats, much as aircraft may be confused by mixed radar beams. The Silphid beetle *Oeceoptoma thoracica*, very common in carrion, has already been mentioned as visiting the fungus *Phallus impudicus* in Europe (Ch. 15). But it is quite likely that these habitats that are not used for breeding may provide fuel for the dispersing insects. Heymons and Von Lengerken[223] who made a complete study of the life-history of this beetle in Germany, state that it breeds in a great many kinds of carrion, including that on the seashore, but also goes to decaying fungi and commonly visits human excrement. Similarly, species of *Necrophorus* will come to hanging carcasses of mammals used as traps, which it is impossible for them to bury. The lists of the Wytham Ecological Survey seem to reflect the very wide-spread character of the insect community visiting or breeding in carrion. These, like all such lists, are never complete or exact, since the full habits of all species are not yet known, therefore the distinction between regular breeders and just visitors is less established than for macrofungi. Of the 280 or so British species of animals associated with carrion, about 100 or 36% have been recorded in the

Wytham area, mostly from carrion itself. These include 190 species of beetles, of which 75 or about 40% have occurred at Wytham, while of 70 species of flies (which have been less thoroughly collected there) 21 or 30% have occurred at Wytham [41]. These are high proportions of the national pool of carrion species to be found on one or two square miles of land: two-fifths of the beetles and a third of the flies, as compared with about a quarter and a tenth respectively for the beetles and flies as a whole from all habitats. I think these high figures are certainly due in part to the mobility of these insects, which is necessary if they are to find the scattered, ephemeral and often quite small and hidden bodies of animals. The numbers given here also point to the enormous preponderance of beetles and flies in these communities, which together form 260 or 93% of all 280 species. Some of them occur on carrion falling in a very wide series of major habitats (mainly on the ground, though also up in nests and holes in trees) right through the terrestrial formation-types in transition marshes, water edges and drift-lines, also in domestic habitats. There is a good deal of evidence that some species prefer one or other of these, though so many are almost universal. Much more work is required to sort out this matter, for the excellent minor habitat records compiled by naturalists like Donisthorpe[102] almost always lack the essential setting of major habitats and their vertical zones.

Fungi also utilize bird food pellets, as has been shown in a fascinating study by Watling[541] of the fungal flora appearing on pellets of the kestrel, *Falco tinnunculus*, on and below open rocky nest ledges in Yorkshire. There was quite a rich mixture of microflora able to exploit the various chemical components of the pellets, though none of them were Basidiomycetes. There were four stages in the succession of species, ending up with fungi that could utilize the keratins of fur. Among the latter was *Onygena corvina*, which also grows on felt and horsehair. The lignin and cellulose users commonly found during succession on the dung of herbi-vorous mammals were absent, and it was noted that a study of an old cast-out hearth-rug, done by Needham and Crossland sixty years earlier, showed the fungi to be nearer in character to those on kestrel pellets than to those on dung! It is not unlikely that fungi are able to utilize such materials in dry conditions where bacterial or animal populations can survive less easily.

In contrast to the very limited fauna of such small bodies of carrion as owl pellets, may be given the instance of the corpse of a dead tawny owl (*Strix aluco*) itself, picked up in Wytham Woods and fully examined for the beetles in it [42]. The body lay on the ground in an oak–sycamore wood having some scrub and bramble, and in a place well removed from any domestic habitats. It was estimated to have been dead about a week. The beetles belonged to three families. Of *Silphidae* there were 8 *Necrophorus humator*, 20 *N. vespilloides*, 6 *N. investigator*, 1 *N. interruptus*, 1 *Thanatophilus rugosus*, 1 *Catops (Sciodrepa) fumatus*; of Histeridae,

1 *Gnathoncus schmidti*; of Staphylinidae, 4 *Ontholestes tesselatus*, 2 *Philonthus marginatus*, 9 *P. succicola*, 1 *P. fimetarius*, 2 *Oxytelus sculpturatus*, 8 *Aleochara curtula*, and 16 unidentified beetles of several species: a total of 80 individuals, some ranking as large insects, belonging to about 16 species. Many of these have been similarly collected on grey squirrels (*Sciurus carolinensis*) a week or two after being hung up at a height of four feet in deciduous woodland and glades in Wytham. The history of fly larvae in this owl corpse was not known, but it is evident that a good many of the beetles attending it were visitors forming a concourse, to gather food but not to breed there. But most of them are regularly found in carrion, and in the right circumstances most or all breed there.

The burying-beetles have received much respectful interest from entomologists, because of their remarkable habits, first fully described by Fabre in the last century. More recently Pukowskii's work[397] in Germany has added a great deal more knowledge about them. They are adapted to deal with rather small bodies and they are discussed now because, besides again illustrating two principles that have already emerged in previous chapters, they also bring in a third which has not been mentioned. The first is that, because they are dealing with dead bodies, their range of prey is extremely wide, including many small mammals, small birds, reptiles and amphibia. The second is that in the course of being processed by the beetles to make an underground food store for their young, the corpses, originally so different in structure, quickly come to look like rather indeterminate lumps of tissue (Plate 53). This is one more instance of the loss of the original distinctive patterns of community as decomposition comes in, a change that has already been shown in litter, soil, dead wood and fungi. The third principle is that these beetles depend for their success on isolating and hiding the carrion as quickly as possible from the main impact of colonization by other insects, and so succeed in preserving each unit not only for one species of carrion-feeder only, but for one breeding pair of that species (Plate 52). The speed of burial must be very vital, especially when blow-flies may arrive, and for this stage of the ritual the *Necrophorus* combine in a team to do the digging. But when the body has been ensconced in its underground crypt, all but one female and perhaps one male are driven out, to the accompaniment of severe and fatal fighting.[146, 397, 526] Fabre noticed a peculiar habit of the *Necrophorus investigator* he studied. Three males and a female were engaged in digging a dead mole into the sand. Every now and then one of them would come out and search the fur and then return to work below. I believe this search may have been for the egg-masses of blow-flies, their chief dangerous competitors. This habit of successfully segregating a food resource with the result that no mixed community of species can develop in it seems to represent rather a high level of ecological civilization, and is found also in some of the larger dung-beetles, in pollen-storing bees, prey-storing wasps, and amongst other creatures in man, whose farmers, foresters and now even his fishermen always hope to canalize into a few species the resources they want.

The only full-dress account of the whole community in natural carrion and its stages of succession is that by Fuller[174] in Canberra in Australia. Putting together records from various species of dead bodies, she ascertained that there were the following insects concerned. Of flies there were 11 species of Calliphoridae (including especially blue-bottles and green-bottles), 12 Muscidae (of which 1 was important), 3 Piophilidae (of which 1 was common), and 15 other lesser species belonging to 11 different families. Of beetles there were 7 Staphylinidæ (of which several were important), 5 Histeridae (2 of them common), 1 of Cleridae which was common, 3 Dermestidae (2 of them common), and 12 other species belonging to 6 families, but none important. In addition there were 7 species in 3 families of parasitic Hymenoptera (of which 1 Chalcid and 1 Pteromalid were common), and 3 non-parasitic, of no importance. Therefore, of this grand total of 79 species belonging to 30 families, about 23 were considered to be 'important', in numbers or in their competitive, predatory or parasitic influence. The ecological succession involves some very complicated timing and food-relationships, since the incidence of certain blow-fly species in Australia changes with the seasonal march of temperature, while there is also a series of succession stages depending on the state of the carrion and its fauna. Perhaps the chief general difference between Australian and British carrion communities is the presence in the former of powerful populations of a blow-fly genus *Chrysomyia* whose maggots not only eat carrion but prey on and control the numbers of the maggots of *Lucilia* and *Calliphora*. Waterhouse[538] in later studies of the carrion insects in sheep carcasses in Australia also emphasized the effective nature both of competition between the blow-fly species, and the activities of predators. The seething masses of maggots (and of the decomposing bacteria as well) give out so much metabolic heat that they can raise the temperature of a carcase 36° F. above that of the surrounding air. It was proved that 10 g. of washed maggots (i.e. without many bacteria) put into a thermos raised the temperature in half an hour from 65° to 100° F.! The dead bodies of lambs and hares attracted much the same community, but *Lucilia* adults did not manage to emerge at the end. Still smaller ones like birds, lizards and mice also had much the same set of species, but only one fly was ever abundant, this being because it is able to get a twelve-hour start over other blow-flies by producing eggs at a more advanced state of development, and this matters in a climate where small bodies dry up rapidly.

This Australian research on carrion communities, and also much of the British work focused on green-bottles of the genus *Lucilia*, has been prompted by the dangers of blow-fly 'strike' in sheep, especially that caused by *Lucilia cuprina* and *L. sericata*, the latter being the species chiefly concerned in this country, where

L. cuprina is absent. Besides developing in carrion, these and less commonly some other species of flies, lay their eggs on live sheep and the larvae develop and damage the superficial layers of tissue. This temporary parasitism is known as myiasis. In Australia particularly, with its enormous population of Merino sheep, this was a great cause of illness and death. Most of the primary 'strike' there had been caused by *Lucilia cuprina*, which is now believed to have invaded the continent from else-where about the eighties of last century and since spread widely in sheep country, though unlike many invaders it occupies the open savannah woodlands and pas-tures where there are sheep, and not so much domestic habitats like gardens.[539] But since substantial control of the situation has now been achieved by the surgical removal or docking of crutch folds and tail and by insecticides, the surveys and analysis of natural reservoirs in carrion have become less necessary.[337] This is a notable instance of the control of a pest and its associated secondary species by altering the micro-habitat structure, as it is the folds and wrinkles especially charac-teristic of the Merino that afford such good oviposition sites at the rear end of the sheep.

In Britain no complete surveys of carrion communities have been done, at least no quantitative analysis of both flies and beetles, and little conclusively about the size and natural population control of carrion populations. Out of a rather dis-jointed literature I shall only select such information as helps to bring out the scale and nature of these communities that assemble with such extraordinary promptness and undergo such intensely crowded population pressures, with dominant species changing until the whole resource is used up. Considering the strong smell of carrion, the quite large numbers of animals dying and (judging by the great abundance and availability of specialized carrion insects everywhere) not being eaten by vertebrates, and the numbers of insects emerging from even a small corpse, it is really surprising that one does not more commonly find the business in progress. The presumption must be that many vertebrates die under close cover, also we know that the disposal of the bodies is so fast that perception of their pres-ence could only be for a short time. And the burying-beetles, under favourable soil conditions, can get a small corpse out of circulation within a day, before its presence is noticeable.

The information on British carrion-flies and beetles is to be found in two rather different areas of literature not usually considered together. The general distri-bution and habits of blow-flies (Calliphoridae) associated with sheep have been defined by MacLeod and Donelly in a series of reports.[312, 311] For mapping dis-tribution great use was made of carrion traps, as well as of other collections throughout the country. Their work has a bearing mainly upon the dispersal and dispersion of these flies in open country where sheep are most commonly kept,[313] and has not been directly concerned with woodland; but it gives a useful indication of the pool of carrion-fly species from which any local community is likely to be recruited. The species of *Lucilia*, that include several capable of causing myiasis in sheep, show a spectrum of habitat preferences from *L. richardsi* and *L. sericata* which prefer open ground and field types and their mixtures at one end, to *L. ampullacea* and *L. caesar*, which tend to haunt shady and sheltered places, at the other; with two other species, *L. illustris* and *L. silvarum*, ranging through all the terrestrial formation-types. (Of the seventh species, *L. bufonivora*, only very few were caught at ordinary carrion baits, at one place in Surrey. The larvae of this species are parasites in the nasal cavities of live toads, and not primarily carrion-livers.) The occurrence of *L. ampullacea* and *L. caesar* in Wytham Woods fits into this picture, though carrion-flies have not yet been extensively collected there. In these sheep blow-fly surveys, which afford the only full geographical knowledge for any British carrion insects, seven other species were also mapped. There were four blue-bottles, with the exceedingly common *Calliphora erythrocephala* and *C. vomitoria* widely distributed (and also frequent on carrion at Wytham), but *C. uralensis* and *C. loewi* northern only; *Phormia terranovae* and *Cynomyia mortuorum*, commoner in the north; and *Acrophaga subalpina*, which occurred from the midlands northward. The nearest carrion-trapping station to Wytham was at Compton in Berkshire, about eighteen miles to the south, and in view of the good dispersal powers of blow-flies it may be taken as defining the pool from which they would be available for Wytham. At Compton all except the two northern blue-bottles and *Acrophaga subalpina* were caught; but as *P. terranovae* and *C. mortuorum*, as well as *Lucilia richardsi* and *L. sericata*, are commoner in open exposed habitats, and since Compton lies in a downland area, they might not be expected to occur, at any rate commonly, in Wytham Woods. Cragg[86] notes of *L. sericata* that 'under shaded conditions such as occur in thick hedgerows and woodland, the species is usually completely absent from the emerging fauna'. I will not try to relay here the much more complete information that exists about other common carrion flies, though some of them (such as species of *Sarcophaga*, *Helomyza*, *Piophila*) often turn up and may be influential.

As regards beetles, we have a thorough primary survey for Wytham Woods and two other localities near Oxford done in 1957-9 by Moore,[332] who used various dead animals and birds for bait. The largest collecting was done in Wytham Woods, where grey squirrels shot during a control campaign were the chief carrion traps, partly placed on the ground and partly hanging, and visited every two weeks from March to November (most carrion communities, like most dung communities, are in abeyance during the winter). A dead cat and one or two other bodies were studied on a water meadow at Marston, near Oxford, and baits were also visited in the open sandy country and adjacent mixed woodlands a Tubney, Berkshire. Of the 40 species found and named (and some of the smalle

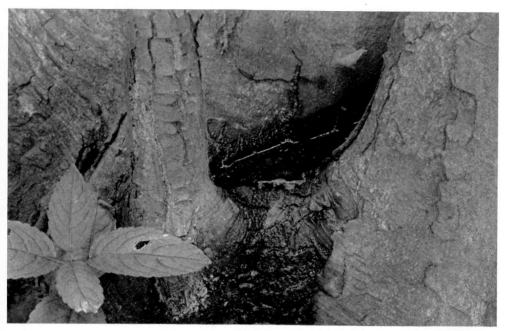

62. Tree-hole in a coppiced sycamore in deciduous woodland (Coding: A 1, W, TR-H) at *c.* 18 in. from the ground, Wytham Woods. It contained larvae of the beetle, *Prionocyphon serricornis.* (Photo D. A. K. 11 Sept. 1950)

63. Marl-pit pond in open farmland (Coding: C 1, o-W), with floating pond-weed, *Potamogeton natans,* a little *Sparganium* reed-swamp, and transition marsh of *Epilobium hirsutum.* (Photo C. S. E. 20 Aug. 1958)

64. Woodland pond (Coding: C 1, W) on Wytham Hill, with dense growth of floating pond-weed, *Potamogeton natans*, in flower. Behind, reed-swamp of *Carex* and *Scirpus lacustris*, and marsh with *Salix atrocinerea* etc. leading to woodland. (Photo E. M. O. Laurie. 1948)

65. Gravel-pit lake (Coding: D 1), seen also from the air in Photo 8, with *Typha latifolia* reed-swamp (white zone) in which sedge-warblers, *Acrocephalus schoenobaenus*, live in summer. Cassington, Oxfordshire. Much of this shallow pool has since grown up with *Salix fragilis* transition scrub. (Photo C. S. E. 20 April 1958)

66. Grisedale Tarn, a small mountain water (Coding: D 1) at *c.* 1770 ft. in the Lake District. (Photo C. S. E. 9 Aug. 1956)

67. Aerial view of a temporary winter lake (above), usually less than 100 acres (Coding: D 1), on Thames-flooded Port Meadow, Oxford. At such times many wild-fowl and wading birds visit it, but at others it is pasture. (Photo Aerofilms Ltd. 18 March 1947)

68. Windermere, the largest English lake (Coding: E 1), with the laboratory of the Freshwater Biological Association at Ferry House. (Photo C. S. E. 16 Aug. 1958)

69. Aerial view of Wytham Park, a valley between two hills from the sides of which springs (marked by white circles) come out in the sand overlying clay. For details see map in Fig. 27. (Photo Hunting Surveys. 30 April 1960)

70. Small stream crossing a woodland glade (Coding: A 3, W) rises under the high scrub behind (Coding: A 4, W). It has some cold-water Boreal relict animals, e.g. *Planaria alpina*. Wychwood Forest, Oxfordshire. (Photo C. S. E. 7 June 1958)

71 & 72. Small woodland stream (Coding: A 3, W) under dense deciduous canopy, Wytham Woods. No green water-plants or algae live in it and the main resource is fallen leaves. Lower photo shows insect emergence traps. (Photos D. A. K. 22 May 1957)

73. Upland torrent stream (Coding: B 4) on Moor House National Nature Reserve, Westmorland, *c.* 1950 ft. (Photo C. S. E. 10 June 1956)

74. The R. Thames at Lechlade, Gloucestershire – a medium-sized lowland river (Coding: C 3) with reed-swamp zone, and cattle pasture. (Photo C. S. E. 9 June 1960)

and more difficult Aleocharine Staphylinidae were not dealt with) 34 occurred in Wytham Woods. At Marston 19 species were found, of which 17 were in common with Wytham; at Tubney 23 species, of which 20 also came at Wytham. Allowing for the greater intensity of collecting at Wytham, this carrion community shows the hall-marks of great uniformity, and by implication exceptional powers of dispersal to be able to find such baits within a few days. A few were confined to one type of locality, as *Trox sabulosus* and *Silpha tristis* at Tubney, and *Dermestes maculatus* (usually a domestic form) at Marston. The latter has, however, been collected once at Wytham, by Mr A. M. Easton. The remaining carrion beetles not recorded from there by Moore, but otherwise entered on the books of the Ecological Survey, are mostly species that have a rather mixed habitat record, chiefly sharing other General habitats like dung, nests and fungi with carrion; or predatory beetles such as the Staphylinids of the genus *Philonthus* with similarly wide habitat range; or peculiar visitors like the dung-beetle *Aphodius obliteratus* walking on the exposed guts of a dead rabbit that contained dung pellets.

The breeding habits of the burying-beetles (the six species of *Necrophorus*) might make one suppose that they would only seek out bodies small enough to tackle with their particular excavating machinery. But on the contrary they appear in large numbers and are very active in the decomposing bodies of larger carrion and have nearly always been found not only in lying but also in hanging bodies of grey squirrels exposed in September in the woods at Wytham for the purposes of class instruction. On 11 September 1950 41 *Necrophorus humator* and 25 *N. vespilloides* were shaken from one dead grey squirrel. Pukowskii's exhaustive investigations[397] in Germany showed that *Necrophorus* are partly carnivorous, and that they devour blow-fly larvae as well as carrion. *N. germanicus*, the largest European species, even attacks *Geotrupes* and kills it – in remarkable battles between these leading performers in carrion and in dung. Since she also determined that *Necrophorus humator*, *N. vespillo*, and *N. vespilloides* overwinter as adults, though *N. interruptus* [= *fossor*] and *N. investigator* do so in the prenymphal stage, the former must be visiting carrion in the autumn to build up their food reserves for hibernation. If this is so, there is more connection between the general communities of larger carrion and the exclusive world of the burying-beetles than might appear at first. Pukowskii also noted that *N. vespilloides* will go into rotting fungi to eat fly larvae, though it cannot breed there.

The dead body of rabbit, mole or wood-pigeon has now been nearly consumed, and those insects that have not perished from the attacks of others or by competition, or been eaten by vertebrates finding the active carrion community, have left on their travels to find another corpse, to collect fuel or to go into hibernation for the following year's work. Some are caught and eaten while in transit. *Necrophorus humator* forms a fraction, though very small, of the food of tawny owls in Wytham

Woods (Ch. 12), and *N. investigator* has been taken at night flying to an ultra-violet trap there.[362] A good many of the carrion, dung and nest insects may be nocturnal, for example *Geotrupes* flies at dusk onwards, and is consumed by owls, foxes and badgers; the dung-beetle *Aphodius rufipes* flies to light at night; the owl-nest beetle *Trox scaber* has also been taken in this way. Of the visiting of flowers and ripe fruit by *Lucilia* and *Calliphora* some instances have been mentioned in Ch. 13. Besides these there are Wytham records for *Lucilia caesar* on the flowers of the cow-parsnip, *Pastinaca sativa*, on limestone grassland, and for *L. ampullacea* of both sexes on ripe blackberries in a deciduous woodland ride [43]. Wilson[551] recorded *L. caesar* on orchard fruit flowers in Surrey. When Cragg and Hobart[88] were trapping, marking and releasing *Lucilia* (mainly *L. caesar*) in North Wales in order to measure their distance of dispersal (which was up to nearly one mile) they noticed that numbers of these flies rested on blackberries with a heavy fruit crop. Therefore it seems likely that at least some carrion-flies seek fuel from various natural stations as they prospect for corpses to breed in, and also that they may store up food, as some biting flies do, to enable them to overwinter and perhaps also to breed successfully.

There must be many ecological contacts between the carrion insects and their outer world. One is that *Lucilia* maggots do not complete even their immediate life-cycle within the dead body but migrate from it before pupating in the soil. Cragg[86] measured movements of *L. sericata* up to 21 feet from dead sheep in North Wales. In Australia the same large-scale emigration has been noticed, with attendant predatory beetles (particularly the large Staphylinid *Creophilus erythrocephalus* which can consume three full-grown maggots per day) that cause considerable mortality.[538] The catching of dung- and carrion-flies by the log-nesting wasp *Metacrabro quadricinctus* has been mentioned in Ch. 14. A more general effect has been studied in Western Australia. Bornemissza[36] surveyed the soil fauna beneath carrion (guinea-pigs were used in the experiments) placed in dry sclerophyll woodland growing on sandy soil. While the carrion was undergoing its main succession stages of decay and occupation by insects, practically the whole of the soil fauna below it disappeared temporarily, only returning after some months and being distinctly different for over a year. These sort of changes must follow their cycle wherever carrion remains for long.

The vertebrate carcase ends up as a pile of bones in which a few beetles adapted to explore these remnants may be found. Among these are *Dermestes* (used by museums for cleaning skeletons) and Nitidulid beetles of the genus *Omosita*. The return eventually of the bone chemicals to the soil is of very great interest, especially to pastoral farmers whose sheep live on base-poor soils, and to any wild mammals that may be faced with similar problems of bone-formation.

Although *Dung* (Plates 54 and 55) has almost completely different communities of primary consumers from those in Carrion, the two have much resemblance in their ecological characters. Both are small units directly derived from live animals; they are scattered in great numbers over major habitats, mostly on the ground; they are being produced all the time, though their communities slow down or cease activity during the winter months; the life of each unit is short; the participants are very mobile and very good at finding their habitat quickly; with this goes an intense exploitation of the food resource, high population densities in small volumes of habitat, and much interaction between them; even with this hot pace of population activity different stages of ecological succession are distinguishable; the whole unit is vulnerable to attack by vertebrate predators; the soil below may be strongly affected for at least a year. Both dung and carrion in Britain have a pool of several hundred species of animals from which particular communities are derived. 320 dung-visiting and dung-breeding species are known to the Wytham Ecological Survey; but it would be misleading to compare with this the smaller number actually from Wytham Woods and fields around it, since no thorough survey of dung communities has yet been undertaken there.

English law states that 'dung is a chattel and may be stolen'. Since this habitat must have existed on land for several hundred million years, it is not surprising to find some insects with very highly developed methods of exploiting it. Just as with carrion, some of the larger beetles specialize in taking away and hiding underground the dung needed for their developing young. This is done either by making balls of dung and rolling them to the burrow, or by rolling dung that is already in conveniently small pellets. In Britain the most elaborate display of this instinctive skill is by the horned dung-beetle *Typhoeus typhoeus*, which can dig vertical galleries in sand to depths of over 3 ft with branched galleries in which rabbit droppings are stored and the eggs laid.[274] In Florida there is a dung-beetle, *Geotrupes profundus*, that makes burrows as much as 9 ft deep in sandy soil.[237] Much has been written about the larger species (that include the Mediterranean scarab) rolling their balls of dung. Mohr[330] mentions, for Illinois, that 'the large beetle, *Pinotus carolinus*, for example, removes so much of a dropping in a single night that larvae of flies, if not removed with it and destroyed in the process, are left to starve and sometimes to dry beneath an inedible crust'. The amount they take away can be as much as 130 g., on average about 50 g.[526] We do not have such titanic monopolists, but I have watched *Geotrupes stercorosus* (= *sylvaticus*) on the rough sheep pasture of the Black Mountains in Wales at about 1600 ft, trundling sheep droppings slowly along the ground. (This species also lives in some British woods[411, 438] and in Germany is known as the Waldmistkäfer or wood dung-beetle.)

There must be a great many other specialized habits by which one or a few species are able to exploit the innumerable smaller units of animal dung without creating anything that would rank as a community. On the other hand what would separately be very small units may accumulate into something larger, as under roosts of birds in trees or bats in caves. But what might be called 'pride of biotope' must be awarded to the communities in the dung of large ungulates, and especially in cattle dung or cow-pats on which all the major community studies have been done. There are also many special accounts of particular insect life-histories, and innumerable casual records by collectors which would perhaps repay a persistent indexer. To understand the status of cattle-dung communities requires a short reference to history. Mohr points out that many of the dung insects now found with cattle in North America probably were formerly dependent upon the great herds of bison or buffalo in the prairies and parkland country (just as the buffalo-bird (*Molothrus ater*, has changed to cattle). In Britain nowadays there is a sharper distinction between the dung-producers in woodland and pasture than formerly, because cattle and sheep do not roam so widely, and woods are usually segregated under forestry management in which grazing would either be impossible, unprofitable or harmful. But formerly grazing was so general that it has accounted for much of the steady erosion of once wooded areas. Deer, being rather better jumpers with protean food-habits and little direct human management, are still able to drop their dung in many different habitats, and it may be that they will do so still more if the present threat of a deer eruption in England materializes. One must suppose therefore that whereas much of England now consists of open agricultural land with woods scattered in it, formerly it consisted of extensive general forest with grassy glades scattered in it, and partly used by cattle. Before that there were the wild cattle; and in late Pliocene times more than a dozen species of large ungulates including elephants, rhinoceros, huge deer, wild horses and cattle. It is from such a historical past that the dung communities have evolved [44]. There are some ecological facts that this helps to explain. For example one of the commonest dung-flies, *Hydrotaea irritans*, which so infuriates the walker through our woods in summer, breeds in cow-pats outside, and may just be following its 'host' through the forest from glade to glade, where however there is little suitable habitat for it. A Syrphid fly, *Rhingia macrocephala*, with carnivorous larvae in dung, visits the glades and rides in Wytham Woods for flowers such as the bugle, *Ajuga reptans*. Coe[73] who worked out its life history, noted this habit of ranging far from its breeding sites, in search of flowers. And the yellow dung-fly *Scopeuma stercorium*, whose adults prey on many other dung-flies,[206] also spends much time hunting in hedgerows and in the woodland edge.

Cattle dung is a first-class habitat because of the relatively large size of cow-pats, their rich food value and the enormous amount produced. The output of dung by a cow [45], measured in Britain, New Zealand and the United States, averages 11-16 cow-pats in 24 hours[207] and the total amount about 50 lb.[534, 330] Not all of this is necessarily dropped in the fields, since cattle may be moved away at night or at certain seasons, and this affects any annual totals one may try to calculate. But as an example, the total fresh dung dropped in a 160-day grazing season was estimated by one American worker to be 7330 lb. or over 3 tons. But the output can be a good deal higher still.[330] No domestic or wild animal in Britain produces more edible habitat [46] than this, except by dying. The total area of ground covered by the dung from such a single cow in a season would be 1260 sq. ft or about 3% of an acre.[534] And in the course of a day cattle grazing in fields walk 2000-3000 yards, more than this on open range,[207] so that the cow-pats get well distributed. But in applying what we know about cow-dung communities (which is our best knowledge) to natural ones two things have to be borne in mind. On the one hand, although the output from a deer or a rabbit may be quite high, the dung units are smaller and cannot possibly support such a large mixture of species living in any one, or even in a small aggregation of them. On the other hand, many of the species, at any rate of beetles, can breed in cow, horse, sheep or deer dung, though there are also apparently some preferences. Landin[283] came to the conclusion from his research on Swedish *Aphodius* that 'the distribution of dung-beetles in different habitats does not depend so much on the kind of dung, as on climatic factors'. A survey of insects in the dung of woodland deer in Britain could test this conclusion further.

The chemical value of dung varies with the kind of feed-stuffs or natural pasture and with other factors, but that it is obviously very high is shown by its importance for farm manure. There is a certain resemblance between the high output of excreta by cows, and the great flow of waste sugar from sucking insects on trees in the form of honeydew, though the latter does not accumulate into aggregations that can support animal communities. Even cow-pats might not be such good habitats were it not for the firm crust that forms quite soon over the surface, and which acts as a skin that retains moisture.[206] But they are apparently not big enough, even with such protection, to build up high temperatures through the accumulation of metabolic heat, as some carrion does. Both Hammer's and Landin's microclimatic measurements in cow-pats show no evidence that this happens. But in larger bodies of manure the heat from metabolism (mainly of bacteria) produces the conditions of a 'hot-bed', in which the species of insects are rather different from those in cow-pats, and which disappear when such manure is spread more thinly on the fields.[158] Many years ago, one treatment recommended for the control of house-flies in farmyard manure heaps was to consolidate the surface with a spade, and so assist the build-up of lethal temperatures inside.

There are three chief monographs on the insect communities of cow-pats: on the general succession among insects by Mohr[330] in Illinois, on the ecology and life-histories of flies by Hammer[206] in Denmark, and more recently measurements and experiments with dung-beetles of the genus *Aphodius* by Landin[283] in Sweden. All three surveys brought out differences between the composition of dung communities in open fields and under shade, though some common species live in both. For Britain there are two smaller surveys of dung communities: by Laurence[286, 287] who bred out a number of flies from cow-pats, and by White[547] who analysed the populations of *Aphodius*, mainly in sheep dung, at Moor House National Nature Reserve in the north Pennine Hills. Among the many collectors who have built up a more vague yet extensive background for this subject Donisthorpe[102] found about 100 species in dung (including manure heaps) during his survey of the beetles in Windsor Forest done over many years. He often recorded the kind of dung concerned.

Mohr worked chiefly on open pasture, where 82 species of insects were breeding in cow-pats. There was a gradual increase in the number both of species and individuals for a week or more, then a decline as the dung got drier, although inside it intense activity was going on. He noticed that the flies and beetles arrived upwind while the dung was still smelling strongly, except for the blood-sucking fly *Haematobia stimulans* which travels on the cattle but drops down instantly to lay eggs in the fresh dung, departing again immediately. His list of species, as in all dung communities and indeed in fungi and carrion as well, consists predominantly of beetles and flies. The 38 species of beetles included 20 Scarabaeidae, of which 10 were *Aphodius*. 17 different families of flies were represented, and 7 species of parasitic Hymenoptera associated with them. Hammer's research was done mainly in the island of Sjaelland, in half a dozen localities, and both in open fields and in places with some shade. In the cow-pats he studied 64 species of flies, but more especially 30 Muscidae and 2 Cordyluridae, and states that 10 other families of flies were present but not worked out. Most of the 64 species also occur in Britain. The initial stage of colonization is crucial. 'The consistency of the dung and its huge content of bacteria make it a medium in which newly hatched larvae with cutaneous respiration would not be expected to thrive. The droppings have often, if they are only a few hours old, a lot of small bubbles just below the crust. They must be formed by the metabolism of the micro-organisms, so no doubt they consist of methane, carbon dioxide, and other gases, which are poisonous in higher concentrations. . . . Great changes take place in the first few hours after defecation, the dropping being aerated by means of numerous beetle tunnels. The beetles, notably species of *Aphodius* and *Sphaeridium*, begin to arrive at the droppings as soon as a few minutes after defecation. . . . The beetles make a tunnel which even in very wet fresh droppings remains open.' The newly hatched larvae of flies that appear in the first day or two are mostly found near the surface where there is most oxygen.[206] As the cow-pat is worked through by insects it becomes honeycombed with galleries. Whereas *Aphodius* species lay eggs in the dung,[283]

Onthophagus and *Geotrupes* burrow into the soil below or near the edge of the cow-pat and store dung in galleries for the larvae,[526] the former laying more eggs than the latter apparently because they have less protection from being eaten.[283] *Geotrupes* is a successful monopolist that may take most of the dung from a cow-pat and so prevent any mixed community of species developing there.[206]

Aphodius is remarkable in the number of species that can coexist in one 'population' of droppings, and partly even in one cow-pat or sheep dropping. In Illinois there were 10 species, on the island of Farö 13 (counting *Colobopterus* as only a subgeneric version of *Aphodius*), on Moor House 16 (out of the 42 recorded British ones). Analysis of these seems to give the usual kind of half or quarter answer about the possible reasons for this successful coexistence. Two of the species at Moor House, *A. prodromus* and *A. sphacelatus*, only visited sheep dung but did not breed in it. But Landin records that both breed in various kinds of dung in Sweden. And although he could prove that some species were more or less abundant according to the degree of shadiness of the major habitat, only one species, *A. zenkeri*, was clearly confined to one zone (woodland). Except for some species avoiding horse droppings, there were no specialists in choice of dung. The seasonal cycle of development at Moor House differs in the species, some wintering as adults, others as eggs, and so on. The relative numbers of course differ also. But at Moor House half of the species were common enough at some period to form more than a tenth of the adults in the dung. So we are left with quite incomplete suggestions as to how differences in manner of life could by themselves bring about continual coexistence in habitat units that are as small and crowded as these. Landin puts forward a novel idea about this situation, suggesting that competition is between *individuals* and not between *species* and that this overcomes the difficulty of finding coexistence in species of apparently identical habits under conditions of crowding and food limitation. I am not at present able to decide whether his interesting experiments are valid proof of the idea, or whether the idea actually solves the dilemma. But it at any rate takes the subject of dung communities into a more advanced stage of thought.

Finally, how do the dung and its inhabitants interact with other parts of the ecosystem? Such interactions are to be seen with soil and vegetation, the food-habits of dung-flies, and the outside enemies of dung insects, as well as in other ways. The former site of a cow-pat is easily distinguished for at least a year after it has run its course as an animal habitat, by the brighter green lush tuft of nitrogen-rich grass that grows there and is avoided by cattle. The latter are said to dislike the smell of the old dung, but it is equally likely that they do not relish high-nitrogen grass. Horses are less particular and have even been used to reduce this pasture pattern. There must be considerable alteration of the soil structure just below a cow-pat, with the burrowing of beetles increasing aeration, and by chemical changes, and the soil fauna probably changes just as it does under carrion [47]. Dung-beetles themselves seem to feed only on the dung mixture, unless they are predators there, but they require hibernation sites, not at present generally identified. Their use of *Brachypodium* tussocks in limestone grassland at Wytham was mentioned in Ch. 6; and I have also found certain small species hibernating in tussocks of *Deschampsia caespitosa* inside deciduous woodland there [48]. The whole subject of hibernation sites for insects, especially those breeding in ephemeral habitats, deserves closer thought. Dung-flies often have other habitats, and Hammer divided their food-habits into five overlapping classes. Three species are obligatory blood-suckers of cattle (and horses too), though one of them breeds on farm premises, not in the fields. Female *Haematobia stimulans* and *Lyperosia irritans* are closely attached to cattle, though the former roosts at night on grass and scrub. Both males and females of the common yellow dung-fly *Scopeuma* (*Scatophaga*) *stercorarium* prey on other flies which they suck. In Denmark the preys included 17 other common dung-flies on and around cow-pats; but it also hunts at a distance, for example in the hedgerows or edge of woods, and is very highly polyphagous. Hobby[227] assembled records of some 50 species of prey in Britain, which can really only be a small sample of the whole diet, and their habitats are extraordinarily varied, some of them being also predators. There is a third small group of dung-flies that are facultative blood-suckers at wounds made by biting flies and so on. The majority of species fall into a fourth group that suck liquid dung as their chief food. Interwoven with these various habits are different degrees of flower-visiting, which for a few species like *Rhingia* is the only food supply, while in some others nectar is additional. Hammer remarks: 'In my opinion nectar is the principal diet of flies from the time they come out of their place of hibernation till the cattle are let out in the field. Later in summer I have seen myself M[usca] autum[nalis] and Morell[ia] on the flowers of *Cotoneaster* and *Heracleum*.' This topic was mentioned in Ch. 13.

Both in Britain and Denmark some birds and mammals attack the dung community on a large scale. Of these starlings are the most conspicuous by day. Plate 54 is of middle-aged cow-pats attacked a few minutes before by rooks. Hammer mentions that both these birds will also commonly seek insects in dung a day or two old. The badger is another visitor to older cow-pats which it turns over to get beetles. Altogether it will be seen that dung, of which the cow-pats discussed are only one of hundreds of kinds that support insect life, if it does not exactly add pure charm to the ecosystem does add the charm of variety, and very well illustrates how a small scattered General habitat is keyed into the rest of the system in which it occurs. There may be a great many more interrelations to be discovered, such as the one that controls cross-pollination of the cuckoo-pint *Arum maculatum* of our woods, which admits a number of small Psychodid midges, mostly *Psychoda phalaenoides* (a dung-fly) attracted to the smell of the spathe, imprisons them and later lets them escape to carry pollen elsewhere.[396, 424]

The phrase *Animal Artefacts* could include an almost illimitable series of structures. Thus it might be held to describe the animal itself, which in a real sense has built its own body, making the body's side-products of secretions, excretions, eggs and young, and eventually leaving a corpse if not eaten first. And it forms a home for parasites: but in this book I have for practical purposes of economical management largely omitted the communities of parasites living in or attached to live animals, though they may run to scores of species. Though some kinds of parasites are highly specific to one host, at any rate at a particular stage of life, many others share them, that is they are polyphagous, as was seen in the oak-gall communities mentioned in Ch. 10. The more usual claim of Animal Artefacts to be one of the chief and universal General Habitats lies in the production of *Nests* and other structural alterations of the environment connected with them, such as burrows and runways (Plate 61). Though the nests of mammals and birds are primarily made for housing the young stages they may also be used by the adults for shelter at other seasons. Among the social insects the nest is a fortress for the whole population, not just for a pair, and of course some birds and mammals have gregarious colonies of nests. Galls lie in the borderline between artificial nests and ordinary cover. In Britain the invertebrate communities of nests are best developed in those of some birds, mammals and ants, with rather fewer in those of bees and wasps. But the nests of a good many birds and some ants do not contain any significant fauna. The highly evolved nest communities are only the main head of a comet whose enormous scattered tail includes all kinds of smaller refuges that one species may provide for another.

Any search for information in this field is like entering a vast rambling museum with many rooms of different sizes, some opening into others, some almost closed from the world; some rooms full of valuables accumulated for one or two centuries, others almost empty, some containing doubtful lumber. Perhaps the largest and best arranged room is that concerned with the inhabitants of ants' nests, or myrmecophiles – parasites, commensals, other guests, predators, as well as less regularly associated or accidental visitors. Weber's ecological survey in North Dakota[544] of a not very distant relative of our large wood-ant, the thatching ant, *Formica rufa obscuripes*, gives one of the best all-round views of the ant-nest as a centre of action and a focus of radiating ecological activities. This species makes low mounds several feet across in the dry sandy prairie, often in neighbourhood of scrub, especially the snowberry, *Symphoricarpos*, on which the ants tend aphid 'flocks'. But they also visit aphids on other plants like rose and wormwood in order to collect excreted sugars, as well as preying on at least 50 insect and spider species, all of which they take back to their nest, which penetrates as much as 5 ft underground. One nest, which it took several people 16 hours to excavate, contained an estimated population of 19,000 ants. The community of myrmecophiles inside the nests comprised about 30 species, of which two-thirds were beetles. Thus the whole complex network of relationships, including bird enemies, must have brought in nearly a hundred species, perhaps more. Donisthorpe[99] found 24 species of myrmecophiles in the nests of wood-ants in Windsor Forest, that number also with *Lasius fuliginosus*, and as many as 36 in the nests of *Lasius brunneus* associated with decaying ancient oak trees.

In a good many places in Britain wood-ants build large nests (Plate 57 [48A]), each inside its own territory and forming a protected base from which to set up hunting raids and pastoral farming on trees and shrubs. The degree of dominance can not only be impressive but quite complete. I have[125] described the territories of *Formica rufa* – forming a system in more than one way like the Balkan countries – in one end of a garden bird sanctuary in the New Forest maintained at one time by the late Dr T. G. Longstaff. I used to hear the children of the house, who ran barefoot, say that this end of the garden 'belongs to the ants'. And the nests of willow warblers (*Phylloscopus trochilus*) only survived outside their radius of influence. On the other hand the ant nests were plundered by their chief enemy in this country, the green woodpecker (*Picus viridis*). The situation was in principle just like that of Weber's thatching ant, with aphid populations cultivated on different trees and shrubs (hawthorn, pine, birch, gorse, broom and probably oak). On the young birches every invertebrate had been destroyed by the ants except for aphids used to collect sugar solution, and kept in small groups guarded by sentries armed with formic acid sprays. In such communities one can see the same progression towards monopoly of resources that has been noted in the larger carrion and dung-beetles, though the monopoly applies to the major habitats around, not to the General Habitat itself. Indeed it is a paradox that the nest faunas of such ants, mostly depending upon wastage or hi-jacking of material that the ants bring home, were no doubt richer in species than the monopolized birch trees outside. The fact that this monopoly is only locally complete (for on oak trees considerable numbers of invertebrates are removed by the ants without sterilizing the fauna of the trees) gives point to the idea that what we call 'dominance' in communities can in extreme instances become 'monopoly of resources'.

An unusual amount is already mapped out about the animals that make substantial nests in the Wytham area, coming as a by-product of the sustained research on populations there; but so far this has not been used to quantify a gradually growing picture of the nest communities themselves. After a brief conspectus of some of the 'host' species that matter, I shall select three special examples applicable to this area but illustrative of general principles as well. There are 11 species of ants on Wytham Hill, for which our knowledge comes mostly from the work of Pontin, together with many records in the Ecological Survey. 5 species of social wasps that make sizeable nests occur, 4 of them commonly. The nests of *Vespula vulgaris*, *V. germanica* and *V. rufa* are made in the ground, those of *V. sylvestris* and *V. norvegica* in the tree or scrub canopy. But the last is scarce and its nest has not yet been identified there. Also until recently there was the hornet *Vespa crabro*, nesting in tree-holes in the woods. Nests of bumble-bees (*Bombus*, with some of their *Psithyrus* parasites) have seldom been identified and do not appear to be as common as the roving queens and workers might suggest, and it is possible that these travel from a distance. At least 8 *Bombus* and 4 *Psithyrus* species occur. There is an occasional wild tree-nest of the hive-bee, *Apis mellifera*. The only large ant colonies actually inside the woodland canopy are those of *Myrmica ruginodis* in old logs (see Ch. 14), most of the other ants living in the edges of wood or scrub, in limestone grassland or in open ground, occasionally in marshes. There are none of the large wood-ants, and *Formica fusca* is very rare. All the ants live in the topsoil, ground zone or in rotting wood at or near ground level. Many of the nests are rather small, though some have populations running into tens of thousands. They carry myrmecophiles, such as the small blind white woodlouse *Platyarthrus hoffmannseggii* and the lilac-coloured springtail *Cyphodurus acinos* [49], and such species are not confined to one species of ant.

By far the most remarkable artefacts made by ants at Wytham are the mounds and underground runways of the small yellow ant *Lasius flavus*, whose periodically spaced low-domed turfy anthills are so well known in undisturbed pastures (Plate 2), though they are now disappearing under intensive farming. On Wytham Hill their extent has shrunk in the last few years, and in order that this ancient and fascinating civilization should not vanish, a five-acre reserve has been established in Wytham Park (Plate 56), grazed by farm cattle and the vegetation managed also in other ways. These ants form one of the chief foods of the green woodpecker *Picus viridis*, this bird commuting between the woodland or parkland canopy with its rotting wood, and the open pasture. The yellow ant survives, however, quite well in subterranean nests that do not have mounds accumulated above them; the special feature of the mounds being the pattern they impart, geometrically, in the vegetation and soil of the mounds, in the fauna within the nests, and as centres that dominate a subterranean zone covering the whole field. (In pastures cow-pats and mole-hills, especially mole fortresses with their nests, are often interspersed, making up a double or triple pattern of different centres of action. The fauna of mole nests is an immensely rich mixture of blood-sucking fleas and mites, and many other nest inhabitants some of which are only found there (Plates 58 and 59). The influence of mole-hills on vegetation is mentioned in Ch. 6. The ecology of *Lasius flavus* populations has become much better known by the recent work of Pontin[394] at Wytham, of Waloff and Blackith[536] at Silwood Park,

Berkshire, and of Haarløv[201] in Denmark, but only a few aspects will be mentioned now. The population of workers in a nest may be anything between 2000 and nearly 25,000. Odum and Pontin[359] used radioactive phosphorus to estimate numbers by marking and recapture and estimated nest populations of 2000-10,000 in some mounds at Wytham [50]. This dense army of workers is engaged both in nest duties (which include transport of soil on to the mounds, tending young, and such things as licking the eggs of aphids to keep them healthy for the later planting on roots[391]), and in travelling along tunnels within a territory beneath the turf to collect food for the nest. Various small preys are captured,[393] including some of the aphid species which are farmed on the roots of plants.[390] On one small patch about 20 yards across, in a mixture of open ground and meadow within the shelter of trees, a dense mixture of *Lasius flavus* and *L. niger* nest populations were found by Pontin to be farming 16 species of aphids and 1 coccid on the roots of various limestone grasses and herbs.[394] At Silwood Park the mound-making populations were farming about 7 kinds of aphids on roots of 4 species of grass and 1 composite.

Each *Lasius flavus* nest is therefore the collecting centre for food materials from a considerable sector of the pasture community of plants and animals. It also shows special features in its vegetation and soil. The larger mounds must certainly be very old institutions, Haarløv calculating that they might take 80-90 years to build, if the ants worked a 150-day year. In the Wytham Park ant reserve many of the mounds are over 2-3 ft across and up to a foot or more high. Although at Silwood Park actual growth of nearly an inch in height and 3 in. in diameter in a year has been recorded, this must be considered against the attacks of woodpeckers (which go on in winter when the ants are inactive) and erosion of the ground by cattle and other causes. And even if mounds of this size can be created in a few decades, it is still most likely that they have been maintained for much longer periods. Thomas[498] made micro-transects across yellow ant mounds in three places on chalk downland and proved (as one can often observe casually) that the vegetation is distinctly different from that of the surrounding pasture, though the exact differences vary locally and are not regularly predictable. Sometimes different species of plants grow on the north and south sides of the mounds. When rabbit populations are abundant their habit of defaecating on anthills adds another factor. In Denmark Haarløv discovered that the soil structure, microclimate and some of the soil microfauna might be different on the north and south sides. *Lasius flavus* colony systems though often dominant in numbers and structure may have *Lasius niger* colonies interspersed among them,[392] and Pontin[394] mapped and partly manipulated some of these mixed systems at Wytham, and was able to prove that effective competition exists between the two species, which tend the same species of aphids though *L. niger* hunts on the ground surface, which *L. flavus* does not.

A second example comes from nests built in the woodland canopy, especially inside holes in trees. As described in Ch. 14, about a third of the breeding birds in terrestrial habitats on Wytham Hill use holes wholly or partly for breeding, and most of these are in the canopy zone. In addition there are others that make substantial nests among the twigs and branches there. All these are rich havens for animal life. To begin with the hole nests have a basic community of invertebrates associated with rotting wood, in such places often in the form of a coarse granular wood-mould mixed with fungal hyphae, and sometimes accumulating to a depth of several feet inside hollow trees. Then besides birds there are grey squirrels, sometimes hornets, probably also bats, using such natural holes. These have lately been supplemented on quite a large scale by nest-boxes, especially for tits and owls. And it has not been uncommon to find competition between different species for the possession of these sites, for example an owl nest mixed with oak twigs brought in by a grey squirrel or the comb of a hornet. In holes and nest-boxes the temperature inside is raised by the presence of sitting birds and their young. In Finland, Nordberg[357] measured differences in the bottom of nests of the great tit and other species that were twice those of the air outside. Birds roosting in winter similarly keep up the temperature, and Kendeigh[263] in Illinois calculated that this confinement afforded a significant saving in heat loss to roosting house sparrows. 'The amount of energy thus conserved may make the difference between survival and death during periods of extreme weather during the winter.' It may also affect the development and survival of any nest fauna.

I shall here confine myself primarily to nests of larger birds. Of such nests at Wytham Hill we know most ecologically about the tawny owl, *Strix aluco*, which has been counted by Southern[464] for a number of years. On this area of about 1000 acres the number of resident pairs increased steadily from 16 in 1947 to 30 in 1958, but the number of pairs actually breeding has fluctuated between 0 and 23, similarly the total number of owlets successfully fledged has varied from 0 to 27, these changes being associated with the fluctuating population levels of the voles and mice required for food. Mr Southern has allowed me to cite some unpublished observations about the location of 27 natural nests recorded by him (though much of the research alluded to has more and more been done with the aid of large nest-boxes like that in Plate 60). Nests occur both inside and along the edges of woodland, but mostly in the latter, and at heights of 6 to over 24 ft. They are fairly evenly distributed in the scrub and tree canopy zones, the commonest trees used being ash and beech, with some also in oak, elm, birch and spruce. None were in sycamore. I have a good deal of information about the invertebrate fauna of six nests (some natural, some in boxes, mainly collected by Southern) that has been partly analysed [51]. The chief point that seems clear is that none of the nest inhabitants are confined to the tawny owl, though one of them, the Scarabaeid beetle

Trox scaber, is very frequent in its nests. From the debris of one nest brought in during September, a total of 217 of these beetles emerged by the following May. This species has also been taken in the nests of the barn owl (*Tyto alba*), little owl (*Athene noctua*);[476] in that of a green woodpecker pair in which starlings later nested;[28] and in others. For Windsor Forest, Donisthorpe[102] noted that this *Trox* occurred in dry carcases, in holes in oaks and elms, and in birds' nests. The tendency for nest inhabitants to utilize a variety of hosts could be proved by many other examples, of which only a few will be given. There is no species of flea confined to the tawny owl, or indeed to British owls, though Rothschild and Clay[414] mention a few that are almost or quite specific to certain birds. According to them *Ceratophyllus gallinae*, common in owl nests (and occurring in that of the tawny owl at Wytham), is known from 65 different bird hosts in Britain. A fly, *Protocalliphora azurea*, whose larvae suck the blood of birds has been rather extensively studied by Owen[365, 366, 370] in the Wytham area, where he bred it from larvae and pupae in the nests of great, blue, marsh and coal tits, starling, wren, magpie and swallow. But it has also been recorded from a number of other species in Britain, nesting in tree-holes, the canopy, near the ground and in buildings. They frequent especially hole nests and those of compact structure.

The Staphylinid beetle *Philonthus subulicornis* (= *fuscus*) and the Histerid *Dendrophilus punctatus* commonly live in tawny owl nests in Wytham Woods. They are predators, and the *Dendrophilus* actively devours fleas.[414] Of this *Philonthus* Donisthorpe[100] wrote: 'In almost every bird's nest I have examined in Windsor Forest during the last decade, and sometimes in abundance, whether in nests at the top of very high fir trees or holes in trees etc. – in nests of hawks, magpies, jackdaws, "French jackdaws" [= apparently woodpeckers], tits etc.' Joy[254] recorded it from an old green woodpecker nest-hole in a beech 'which had been occupied by the usual sequence of lodgers, viz., green woodpecker, starlings and bats.' There are other records of the kind. Spittle[478] also took this species in grey squirrel dreys. *Dendrophilus punctatus* has a rather wide range of habitats, in carrion, rotting wood and ant nests,[168] as well as those of birds. In Windsor Forest it has been taken in the nests of *Lasius brunneus*, that of a red squirrel, and is abundant in those of birds.[102] The valuable series of collections by Spittle includes records of it from nests of heron,[473] carrion crow,[474] tawny owl and barn owl.[476] Nordberg[357] made an immense collection of invertebrates (including mites, which formed about half the 523 species) from the nests of 56 kinds of birds in Finland, and 19 species had *D. punctatus*, these including such widely different forms and nest-sites as kestrel, swallow, great spotted woodpecker, titmice, carrion crow, and even an aquatic bird, the goosander, *Mergus merganser*. The last is explained by its habit of nesting in holes in trees and banks.

A third beetle, which has been found in robins' nests in Wytham Woods[173] but is not yet identified among the owl nest materials, is the small Staphylinid *Atheta nigricornis*. Spittle noted it in nests of the sand-martin,[475] heron,[473] carrion crow,[474] little owl, tawny owl and barn owl,[476] as well as in dreys of the red[477] and grey[478] squirrels. In Finland[357] it turned up in nests of 23 species of birds as disparate as the redstart, great tit, chaffinch, kestrel, Tengmalm's owl and the white-tailed eagle. It seems quite certain that nest specificity is the exception and wide acceptance, survival and probably breeding the usual rule. To carry this analysis further one would need more complete records of the breeding and of the frequency of breeding by such species in the nests of different hosts, in order to construct a picture as good as that obtained by Paviour-Smith for fungus beetle communities and the headquarters of species (Ch. 15). It seems to follow that *Philonthus subulicornis* or *Ceratophyllus gallinae* depend on limitations of habitat that follow very broad rules, such as 'hole nest' or 'canopy nest' or structural features like compactness and permanence. But the highly specific parasite or other nest inhabitant has its own interest, and I will end by referring to one situation that has had an enormous effect upon the whole West European and British ecosystems. This is the rabbit flea *Spilopsyllus cuniculi* as a carrier, and in this country probably the sole effective carrier, of the virus of myxomatosis among wild rabbits. It was discovered by Mead-Briggs and Rudge[42] that in order to mature their ovaries these fleas must have a blood-meal from a pregnant doe rabbit, or, as has since been found,[41] from a nestling rabbit less than a week old. The larvae then develop inside the rabbit's breeding nest. This discovery fixes the underground breeding nest as the hub of the whole cycle of myxomatosis epidemic, whose effects upon vegetation and wild life have been colossal and are still continuing.

Although this book does not attempt to canvass the communities of domestic habitats, most of which are fragments of natural ones mixed with foreign invading species, the ecological survey by Woodroffe[555] of birds' nests in buildings deserves mention for its excellent quality and the contrast it offers to natural situations in a wood. He examined, though without heat-extracting or breeding-out, a large number of nests of sparrows (*Passer domesticus*), jackdaws (*Corvus monedula*), swallows (*Hirundo rustica*), house-martins (*Chelidon urbicus*) and domestic pigeons (*Columba livia*). In these some 114 species of insects and mites were found, comprising 13 ectoparasites, 76 scavengers and 25 predators. Most of the nests were dry or very dry, and the faunal lists though having a certain number of species in common with, for example, tawny owl nests at Wytham, are markedly different, especially in levels of abundance. Woodroffe concluded that 'Such a group of species occurs in no other natural habitat in this country, although fragments of it occur in such situations as the nests of rodents and social insects and beneath the bark of trees. . . . Except when they are associated with buildings, birds' nests in our climate are rarely dry. Even when situated in holes in trees, the nests tend to be intermediate in type, some part usually being affected by seepage of rain water. Probably only house-martins' nests, situated under cliff ledges, and the nests of swifts and jack-daws, in crevices and fissures in the rock, are sufficiently protected to provide, occasionally, a really dry nest. Before this community was affected by human activity many of its constituent species must have been rare insects, and this is still true of the entirely rural parts of the country.' A good number of these domestic dry nests carry scavenging insects and mites commonly living in houses and stored products, and capable of doing damage. The annual invasions of clothes moths, meal-worm beetles and carpet beetles into houses usually come from birds' nests.[556] Conversely at least some birds' nest species have an alternate habitat away from houses. One of these is the varied carpet beetle *Anthrenus verbasci* (a well-known museum pest), which visits flowers, including the hogweed, *Heracleum sphon-dylium*, to feed on nectar and pollen.[557]

CHAPTER 17

Woods and Water Bodies

IN A BOOK that concentrates chiefly upon terrestrial communities and can at most give only an outline of the characters of some of these, it is not practicable to allot an equally large space to aquatic communities, for many of which there are in any case special books and monographs. However, the interspersion together of land habitats and water bodies is part of the whole pattern and needs some mention. There are the rich Transition habitats of marsh and the riparian zone that unite the two, while the flow of water systems influences even more fundamentally the soils and microclimates of land habitats. The water bodies and marshes of woodland have received comparatively little attention. This has happened partly because many of these waters lack green plants and so have not entered directly into the surveys of plant ecologists. Also many of them look unattractive to the naturalist or appear small and unimportant features of a wood. Wytham Woods has an exceptionally rich profusion of springs, spring flushes, marshes and streams which I will now try to fit into the general pattern of habitats already described.

In Ch. 4 the broad classification of all water bodies according to size and speed, suggested by Elton and Miller in 1954,[137] is mentioned and a representative series of these illustrated in Plates 62-74. In the Wytham Woods area about half the 25 possible combinations shown in Fig. 3 (p. 75) occur, and several more not far outside it. It is chiefly the very large lakes and rivers and complete torrent streams that are lacking, and it should be added that one or two very large items hardly exist in Britain at all. In a short paper in 1956 about the Nemourid stone-flies living on Wytham Hill[132] I described the general conditions of the springs and streams there. Since then the Ecological Survey has mapped them more thoroughly and the result is seen in Fig. 27 [52]. On this map it is very conspicuous that the springs and spring flushes arise predominantly between the 300 and 400 ft contours that run round the middle zone of the hill in a rough figure-of-eight fashion. I have explained in Ch. 3 how these springs are caused by the rainwater sinking into the upper limestone reef and intermediate sands and coming out in the latter especially where they meet an impermeable layer of Oxford Clay. Although there are outlets all round the hill (and this map only includes the main ones – there are many minor marshy spots and occasional flushes) far more come on the easterly slopes. This is by reason of the south-easterly dip in the Jurassic strata, so that more subterranean water is carried in that general direction. But there are many minor complexities of the internal geology, as well as a good deal of surface slipping, that create further local variations. One of the chief of these is,

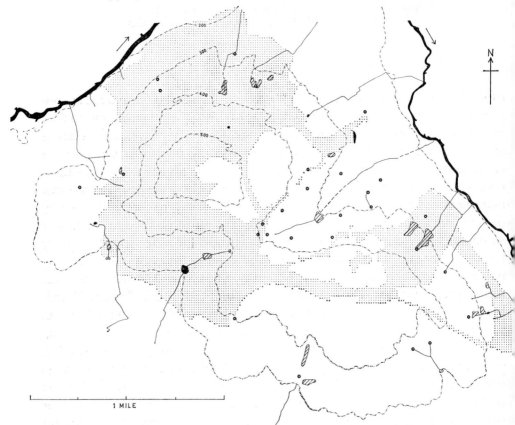

FIG. 27. Distribution of water bodies on Wytham Hill. *Dot-dash:* contours. *Stipple:* woodland and scrub and some natural grassland enclaves. *White:* farmland. *Cross-hatched:* marshes. *Circles:* springs. *Thin lines:* streams. *Black patches:* ponds. *Thick black:* rivers. The springs mostly rise between 300 and 400 ft. (Map prepared by C. A. Elbourn, drawn by A. J. Dunford)

as was explained in that chapter, the continued washing out of the sands over many thousands of years that has undermined the overlying coral reef and made large sections of it come away and gradually slide downhill. The map also differentiates those areas of the Hill (stippled) having a canopy of woodland or scrub from the open parts with farm fields. This stippled area does however also include the small natural grassland areas, in order to make the map as simple as possible;

but as a matter of fact all of these are on dry ground with no springs or ponds. Here then is a central collecting ground from which small streams radiate partly in woodland and partly in the open, all eventually reaching the R. Thames (those entering the Seacourt Stream also join the main river further down). This situation is important for understanding some of the cold water elements in the fauna that seem to be relicts from Boreal times coming into the Thames–Rhine system and now surviving here only in some of the cold head-waters, whose coolness is enhanced by the protection of woodland canopy.

The following brief analysis of the smaller water bodies of woodland is only designed to put the chessmen on the board in their normal starting positions, not to play any complicated ecological game with them. Our knowledge is still at a rather early stage, though it has undoubtedly brought out already the unexpected richness of habitats and communities that might at first glance appear to be little more than ecological slums. To begin with I must mention a series of very small habitats that can only just be counted as water bodies at all, though they do have water trickling in them. These are the sap flows, that under certain conditions develop into what have been called slime fluxes. In Ch. 10 the activities of sap-sucking insects in creating honeydew as a waste product have been described. Sap flows, usually on mature trees, occur where there has been a wound or leak in the bark letting out the sugary sap but may be augmented by rain trickles. They frequently become infected with yeasts and other micro-organisms and attract visiting insects, some of which are able to breed in them. It is not worth saying very much about this kind of community here, but it does form a bridge between the General habitats and the Aquatic habitats. In the Survey it has been included in the former, really on the ground that Aquatic habitats come directly from rain-water and not through the medium of trees. Information about them in Wytham Woods is only episodic, though they certainly occur as scattered units and some of the regular sap-breeding flies have been recorded there. Thus I have watched an adult *Brachyopa sensilis*, a Syrphid fly that breeds in slime flows, hovering so exactly still in the air a few inches from a leaking branch on a large horse-chestnut tree that a glass tube could be placed over it quite easily.

Sap flows are not all of the same kind, at least they develop in different ways, and turn different colours which indicate their properties. Robinson[413] analysed the small community living in a brown sap flow on an elm in Sheffield over two years. In the spring and early summer there was a dark brown slimy flow that dried partly in winter. In this there were 8 species of animals: feeding on the slime itself a Tyroglyphid mite *Hericia hericia*, the main prey of a Staphylinid beetle *Thamiarea hospita*, and the larvae of 3 kinds of flies, *Brachyopa sensilis*, a Ceratopogonid *Dasyhelea obscura*, and the only British Aulacigastrid *Aulacigaster leucopeza*. The larvae of 3 species of flies preyed on the others: 2 Dolichopodids of the genus

Systemus and an Anthomyiid of the genus *Phaonia*. Somewhat similar communities had been found earlier by Keilin[258, 259] in sap flows on elm and horse-chestnut at Cambridge. Quite different in character are the white slime flows that develop on oak trees and whose use as a major food resource by hornets, *Vespa crabro*, in Epping Forest, has been described by Vere.[524] Whereas the brown elm flux studied by Robinson had a pH of 8·7, the white oak ones had the remarkably acid value of 3·5. Wilson[549] made a rather full record of the visitors to white slime flows on an oak at Wisley, Surrey. Such flows are evidently colonized by yeasts and they give off a strong smell of beer or cider mixed with other scents, which attracts a large number of insect visitors, including butterflies, flies, beetles, wasps, Psocids and bugs. But these are really concourses (Ch. 13) with only elementary food-chains involved.

The smallest true water body commonly found in woods (though chiefly where there are old trees) is the tree-hole full of rainwater. The distinction between these and the sap flows is illustrated by an experience of Keilin,[259] who was working on a relatively huge water-hole inside the trunk of a horse-chestnut at Cambridge. A large hole at about 6 ft led into a reservoir 3 ft 9 in. deep in the trunk, and this was always half full of a clear brown water over a bottom covered with wood debris. 'In order to avoid the frequent overflows of the water during the heavy rains and the drowning of insects living above the usual water level, two holes were drilled in the side of the tree about 14 inches beneath the natural opening of the reservoir. After a year these two holes became transformed into two characteristic wounds with sap-exudation or "slime flux".' And the faunas of the two habitats were quite different. This boring into trees is just what the goat moth, *Cossus cossus*, does, and the resulting slime fluxes attract many beetles.[102]

A good deal of the rain that is intercepted by the tree canopy trickles down the branches, and is collected rather in the fashion of a river basin whose tributaries eventually join up into a main channel. The paths of trickle strongly affect the distribution of epiphytic mosses and lichens on the tree (see Ch. 10 and Plate 27), and if the structure of the tree produces any small external cups or holes between branch and trunk or in other ways, a tree water-hole is formed. Most of these are temporary, and one of the commonest mosquitoes in them, *Aedes geniculatus*, lays its eggs on the side of the hole where they may dry and later on hatch when more rain comes to raise the level again.[317] Another kind of hole is formed by heart-rot in the core of a trunk, as with the horse-chestnut studied by Keilin. That particular tree-hole was watched for seven years, and thereafter perpetuated artificially by keeping part of the felled trunk, which went on supporting a rich fauna for at least five years more.[260] There are three British mosquitoes that live only in tree-holes, external or internal: *Anopheles plumbeus*, *Aedes (Finlaya) geniculatus* and *Orthopodomyia pulchripalpis*.[317] The first two occur in tree-holes in Wytham

Woods, but the third is very local in Britain. All three species were living together in Keilin's horse-chestnut hole and MacGregor[310] similarly found all three in one beech tree-hole in Epping Forest. All three were collected by Edwards[114] in tree-holes in Hyde Park, London. Marshall[317] states that *Anopheles plumbeus* and *Aedes geniculatus* commonly occur together. There is a small list of other Diptera that are confined to or at any rate characteristic of tree-holes [53], including Syrphids such as *Eristalis (Tubifera) tenax*[98] and *Mallota cimbiciformis*,[74] but these have not yet been identified from such places in Wytham Woods, though some of the species do occur in the area. The larvae of a Helodid beetle, *Prionocyphon serricornis*, is not uncommon in Wytham tree-holes, its usual habitat (Plate 62).

Besides the more easily visible insect larvae that form the main biomass of this small compact community, there is a microfauna that includes copepods, nematodes, rotifers and Protozoa, especially ciliates. The whole thing is based on decaying wood and usually also leaves, twigs and sometimes debris from nests as well. Scourfield[434] found a small copepod *Moraria arboricola* in beech and hornbeam water-holes in Epping Forest – his animals lived for $4\frac{1}{2}$ years in a 3×1 in. glass tube with the original organic sediment and additions of water. It has since been found in other localities, mainly in beeches, and occasionally it lives in other places than tree-holes.[435, 200] A second species, *M. varica*, has similar habits. But we still have no comprehensive ecological survey of tree water-holes such as has been done in the United States by two army doctors, Jenkins and Carpenter,[245] whose work brings out some interesting general facts. First, there are no tree-hole mosquitoes in conifers, apart from one *Aedes* with a special habitat deep inside trunk holes of gums and occasionally swamp cypress. Secondly, three of the species of *Aedes* live in a wide range of broad-leaved trees, though the fourth seems to be confined to willows. Thirdly, the three genera that have tree-hole species here also come (with different species) in American tree-holes. Fourthly, a special feature found in North American tree-holes is *Megarhinus rutilus*, a large mosquito whose larvae prey on those of the other mosquitoes, and whose adult females feed on nectar and plant juices, and are not blood-suckers.

Aedes geniculatus and *Anopheles plumbeus*, like their American analogues, frequent tree-holes in a very wide variety of deciduous trees in Britain. According to Marshall[317] both have occurred in oak, ash, sycamore, beech, elm, lime, sweet-chestnut and horse-chestnut; the former also in hornbeam and the latter also in birch. Experience of Wytham Woods points to old beeches and coppiced sycamores being the usual sites for inhabited water-holes, but they have also been found in ash and other trees. This community, though specialized and very small, is evidently spread generally through deciduous woodland, and is confined to trees, and in natural woodland is especially characteristic of old trees. Of its extra-mural relations we do not know very much, except that *Aedes geniculatus* is an active man-biter and that it spreads through considerable parts of Wytham Woods. *Anopheles plumbeus* is also a known man-biter.[317]

The small streams on the middle and lower slopes of Wytham Hill that have been mentioned may either rise from springs in the open pasture or in pasture that has now been ploughed up, or under the shade of the woodland canopy. Out in the open they may start as a flush of luxuriant grass, or are surrounded by rushes, or there may be an old stone or iron cattle trough around which grow watercress (*Nasturtium*) or other marsh plants. The head pools sometimes have a good growth of green algae and diatoms, and I have once seen the remarkable tree-like alga *Batrachospermum moniliforme* [54]; but if the water is much disturbed there will be a clear mud bottom. But inside the woods the same stream looks remarkably different, and makes one think of the unkempt and dank forest described by Mickiewicz (Ch. 10). In mid-winter one sees a laminated deposit of fallen dead leaves, not everywhere but in patches, lying on the muddy silt bottom. In this rather unpromising-looking 'aquatic leaf-litter', which does not appear particularly rotten though partly softened by long immersion, several kinds of small animals may be found crawling between the leaves, and if they are kept indoors can be observed feeding on the leaf surface or eating the edges of holes in them. The commonest animals are shrimps, *Gammarus pulex*; the nymphs of stone-flies, usually *Nemoura erratica*; and very small caddis larvae, including *Crunoecia irrorata*, bearing cases made of sand and bits of dead leaf. These woodland streams are only a few feet wide, and often only an inch or two deep, cold, fairly fast flowing, with bottoms of sandy silt usually with black mud underneath, littered with leaves, twigs and other debris, and almost without any trace of aquatic plants, although there may be an occasional patch of diatoms and sometimes tall sedges such as *Carex pendula* grow along the margins. At this time of the year some of the dead leaves are already partly skeletonized by the animals.

By the summer most of the dead leaves have disappeared, except for harder species like oak and hawthorn; the softer ones like ash, sycamore, elm, hazel and sallow are fairly quickly attacked or decomposed. The order of preference on the whole seems to be much the same among these stream animals as among the worms and molluscs in terrestrial litter investigated by Lindquist (Ch. 12). But the only systematic experiments so far published have been those by Priesner[395] in Austria upon the huge larvae of the crane-fly *Tipula maxima* which is common also in woodland streams at Wytham, where the larvae live in the mud both under water and in the waterlogged margins. He tested their preferences for 15 species of tree leaves. For those species common in Wytham Woods the order of preference was ash, wych elm, oak, field maple, beech and birch. In the whole series oak came 10th, beech 13th, while ash was 3rd. Oak and beech leaves in these streams seem to be avoided by most of the animals, at any rate for many months.

The water is so saturated with calcium bicarbonate that any object lying there gets covered within a year with a hard coat of calcium carbonate crystals, if it is not eaten or decomposed. Thus the stream edges and bottom are strewn with a curious collection of 'fossil' leaves, acorn cups, twigs and such-like. By the late autumn there is a new fall of leaves and the seasonal round starts once more.

The stone-flies at any rate have an annual cycle geared to the abundance of leaf litter, as they usually emerge from the water in spring and early summer, and only small nymphs are present in high summer. *Nemoura erratica* adults have been found from April to June in Wytham Woods, but there are earlier and later records elsewhere. In the Lake District Hynes found them most commonly in March.[132] How *Gammarus* survives the year is at present an unanswered question. In practically every spring and stream on Wytham Hill it can just by casual inspection be seen to form the most massive population present, and it equally occurs in those stream stretches that are in the open. But there is one woodland stream (known as Stream 8) in the NE. part of the hill that rises under dense canopy and flows down through thick woodland to the edge, where it peters out entirely, being now separated from its former lower course that still enters the Thames. In 1949 this stream dried up completely and all the *Gammarus* died out and have not been able to recolonize from below. But the leaf litter still disappears, partly through the work of stone-flies, caddis and other invertebrates.

The two dominant features of these small streams right inside the woods are the absence of green water-plants and algae, and the fact that dead leaves are the central food resource (and also during much of the year cover) for the inhabitants. There is some evidence that some of the latter (including *Gammarus*) are nocturnal and mostly keep under cover by day. But besides the annual main leaf-fall, which consists of leaves from which nitrogen has largely been withdrawn, there are other small items falling from the plant layers above all round the year. Preliminary measurements by Ovington[364] proved that in some woodlands tree flowers might be important additions. I have noticed that a green leaf of sycamore, poplar or other softer species falling into a spring or stream will at once be attacked by animals. And it has to be remembered that there are supplies of leaves not only from the higher canopy (where nevertheless wind is most likely to dislodge them) but from elder and sallow and other shrubs, from woodland field-layer plants like dog's mercury (shown by Lindquist to be edible to earthworms), and any marginal growth of *Carex*. Besides these there are flowers, fruits, excreta of caterpillars and so on. All these aspects bristle with problems needing analysis and quantification [55]. Meanwhile it is possible to give a general idea of the nature and scale of the whole community in such a stream, from an ecological survey carried out in 1955-8 by Mr D. H. Eccles at the Bureau of Animal Population. This survey could not be quite completed before Mr Eccles returned to Africa, but he left the records and specimens with the Ecological Survey. They are of particular value because of his skill in handling the taxonomic difficulties presented by many of the insects, especially the flies. The following summary is based upon a preliminary analysis of the material, carried out with the help of Mr C. A. Elbourn [55A]. The survey was done on a single stream (Plate 71), one of those in the SE. part of Fig. 27. This stream (known as Stream 5) rises in a pasture field, flows for 150 yards before entering a broad strip of deciduous woodland (Marleywood Plantation – planted in the early nineteenth century and mentioned in Ch. 3), where it continues for another 150 yards before emerging again to flow down into the Seacourt Stream, which in turn eventually joins the Thames. Its width was about 3-6 ft but the flow very shallow, usually only several inches deep, on which account I have classified it in the smallest category of flowing water, as A 3. The only marsh plants are patches of *Carex pendula* which is able to withstand a good deal of shade – but other stretches of the margin have only bare silty banks. The only aquatic plants found by Eccles were one patch of blue-green algae on a minute cascade, and a single diatom frustule in the gut of a nematode! The temperature of this spring-fed stream usually remained low, fluctuating with rainfall and air temperatures. Readings of water temperature, though not taken each day, gave enough records to indicate that it remained below 12° C. between October and May and did not rise above 16·4° C. in June to September. Macan[305] analysed the temperature regime of a small moorland stream in the Lake District that crossed a wood. His transect downwards showed that, from where the stream entered the wood, the water temperature fell steadily by a total of 7·6° C. But this difference disappeared on wet days.

Eccles' ecological survey was done by four methods, which taken together provided a rather complete picture of the animal community. These were: general collecting both in and on the margin of the stream; breeding out insect adults from their aquatic larvae and pupae; analysis of core samples through aquatic litter and stream bottom, by means of a flotation method; and traps (Plate 72) that caught adults emerging from the water. The resulting list of species known or fairly certainly known to live in the stream, at least in their early stages (that is, for most of their life) comprised the following groups. There were 2 species of planarian worms (including *Planaria*, now *Crenobia, alpina*); at least 5 nematodes; 1 rotifer, 1 water snail and two small bivalves; 5 water-mites (including one Halacaridae); 3 copepods; 6 ostracods; *Gammarus pulex*; 1 surface-living Collembolan; 1 stone-fly (*Plecoptera*), *Nemoura erratica;* 2 mayflies (Ephemeroptera); 1 surface-running bug, *Velia caprai;* 6 caddis-flies; 5 small water beetles (2 Dytiscidae, 2 Hydrophilidae, 1 Helodidae, the last having an adult that is not aquatic and sits on Transition vegetation); and a large host of fly species (Diptera). The last comprised 10 families: 6 crane-flies (Tipulidae), including *Tipula maxima*; 3 Ptychopteridae, whose larvae breathe air through a long telescopic 'tail' reaching to the surface; 13 owl midges and allies (Psychodidae); 1 Culicidae (*Dixa submaculata*, not a mosquito); at least 32 non-biting midges of the family Chironomidae; 10 midges of the family Ceratopogonidae, of which *Culicoides obsoletus* was biting man by the stream and does so elsewhere in Wytham Woods; 2 black flies, Simuliidae (of which *Simulium erythrocephalum* bites man in Wytham Woods and elsewhere); 7 predatory Empidae; 4 small flies of the family Sphaeroceridae; 1 Ephydridae. I have omitted several fly records that may represent accidental presence, but the main list, subject to a few changes when life-histories are more completely known, is of species that actually live in the stream during their early life. These flies form two-thirds of the surprising total of 121 species, and besides these some other aquatic insects were taken near the stream and may also have grown up in it. The impression left is of a very rich community for such a limited habitat, and one whose main basis is the annual supply of dead and some living leaves, supplemented by a myriad of smaller items from above [55B]. But beyond knowing that several common animals break up and eat the softer dead leaves, and sometimes the harder ones as well; that the resulting fragments and excreta must form a further resource for smaller forms; and that the main resource has mostly disappeared or become calcified within a year; that some of the species (such as some caddis) are predators and others (such as water-mites) partly parasites; we can only partly comprehend the inner workings of the system.

These head-springs and streams on Wytham Hill also provide some evidence of ancient historical survivors. In a spring trough situated in open pasture on the side of the Wytham Park (Plate 69, bottom, right) Efford[116] discovered two subterranean Crustacea that had evidently been washed to the surface from the underground waters of the Calcareous Grit sands in the hill. One was a single individual of the minute (1 mm. long) Anaspidacean *Bathynella chapuisi*, evolved from an order that flourished in Carboniferous times. This species is widely known in Europe, where it lives mainly in interstitial water in underground sands.[350] In this country it was thought to be confined to some stone quarries in Wiltshire, but recently Spooner[479] has obtained it by tapping underground gravels on the edge of Dartmoor, and also a Thames gravel terrace near Pangbourne. In 1960 it was discovered in the silt of a pool in a cave in Yorkshire.[218]

The second species was the blind well-shrimp, *Niphargus aquilex*, which turned up more than once in the Wytham spring and appears not uncommonly in wells in the south of England. I have pumped it up from a house well in the gravel at Kidlington, Oxfordshire, 4 miles NE. of Wytham across the Thames Valley. In July 1922 my brother the late Geoffrey Elton found this shrimp in a swampy mossy spring trickle full of dead leaves under the canopy of an alder wood near Petersfield, Hampshire, where I collected some that were named by the late Dr

W. T. Calman. These must also have been flooded out to the surface, since the pool became dried up afterwards. Such interstitial-living subterranean animals are just one facet of the more extensive cave fauna whose character and distribution has been summarized by Hazelton and Glennie.[218]

The second ancient element consists of animals permanently living in these head-streams both inside or outside woods. These appear to be cold-water forms that were much more widely distributed in earlier millennia, having either survived the last glaciation in Britain or migrated afterwards from Europe – which would mean they must have arrived by Boreal times, and are now confined to isolated localities. *Planaria alpina* is a particularly good example of this. It has been found in four of the streams or head-springs on Wytham Hill, under shade, and in similar places in Wychwood Forest, Oxfordshire. One of these at Wytham (Spring 2) was described by me[132] in 1956: a shallow muddy pan under a groove of grey poplars (*Populus canescens*), with water never more than 2 in. deep yet always flowing even in the driest summers, cold water that plunges underground again after running about 15 ft. Although the shelter of woods or scrub must certainly help to keep the water cooler than it might otherwise be, and *Planaria alpina* in the south of England is most often found in such streams, this shelter may not always be essential right at the cold spring source. Spring 2 lies in the contour of what was once a pond, and a sub-fossil specimen of the marsh snail *Succinia pfeifferi* there indicates that it once had a non-woodland marsh.

Another instance of a relict that comes in such streams, and is almost entirely confined to those with woody canopy, is the minute water-mite *Feltria romijni*, on which Efford[117, 120] has made a very complete population study at Wytham, and extended the survey also to some other parts of the British Isles.[119] It has been found by him in some other places around Oxford (Wychwood Forest (Plate 70) and Burford in Oxfordshire, and Cothill in Berkshire); and it also occurs in northern England, Wales and Ireland. He got five species of water-mites in Spring 5A at Wytham, a spring very like and not far from Spring 5 studied by Eccles, but with a heavier growth of *Carex pendula* at the margins. All these mites have free-living adults but larvae parasitic on Chironomid flies, by which means they get dispersed. *Feltria romijni* appears to be entirely confined to one extremely small midge (only 1 mm. in length), *Tanytarsus flavidulus*. The small case-bearing larvae of this fly tend to aggregate on parts of the stream bottom where detritus of dead leaves broken up by larger animals accumulates. In May the number of *T. flavidulus* emerging per square metre per day was estimated to be over 1500.[118] Only in some Irish localities does this fly live in completely exposed streams, though sometimes it comes under *Phragmites* reed-swamp and not trees. The food of the water-mite is not known for certain, but its structure suggests that it is predatory on very small animals or their eggs. One other feature of the life of these head-stream water-mites will be mentioned. Of the five species, *F. romijni* has only one host fly, but the other four are less specialized: *Lebertia glabra* had 3 host species, *Sperchon glandulosus* and *Ljania papillata* 5, and *Atractides nodipalpis* 8. Here again one sees the progressive ramification of the food-chains that has been discussed at many stages in this book.

Although we have much to learn about the inner relationships of these woodland dead-leaf-based communities, a little is beginning to become clear about the species of stone-flies.[132] These are entirely represented by the small family Nemouridae, of which 11 species are known in Britain, and of these 6 live on Wytham Hill. Most of them have nymphs that eat dead leaves, though not always under dense woody canopy. *Nemoura erratica* is however highly characteristic of shaded woodland streams both at Wytham and elsewhere in Britain and also in Scandinavia. A larger species, *Nemoura variegata* (= *cinerea*[271]), lives in streams and brooks, usually with overhanging trees or scrub, and may even live in stagnant water. Its nymphs will eat not only dead leaves of trees and shrubs but also those of *Carex*. In the middle of Wytham Park there is a place called Wormstall Duck Pond, originally formed in the nineteenth century by damning up a cold stream. Now it has no ducks because there is no pond, but there are four species of Nemouridae living in what has become a rather cold stream marsh with multiple channels running over silt and shaded by sallows (*Salix atrocinerea*), willows and some other trees. Here *Nemoura erratica*, the dominant stone-fly in the woods above, and *N. variegata* the common one in the lower streams round Oxford, live together; also *Nemoura dubitans*, an extremely local species whose nymphs were described from here by Hynes,[243] and *Nemurella inconspicua* (= *picteti*) [56]. With them also, of course, *Gammarus pulex*. In one or other cool stream or spring on the hill *Nemoura cambrica* and *Amphinemura standfussi* have also been taken. It is evident with most of these species, from my own observations and those of specialists like Brinck in Sweden,[43] that the nymphs feed on a variety of soft leaves and are not monophagous. But Hynes[242] was able to rear *Amphinemura standfussi* on dead oak leaves. He also discovered by looking at the gut contents of nymphs that *Nemoura variegata* eats algae as well as leaves, if these are present in a stream. There is an interesting habit of the adults that further binds them to woody surroundings: *N. erratica*, *N. variegata* and *Nemurella inconspicua* in Sweden feed upon the lichen and algal growth on fallen twigs and branches near the streams. Hynes[242] has further proved by experiment that *N. variegata* females require such food in order to ripen eggs, and that unfed adults did not copulate.

Small woodland ponds under thick tree canopy have some of the ecological characteristics of woodland streams, in that they are cool and dead leaves accumulating on the bottom provide one of the main food supplies for animals. But the species of animals are very different from those in woodland streams. Mosquitoes are often found in such places, and Marshall's description[317] of the habitats of, for example, species of *Aedes*, provides a whole series from ponds under thick canopy to open ponds, and then also from fresh to brackish or saline waters. The large *Aedes rusticus* lives in ditches or woodland ponds with scrub or deciduous trees round, and Marshall gives a photograph of a hazel leaf partly skeletonized by the larvae. *Aedes cantans* also comes in such pools, including temporary ones, and disappears if surrounding woody vegetation is cut.[317] There is another influence of woodland that is not so often realized. In May 1940 I visited a small pond in Bagley Wood, Berkshire, which lay completely under the canopy of an oak-birch wood on gravel soil over clay. Here there were *Aedes rusticus* and *A. cantans*, both attacking man. But when I saw it again, in June 1945, the wood had been clear-felled up to the edge of the hollow where the pond had stood, and there was now no standing water, only a slightly marshy bottom covered with *Polygonum hydropiper* and *Glyceria*. It appeared that the original canopy had been sufficient to prevent progressive evaporation of the pond.

In the Ecological Survey ponds have been divided into 'Woody' and 'Non-woody' (see Ch. 4), with the implication that Woody ponds are either under the canopy of trees or scrub, or shaded by them on the edge of woodland or scrub. It is clear, however, that the larger the pond is, the less will be the influence of the Woody element; also that this will be less on the edge than in the middle of woodland or scrub. There are three main features that dominate a Woody pond. First is protection from wind and high evaporation; secondly the shade that discourages aquatic green vegetation; and thirdly the leaf-fall that provides an alternative resource. The largest pond in Wytham Woods (Pond 1) lies on the west slope between the two parts of the hill, and is fed by a spring stream from above that was damned up between 1872 and 1898. When full it is about 60 yd. across, and 3-4 ft deep. It is entirely surrounded by woodland and scrub and is in a very sheltered position (Plate 64). But the woody vegetation, although supplying some of the resources, is not by any means dominant in its influence, and the pond has a rich vegetation, with layers of submerged plants, floating pond-weed (*Potamogeton natans*), reed-swamp of mares-tail (*Hippuris vulgaris*), bulrush (*Scirpus lacustris*), reed-mace (*Typha latifolia*) and sedges, and then marsh zones above the margin. This pond therefore is really in woodland 'edge', and does not represent the extreme conditions of those under dense canopy. However, when the pond was examined during a drought in 1947 the bottom was found to have dead leaves of various kinds, terrestrial and aquatic, to a depth of 22 in. A careful survey was done in the years 1944-8 by Miss E. M. O. Laurie (now Mrs Isserlis), working at the Bureau of Animal Population, and the records and specimens are with the Ecological Survey. At this period she established the existence of at least 116 species of animals there, and in this list of species *only one*, *Gammarus pulex*, occurs also in Stream 5 that I have described above. This means to say that a small woodland stream under canopy, and a dammed-up pond below in a large woodland glade, could together contribute something like 250 species of animals to the system in which they lie. One example only will be mentioned of the Woody influence upon Pond 1 animals: the caddis larvae of *Glyophotaelius pellucidus*, whose case is there made from dead leaves of the marsh sallow, *Salix atrocinerea*.

The immense network of river and subsidiary channels, cuts and ditches that meanders down the great bend in the Thames from which Wytham takes its Saxon name contains rich communities that have as yet hardly been explored, though the increasing pressures of mechanical drainage and the possible dangers from the run-off of toxic chemicals from the land invite (before it is too late) a proper survey such as has already been begun at the freshwater station of Reading University down-river. But I shall refer to two ways in which the river system influences the Wytham area. One is through the food supply of herons; the other by the effects of flood waters on the dispersal of animals (dealt with in the next chapter). The heronry in Wytham Woods, of which an annual census has been made since 1928, depends for food largely upon the animals living in these valley channels, which include not only the Thames system but those of the rivers Windrush, Evenlode and Cherwell converging near Oxford, as well as the Ock and Thame a little to the south. The heronry has been at Wytham for a long time, though its exact site within the woodland changes from time to time, being either in deciduous or coniferous trees and at heights of 30-60 ft. The number of nests has varied from 6 to 28 [57], that is the number of breeding birds has been less than 60. Owen[367, 369] has analysed the food brought back by their parents to the younger nestlings, by persuading the latter to regurgitate some of their meals, and he estimated that a nestling must consume on the average about 150 kg. of fresh food (mainly fish) during its nestling life, which occurs from about the end of March or early April to early July, sometimes a little later. Some young birds died, probably through not getting enough to eat. The diet of the Wytham birds included the following species: trout* (*Salmo trutta*), pike* (*Esox lucius*), carp* (*Cyprinus carpio*), gudgeon (*Gobio gobio*), tench* (*Tinca tinca*), minnow (*Phoxinus phoxinus*), roach (*Rutilus rutilus*), bleak (*Alburnus alburnus*), eels (*Anguilla anguilla*), perch (*Perca fluviatilis*), ruffe* (*Acerina cernua*), three-spined stickleback (*Gasterosteus aculeatus*), water vole (*Arvicola amphibius*), water shrew* (*Neomys fodiens*), several terrestrial small mammals*, large water beetles* (*Dytiscus*), dragonflies (*Agrion splendens*), and a few other animals. The species marked with an asterisk were only eaten in small numbers. Of the larger prey, that is over 100 mm. long, the roach formed half. Of the smaller ones, minnows and three-spined sticklebacks were predominant, the latter being about half. These proportions do not represent just the abundance of fish, but the fish that can be caught by a heron in shallow water.

Among absentees from this list one notices, for example, the chub (*Squalius cephalus*), barbel (*Barbus barbus*) and dace (*Leuciscus leuciscus*).

The dietary recorded for Wytham is the result of searching by the herons in a variety of water bodies. The roach is very abundant in the main flowing waters; while the stickleback is largely absent from large rivers and typically found in ditches and other small and slow waters, and in ponds. I have frequently noticed, in the course of early morning expeditions to the river to look for birds, that herons are to be seen on the R. Thames margin but usually fly off when the first anglers arrive, perhaps at about 8 a.m. The force of these rival fish-catchers in the Oxford area is very large, and although many of them throw back the fish they catch, this does not prevent their presence from driving off fishing herons. I think that when they are unable to work the main rivers the herons retire to the hinterland of smaller waters and there collect sticklebacks, among other foods. Confirmation of this idea is perhaps given by the fact that in the extremely dry summer of 1959, when most of the ditches and small water bodies dried up completely, herons were to be seen in much larger numbers than usual by the riverside and in fields close by. Heronries are usually placed in woods, but the diet varies very much in accordance with the kind of country round them. Owen also analysed the diet of young herons in an oak wood at High Halstow on the coast of Kent, near the Thames estuary. Here the number of fish species eaten was much less, mainly eels, three-spined sticklebacks and also ten-spined (*Pygosteus pungitius*), together with a great many brackish water prawns, *Palaemonetes varians*.

Having noticed the sap-flows, tree-holes, springs, streams and ponds that are closely dependent for their character and basic resources upon woodland, and the use by herons of the woods as a base for collecting fish from the surrounding rivers, ditches and other waters, it remains to mention the marshes of woodland. On Wytham Hill these are well developed where spring flushes come out, and there is a very strong difference in the vegetation and general structure of those in pasture fields outside, and those under or in the shelter of tree and scrub canopy. The former have poorly developed variety, because of the trampling by cattle, and are usually composed of rushes (*Juncus*) with a few other plants such as *Epilobium parviflorum*. Their fauna has not been looked at. Inside the woods there are much richer communities and some of the marshes are quite large (Plate 75). In summer there is a lush vegetation (in wet years over head height) of such plants as *Carex riparia, Equisetum telmateia, Epilobium hirsutum, Eupatorium cannabinum* and *Angelica sylvestris*. Formerly there was also a very rich mixture of mosses and liverworts on the ground underneath, but as Jones[253] has pointed out, the disappearance of rabbits through myxomatosis has resulted in densification of the vegetation and an impoverishment of this ground zone of bryophytes. Before that time one commonly found signs of rabbits in these marshes, where they attacked the yellow iris, *Iris pseudacorus*, and other plants. This dense field layer produces a litter zone that is extremely rich in animal life, both in species and numbers, and in winter to spring it falls down to a temporary Open Ground condition (Plate 76 shows the onset of spring growth). Some of the animals are exactly the same as those in the terrestrial litter of the wood: thus Todd[507] recorded eight common harvestmen (Opiliones) in Wytham woodland marshes. Many of the common snails and slugs in these marshes have a similarly wide habitat range, though the litter they feed on comes mainly from different plants that do not grow under the terrestrial canopy. There are, however, two species of snails, *Clausilia rolphii* and *Azeca goodalli*, that are here virtually confined to woodland marshes, though both have elsewhere been found as inhabitants of ordinary woodland or hedgerow litter.[122] Another snail, *Arianta arbustorum*, though not rare in the latter, is enormously more abundant in the marshes, which are really important components in the whole ecosystem.

Knowledge of Transition communities has recently been advanced considerably by the work of W. W. Murdoch at the Bureau of Animal Population. This was done partly on a marsh by Pond 1 in Wytham Woods, and partly in the edge of a large marsh of reed-grass, *Phalaris arundinacea*, by Blenheim Park Lake in Oxfordshire [58]. There are over 100 species of British beetles in the family Carabidae that inhabit Transition marshes and other zones (often quite narrow) bordering water bodies. For example, the bare or gravelly mud on damp river-banks has a rich fauna in which such beetles are abundant. An analysis by Murdoch of what is known of about 80 of these species (of which 24 occur in the Wytham area) suggested that they fall broadly into two categories: (1) inhabitants of zones carrying a good field layer of vegetation in summer and consequently thick litter that persists through the winter, (2) those of zones with poor vegetation cover or none at all. He concluded that 'it seems to matter very little to the beetles what species of plants form the habitat'. This subdivision exists both within woodland and outside it and again emphasizes the wide spread of species that depend directly or through their prey upon rotting vegetation. *Agonum fuliginosum*, on which Murdoch has done a full population analysis, is one of the species that lives in thick marsh, while *Agonum ruficorne* is usually absent from such thick litter and occurs on the bare margins of woodland streams under thick canopy. But the latter, for example, has a tremendous range of habitat. I have taken it on the stony margins of Welsh mountain torrents and in a stream trickle just above H.W.M. on a sea-cliff in Pembrokeshire.

One last example will illustrate the structural miscellany that is to be found in Transition zones. Over much of Lowland England near rivers and smaller water bodies, including still ones, the pollard willow is a conspicuous element in the landscape (Plates 77 and 78). These are trees, usually of the crack willow *Salix fragilis*, planted originally and now often very old, whose shoots are cut every few years (typically about 10 to 15) and used for making hurdles and so on though nowadays they tend to be left without further cutting. The crown of such trees is expanded into a platform or depression up to several feet across, on which leaf and twig debris accumulate, and here develops a remarkable chance assemblage of terrestrial plants. Some of the plant seeds are wind-blown, but many are brought by berry-eating birds, and it is not rare to see ivy, hawthorn or elder growing there. Among surveys of this epiphytic flora I will mention four. Church[69] in his 'Plant-life of the Oxford District' mentions some species, and remarks that 'a willow can be so pollarded half a dozen times before badly decaying: they become hollow shells in 50 years'. Gunther[199] counted the plants growing on 114 pollard willows along branches of the Cherwell in 'Mesopotamia' at Oxford. In 1888-90 there were 183 species, in 1900 there were 138, and in 1911 only 90, a few of the trees having died meanwhile. Thompson[501] counted about 103 species of vascular plants growing on pollard willows and alders along the River Chew in Somerset, where deep floods up to 10 ft brought some of the seeds. Bingley[26] more recently cites a survey by J. F. M. and M. Cannon of riverside willows near Flatford Mill in Suffolk, where 35 species occurred in the crowns which were at about 9 ft. He also noted that the invertebrate fauna living thus above the ground contains typical litter animals such as earthworms, millipedes and such like. Although such communities may also come on willows growing away from water, it is to be supposed that the damper microclimate near water has some importance. These epiphytic 'gardens', besides demonstrating the decisive results of introducing a new structural feature into a habitat system, may also remind us of some of the structural and biological richness that undoubtedly existed in Miocene and Pliocene times, even in temperate forests [59], and which has been lost in our glacially smashed landscape. That dampness encourages the development of such epiphytic growth is illustrated by Tansley's account[493] of the vascular epiphytes growing on procumbent oak trunks and on branches in Wistman's Wood in the very wet climate of Dartmoor, Devon, of which he remarked: 'It is obvious that the habitat provided by the layer of humus accumulating on the upper surfaces of the horizontal trunks and branches is not very different from the similar layers on the rocks of the woodland floor.'

CHAPTER 18

Dispersal and Invaders

THE WHOLE TERRESTRIAL and freshwater ecosystem that has been analysed into its component parts in the previous chapters has two outstanding characteristics: its complexity and its comparative stability. Most ecological work has to be concerned with relatively small parts of a population or a community, and this is a sound procedure, up to a point, for obtaining the solid material for building up knowledge of the whole. I have approached the matter from the opposite point of view: looking at the whole ecosystem as a piece of ecological machinery, breaking it down into component parts according to a set of consistent ideas, and then using what information exists to fit these components again into an integrated whole. By treating the problem this way, one is forced to consider the scale on which species mixtures are organized, and the relationships between the different component communities. But doing this is a formidable job that could still only be attempted for a place like Wytham Woods which has a wealth of information – not just information about animals, but information organized in the right way and collected at the two levels of population and community. I remember two friends of my youth who decided to take the family piano to pieces while their parents were out of the house one evening, and were very disconcerted to find that they could not put it together again, so that it just lay about in twanging tangled heaps. I would wish to have the skill of a more mature mathematical colleague who, having bought a new typewriter, took it apart and reassembled it the same evening, because he just wanted to understand how it worked. There are, however, also some features of the ecosystem as a whole that will now be discussed.

In another book, about invading species,[133] I have given the reasons for thinking that simple communities, that is communities with few species, are usually less able to withstand invasion by new animals or plants coming from without than are large and complex communities such as have been described in the last twelve chapters here. Briefly, the following reasons were advanced in support of this belief: mathematical conclusions about the interactions of simple population mixtures; laboratory experiments with only very few species interacting, and with or without the stabilizing tendency of cover, that is, more varied habitat structure; the vulnerability to invasion of oceanic island communities of animals and plants; the frequency of outbreaks and of successful invasions in the simplified communities of farmland; the apparent scarcity of outbreaks of population in tropical rain forests; and the interaction of enemies and parasites with orchard pests, and the unexpected results of reducing this community by toxic chemicals.

In putting forward these ideas, which seem to have been rather widely accepted as reasonable ones, I overlooked the essential difference between *instability* and *vulnerability* in communities. A tremendously intricate ecosystem like that of Wytham Hill and its environs is not highly vulnerable to invaders from without, as I shall show in this chapter. It is also highly stable, in the sense that most of the species persist there successfully, albeit with the kind of fluctuations that are an inherent feature of such populations. Oceanic islands, by all accounts, were also stable systems, apart from climatic disasters like storms and tidal waves and volcanic outbursts; but these very exiguous communities have proved extremely vulnerable to invasions. One could therefore say that both Wytham Hill and a coral island could have stable communities, but that the latter is very vulnerable. The distinction, I think, rests on the genetic adjustment between species. It seems to be possible, somewhere in the range between the mathematical models and glass-jar experiments with one to three species together, and the deep organization of some thousands of species at Wytham, to have communities of a few score or hundred forms that could be genetically adjusted to live in fairly good equilibrium. What these communities lack is the immediate compensatory arrangements that exist in multiple food-chains and the flexible food-habits and behaviour of many hundreds or some thousands of species – the machinery that I referred to a long time ago[124] as a sort of fire-brigade system, which we suppose to be exceptionally highly evolved in the tropics. It is therefore worth suggesting that 'ecological resistance to invaders', an undoubted feature of highly organized communities, has at least these two elements: rather prompt compensatory reactions of an ecological kind, and rather slower ones of a genetic nature. The latter have been discussed in a very interesting way by Pimentel,[386] who looks to them for a powerful means of population control, a theory that seems to depend very much for its success on the rate of reaction possible by any purely genetic mechanism – and this still needs to be defined.

These ideas about invasions were evolved from a contemplation of the increasing number of species transported intentionally or by accident through the agency of man, between continents, from continents to islands, from one lake or one sea to another; and also in the historical light of the past faunal or floral isolation of these lands and waters which man's activities are now breaking down, especially those that developed during the Tertiary Period and are generally known as Wallace's Realms. But the conclusions that can be made about stability of communities under the impact of invasion do not rest only on this kind of evidence.

There are, in a very rough classification, three kinds of dispersal movements among animal populations. First come the normal movements, which may either be rather random or may be highly ritualized, of species that live in the place or at any rate visit it regularly and form part of its main faunal list. The second are random mass bombardments by native species from outside the home area, and especially those brought by active migration, by aeroplankton and by river floods. The third are genuine invaders carried by man from abroad, old or new, some of which have little impact and disappear, while others come to stay. Between these three broad categories there are many borderline sorts of movement, and from ignorance we do not always know in what category to place a species. For example, when one finds a water-strider, *Gerris lacustris*, arriving to skate on the surface of an entirely temporary spring pool in Wytham Woods, it will be assumed that it came from the river back-waters, or perhaps a larger pond; but for all we know, it may have flown from Wiltshire or France. And when a very old invader like the rabbit recolonizes the hill from neighbouring land, it does not now matter very much that the original rabbits entered Britain in Norman times.

It will by now be evident that a large part of the ecosystem consists of small interspersed components composed of different communities, and that even the larger matrix, say of woodland, in which they are set is itself a pattern of individual plant units or groups of plants. An organization of this type with an involved pattern of interspersion can only continue to exist, or to exist in a stable form, with a tremendous amount of local dispersal movement among most of the animals. Indeed, Southwood[467] has put forward the theory that the primary adaptive reason for much animal dispersal and migration is the changing locus and nature of habitats – a phenomenon seen most clearly in some of the temporary general habitats like carrion, dung and nests. This movement in turn brings up problems of fuelling by which to perform the movements, a subject that has re-curred in a number of previous chapters, but especially in Ch. 13. Nearly all this kind of local dispersal takes place in the warmer months of the year. Entomologists very well know that there are certain days, especially towards evening, when very large numbers of small insects such as beetles fly in the air not very far above the vegetation; and this applies similarly to the activities of insects like moths on certain nights. Omer-Cooper and Tottenham[82] have described how one of them swept the air with a net for a total of six hours towards dusk on four days in July, on Wicken Fen near Cambridge, and captured over 7000 beetles belonging to 81 species. And although this nature reserve has been very extensively collected over by expert entomologists (albeit without recording any adequate information about the habitats), 25 of these species had not previously been recorded there, and nearly two-thirds of the specimens were in this group. 98% were rove-beetles (Staphylinidae). It is pretty certain that most land areas have aerial transit on this sort of scale going on whenever the weather is 'right', and it is well known that the mass flights of moths at night contain many species that are not living in the habitat where the collecting is done. In June 1963 Professor F. C. Evans collected flying insects in the middle of an open grassland area on the top of Wytham Hill using a trap modelled on the 'Malaise'. This trap is a passive one, in that it does not contain attractants such as bait or chemicals, nor is it lit up. It has four wings of textile forming bays up to 5 ft from the ground level that catch insects flying from any direction, and these make their way into a funnel trap at the top. The catches were rich in species, some of which were not grassland forms at all, and Prof. Evans informed me that he had had similar experience with this kind of trap on an old field in Michigan.

The same kind of wide dispersal movement goes on among aquatic insects, and a good deal has been published about the colonization of waters by beetles and bugs. Fernando[153, 154] carried out some experiments with traps designed to measure the amount and nature of this movement. He put out 4-ft square tanks and also sloping glass sheets with water traps at the base which attracted the flying insects. One set of experiments was done in Wytham Woods (partly near Pond 1) and the other by gravel-pit pools at Cassington, not far away. One of the commonest arrivals was a small Hydrophilid beetle *Helophilus brevipalpis*; in one set of tests lasting from 26 March to 21 October over 2000 were caught, and sometimes more than a hundred might arrive in one day. In this combined series of experiments 11 species of Hydrophilidae and 10 Dytiscidae were thus caught on migration. Of Hemiptera, 3 species of Corixidae and 2 of Gerridae (water-striders) were taken in these traps at Wytham and some other Corixidae also at Cassington.

Superimposed upon all this small-scale local movement is the rain of small insects coming down from 'aeroplankton', that mixed assemblage of floating or partly flying species carried into the High Air up to several thousand feet and dispersed evidently over great distances before descending to earth. In these upper regions they form the food of the swift (*Apus apus*).[281] A useful summary of this technically complicated field of ecology is given by Freeman[170, 171] who (in collaboration with A. C. Hardy) trapped insects and spiders in nets on high wireless masts in Lincolnshire, taking them at heights of 10, 177 and 277 ft, expressing the catches in numbers per million cubic feet of air. There was considerable difference between the species caught at low level near the ground and those from higher up, the latter forming the real aeroplankton, and the former being part of the normal working population that I have already mentioned, taken during their local dispersal. Freeman took altogether 342 species, Diptera, Hemiptera (especially aphids) and Hymenoptera being commonest. To these he added 20 species of spiders, and even a few mites. It is a fair inference from this and other equally solid work at Rothamsted and elsewhere, that the Wytham area must be under constant bombardment by floating small insects, many of which (such as aphids) may be really key species in the communities to which they belong. To these again we should add larger forms like butterflies that undertake directed and powerful migrations often from great distances and from abroad. Migrant birds form another category that connects any area of Britain to the ecology of foreign parts.

The winter floods of the upper Thames Valley are very well known to those of us who live there, and have been well described by Church[69] in 1922: 'When Port Meadow, Osney Fields, Iffley Fields, and the Cherwell Meadows are under water, the aspect of the country returns to its primary winter condition, with hamlets spaced along the flood-margin and the town on its gravel bank, appearing from the surrounding hills as more or less isolated in a broad lake.' Although control of this water is more exact than formerly, it is still necessary for the salvation of the lower Thames settlements to retain some of this flood-water above (Plates 67, 81 and 82). These floods wash out from their homes enormous numbers of invertebrate animals, winged and wingless, which must be carried for long distances. As the floods recede these are left behind in the flood rubbish, and many of the animals are still alive. The extent of this natural invasion from above, implying a good deal of natural recruitment as well, can be illustrated by two examples. At the end of April 1908 an unusual snow-storm followed by heavy rains raised floods in the R. Thames and Cherwell valleys. Walker[531] and Champion fished out flood refuse caught against a foot-bridge at Water Eaton just above Oxford on the Cherwell, and found it 'literally seething with beetles', of which they counted 340 species. In addition there were thousands of ants, *Myrmica 'rubra'*, which were seen to be making new communities in the drier parts of the flood refuse. Some of the beetles whose names are given certainly belong to Transition zones, but others come from various terrestrial or general habitats. Easton[112] recorded the beetles he found in flood rubbish on the R. Mole in Surrey in November, and by the R. Thames at Shillingford in December 1946. He got 3795 beetles, and altogether, a total of 327 species. There were 152 species at the first place, and 272 at the second. Their original habitats were certainly extremely varied.

Strictly speaking it is not possible to prove that the fauna of a place like Wytham Hill remains unchanged over twenty years, and we do know of certain species having arrived and others having vanished, perhaps temporarily. Nevertheless general experience, which includes the study of a good many species during prolonged investigations on their populations, makes it pretty certain that the whole system is stable in composition and does not radically change from year to year. But it is subjected to this ceaseless bombardment by species from outside. These species must either exist already on the area, in which case the additional forces arriving may not have much effect on the balance of populations; or they must fail to establish themselves, either because they could not in any case live in the habitats there or because the community has its own biotic properties that go to make what can be called 'ecological resistance'. Rather better evidence about this comes from the fate of foreign invaders, to which I will turn. In the following notes about invaders at Wytham I shall omit reference to Domestic habitats.

The rabbit seems to have been brought into Britain between the time of Domesday Book in 1086 and the twelfth century, and it is usually said that the introduction came with the Normans from France.[502] It has to be admitted that its profound influence on the vegetation of Britain, especially realized by us since the fall in numbers after the pandemic of myxomatosis in 1953-4, proves that even the complex communities here were unable to cushion off the shock of this invader entirely. With it at some unknown date must also have come the rabbit flea, *Spilopsyllus cuniculi*, although we do not know whether this or other invading parasites are Norman, Tudor or Victorian. This flea is common on the surviving rabbits at Wytham [60]. The myxoma virus lives in the native wild rabbit of South America, was released in France in 1952, reached Kent in 1953, and spread with remarkable speed during the following two years. The first rabbit dying of myxomatosis in Wytham Woods was picked up by Professor Thomas Park and myself on 20 September 1954. The numbers soon dropped low and have remained so, under careful control. The scars of earlier outbreaks, especially before 1945, can be seen on the trunks of sycamores and beeches in many places, and the selective effect of their attacks on scrub has left large stands of elder, *Sambucus nigra*. The falling off in rabbit pressure has brought about protean changes in open ground and field-type vegetation on the Hill.

The North American grey squirrel (*Sciurus carolinensis*) was introduced at a number of centres in Britain from the latter part of the nineteenth century onwards. Fortunately it is possible to determine approximately when they reached Wytham Woods and replaced the native red squirrels (*Sciurus vulgaris*) that formerly lived there. Lord Hurcomb, who lived in Oxford in his youth, has informed me that red squirrels could be seen on the eastern edge of Wytham Woods and to a lesser extent on the other side, in the middle and late nineties of last century, and for a few years later, say up to the first World War. The Hon. Geoffrey Bourke who was agent for the Wytham Abbey Estate in 1921-4 has given me a further valuable record. 'Grey squirrels were predominant, though there were a few red squirrels on the property, particularly in the woods on the southern boundary of the estate. . . . To the best of my recollection I never saw a red squirrel in any of the woods on the northern half of the Estate.' I myself recorded two grey squirrels on a keeper's gibbet in the woods in December 1926. By the time this estate came into the hands of the University in 1943, no red squirrels survived, and the grey species was very numerous and still survives in spite of local control. This change-over of the two species, the biological mechanism of which is still quite unknown, also happened in the City of Oxford about the same time [61]. The grey squirrel brought its flea, *Orchopeas wickhami*, with it to Britain, as well as other parasites that include at least one North American species of louse, *Hoplopleura sciuricola*.[500] Dr M. J. Cotton has collected the flea both from

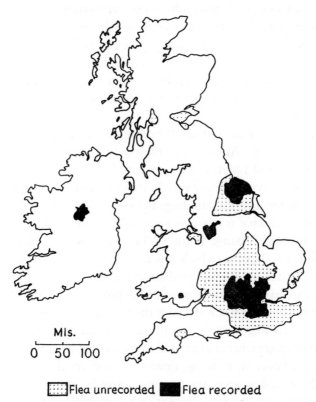

Mls.

0   50   100

[:::] Flea unrecorded   ■ Flea recorded

FIG. 28. Main distribution areas up to 1936 of the flea, *Orchopeas wickhami*, brought by the invading North American grey squirrel, *Sciurus carolinensis*. The flea mostly spread more slowly than its host. (After R. B. Freeman, 1941)

squirrels and their nests at Wytham [60]. The map in Fig. 28, based on a survey by Freeman,[172] using field material accumulated by Middleton during his investigation into the spread of the grey squirrel, shows that the flea usually lagged behind its host. Besides *O. wickhami* the one ordinarily found on the red squirrel, *Monopsyllus sciurorum*, was very frequently found on grey squirrels. Freeman noted that it 'was very frequent and it is probable that it can establish permanent breeding colonies, though it was never found in such numbers as *O. wickhami*, the index for 187 specimens being 3·9 compared with 10·65'.

367

One of the most interesting clashes between invading species is the tremendous and often lethal damage done by grey squirrels at Wytham and elsewhere to sycamores, *Acer pseudo-platanus*, whose bark they strip on a considerable scale. The sycamore, introduced from Europe several centuries ago, was planted in Wytham Woods in the first half of the nineteenth century, and is still very common, chiefly in the form of coppiced trees. It is this younger growth that the squirrels damage. Therefore these two invading species have not yet arrived at a balanced state [62]. Of birds, there are singularly few invaders from abroad, other than long-standing introductions like the pheasant (*Phasianus colchicus*) which even in the absence of protection by keepers is still able to maintain a breeding population. The little owl, *Athene noctua*, which was brought in from Europe to this country in the nineteenth century, is not common in the area, though it has been recorded in the open parts there.

The rabbit has been a truly dominant herbivore and the grey squirrel is capable of much general damage. At first sight they would appear to contradict the idea that complex woodland systems can resist invaders. But, for what it is worth, it could be said that the whole larger vertebrate section of the community of woodlands and their immediate surroundings nowadays lacks some of the features of primeval forests, and what is more, is very unlikely to get them back again. The most obvious historical change is the decline or extinction of larger predatory mammals such as pine marten (which attack squirrels among other species), polecat (the tame ferret is still an effective predator if it gets the chance) and wild cat, also some of the larger hawks.[128] In support of the notion that rabbits became general pests because they had too few enemies is the historical fact that rabbits were for a long time after their introduction locally kept in managed warrens,[502] and only became abundant everywhere in the wild in recent centuries, when forest land was disappearing, predators were being destroyed, and finally a self-preserving industry for killing rabbits grew up. But one must be careful not to build up an argument that becomes circular, since if these successful invaders are not in fact invading a natural system, the argument loses part of its meaning. It may be that, as seems to have happened in many parts of the world, there are a few invaders that are highly successful in penetrating a seral forest ecosystem; though their effects may be severe, extremely few species achieve this success. The interspersion of our surviving woodlands with agricultural land also complicates this issue, as with the fallow deer (*Dama dama*), originally an introduction to Britain centuries past, kept in parks, and now quite common in woodlands – for example in the Oxford region they live in Wytham Woods, Wychwood Forest and Bernwood Forest. But in such places it seems certain that they get much of their food from agricultural crops.

Among the thousands of invertebrates in Wytham Woods only a few are known to be invaders from abroad at any rate in fairly modern times. Although it is not simple to establish a negative proposition, I feel satisfied that the number of these invaders is small, indeed extraordinarily small. Three insects will be mentioned. Among the oak galls discussed in Ch. 11, the largest on oak foliage is the marble gall, *Andricus kollari*, which may occur in great abundance on the twigs of young oak trees, where the gall-wasp develops inside the leaf buds. It has an alternate generation, *A. kollari* forma *circulans*, that has been found only on the Turkey oak, *Quercus cerris*; but as this alien oak from south-east Europe does not grow everywhere in the range of the gall-wasp, it seems likely that its life-history does not always include this change of host trees. *Andricus kollari* is the only oak gall known to be a recent invader, its history having been summarized by Connold.[80] It was first observed in 1834 near Exeter in Devon, and by mid-century was already abundant in Somerset and Gloucestershire. About this time its spread round London was probably accelerated by a specialist who distributed samples to observers. Connold remarked in 1908: 'Now the gall may be found in almost every hedgerow, where there is oak, throughout the whole of Britain, in some districts in great abundance.' It has been suggested, because a foreign gall used to be imported for dyeing purposes, that *A. kollari* arrived in the same way; but there is no direct historical evidence about this. The galls are capable of distorting the twigs of young oaks (they do not come on mature ones), but to what extent they are seriously harmful in natural woodland is less certain. I have never seen heavy damage in real woodland edges of Wytham, and the species seems to have settled down among the many other species of oak gall, partly sharing their parasites. When these galls are hard and empty they actually add a new form of cover to the other complicated woodland structures (Ch. 11).

In the course of her investigations into the population ecology of the beetle *Cis bilamellatus* that commonly breeds in abundance in the dead brackets of the fungus *Polyporus betulinus* on birch trees (see Ch. 15), Paviour-Smith[453] undertook a survey of its spread and distribution in Britain. This beetle was first noticed in 1884 at West Wickham in Surrey, and in view of the excellence of beetle-collecting in Britain there is no doubt that it was a new arrival in this country not long before this date. It is an Australian species very probably brought here accidentally in dry bracket fungus specimens sent to museums, perhaps to Kew Herbarium. Its subsequent spread was from the London area and the first survey map published in 1960 gave a clear picture of the zones of spread which by then had reached the south and east coasts, south Wales and the Midlands and up into Cheshire and Yorkshire. Later information, not yet published, has extended this range somewhat. From 1906 onwards Walker published an extensive series of reports about beetles in the Oxford district (Ch. 3), but it was not until 1935 that he recorded *Cis bilamellatus*, in Wytham Woods.[532] This falls within a decade when the beetle was spreading rather rapidly northwards: thus it was recorded in 1936 at Watlington 13 miles south of Oxford, and from Cheshire in 1942. By the 1950s the beetles were very common in Wytham Woods. Although it has been found breeding in several other kinds of macrofungi on trees, there is no doubt that the birch-bracket is its primary headquarters. There is also no doubt that in this habitat it is dominant and successful; but since it eats only brackets that are already dead it is incapable of being an 'outbreak species' in the ordinary sense. Its relationship to other Ciid beetles inhabiting the same fungus remains to be worked out completely.

Because of the impact of some introduced placental mammals on the native communities of Australia it used to be said that the Australian fauna was, from its long isolation, highly vulnerable to invaders and conversely would not be success-ful elsewhere. But this proposition can no longer be held, at any rate for insects. A very dangerous orchard pest, the fluted scale-insect *Icerya purchasi*, has invaded orchards in other continents, and at the present time there are beetles from Australia invading British stored products and domestic habitats.[133] Another recent invader is the small beetle *Lathridius bifasciatus*, a very visibly distinct species belonging to a family that lives by eating moulds. This was first noticed in Britain in 1949 by Lewis[291] who has contributed further knowledge about its spread, at present confined to the south-eastern region of England. It was first found in Wytham Woods in 1960 [63] and is unlikely to have been overlooked much before that time. Like many of its allies, this beetle is not strictly confined to one habitat, since the moulds on which it depends occur widely. So far it has turned up in heaps of dead vegetable matter, in old haystacks, in fungi and the like. The Wytham records were from the edges of deciduous woodland. As far as I know, it has not been found anywhere in immense numbers, but it is certainly living in the wild, as well as in semi-natural, agricultural and domestic habitats.

Although the rabbit, grey squirrel, fallow deer, pheasant, little owl, and any parasites they brought with them, the oak-apple gall wasp and the two Australian beetles do not constitute the whole force of invading animals in Wytham Woods, they are the ones about which most is known, and I do not believe there are more than a few others to be detected outside artificial habitats. Some more may be expected in the future. Thus, taking the Wytham area as a whole, the muntjac or barking deer (*Muntiacus* sp.), spreading from Bedfordshire, cannot be far away; two amphipods, *Orchestia bottae* in the Thames, and *Eucrangonyx gracilis* in ponds, have established at Oxford; also the collared dove, *Streptopelia decaocto*, is not far away, though so far this bird has been confined to Domestic habitats. Only with the squirrels do we know for certain that a native species has been replaced by the invader. Only the first two species have seriously damaged any part of the wood-land system, and the population level of the rabbit has been brought down heavily by a further invader, the myxoma virus, which found the necessary flea vector (also an invader originally) already here. (On the other hand, the fungus disease of the English elm, caused by *Cerastomella ulmi*, which found native bark-beetle vectors, has not extinguished elm trees in Britain; at Wytham, where the disease is present, the trees growing in the woodlands and their edge have not greatly been damaged.) In Wytham Woods at any rate, the chief damage by grey squirrels is to another invader, the sycamore. The oak mildew, *Microsphaera alphitoides*, was first seen in Europe in 1907 and quickly spread in a year, also reaching Britain. It is thought to have been brought accidentally, from North America. It is not ordinarily severe, but can damage badly the secondary growth of shoots after caterpillar defoliation (Ch. 10).[252]

The introduction of exotic plants, and especially of trees, raises a different kind of question, for so many of them are unlikely to become invaders in the ordinary sense, or are maintained under artificial management of gardens, parks and forestry plantations. A few of them have, however, shown strong competitive powers, among them the sycamore, which reproduces abundantly in Wytham Woods, making groves of self-sown saplings and is sufficiently invasive to provoke repressive management. *Rhododendron ponticum* elsewhere (usually in more acid soils) has become a severe problem in the scrub layer of woodlands. The fauna on such alien species is always limited or absent, though it may sometimes be abundant in numbers; and many foreign trees and shrubs have no animals living on them at all, or perhaps one or two kinds only. I have drawn attention to the relative poverty in species attached only to the sycamore (Ch. 10), though its special aphid happens to flourish very much and support a large community of native British predators and parasites overlapping from other trees. I have also shown[133] that *Rhododendron ponticum*, which has been in Britain for at least 200 years, has gradually been acquiring an insect fauna comprised of one or two native species and several alien invaders, one of which is the cause and possibly the vector of a serious fungal disease. The common larch (*Larix decidua*), introduced about the beginning of the seventeenth century, also has a modest insect fauna of its own by now, as well as attracting native forms. Three of these have been noted in Wytham Woods: a longicorn, *Tetropium gabrieli*, and the huge sawfly, *Urocerus* (*Sirex*) *gigas*. The large parasite of the latter, *Rhyssa persuasoria*, is also there [64]. I have suggested that the invasive power of some alien trees and shrubs may partly be helped by the absence of any large animal community attached to them; but this is a speculation at present. However, the relative poverty in animal life of so many planted forest trees is important in any case, for it has the effect of making large areas of woodland, especially conifer woodland, relatively uninteresting so far as their animal communities are concerned. A few years ago I was asked by an organization that was printing a new Atlas of this country, whether it would be a good plan to combine on one map all the nature reserves, bird sanctuaries and so on, with the

Forestry Commission's State Forests. My reply was a suggestion that, on the contrary, the latter could well be combined with the map of urban areas, and the whole lot labelled 'biological deserts'!

Often the food-chains on alien plants are still very simple. In August 1949 I looked at the fauna on foliage of a 28-year-old plantation of Douglas fir, *Pseudotsuga taxifolia*, in Wytham Woods. The only abundant herbivore, possibly the only one really resident on the trees, was the aphid *Adelges cooleyi* originally imported with this tree from eastern North America. Every twig had on it the white woolly tufts that cover the egg-masses. With it were native ladybirds, *Aphidecta obliterata*, which have become the best-known enemy of this aphid both in Britain and Europe, though this species is also found on other conifers including Scots pine. *A. cooleyi* is either confined to the Douglas fir or locally may have an alternate phase on Sitka spruce, *Picea sitchensis*, another alien.[163] It seems that not only have native predators colonized trees like the sycamore and Douglas fir (which have suitable herbivore key animals), but some native herbivorous insects have also moved on to them. Styles[486] has recorded some of the polyphagous moths that have begun to live on planted foreign conifers. Thus, a Tortricid moth, *Syndemis musculana*, previously known from bramble, birch and oak in Britain, has become common on larches. These two processes, the slow following invasions of animals after their host plants, and the changing or extended habits of native species, foreshadow a gradual building-up of some semblance of richness in the communities living on invading species. But meanwhile increasing areas of Britain are becoming clothed with simplified vegetation inhabited by a simplified fauna, while the natural surviving ecosystems composed of what Church,[69] writing sardonically about garden introductions, once called 'the honest free-fighters of the wild' are retreating into relatively small island fortresses. The fascinating thing is that these fortresses do to a great extent repel the inroads of invaders or are able to absorb them into their capacious species network.

I have left to the last a consideration of the extraordinary phenomenon of the defoliation of native oak trees by native moths, described in Ch. 10. Any theory about the stability of natural communities must take account of this apparently large exception. I have for many years made notes of any instances in which natural or semi-natural vegetation is destroyed by its native herbivores, and it does seem that defoliation, or serious damage to the machinery of the plant, is either comparatively rare or occurs only on individual plants or small patches of plants. And I can recollect no instance of extinction of a species locally through such a happening. But in oak trees defoliation is common, serious and often spectacular. It is worth examining first of all what we mean by 'stability' in a community. It obviously does not mean constant populations, for these are seldom found; nor does it mean absence of large fluctuations in numbers of animals, for these also are not infrequent. It chiefly means two things: that most of the species under observation survive on the area over a number of years, that is, the species composition does not change much; and that herbivores do not increase to a level that destroys the biological machinery of plants or of other features of the habitat on which they depend. Most herbivores do not increase up to this danger level: how this limit is regulated we do not yet know. Defoliation does not seem to destroy oak trees very often: many can probably live for hundreds of years in face of it. This meets the first condition. That the biological machinery is not destroyed also follows, and furthermore the tree produces a large second crop of leaves to replace what has been lost. I think this gives the clue required, for most other forest trees that grow with the oak are unable to replace their first crop of leaves in the same season. Then there is the fact that the oak trees show individual differences, probably genetic, in defoliation (Ch. 10). If defoliation is indeed a disadvantage in the long run (it does slow down the rate of growth), the oak population may actually be in process of adaptation, but taking a long time because of the great longevity of the existing trees. Alternatively, defoliation of the first leaves may produce some corresponding advantage, about which any trained evolutionist could invent many theories (as that greater light intensity on the forest floor encourages the field layer below oak canopy, and therefore creates a better climate for decay of oak leaves). When an oak is defoliated the caterpillars responsible develop and leave the trees before this point is reached. The foliage produced in replacement is relatively sterile of animals. But, as in most woods there are other undefoliated trees that have kept their rich animal community there can be recolonization from them. Thus the system as a whole can without deception be termed 'stable'.

CHAPTER 19

The Whole Pattern

THE EXPLORATION of communities and ecosystems can be followed by many routes, all of them very difficult. The journey is slow, like taking a camel caravan over dry country. The white bones of some earlier expeditions lie on the sand, having failed to carry their loads of physiological concepts, graeco-roman technical terms or useless adaptive 'explanations' even to the first oasis on the way. Others, loaded differently, with great burdens of species lists, coefficients of association and trellis diagrams, algebraic 'habitat niches', or primitive food-cycle diagrams, have gone further, perhaps to the second or third oases. The outcome is still to be decided, and I believe it will serve little purpose to drag into the present statement of conclusions all these other methods of approach to the problem. Our own journey has been in two parts: in the first ten years workable methods of handling large amounts of information from field investigations without losing track of their validity or meaning were devised and set up in action. These are recounted in Ch. 1-5, where the patterns of interspersion are analysed into their components and the criteria for arranging them discussed. In the second ten years, the methods have been consistently applied to the elucidation of a terrestrial ecosystem with its concomitant small water bodies (Ch. 6-18). From the second oasis camp it is now possible to look back and try to assess what discoveries have been made during the journey.

Underlying this kind of survey is the belief that ecologists have to some extent been dazzled by the technical and mathematical triumphs of physics and chemistry, and have embarked on various quantitative investigations without fully taking into account the whole context in which their populations live in nature. But there is also something else behind the approach described in this book. It is that the large number of species of plants and animals and micro-organisms, and a good many real problems in taxonomy, have made animal ecologists hesitant to investigate whole ecosystems – plant, animal and environment. I believe that at every level in science this sort of view is natural, and that one has to make a considerable effort to break through from one level of study to another above it, and while doing so to forge through the apparent complexities to a higher level of integration

374

and arrive at simple ideas applicable to that higher level but invisible from the jungle below. At each stage the synoptic view will appear superficial and incomplete to the person working at a less synoptic level. The only way, however, to decide whether or not a particular method of ecological survey is rewarding in this way is to show whether it has produced some new concepts of the structure of natural systems, which is what this chapter essays to do. The conclusions can best be traced through a series of propositions, some of which are perhaps self-evident once pointed out, others rest on the evidence given in the main body of the text, and still others are reasonable speculations; while all can be tied together in a logical whole.

1. The pyramid of numbers, really a pyramid of consumer layers, is matched by what I have called (Ch. 9) the inverse pyramid of habitats. A great many herbivorous animal species are confined to one species or one genus or at any rate very few species of plants, and their populations (except when purely in transit from one locus to another) therefore closely reflect the primary pattern of interspersed plant species in the vegetation. But even at this stage there are also polyphagous herbivores that have a wide range of host plants. At the level of the secondary consumers, the predators usually have much wider habitat range than each of their food species, and this applies also to a good many parasites, though the latter may often be confined to one host species, and therefore still reflect its distribution – whether this in turn is limited to one or to more species of plants. And here again different life functions help to spread the habitat range, as with *Anthocoris nemorum* mentioned in Ch. 11, which has not only wide choices of food, but requirements also for hibernation and egg-laying sites. At a still higher level, as with shrews or insectivorous birds like tits, the habitats visited are numerous and visits are frequently geared to seasonal production of resources. Above this again may be even wider ranging predators like hawks and owls.

2. The effect of the inverse pyramid of habitats is that the original pattern of herbivores keyed on to the interspersion of plant species becomes progressively blurred, though not lost, with progression up the food-chains. The second process that reinforces this is the decay of living matter, plant and animal. Decay, through the action of bacteria or fungi upon dying and dead organic matter, evidently tends to break down the structural and chemical characteristics that we know or assume to be the limiting conditions for herbivorous species, and to produce in due course a series of media and food resources that are more similar, so far as the animals eating and living in them are concerned, than the living plant tissues. This conclusion rests more on the empirical evidence from ecological survey than upon an objective proof that the main forms of decaying matter, such as leaves, wood, carrion and dung, each consist of chemically similar entities. They certainly are not uniform; yet the animals that exploit them show far less limitation to the

species from which the decaying matter is derived than would the original herbivores. I will refer to such animals as 'saprophagous', using this term as a portmanteau one to include a variety of feeding habits that have in common the fact that live green plant products are *not* eaten. That most saprophagous animals are usually relatively indiscriminate in their choice of food has been thoroughly proven for soil, litter, dead wood, macrofungi, carrion, dung, nest and woodland aquatic litter species. It follows therefore that the inverse pyramid of habitats is not a conspicuous feature of food-chains based upon dying and dead matter. Both saprophagous and predatory animals may range widely (Ch. 16).

3. Since most dead material falls eventually to the ground where it is either used up or becomes (after some processing by animals and micro-organisms) incorporated into the soil, the lower strata of terrestrial formation-types have more resemblance in their animal communities than the green 'canopy' of whatever level.

4. When vegetation dies and the parts of plants fall to the ground, these retain their recognizable specific structure for a long time after they have begun to converge into the greater similarities of decaying matter. Thus bracken litter looks superficially quite different from oak–ash litter, and logs of different species can be identified for some years after they fall, nevertheless any such identifications rather cloak the profound common denominators introduced by the fact of death in the tissues and the invasion of decay organisms. The original specificity is however often partly retained in the macrofungus fruiting bodies that develop on dying and dead wood – not usually completely, but in the sense that most of these fungi show strong host preferences or groups of preferences. To this extent the loss of identity implicit in death and decay is checked or even apparently reversed, and it may be relevant that many of the most imposing bracket fungi have in fact begun life while the tree or shrub was alive, and are unable to establish after their death. The patterns of habitat and community distribution that develop were explained in Ch. 15.

5. Dead plant matter tends to fall below its parent plant, and to that extent repeat on the ground the canopy pattern above. The lighter materials, however, have a considerable amount of mechanical drift laterally through wind currents, especially leaves and those tree fruits adapted to the purpose. The heavier ones, such as acorns and branches and trunks, fall straight down, and the latter retain the original pattern for many years, though decay causes them to bring about resemblances between, say logs, of different tree species. These fallen units are always smaller than the original canopy unit.

6. In so far as animals have strong lateral movements, these further emphasize the loss of the original patterning of populations perceptible in the green-plant herbivores. Thus the three processes – polyphagy with wider habitat range, decay of living matter, and lateral movements, all combine towards the same result, that

75. Aerial view of Marley Wood, Wytham Hill, with two large woodland spring marshes, lower left (Coding: A-T/O (W)). (Photo Hunting Surveys. 30 April 1960)

76. Woodland spring marsh in Wytham Woods, with young great horsetail (*Equisetum telmateia*), hemp agrimony (*Eupatorium cannabinum*), and *Valerianella dioica* (in flower). The litter fauna is extremely rich. (Photo V. Todd[507] *c.* 1948)

77. Pollard willow, *Salix fragilis*, transition zone on the bank of the R. Thames at Wolvercote, Oxfordshire. (Photo C. S. E. 9 March 1958)

78. A slow stream at Ferry Hinksey, Oxford, August 1921 (Coding: A/B 2); with emergent arrow-head, *Sagittaria*, and transition zone with pollard willows. (From A. H. Church, 1922)

79. Tidal salt-marsh zones on Scolt Head Island, Norfolk (Coding: A-T, Saline, Shingle). *Suaeda fruticosa* at H. W. M. (r.), and sand-dunes beyond. (Photo C. S. E. 20 June 1957)

80. Intertidal sands and cliff grassland at Marloes Bay, Pembrokeshire; with rocks projecting through the sand (see Photos 83 and 84). (Photo C. S. E. 23 July 1947)

81. Vertical aerial view of the N.E. bend in the R. Thames by Wytham Hill, with flood meadows, pollard willows by ditches, etc., and old meanders between river and Seacourt Stream on r. (Photo Hunting Surveys. 30 April 1960)

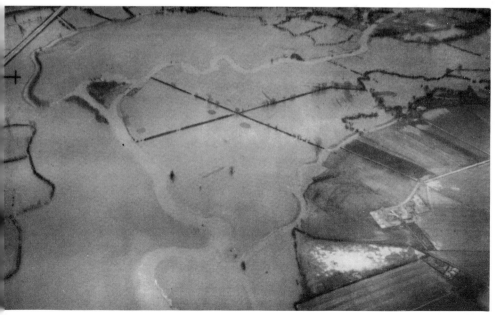

82. Oblique aerial view of the R. Thames bend shown in Photo 81, with spring floods. (Photo Aerofilms. 18 March 1947)

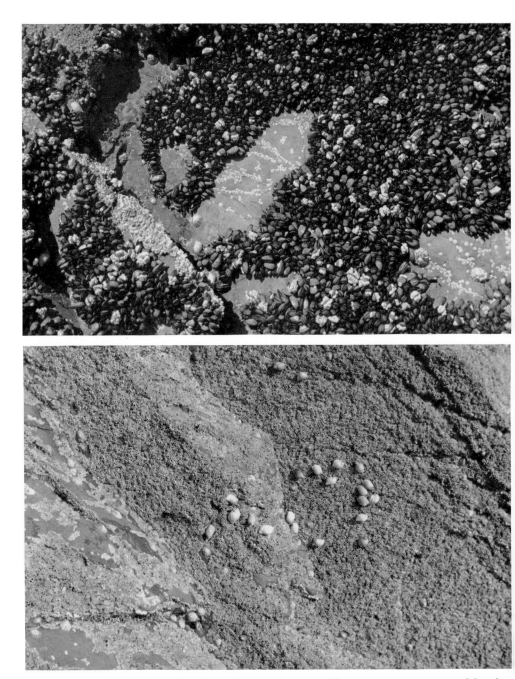

83 & 84. Barnacle (*Balanus balanoides*) and mussel (*Mytilus edulis*) communities on intertidal rock at Marloes Bay (Photo 80), with the barnacle's chief enemy *Nucella lapellus* (among killed barnacles on lower photo). (Photos C. S. E. 29 Aug. 1956 & 27 Aug. 1961)

85. The sacred Lake of Bogdo-ola, at 6000 ft in mountains at the west end of Outer Mongolia: an ancient conservation area. (From D. Carruthers, 1914)

86. Water and swamp vegetation returning in a gravel pit near Standlake, Oxfordshire, while machinery still excavates close by. The modern conservation problem is how to combine exploitation of land with survival of wild life. (Photo C. S. E. 6 July 1958)

87. Seral communities by a lane in Berkshire, with field-type of grass and flowers such as *Anthriscus sylvestris*, hawthorn and hazel hedge, and English elms. The preservation of plant and animal communities like these can enhance the richness and interest of an exploited countryside.
(Photo C. S. E. 22 May 1960)

is the gradual dissolving of the primary community pattern towards one that is more randomized.

7. Some other activities of animals also have similar influence: for example honeydew is a common food substance produced by a variety of different sucking insects living on different trees. Flowers, considered as fuel stations, are to a considerable extent interchangeable since all produce much the same kind of nectar, or in the case of pollen something fundamentally similar. Again, a great many insects have at least two habitats that are necessary for their whole life-history, the larval longicorn beetle in a log having an adult seeking scrub flowers, or the aquatic fly that emerges and has a mating dance in some transition habitat, or seeks a blood meal from a terrestrial mammal or bird.

8. All this leads to another aspect of the situation: no habitat component with its animal community is a closed system. Though for many practical working purposes the structural boundaries are highly useful and informative, they are constantly passed by population movement, either to similar components elsewhere, or to different components with equally suitable resources, or to different components for some other biological function – perhaps a life-history requirement. An ecological survey enables these phenomena to be docketed and studied in a rational way.

9. By saying that the community is not a closed system, one is really making somewhat the same verdict as a physicist who describes the 'field system' of a particle or a magnetic source, with lines of influence spreading from an active centre (Ch. 9). One is saying that every community unit is partly interlocked with others, not necessarily its nearest neighbours, though often so. At present we can describe this interlocking or what I have called 'girder system' (Ch. 10), and show that it is a universal and widespread property of ecosystems. But it is still too early to be able to prove directly that the biotic linkages have this or that effect upon the level of populations or other dynamic controls. We can, again, only approach the matter empirically, as I have done in the previous chapter. These conclusions can be recapitulated as follows.

10. There are a number of lines of evidence suggesting that simple communities, that is communities with few species, can exist in a stable state, albeit with such fluctuations as occur in all natural systems (Ch. 18). But it appears that they are much more vulnerable to invasion by species from other countries than are the more complex communities such as live in Wytham Woods. If this proposition is true the fact of complexity would seem to carry with it some stabilizing property. It is reasonable to suggest, though it cannot be yet proved, that the interlocking of biotic connections right through a terrestrial ecosystem is one of the chief reasons for this property. In turn, if this is really the case, the girder system must have some effect either in controlling numbers or at any rate in damping down

fluctuations or slowing down deviations from the norm. Whether this be a true explanation or not, it at any rate shows that ecological survey is relevant to the further investigation of such stability.

11. So far this chain of argument has been concerned with how the pattern of distribution in the habitats and communities changes from the distinct one of the plant canopy or carpet to a relatively more random one, or at any rate to one that is less easily traceable to the arrangement of the original plant interspersion and its resulting food-chains. But meanwhile a whole series of secondary patterns have been forming, this time through the activities of the animals themselves, which may in turn create new secondary patterns in the vegetation. Thus when a powerful polyphagous herbivore like the cow, feeding fairly randomly on a newly occupied pasture (it certainly has been proved to cover the whole ground very thoroughly) deposits its large parcels of dung, a new pattern is set up that has two main effects on the pasture system: the numerous scattered cow-pats attract a rich special community of animals, and they also alter the pattern of grass subsequently growing on the patches so that cattle tend to avoid feeding on them. The distribution of cow-pats bears no relation at all to the plan of the original plant carpet from which the cattle food has been taken. There are many other less conspicuous examples of the same process, where dung or carrion are produced (Ch. 16). Similarly, the territorial organization of yellow ants in pasture sets up entirely new 'fields of force' which also not only alter the local vegetation mixture, but can change the distribution of dung from the concentration of rabbits on the hillocks for purposes of defaecation. Mole-hills also affect the plant carpet. There are a great many vertebrate activities, such as nesting or foraging or territorial behaviour, that set up repeated centres of action or other types of new patterning.

12. A further influence of animals is that they are by their active movements able to a considerable extent to reverse the transfer of organic matter that fell to the ground by the force of gravity, in their diel or seasonal migrations up the trunks of trees, or by other free movements (Ch. 12).

13. We already know that the ecological machinery of any community, of any habitat component, or of any one similar unit of which it is composed, is kept going by the movements of animals that result in contacts between consumer and consumed, as well as in very many influences upon the habitat that are equally important though they may not involve a direct act of feeding. Some of these movements are frequent, others only important at certain stages of life. The patchy pattern of interspersion that so many habitat components have, as well as the short-lived nature of some of them, necessitate many journeys in transit across other habitats, or between different habitats required for the whole life needs. In a great many of these communities, at any rate in the height of their season, population densities of these mixtures of species can be very high, that is contacts are often at an in-

tense level. To the ordinary movements within and between habitats (with among the higher consumers very wide habitat ranges), are to be added those pressures from outside the whole local ecosystem that I have described in Ch. 18, these being roughly divisible into reinforcements of native species of animals brought by air drift or flood or by active migration, and to some extent by man (Ch. 3); and invaders brought in from abroad.

14. These continual movements, contacts and ecological events of all kinds may have, if natural selection at the present day has any meaning in adjusted communities, a considerable effect upon the total efficiency of any community or mixed ecosystem. That is to say, one may reasonably postulate that the interlocking girder connections that I have been concerned with in this book, will tend to keep individual species and those immediately involved with them, and therefore consequently the whole system, up to the mark and able to resist invaders and are likely to damp most fluctuations within it. This is a theoretical suggestion that puts special weight upon interspersion and movements, and seeks to explain the converging evidence that such systems show ecological resistance, and are therefore in good shape both ecologically and genetically.

15. Finally there is the curious subject of monopoly, already alluded to in Ch. 16. It is usually found that communities have some species dominant in numbers (or other index of importance), and much has been written about this aspect of diversity. But sometimes a species of plant or animal gets so powerful (or highly specialized to some habitat difficult to live in physically) that it is the main or only one occupying at any rate the key consumer layer of that community. Examples among plants are *Brachypodium pinnatum* (Ch. 6), sometimes *Calluna* heath (Ch. 7), marram dune (Ch. 8) and rabbit-rejected elder scrub (Ch. 9). Among animals it has been noticed in *Glomeris* (Ch. 6), among ants and locally among burying-beetles and dung-beetles (Ch. 16). There are three aspects of such monopoly or almost complete dominance to be noticed here. First, some plants in this category have very few species of herbivorous animals eating them. *Brachypodium pinnatum* is an example. They may, however, harbour visiting species (as with hibernators in tussocks) or have a rich community living on the products of their decay. Introduced plants, such as garden forms, often have no herbivores at all and therefore no food-chains exploiting them (Ch. 18). When these form pure stands, as often happens in conifer forestry, there is plant monopoly and a poor animal community. Secondly, there are no instances known to me in which one species of animal completely monopolizes all the resources on an area, and even burying-beetles and dung-beetles that tend to do this only succeed in getting some of the dead mice or cow-dung that is being produced, though they take the whole parcel of what they do use. And even among monopolist ants there are commensals in their nests that can hi-jack some of the resources brought back. And all such monopolists in one

379

key consumer layer are subject to further attack by predators and parasites along the food-chains. The third point is that the tendency towards monopoly, shown in the widespread occurrence of relative dominance in communities, seldom goes the whole way – from which fact we can draw two further conclusions: that there are strong ecological and evolutionary forces against monopoly in nature, and that (as distinct from pure cultures in man's crops and forests) it is not common enough to alter the general picture in natural communities of complexity and full development of species networks.

★   ★   ★

It is now clear that we need to use several different tools for studying food-chains in their actual three-dimensional paths in nature. So far, most diagrams of food-relations have been of an essentially abstract nature, themes without coordinates. In undertaking further analysis along these lines, it is useful to separate the four following features of the food-habits of animals. The first is whether they eat more than one species, that is are polyphagous, leaving open whether all *individuals* of the population are actually polyphagous in the place where they live. The second is whether the food is taken from more than one consumer layer, for this happens a good deal more frequently even among herbivores than is realized. The third is whether they take food from more than one habitat component (however defined laterally and vertically). The fourth is whether they eat live or fresh food, that is are herbivores, predators or parasites; or else eat dead or decaying plants or animals, with or without the concomitant microflora associated with decay, in other words are in the broad sense saprophagous. The identification of all these four contexts for a species and for its associates, would give us a really good working chart of communities and the habitats they use. The ecological survey described and drawn upon in this book has attempted to open up such a field without claiming to give any complete picture yet. Without such a spatially and functionally defined plan of communities any study of 'productivity' in terrestrial communities is bound to be shaky, to say the least. In this connection it should be underlined also that the term 'energy flow' often used to connote the transfer of energy along the food-chains is a rather unfortunate one, in so far as such a large amount of feeding, and nearly all feeding by predators, is of a highly staccato nature. Finally, an ecological survey of this kind can put in the many interrelationships that are not described by the food-chains alone, among them many necessary features (usually structural ones) for resting, seasonal diapause, pupation, mating, nesting, nesting materials, drinking and so on.

Two more topics will be mentioned before closing this book: the regulation of numbers in populations and conservation ecology. The whole field of population control in nature and theories about how it works has got into a rather peculiar state where a number of strongly held views exist that are at first sight incompatible with one another. Thus regulation of numbers has been attributed to the quantity of food, the quality of food, space, enemies, parasites, interspecific competition, self-regulation by competition (real or ritual), climatic disaster and the like. What is needed now in animal ecology is a sort of Ecumenical movement, or more precisely the development of a general comparative ecology of population limitation. For if one fact is certain it is that somewhere at some time in some species every one of these processes will be found acting as the chief or even the only limit to numbers. Similarly, somewhere at some time in some species, almost every conceivable combination of these factors will be operating in complex interaction. And a particular species may not be limited in the same fashion at different times and places. And there will no doubt be further subtle processes, at present unknown or only suspected, to add to the rest. It is extremely important that one should be able justifiably to hold such an ecumenical view, because if complexity in ecosystems results in more complicated inter-regulatory processes between species, the chain of arguments given in this chapter is a reasonable one. But if, for example, each species, though having food-chain and other relationships, had its numbers solely controlled by its own self-regulatory adaptations and behaviour, the picture would look quite different.

There is, however, no doubt at all that interspecific relations do result in control of or changes in numbers; and often in changes of population structure (which are in themselves part of the community scenery) without actually controlling upper limits of density. As the best example that exists of an open-minded field investigation of this situation, I have included two photographs (Plates 83 and 84) of the *Balanus balanoides* community of the intertidal seashore in west Wales. This same community was analysed quantitatively on the Island of Cumbrae in Scotland by Connell[79] over nearly three years. Space limited the colonization of rock surfaces. Protection from waves affected the actual density. Overcrowding of barnacles produced growth-forms that made them vulnerable to storms. The presence of limpets (*Patella*) controlled the growth of algae, itself adverse to survival of limpets. Exclusion cages proved that their chief enemy, the gastropod *Thais* (*Nucella* or *Purpura*) *lapillus* selected the larger barnacles and altered the age structure of these populations, so that the age structure varied with level on the shore, because the predators were absent at higher levels. He concluded: 'The barnacle zonation on the intertidal shore seems to be bounded at the top by deleterious physical factors (weather), at the bottom by biological ones (competition for space and predation).' There are also other aspects that include competition between different species of barnacles at certain levels. It is, of course, not be to concluded from Connell's work that all populations have so many processes affecting their numbers, and we know of some species that seem to have rather few critical controlling factors. But it is certain from Brian's study (Ch. 7) of ant populations on the maritime heathland near Poole Harbour in Dorset, that interspecific relationships can be quite decisive in determining distribution and numbers, and therefore that a theory about the effects of communities upon population balance could be quite valid.

In 1953 Aldo Leopold,[289] the great natural philosopher of conservation in North America, wrote that 'one of the penalties of an ecological education is that one lives alone in a world of wounds. Much of the damage inflicted on land is quite invisible to laymen.' As a matter of fact much of it has been largely invisible to ecologists also, at any rate in this country. The Nature Conservancy is doing much to change this, but it might still be true to ask, as Leopold did: 'Have we learned this first principle of conservation: to preserve all the parts of the land mechanism? No, because even the scientist does not yet recognize all of them.' I do not take the extreme kind of view about nature expressed by the poet Pope in his *Essay on Man* (1733), when he said:

> From Nature's chain whatever link you strike
> Tenth, or tenth thousandth, breaks the chain alike.

Communities contain too many methods of compensation and the substitution of one species for another for it to be possible to claim that all species are functionally important in a community, though they certainly are from other (including ethical) points of view. In the ethical field, we might perhaps apply here a remark in *The Pilgrim's Progress*: 'For, said they, all things must be managed here for the supporting of the weak, as well as to the warning of the unruly.' The case for general conservation is threefold and has been discussed by me in an earlier book.[133] It is moral, as just indicated – no power without responsibility. It is also based on interest, whether personal, educational, or purely scientific – the deep study of the world as it was when man found it, or those parts still keeping some of the character and potentialities of that earlier untamed richness. Paul Errington[139] in an essay on 'The pricelessness of untampered Nature' published in the *Journal of Wildlife Management* in 1963 asked the sinister question: 'Where can people who live in this region expect to find anything with the sanction of a thousand years behind it?' Thirdly it is an economic question, a question of human survival, or at the very least man's survival in environments that are worth surviving in. The picture does not need to be etched in detail here, for by now everyone knows that natural habitat and communities are fast being removed, and that the quality of the environment is being hazarded by such things as toxic chemicals and radioactive fall-out, besides being radically simplified in order to grow crops and new forests. On top of this there is a steady bombardment of alien species from other lands and waters, with consequent explosions after the arrival of some of them.

Near the end of his sardonic and terrifying allegory 'War with the newts' Karel Čapek communes with himself. His *alter ego* suggests that perhaps some disease may arise and happen to wipe out the newts that are threatening mankind. The author replies: 'Must Nature always be asked to straighten out the mess that man has made?' This was before myxomatosis was let loose in Europe!

The notion of conservation used to be entirely protective and local. The lake basin of Bogdo-ola in central Asia shown in Plate 85 must have been one of the earliest sanctuaries of this kind. Carruthers[63] remarks that an earlier explorer found a notice put up near the lake, saying: 'It is forbidden, under penalty of instant death, to violate the tranquillity of this holy land. There must not only be no shooting and no tree-cutting, but the cattle may not even be pastured here, that they may not trample underfoot the herbage belonging to God's creatures.' In contrast with this rather dream-like stage of conservation by Buddhist priests, is the modern problem illustrated by the gravel-pit and its ecological recovery shown in Plate 86 [65]. Modern conservation certainly has its quota of Bogdo-olas where life is entirely safe, but its chief problem remains that of fashioning over the whole extent of occupied and exploited land a mosaic of landscape and many small habitats in it that is as rich as possible consistently with keeping the necessary productivity of land and its use by man for so many different purposes. There are two dangers that are now being more widely discussed than formerly. The first is that in giving priority to economic productivity, especially in regard to the production of large cash crops from the land, the human environment itself may gradually become dull, unvaried, charmless, and treated like a factory rather than a place to live in. The second is that oversimplified communities contain within themselves flaws of organization that render them vulnerable to invaders of unfamiliar kinds, especially those that have evolved in other continental areas. Just how we are to maintain ecological arrangements that will help to solve this dilemma is not yet certainly known, but there are two things that should be done. One is to maintain the maximum variety of natural and semi-natural habitats and their communities in the landscape, as possible buffers against invasions and unbalance. This means preserving *in as rich a form as possible* all the communities that may be interspersed among croplands, especially woods, scrub, roadside and field hedgerows and meadows (Ch. 9 and Plate 87), as well as various habitats transitional to water; also as reservoirs of species (and quite apart from their intrinsic interest) the rich maritime terrestrial communities (Ch. 8). Among all these again is the intricate network of small water bodies (Ch. 17). The second thing we can do is to discover how life is organized and the balance maintained in natural deciduous woodland with its associated 'furniture' of dying and dead organic resources and their communities, as well as in the seral stages leading up to the full forest. For it is in woodland (in this country deciduous woodland) that the highest diversity of habitat has been evolved on land and relationships and population pressures exist in their most elaborate form. But the study of this system, as exemplified in Wytham Woods, requires continuity over many years and a flexible approach that allows much individual research on different parts of the system, combined with a permanent survey that can gradually improve the 'ecological map' – a three-dimensional and somewhat changeable map of the sharing of matter and energy between species, and their movements through consumer layers and habitat components, from the living and the dead resources, by day and night and by season. By learning to understand more about this system, and how the ecological forces within it are controlled, we shall be better prepared to face conservation problems generally, and perhaps may begin to understand just what so often goes wrong in the artificially simplified croplands and planted forests that, after all, form the major part of our surroundings, at any rate in the lowlands where most people live.

The Ecological Survey at Wytham has tried to make a blue-print or plan of the organization of communities on Wytham Hill – perhaps it has done more than that, and already laid some sort of foundations too. The methods have served well and have brought some new principles into focus. Much more remains to be harvested and this is a task for the years ahead.

References

Reference numbers in the text are in superior figures

1. AKOPYAN, M. M. 1953. ['The fate of corpses of ground squirrels [susliks] on the steppe'], *Zool. Zh.* 32: 1014-19.
2. ALEXANDER, W. B. 1933. 'The rook population of the Upper Thames region', *J. Anim. Ecol.* 2: 24-35.
3. ALLAN, P. B. M. 1949. *Larval foodplants: a vade-mecum for the lepidopterist*, London.
4. ALLEN, A. A. 1960 'A few notable and unexpected beetles on Blackheath (S.E.)', *Ent. Mon. Mag.* 96: 272.
5. ANASIEWICZ, A. 1962. ['Observations of *Cantharis* L. occurring on winter rape'], *Ekol. Polsk.* Ser. A, 10: 295-305.
6. ANDERSEN, J. 1954. 'The food of the Danish badger (*Meles meles danicus* Degerbøl)', *Danish Rev. Game Biol.* 3 (1): 1-75.
7. ANDERSON, N. H. 1962. 'Studies on overwintering of *Anthocoris* (Hem., Anthocoridae)', *Ent. Mon. Mag.* 98: 1-3.
8. ARDÖ, P. 1957. 'Studies in the marine shore dune ecosystem with special reference to the Dipterous fauna', *Opusc. Ent.*, Suppl. 14: 1-255.
9. ARKELL, W. J. 1928. 'Aspects of the ecology of certain fossil coral reefs', *J. Ecol.* 16: 134-49.
10. ARKELL, W. J. C. 1945. 'The geology of Wytham Hills', unpublished MS of Survey done in 1943, Geology Dept, Oxford University. Reproduced also in OSMASTON, F. C., 1959, Appendix X.
11. ARKELL, W. J. 1947. *The geology of Oxford*, Oxford.
12. ASKEW, R. R. 1960. 'The biology of some gall wasps (Hymenoptera, Cynipidae) on oak', D. Phil. Thesis, Oxford University.
13. ASKEW, R. R. 1961. 'On the biology of the inhabitants of oak galls of Cynipidae (Hymenoptera) in Britain', *Trans. Soc. Brit. Ent.* 14: 237-68.
14. AUBROOK, E. W. 1939. 'Insects bred from owl-pellets', *Ent. Mon. Mag.* 75: 88.
15. AUDY, J. R. 1956. 'Trombiculid mites infesting birds, reptiles, and arthropods in Malaya, with a taxonomic revision . . .', *Bull. Raffles Mus.* 28: 27-80.
16. BALOGH, J. & LOKSA, I. 1956. 'Untersuchungen über die zoozönose des luzernenfeldes: strukturzönologische Abhandlung', *Acta Zool. Hung.* 2: 17-114.
17. BANKS, C. J. 1954. 'Random and non-random distributions of Coccinellidae', *J. Soc. Brit. Ent.* 4: 211-15.
18. BANKS, C. J. 1955. 'An ecological study of Coccinellidae (Col.) associated with *Aphis fabae* Scop. on *Vicia faba*', *Bull. Ent. Res.* 46: 561-87.

19. BARKMAN, J. J. 1958. *Phytosociology and ecology of cryptogamic epiphytes*, Assen, Netherlands.

20. BARNES, H. F. 1951. *Gall midges of economic importance. Vol. V. Gall midges of trees*, London.

21. BASSEY, E. A. 1950. *Morphology and taxonomy of Fungi*, Philadelphia & Toronto.

22. BENSON, R. B. 1952. 'Hymenoptera. 2. Symphyta. Section (b)', *Handb. Ident. Brit. Insects*, 6 [Pt 2(b)]: 51-137.

23. BETTS, M. M. 1955. 'The food of titmice in oak woodland', *J. Anim. Ecol.* 24: 282-323.

24. BEVEN, G. 1964. 'The feeding sites of birds in grassland with thick scrub. Some comparisons with dense oakwood', *Lond. Nat.*: 86-109.

25. BILHAM, E. G. 1938. *The climate of the British Isles . . .*, London.

26. BINGLEY, F. J. 1959. 'Nature in miniature', No. 7 in 'The world of Nature: a series of seven broadcasts describing the processes at work in a variety of natural habitats', B.B.C., London. pp. 27-9.

27. BLAIR, H. G. 1946. 'On the economy of the oak marble gall (*Cynips kollari*, Hartig)', *Proc. S. Lond. Ent. Nat. Hist. Soc.* 1945-6: 79-83.

28. BLAIR, K. G. 1949. 'Coleoptera and Diptera from an old nest of the green wood-pecker', *Ent. Mon. Mag.* 85: 48.

29. BLAIR, K. G. 1951. 'The habitat of *Staphylinus ater* Grav. (Col., Staphylinidae.)', *Ent. Mon. Mag.* 87: 287.

30. BLAIR, K. G. 1951. 'Some parasites of *Hylesinus fraxini* Panz. and *H. oleiperda* F. (Col., Scolytidae)', *Ent. Mon. Mag.* 87: 89.

31. BLANQUET, J. BRAUN-, FULLER, G. D. & CONARD, H. S. 1932. *Plant sociology: the study of plant communities*, New York, etc. P. 32.

32. BLEGVAD, H. 1926. 'Continued studies on the quantity of fish food in the sea bottom', *Rep. Danish Biol. Sta.* 31: 27-56.

33. [BOCOCK, K. L.] 1962. 'Changes in the amount of nitrogen in decomposing leaf litter', *Rep. Nature Conservancy* for year ended 30 Sept. 1962.

34. BODENHEIMER, F. S. 1938. *Problems of animal ecology*, Oxford.

35. BORNEBUSCH, C. H. 1930. *The fauna of forest soil . . .*, Copenhagen.

36. BORNEMISSZA, G. F. 1957. 'An analysis of arthropod succession in carrion and the effect of its decomposition on the soil fauna', *Aust. J. Zool.* 5: 1-12.

37. BOYD, J. M. 1957. 'Comparative aspects of the ecology of Lumbricadae on grazed and ungrazed natural maritime grassland', *Oikos*, 8: 107-21.

38. BOYD, J. M. 1960. 'Studies of the differences between the fauna of grazed and ungrazed grassland in Tiree, Argyll', *Proc. Zool. Soc. Lond.* 135: 33-54.

39. BRERETON, J. LE G. 1957. 'The distribution of woodland isopods', *Oikos*, 8: 85-106.

40. BRIAN, M. V. 1952. 'The structure of a dense natural ant population', *J. Anim. Ecol.* 21: 12-24.

41. BRIGGS, A. R. MEAD- 1964. 'A correlation between development of the ovaries and of the midgut epithelium in the rabbit flea, *Spilopsyllus cuniculi*', *Nature, Lond.* 201: 1303-5.

42. BRIGGS, A. R. MEAD- & RUDGE, A. J. B. 1960. 'Breeding of the rabbit flea,

Spilopsyllus cuniculi (Dale): requirement of a "factor" from a pregnant rabbit for ovarian maturation', *Nature, Lond.* 187: 1136-7.

43. BRINCK, P. 1949. 'Studies on Swedish stoneflies (Plecoptera)', *Opusc. Ent.*, Suppl. 11: 1-250.

44. BRINDLE, A. 1953. 'Diptera of the Pendle Hill area. II. Tipulidae, Trichoceridae, Anisopodidae and Ptychopteridae', *Northw. Nat.* N.S., 1: 55-65.

45. BRINDLE, A. 1962. 'Taxonomic notes on the larvae of British Diptera. 11. Trichoceridae and Anisopodidae', *Entomologist*, 95: 285-8.

46. BRISTOWE, W. S. 1939. *The comity of spiders*, London. Vol. 1.

47. BROADHEAD, E. 1958. 'The Psocid fauna of larch trees in northern England – an ecological study of mixed species populations exploiting a common resource', *J. Anim. Ecol.* 27: 217-63.

48. BROADHEAD, E. & DATTA, B. 1960. 'The taxonomy and ecology of British species of *Peripsocus* Hagen (Corrodentia, Pseudocaeciliidae)', *Trans. Soc. Brit. Ent.* 14: 131-46.

49. BROWN, L. E. 1956. 'Field experiments on the activity of the small mammals, *Apodemus, Clethrionomys* and *Microtus*', *Proc. Zool. Soc. Lond.* 126: 549-64.

50. BROWN, J. M. B. 1953. 'Studies on British beechwoods', *Bull. For. Comm., Lond.* 20: 1-100.

51. BUKHOVSKII, V. 1936. ['The population of invertebrates of the Crimean beech forest'], *Trans. State Reserves*, Ser. 2, 1: 5-103. (In Russian, summary in German. Translation by J. D. Jackson in Bureau of Animal Population, Oxford.)

52. BURGER, H. 1940. 'Holz, Blattmenge und Zuwachs. 4. Ein 80 jähriger Buchenbestand', *Mitt. Schweiz. ZentAnst. Forstl. Versuchsw.* 21: 307-48.

53. BURGER, H. 1947. 'Holz, Blattmenge und Zuwachs. 8. Die Eiche', *Mitt. Schweiz. ZentAnst. Forstl. Versuchsw.* 25: 211-79.

54. BURGER, H. 1950. 'Holz, Blattmenge und Zuwachs. 10. Die Buche', *Mitt. Schweiz. ZentAnst. Forstl. Versuchsw.* 26: 419-68.

55. BUTLER, E. A. 1923. *A biology of the British Hemiptera-Heteroptera*, London.

56. BUTLER, P. M. 1951. 'Notes on the general zoology of Spurn', *Naturalist*: 83-5.

57. BUTLER, P. M. & HINCKS, W. D. 1954. 'The entomology of Spurn Peninsula. Conclusions', *Naturalist* : 107-9.

58. BUXTON, P. A. 1935. 'Changes in the composition of adult *Culex pipiens* during hibernation', *Parasitology*, 27: 263-5.

59. BUXTON, P. A. 1954. 'British Diptera associated with fungi. 2. Diptera bred from Myxomycetes', *Proc. R. Ent. Soc. Lond.* Ser. A, 29: 163-71.

60. BUXTON, P. A. 1960. 'British Diptera associated with fungi. III. Flies of all families reared from about 150 species of fungi', *Ent. Mon. Mag.* 96: 61-94.

61. CABORN, J. M. 1957. 'Shelterbelts and microclimate', *Bull. For. Comm., Lond.* 29: 1-135.

62. CAMPBELL, B. 1953. *Finding nests*, London.

63. CARRUTHERS, D. 1914. *Unknown Mongolia: a record of travel and exploration in north-west Mongolia and Dzungaria*, London. Vol. 1.

64. CARTWRIGHT, K. ST.G. & FINDLAY, W. P. K. 1958. *Decay of timber and its prevention*, 2nd ed. London.

65. CHAMBERS, V. H. 1946. 'An examination of the pollen loads of *Andrena*: the species that visit fruit trees', *J. Anim. Ecol.* 15: 9-21.

66. CHITTY, D. 1937. 'A ringing technique for small mammals', *J. Anim. Ecol.* 6: 36-53.

67. CHITTY, D. 1938. 'A laboratory study of pellet formation in the short-eared owl (*Asio flammeus*)', *Proc. Zool. Soc. Lond.* Ser. A, 108: 267-87.

68. CHRISTENSEN, B. SCHJØTZ-. 1957. 'The beetle fauna of the Corynephoretum in the ground of the Mols Laboratory with special reference to *Cardiophorus asellus* Er. (Elateridae)', *Natura Jutlandica*, 6-7: 1-120.

69. CHURCH, A. H. 1922. 'Introduction to the plant-life of the Oxford District. I. General review', *Bot. Mem.* 13: 1-103. Oxford.

70. CHURCH, A. H. 1925. 'Introduction to the plant-life of the Oxford District. II. The annual succession. (Jan.–June)', *Bot. Mem.* 14:1-71. ibid. ('July–December'), 15: 1-63. Oxford.

71. CLAPHAM, A. R., TUTIN, T. G. & WARBURG, E. F. 1952. *Flora of the British Isles*, Cambridge.

71a. CLARK, E. J. 1948. 'Studies in the ecology of British grasshoppers', *Trans. R. Ent. Soc. Lond.* 99: 173-222.

72. CLEMENTS, A. N. 1963. *The physiology of mosquitoes*, Oxford etc.

73. COE, R. L. 1942. '*Rhingia campestris* Meigen (Dipt., Syrphidae): an account of its life-history and descriptions of the early stages', *Ent. Mon. Mag.* 78: 121-30.

74. COE, R. L. 1953. '*Mallota cimbiciformis* Fallén (Diptera: Syrphidae) breeding in Hyde Park, London . . .', *Ent. Gaz.* 4: 282-6.

74a. COLLIN, J. E. 1955. 'Genera and species of Anthomiidae allied to *Chirosia* (Diptera)', *J. Soc. Brit. Ent.* 5: 94-100.

75. COLLYER, E. 1953. 'Biology of some predatory insects and mites associated with the fruit tree red spider mite (*Metatetranychus ulmi* (Koch)) in south-eastern England. II. Some important predators of the mite', *J. Hort. Sci.* 28: 85-97.

76. COLQUHOUN, M. K. 1942. 'A natural population of *Coccinella septempunctata* in Norfolk', *Entomologist*, 75: 40-1.

77. COLQUHOUN, M. K. 1951. 'The wood pigeon in Britain . . .', *Agric. Res. Coun. Rep. Ser.* 10: 1-69. London.

78. CONCHOLOGICAL SOCIETY OF GREAT BRITAIN & IRELAND. 1951. 'Census of the distribution of British non-marine Mollusca', *J. Conch.* 23: 171-244.

79. CONNELL, J. H. 1961. 'Effects of competition, predation by *Thais lapillus*, and other factors on natural populations of the barnacle *Balanus balanoides*', *Ecol. Monogr.* 31: 61-104.

80. CONNOLD, E. T. 1908. *British oak galls*, London.

81. CONWAY, V. M. 1955. 'The Moor House National Nature Reserve Westmorland', *Handb. Soc. Prom. Nat. Res.*: 7-13.

82. COOPER, J. OMER- & TOTTENHAM, C. E. 1934. 'Coleoptera taken in the air at Wicken Fen', *Ent. Mon. Mag.* 70: 231-4.

83. COULSON, J. C. 1959. 'Observations on the Tipulidae (Diptera) of the Moor House Nature Reserve, Westmorland', *Trans. R. Ent. Soc. Lond.* 111: 157-74.

84. COULSON, J. C. 1961. 'The biology of *Tipula subnodicornis* Zetterstedt, with comparative observations on *Tipula paludosa* Meigen', *J. Anim. Ecol.* 31: 1-21.

85. COX, J. C. 1905. *The Royal Forests of England*, London.
86. CRAGG, J. B. 1955. 'The natural history of sheep blowflies in Britain', *Ann. Appl. Biol.* 42: 197-207.
87. CRAGG, J. B. 1961. 'Some aspects of the ecology of moorland animals', *J. Ecol.* 49: 477-506.
88. CRAGG, J. B. & HOBART, J. 1955. 'A study of a field population of the blowflies *Lucilia caesar* (L.) and *L. sericata* (Mg.)', *Ann. Appl. Biol.* 43: 643-63.
89. CRISP, G. & LLOYD, L. 1954. 'The community of insects in a patch of woodland mud', *Trans. R. Ent. Soc. Lond.* 105: 269-314.
90. DELANY, M. J. 1953. 'Studies on the microclimate of *Calluna* heathland', *J. Anim. Ecol.* 22: 227-39.
91. DELANY, M. J. 1956. 'The animal communities of three areas of pioneer heath in south-west England', *J. Anim. Ecol.* 25: 112-26.
92. DE LEERSNYDER, M. & HOESTLANDT, H. 1958. 'Extension du gastropode méditerranéen, *Cochlicella acuta* (Müller), dans le sud-est de l'Angleterre', *J. Conch.* 24: 253-64.
93. DERKSEN, W. 1941. 'Die Succession der Pterygoten Insekten im abstorbenen Buchenholz', *Z. Morph. Ökol. Tiere*, 37: 683-734.
94. DIVER, C. & DIVER, P. 1933. 'Contributions towards a survey of the plants and animals of South Haven Peninsula, Studland Heath, Dorset. III. Orthoptera', *J. Anim. Ecol.* 2: 36-69.
95. DIVER, C. & GOOD, R. D'O. 1934. 'The South Haven Peninsula survey (Studland Heath, Dorset): general scheme of the survey', *J. Anim. Ecol.* 3: 129-32.
96. DIXON, A. F. G. 1959. 'An experimental study of the searching behaviour of the predatory Coccinellid beetle *Adalia decempunctata* (L.)', *J. Anim. Ecol.* 28: 259-81.
97. DIXON, A. F. G. 1963. 'Reproductive activity of the sycamore aphid, *Drepanosiphum platanoides* (Schr.) (Hemiptera, Aphididae)', *J. Anim. Ecol.* 32: 33-48.
98. DIXON, T. J. 1960. 'Key to and descriptions of the third instar larvae of some species of Syrphidae (Diptera) occurring in Britain', *Trans. R. Ent. Soc. Lond.* 112: 345-79.
99. DONISTHORPE, H. 1930. 'The ants (Formicidae) and guests (myrmecophiles) of Windsor Forest and District', *Ent. Rec.* 42 (Suppl.): (1)-(18).
100. DONISTHORPE, H. 1931. 'A note on some bird's nest Coleoptera', *Ent. Mon. Mag.* 67: 57-8.
101. DONISTHORPE, H. 1935. 'The British fungicolous Coleoptera', *Ent. Mon. Mag.* 71: 21-31.
102. DONISTHORPE, H. ST. J. K. 1939. *A preliminary list of the Coleoptera of Windsor Forest*, London.
103. DONISTHORPE, H. 1943. 'Coastal insects found inland', *Ent. Mon. Mag.* 79: 125.
104. DOWNES, J. A. 1955. 'The food habits and description of *Atrichopogon pollinivorus* sp. n. (Diptera: Ceratopogonidae)', *Trans. R. Ent. Soc. Lond.* 106: 439-53.
105. DRUCE, G. C. 1886. *The Flora of Oxfordshire . . .*, Oxford.
106. DRUCE, G. C. 1897. *The Flora of Berkshire . . .*, Oxford.
107. DRUCE, G. C. 1915. 'The saline spring at Marcham', *Proc. Ashmol. Nat. Hist. Soc.* for 1914: 34-5.

108. DUFFEY, E. 1956. 'Aerial dispersal in a known spider population', *J. Anim. Ecol.* 25: 85-111.

109. DUFFEY, E. 1962. 'A population study of spiders in limestone grassland. The field-layer fauna', *Oikos*, 13: 15-34.

110. DUFFEY, E. 1962. 'A population study of spiders in limestone grassland. Description of study area, sampling methods and population characteristics', *J. Anim. Ecol.* 31: 571-99.

111. DUFFY, E. A. J. 1953. 'Coleoptera (Scolytidae and Platypodidae')', *Handb. Ident. Brit. Insects,* 5, Pt 15: 1-20.

112. EASTON, A. M. 1947. 'The Coleoptera of flood-refuse. A comparison of samples from Surrey and Oxfordshire', *Ent. Mon. Mag.* 83: 113-15.

113. EDWARDS, C. A. & HEATH, G. W. 1963. 'The role of soil animals in breakdown of leaf material', In *Soil organisms* . . . (Colloquium, ed. by J. Doeksen & J. Van den Drift), Amsterdam. Pp. 76-84.

114. EDWARDS, F. W. 1928. '*Orthopodomyia pulchripalpis* Rond. in the London district', *Entomologist*: 213.

115. EDWARDS, F. W., OLDROYD, H. & SMART, J. 1939. *British blood-sucking flies,* London.

116. EFFORD, I. E. 1959. 'Rediscovery of *Bathynella chappuisi* Delachaux in Britain', *Nature, Lond.* 184: 558-9.

117. EFFORD, I. E. 1960. 'A population study on water-mites (Hydracarina)', D.Phil. Thesis, Oxford University.

118. EFFORD, I. E. 1960. 'Observations on the biology of *Tanytarsus* (*Stempellina*) *flavidulus* (Edwards) (Dipt., Chironomidae)', *Ent. Mon. Mag.* 96: 201-3.

119. EFFORD, I. E. 1962. 'The taxonomy, distribution and habitat of the watermite, *Feltria romijni* Besseling, 1930', *Hydrobiologia,* 19: 161-78.

120. EFFORD, I. E. 1963. 'The parasitic ecology of some water-mites', *J. Anim. Ecol.* 32: 141-56.

121. EKBLAW, E. 1947. *The concise dictionary of English place-names,* Oxford. 3rd ed.

121a. ELBOURN, C. A. 1965. 'The fauna of a calcareous woodland stream in Berkshire', *Ent. Mon. Mag.* 101: 25-30.

122. ELLIS, A. E. 1926. *British snails* . . ., Oxford.

123. ELTON, C. S. 1925. 'The dispersal of insects to Spitsbergen', *Trans. Ent. Soc. Lond.* 73: 289-99.

124. ELTON, C. 1927. *Animal ecology,* London.

125. ELTON, C. 1932. 'Territory among wood ants (*Formica rufa* L.) at Picket Hill', *J. Anim. Ecol.* 1: 69-76.

126. ELTON, C. 1935. 'A reconnaissance of woodland bird communities in England and Wales', *J. Anim. Ecol.* 4: 127-36.

127. ELTON, C. 1939. 'On the nature of cover', *J. Wildlife Mgmt,* 3: 332-8.

128. ELTON, C. 1942. *Voles mice and lemmings: problems in population dynamics,* Oxford.

129. ELTON, C. 1947. 'Some Orthoptera from Shropshire and Pembrokeshire', *Ent. Mon. Mag.* 83: 42.

130. ELTON, C. 1949. 'Population interspersion: an essay on animal community patterns', *J. Ecol.* 37: 1-23.

131. ELTON, C. 1951. 'The habitat of *Staphylinus ater* Gr. (Col., Staphylinidae)', *Ent. Mon. Mag.* 87: 175.

132. ELTON, C. S. 1956. 'Stoneflies (Plecoptera, Nemouridae), a component of the aquatic leaf-litter fauna in Wytham Woods, Berkshire', *Ent. Mon. Mag.* 92: 231-6.

133. ELTON, C. S. 1958. *The ecology of invasions by animals and plants*, London.

134. ELTON, C. S. 1959. 'Swarming of male *Culex pipiens* L. (Dipt., Culicidae)', *Ent. Mon. Mag.* 95: 189-90.

135. ELTON, C. S. 1960. '*Prionychus ater* (F.) (Col., Alleculidae) in Wytham Woods, Berkshire', *Ent. Mon. Mag.* 96: 176-7.

136. ELTON, C. S., FORD, E. B., BAKER, J. R. & GARDNER, A. D. 1931. 'The health and parasites of a wild mouse population', *Proc. Zool. Soc. Lond.*: 657-721.

137. ELTON, C. S. & MILLER, R. S. 1954. 'The ecological survey of animal communities: with a practical system of classifying habitats by structural characters', *J. Ecol.* 42: 460-96.

138. ELTON, O. (Translator) 1940. 'Passages from Mickiewicz's *Pan Tadeusz*', *Slavonic Yearb.* 19: 1-15.

139. ERRINGTON, P. L. 1963. 'The pricelessness of untampered Nature', *J. Wildlife Mgmt*, 27: 313-20.

140. EVANS, A. C. 1948. 'The identity of earthworms stored by moles', *Proc. Zool. Soc. Lond.* 118: 256-9.

141. EVANS, A. C. & GUILD, W. J. MCL. 1948. 'Studies on the relationship between earthworms and soil fertility. IV. On the life cycles of some British Lumbricidae', *Ann. Appl. Biol.* 35: 471-84.

142. EVANS, A. C. & GUILD, W. J. MCL. 1948. *op. cit.* V, 'Field population', *Ann. Appl. Biol.* 35: 485-93.

143. EVANS, F. C. 1942. 'Studies of a small mammal population in Bagley Wood, Berkshire', *J. Anim. Ecol.* 11: 182-97.

144. EVANS, F. C. & DAHL, E. 1955. 'The vegetational structure of an abandoned field in southeastern Michigan and its relation to environmental factors', *Ecology*, 36: 685-706.

145. EVANS, F. C. & LANHAM, U. N. 1960. 'Distortion of the pyramid of numbers in a grassland insect community', *Science*, 131: 1531-2.

146. FABRE, J.-H. 1913 ed. *Les merveilles de l'instinct chez les insectes*, Ch. 5, 'Les necrophores. – L'enterrement'*, Paris.

147. FABRE, J.-H. 1919. *The glow-worm and other beetles* (orig. publ. 1913 in *Century Mag.* 87: 105-12), London.

148. FAGER, E. W. 1955. 'A study of invertebrate populations in decaying wood', D.Phil. Thesis, Oxford University.

149. FAGER, E. W. 1957. 'Determination and analysis of recurrent groups', *Ecology*, 38: 586-95.

150. FARROW, E. P. 1925. *Plant life on East Anglian heaths . . .*, Cambridge.

151. FENTON, F. A. 1959. 'The effect of several insecticides on the total arthropod population in alfalfa', *J. Econ. Ent.* 52: 428-32.

152. FERGUSON, W. S. & ARMITAGE, E. R. 1944. 'The chemical composition of bracken (*Pteridium aquilinum*)', *J. Agric. Res.* 34: 165-71.

153. FERNANDO, C. H. 1958. 'The colonization of small freshwater habitats by aquatic insects. 1. General discussion, methods and colonization in the aquatic Coleoptera', *Ceylon J. Sci.* (Biol. Sci.), 1: 117-54.

154. FERNANDO, C. H. 1959. 'The colonization of small freshwater habitats by aquatic insects. 2. Hemiptera (the water-bugs)', *Ceylon J. Sci.* (Biol. Sci.), 2: 5-32.

155. FICHTER, E. 1954. 'An ecological study of invertebrates of grassland and deciduous shrub savannah in Eastern Nebraska', *Amer. Midl. Nat.* 51: 321-439.

156. FISHER, J. & LOCKLEY, R. M. 1954. *Sea-birds: an introduction to the natural history of the sea-birds of the North Atlantic*, London.

157. FISHER, R. C. 1936. 'Insects attacking the timber of English oak', *Forestry*, 10: 47-57.

158. FLINT, J. H. 1964. 'Insects from a hot manure heap', *Naturalist*: 56.

159. FOGH, T. WEIS-. 1952. 'Fat combustion and metabolic rate of flying locusts (*Schistocerca gregaria* Forskål)', *Phil. Trans.* Ser. B, 237: 1-36.

160. FORD, J. 1937. 'Fluctuations in natural populations of Collembola and Acarina', *J. Anim. Ecol.* 6: 98-111.

161. FORD, L. T. 1949. *A guide to the smaller British Lepidoptera . . .*, London.

162. FOREL, F. A. 1892, 1895, 1904. *Le Léman. Monographie limnologique*, Lausanne. 3 vols.

163. FORESTRY COMMISSION. 1946. '*Adelges* attacking spruce and other conifers', *Leafl. For. Comm., Lond.* 7: 1-5.

164. FORESTRY COMMISSION. 1962. 'Elm disease, *Ceratocystis ulmi*', *Leafl. For. Comm., Lond.* 19: 1-7.

165. FORESTRY COMMISSION. 1962. 'The grey squirrel: a woodland pest', *Leafl. For. Comm., Lond.* 31: 1-18.

166. FORREST, H. E. 1899. *The fauna of Shropshire . . .*, Shrewsbury & London.

167. FOWLER, [W. W.] 1888. *The Coleoptera of the British Islands . . .*, London. Vol. 2.

168. FOWLER, [W. W.] 1889. *op. cit.*, Vol. 3.

169. FOWLER, [W. W.] 1890. *op. cit.*, Vol. 4.

170. FREEMAN, J. A. 1945. 'Studies in the distribution of insects in aerial currents: the insect population of the air from ground level to 300 feet', *J. Anim. Ecol.* 14: 128-54.

171. FREEMAN, J. A. 1946. 'The distribution of spiders and mites up to 300 ft. in the air', *J. Anim. Ecol.* 15: 69-74.

172. FREEMAN, R. B. 1941. 'The distribution of *Orchopeas wickhami* (Baker) (Siphonaptera), in relation to its host the American grey squirrel', *Ent. Mon. Mag.* 77: 82-9.

173. FREEMAN, R. B. 1946. 'Coleoptera from nests of the robin', *Ent. Mon. Mag.* 82: 217.

174. FULLER, M. E. 1934. 'The insect inhabitants of carrion: a study in animal ecology', *Bull. Coun. Sci. Industr. Res. Aust.* 82: 1-62.

175. GALECKA, B. 1962. ['Influence of patches of wood in fields on changes in numbers of potato aphids and the predatory Coccinellidae'], *Ekol. Polsk*, Ser. A, 10: 21-44.

176. GEIGER, R. 1950. *The climate near the ground* (transl. M. N. Stewart *et al.*), Cambridge, Mass.

177. GERARD, B. M. 1963. 'The activities of some species of Lumbricidae in pastureland', in *Soil organisms . . .* (Colloquium, ed. J. Doeksen & J. Van der Drift), Amsterdam. Pp. 49-54.

178. GERARD, B. M. 1964. 'A synopsis of the British Lumbricidae', *Synops. Brit. Fauna* (Linn. Soc.) 6: 1-58.

179. GIBB, J. 1950. 'The breeding biology of the great and blue titmice', *Ibis*, 92: 507-39.

180. GIBB, J. 1954. 'Feeding ecology of tits, with notes on treecreeper and goldcrest', *Ibis*, 96: 513-43.

181. GILBERT, O. & BOCOCK, K. L. 1960. 'Changes in leaf litter when placed on the surface of soils with contrasting humus types. II. Changes in the nitrogen content of oak and ash leaf litter', *J. Soil Sci.* 11: 10-19.

182. GILLHAM, M. E. 1953. 'An ecological account of the vegetation of Grassholm Island, Pembrokeshire', *J. Ecol.* 41: 84-99.

183. GILLHAM, M. E. 1955. 'Ecology of the Pembrokeshire islands. III. The effect of grazing on the vegetation', *J. Ecol.* 43: 172-206.

184. GILLHAM, M. E. 1956. *op. cit.* IV, 'Effects of treading and burrowing by birds and mammals', *J. Ecol.* 44: 51-82.

185. GIMINGHAM, C. H. 1960. 'Biological Flora of the British Isles . . . *Calluna vulgaris* (L.) Hull', *J. Ecol.* 48: 455-83.

186. GLEGG, W. E. 1926. 'Epping Forest Report', *London Nat.* for 1925: 35-6 (see also 1927, *London Nat.* for 1926: 55-6).

187. GOATER, B. 1957. 'Autumn moths at elder berries', *Ent. Rec.* 69: 46-7.

188. GODFREY, G. K. 1953. 'The food of *Microtus agrestis hirtus* (Bellamy, 1839) in Wytham, Berkshire', *Säugetierk. Mitt.* 1: 148-51.

189. GODFREY, G. K. 1955. 'Observations on the nature of the decline in numbers of *Microtus* populations', *J. Mammal.* 36: 209-14.

190. GODFREY, G. & CROWCROFT, P. 1960. *The life of the mole* (Talpa europaea Linnaeus), London.

191. GODWIN, H. 1943. 'Biological Flora of the British Isles. Rhamnaceae. *Rhamnus cathartica* L., *Frangula alnus* Miller (*Rhamnus Frangula* L.) . . .', *J. Ecol.* 31: 66-92.

192. GODWIN, H. 1956. *The history of the British flora; a factual basis for phytogeography*, Cambridge.

193. GODWIN, H. 1960. 'The history of weeds in Britain', in *The biology of weeds* (ed. J. L. Harper), Oxford. Pp. 1-10.

194. GRAYSON, A. J. & JONES, E. W. 1955. *Notes on the history of the Wytham Estate with special reference to the woodlands*, Imperial Forestry Institute, Oxford. 28 pp.+ 2 maps.

195. GREEN, J. 1950. 'The feeding habits of *Cylindronotus laevioctostriatus* (Goeze) (Col., Tenebrionidae)', *Ent. Mon. Mag.* 86: 92-3.

196. GREEN, J. 1951. 'The food of *Cylindronotus laevioctostriatus* (Goeze) (Col., Tenebrionidae) and its larva', *Ent. Mon. Mag.* 87: 19.

197. GREEN, J. 1951. 'The distribution of *Staphylinus ater* Gr. (Col., Staphylinidae) on Skokholm Island, Pembrokeshire', *Ent. Mon. Mag.* 87: 106-7.

198. GUILD, W. J. McL. 1948. 'Studies on the relationship between earthworms and soil fertility. III. The effect of soil type on the structure of earthworm populations', *Ann. Appl. Biol.* 35: 181-92.

199. GUNTHER, R. T. 1912. *Oxford gardens, based upon Daubeny's Popular Guide to the Physick Garden of Oxford* . . ., Oxford. Appendix I. 'The gardens of the winds and the birds in Mesopotamia.'

200. GURNEY, R. 1932. *British fresh-water Copepoda*. London. Vol. 2.

201. HAARLØV, N. 1960. 'Microarthropods from Danish soils: ecology, phenology', *Oikos*, Suppl. 3: 1-176.

202. HALL, D. G. 1948. 'The blowflies of North America', The Thomas Say Foundation, Vol. 4. Baltimore.

203. HAMM, A. H. 1918. 'Sapyga clavicornis L. and other Hymenoptera, in old posts at Oxford', *Ent. Mon. Mag.* 54: 184-5.

204. HAMM, A. H. & RICHARDS, O. W. 1926. 'The biology of the British Crabronidae', *Trans. Ent. Soc. Lond.* 74: 297-331.

205. HAMMER, M. 1944. 'Studies on the Oribatids and Collemboles of Greenland', *Medd. Grønland*, 141(3): 1-210.

206. HAMMER, O. 1941. 'Biological and ecological investigations on flies associated with pasturing cattle and their excrement', *Vidensk. Medd. Dansk. Naturh. Foren. Kbh.* 105: 1-257.

207. HANCOCK, J. 1953. 'The grazing behaviour of cattle', *Anim. Breed. Abstr.* 21: 1-13.

208. HANSEN, V. 1927. *Danmarks Fauna. Biller. VII. Bladbiller og Bønnebiller (Chrysomelidae and Lariidae)*, Copenhagen.

209. HANSON, H. S. 1937. 'Notes on the ecology and control of pine beetles in Great Britain', *Bull. Ent. Res.* 28: 185-236.

210. HANSON, H. S. 1940. 'Further notes on the ecology and control of pine beetles in Great Britain', *Bull. Ent. Res.* 30: 483-536.

211. HARDY, A. C. 1924. 'The herring in relation to its animate environment. Part I', *Fish Invest., Lond.* Ser. 2, 7(3): 1-53.

212. HARDY, A. C. 1949. 'Zoology outside the laboratory', *Rep. Brit. Ass.* 6: 213-23.

213. HARPER, J. L. & WOOD, W. A. 1957. 'Biological Flora of the British Isles. *Senecio jacobaea* L.', *J. Ecol.* 45: 617-37.

214. HARTLEY, C. H. & DUNBAR, M. J. 1938. 'On the hydrographic mechanism of the so-called brown zones associated with tidal glaciers', *J. Mar. Res.* 1: 305-11.

215. HARTLEY, C. H. & FISHER, J. 1936. 'The marine foods of birds in an inland fjord region in West Spitsbergen. Part 2. Birds', *J. Anim. Ecol.* 5: 370-89.

216. HARTLEY, P. H. T. 1953. 'An ecological study of the feeding habits of the English titmice', *J. Anim. Ecol.* 22: 261-88.

217. HARTLEY, P. H. T. 1954. 'Wild fruits in the diet of British thrushes. A study in the ecology of closely allied species', *Brit. Birds*, 47: 97-107.

218. HAZELTON, M. & GLENNIE, E. A. 1962. 'Cave fauna and flora', Ch. 9 in *British caving: an introduction to speleology*, (ed. C. H. D. Cullingford). London.

219. HEGINBOTHAM, C. D. 1946. 'Wiltshire mollusc collectors', *Wiltsh. Archaeol. Nat. Hist. Mag.* 51: 457.

220. HENSLOW, G. 1901. *Poisonous plants in field and garden*, London.

221. HEPBURN, I. 1952. *Flowers of the coast*, London.

222. HERING, E. M. 1951. *Biology of the leaf miners*, 's-Gravenhage, Netherlands.

223. HEYMONS, R. & VON LENGERKEN, H. 1931. 'Studien über die Lebenserscheinungen der Silphini (Coleopt.). VII. Oeceoptoma thoracica L.', *Z. Morph. Ökol. Tiere*, 20: 691-706.

224. HILL, A. R. 1957. 'The biology of *Anthocoris nemorum* (L.) in Scotland (Hemiptera: Anthocoridae)', *Trans. R. Ent. Soc. Lond.* 109: 379-94.

225. HINCKS, W. D. et al. 1951-4. 'The entomology of Spurn Peninsula', *Naturalist*, 1951: 75-86, 139-46, 183-90; 1952: 131-8, 169-76; 1953: 125-40, 157-72; 1954: 74-8, 95-109.

226. HINCKS, W. D. 1951. 'The entomology of Spurn Peninsula. III. General entomology of the areas', *Naturalist*, 85-6.

227. HOBBY, B. M. 1931. 'List of the prey of dung-flies (Diptera, Cordyluridae)', *Trans. Ent. Soc. S. Engl.* 7: 35-9.

228. HOBBY, B. M. 1957. 'A swarm of Sepsidae (Dipt.)', *Ent. Mon. Mag.* 93: 34.

229. HOBBY, B. M. & KILLINGTON, F. J. 1934. 'The feeding habits of British Mecoptera; with a synopsis of the British species', *Trans. Soc. Brit. Ent.* 1: 39-49.

230. HOCKING, B. 1953. 'The intrinsic range and speed of flight of insects', *Trans. R. Ent. Soc. Lond.* 104: 222-345.

231. HOEL, A. 1915. 'D'ou vient le renne du Spitsberg?', *Géographie*, 30: 443-8.

232. HOLDGATE, M. W. 1963. 'Observations in the South Sandwich Islands, 1962', *Polar Rec.* 11: 394-405.

233. HOLLOM, P. A. D. 1955. *The popular handbook of British birds*, London.

234. HOLLOWAY, P. H. 1951. 'Insects and ivy-bloom', *Ent. Rec.* 63: 275-7.

235. HOOKER, J. D. 1891. *Himalayan journals; or, notes of a naturalist in Bengal, the Sikkim and Nepal Himalayas, the Khasia Mountains, etc*, London. 2 vols. (orig. publ. 1854).

236. HOPF, H. S. 1938. 'Investigations into the nutrition of the ash-bark beetle, *Hylesinus fraxini* Panz.', *Ann. Appl. Biol.* 25: 390-405.

237. HOWDEN, H. F. 1952. 'A new name for *Geotrupes* (*Peltotrupes*) *chalybeus* LeConte, with a description of the larva and its biology (Scarabaeidae)', *Coleopterists' Bull.* 6: 41-8.

238. HOWES, F. N. 1945. *Plants and beekeeping . . .*, London.

239. HUBBARD, C. E. 1954. *Grasses . . .*, Harmondsworth, Middlesex.

240. [HUSSEY, N. W.] 1956. 'Oak leaf roller moth', *Leafl. For. Comm. Lond.*, 10: 1-7.

241. HUXLEY, T. 1959. 'The food of woodlice with reference to the break-down of dead plants' (unpublished report to the Nature Conservancy, Edinburgh & London).

242. HYNES, H. B. N. 1941. 'The taxonomy and ecology of the nymphs of British Plecoptera with notes on the adults and eggs', *Trans. R. Ent. Soc. Lond.* 91: 459-557.

243. HYNES, H. B. N. 1963. 'The gill-less Nemourid nymphs of Britain (Plecoptera)', *Proc. R. Ent. Soc. Lond.* Ser. A, 38: 70-6.

243a. IMMS, A. D. 1947. *Insect natural history*, London.

244. JANSSEN, W. 1963. 'Untersuchungen zur Morphologie und Ökologie von *Cantharis* L. and *Rhagonycha* Eschsch. (Cantharidae, Col.)', *Z. Wiss. Zool.* 169: 115-202.

245. JENKINS, D. W. & CARPENTER, S. J. 1947. 'Ecology of the tree hole breeding mosquitoes of Nearctic North America', *Ecol. Monogr.* 16: 31-47.

246. JENSEN, M. 1961. *Shelter effect: investigations into the aerodynamics of shelter and its effects on climate and crops*, Copenhagen.

247. JENSEN, P. BOYSEN. 1915. 'Studies concerning the organic matter of the sea bottom', *Rep. Danish Biol. Sta.* 22: 1-39.

248. JOHNSON, S. 1816 ed. *A journey to the Western Islands of Scotland*, London.

249. JONES, E. W. 1945. 'The structure and reproduction of the virgin forest of the North Temperate Zone', *New Phytol.* 44: 130-48.

250. JONES, E. W. 1945. 'Biological Flora of the British Isles. *Acer* L.', *J. Ecol.* 32: 215-52.

251. JONES, E. W. 1952. 'A bryophyte Flora of Berkshire and Oxfordshire. I. Hepaticae and Sphagna', *Trans. Brit. Bryol. Soc.* 2: 19-50. *ibid.* 1953. *op. cit.* 'II. Musci', *ibid.* 2: 220-77.

252. JONES, E. W. 1959. 'Biological Flora of the British Isles. *Quercus* L.', *J. Ecol.* 47: 169-222.

253. JONES, E. W. 1959. 'Wytham vegetation. Noteworthy botanical features', Appendix 9, in OSMASTON, F. C., 1959.

254. JOY, N. 1906. 'Coleoptera from old birds' nests', *Ent. Mon. Mag.* 42: 39-40.

255. JOY, N. H. 1932. *A practical handbook of British beetles*, London. Vol. 1.

256. JUDENKO, E., JOHNSON, C. G. & TAYLOR, L. R. 1952. 'The effect of *Aphis fabae* Scop. on the growth and yield of field beans in a garden plot', *Plant Pathology*, 1: 60-3.

257. KEILIN, D. 1911. 'On the parasitism of the larvae of *Pollenia rudis* Fab. in *Allolobophora chlorotica* Savigny', *Proc. Ent. Soc. Wash.* 13: 182-4.

258. KEILIN, D. 1921. 'On the life-history of *Dasyhelea obscura*, Winnertz (Diptera, Nematocera, Ceratopogonidae) . . .', *Ann. Mag. Nat. Hist.* Ser. 9, 8: 576-90.

259. KEILIN, D. 1927. 'Fauna of a horse-chestnut tree (*Aesculus hippocastanum*). Dipterous larvae and their parasites', *Parasitology*, 19: 368-74.

260. KEILIN, D. 1932. 'On the water reservoir of a horse-chestnut tree', *Parasitology*, 24: 280-2.

261. KEILIN, D. & TATE, P. 1940. 'The early stages of the families Trichoceridae and Anisopodidae (= Rhyphidae) (Diptera: Nematocera)', *Trans. R. Ent. Soc. Lond.* 90: 39-62.

262. KEMPSON, D., LLOYD, M. & GHELARDI, R. 1963. 'A new extractor for woodland litter', *Pedobiologia*, 3: 1-21.

263. KENDEIGH, S. C. 1961. 'Energy of birds conserved by roosting in cavities', *Wilson Bull.* 73: 140-7.

264. KERSHAW, K. A. 1963. 'Lichens', *Endeavour*, 22: 65-9.

265. KEVAN, D. K. McE. 1951. '*Platycleis occidentalis occidentalis* Zeuner (Orthoptera, Tettigoniidae) in the Midlands', *J. Soc. Brit. Ent.* 4: 42-3.

266. KEVAN, D. K. McE. 1952. 'A summary of the recorded distribution of British Orthopteroids', *Trans. Soc. Brit. Ent.* 11: 165-80.

267. KEVAN, D. K. McE. 1954. 'Further notes on the distribution of British Orthopteroids', *J. Soc. Brit. Ent.* 5: 65-71.

268. KIKKAWA, J. 1964. 'Movement, activity and distribution of the small rodents *Clethrionomys glareolus* and *Apodemus sylvaticus* in woodland', *J. Anim. Ecol.* 33: 259-99.

269. KIKUCHI, T. 1962. 'Studies on the coaction among insects visiting flowers. II.

Dominance relationship in the so-called drone fly group', *Sci. Rep. Tôhoku Univ. Ser. 4* (Biol.), 28: 47-51.

270. KILLINGTON, F. J. 1936-7. *A monograph of the British Neuroptera*, Ray Society, London. 2 vols.

271. KIMMINS, D. E. 1950. 'Plecoptera (stone-flies)', *Handb. Ident. Brit. Insects*, 1, Pt 6: 1-18.

272. KROGERUS, R. 1932. 'Uber die Ökologie und Verbreitung der Arthropoden der Triebsandgebiete an den Küsten Finnlands', *Acta Zool Fenn.* 12: 1-308.

273. KURTH, A., WEIDMANN, A. & THOMMEN, F. 1960. 'Beitrag zur Kenntnis der Waldverhältnisse im Schweizerischen Nationalpark', *Ergebn. Wiss. Unters. Schweiz. NatParks*, 8 (Suppl.): 1-378.

274. KUYTEN, P. 1960. 'Verhaltensbeobachtungen am Dreihornmistkäfer (*Typhoeus typhoeus* L., Col. Scarab.)', *Ent. Z.* 70: 223-33.

275. LACK, D. 1933. 'Habitat selection in birds with special reference to the effects of afforestation on the Breckland avifauna', *J. Anim. Ecol.* 2: 239-62.

276. LACK, D. 1935. 'The breeding bird population of British heaths and moorland', *J. Anim. Ecol.* 4: 43-51.

277. LACK, D. 1939. 'Further changes in the Breckland avifauna caused by afforestation', *J. Anim. Ecol.* 8: 277-85.

278. LACK, D. 1955. 'British tits (*Parus* spp.) in nesting boxes', *Ardea*, 43: 50-84.

279. LACK, D. 1958. 'A quantitative breeding study of British tits', *Ardea*, 46: 91-124.

280. LACK, D. & LACK, E. 1958. 'The nesting of the long-tailed tit', *Bird Study*, 5: 1-19.

281. LACK, D. & OWEN, D. F. 1955. 'The food of the swift', *J. Anim. Ecol.* 24: 120-36.

282. LACK, D. & VENABLES, L. S. V. 1939. 'The habitat distribution of British woodland birds', *J. Anim. Ecol.* 8: 39-71.

283. LANDIN, B.-O. 1961. 'Ecological studies on dung-beetles (Col. Scarabaeidae)', *Opusc. Ent.*, Suppl. 19: 1-228.

284. LARKIN, P. A. & ELBOURN, C. A. 1964. 'Some observations on the fauna of dead wood in live oak trees', *Oikos*, 15: 79-92.

285. LAST, H. 1951. '*Ocypus ater* Grav. (Col., Staphylinidae)', *Ent. Mon. Mag.* 87: 250.

286. LAURENCE, B. R. 1953. 'Some Diptera bred from cow dung', *Ent. Mon. Mag.* 89: 281-3.

287. LAURENCE, B. R. 1955. 'Diptera. Flies associated with cow dung', *Ent. Rec.* 67: 123-6.

288. LEIUS, K. 1960. 'Attractiveness of different foods and flowers to the adults of some Hymenopterous parasites', *Canad. Ent.* 92: 369-76.

289. LEOPOLD, L. B. (ed.) 1953. *Round River: from the journals of Aldo Leopold*, New York.

290. LETTS, M. (transl. & ed.) 1926. *Pero Tafur: travels and adventures 1435-1439*, London.

291. LEWIS, E. 1959. 'Note on two Australian beetles now established in Britain', *Proc. Croydon Nat. Hist. Sci. Soc.*: 267-8.

292. LEWIS, T. 1959. 'The annual cycle of *Limothrips cerealium* Haliday (Thysanoptera) and its distribution in a wheat field', *Ent. Exp. Appl.* 2: 187-203.

293. LINDQUIST, B. 1938. 'Dalby Söderskog: en skansk lövskog i forntid och nutid', Stockholm. 273 pp. (Reprinted from *Acta Phytogeogr. Suec.* 10, No. 1.)

294. LINDQUIST, B. 1941. 'Undersökningar över några Skandinaviska daggmaskarters betydelse för lövförnans omvandling och för mulljordens struktur i svensk skogsmark', *Svenska SkogsvFören. Tidskr.* 39: 179-242.

295. LINDQUIST, B. 1942. 'Experimentalle Untersuchungen über die Bedeutung einiger Landmollusken für die Zersetzung der Waldstreu', *K. Fysiogr. Sällsk. Lund Förh.* 11: 144-56.

296. LLOYD, M. 1963. 'Numerical observations on movements of animals between beech litter and fallen branches', *J. Anim. Ecol.* 32: 157-63.

297. LOCKET, G. H. & MILLIDGE, A. F. 1953. *British spiders*, London, Vol. 2.

298. LOCKIE, J. D. 1955. 'The breeding and feeding of jackdaws and rooks, with notes on carrion crows and other Corvidae', *Ibis*, 97: 341-69.

299. LOCKIE, J. D. 1959. 'The food of nestling rooks near Oxford', *Brit. Birds*, 52: 332-4.

300. LONG, H. C. 1924. *Plants poisonous to live stock*, Cambridge.

301. LOTKA, A. 1925. *Elements of physical biology*, Baltimore.

302. LUCAS, W. J. 1920. *A monograph of the British Orthoptera*, London.

303. LUCAS, W. J. 1925. 'Notes on British Orthoptera (including Dermaptera) in 1924', *Entomologist*, 58: 81-6.

304. LÜHMANN, M. 1933. 'Beitrag zur Biologie des Schneeballkäfers *Galerucella viburni* Payk. . . .', *Z. Angew. Ent.* 20: 531-64.

305. MACAN, T. T. 1959. 'The temperature of a small stony stream', *Hydrobiologia*, 12: 89-106.

306. McCUBBIN, W. A. 1954. 'The plant quarantine problem', *Ann. Cryptog. Phytopath., Copenhagen*, 11: 1-255.

307. MACFADYEN, A. 1955. 'A comparison of methods for extracting soil arthropods', in *Soil Zoology* . . . (ed. D. K. McE. Kevan), London. Pp. 315-32.

308. MACFADYEN, A. 1961. 'Improved funnel-type extractors for soil arthropods', *J. Anim. Ecol.* 30: 171-84.

309. MACFADYEN, A. 1963. *Animal ecology: aims and methods*, London.

310. MACGREGOR, M. E. 1929. 'The significance of the pH in the development of mosquito larvae', *Parasitology*, 21: 132-57.

311. MACLEOD, J. 1963. 'Further records of distribution of blowflies in Great Britain', *Bull. Ent. Res.* 54: 113-17.

312. MACLEOD, J. & DONNELLY, J. 1956. 'The geographical distribution of blowflies in Great Britain', *Bull. Ent. Res.* 47: 597-619.

313. MACLEOD, J. & DONNELLY, J. 1963. 'Dispersal and interspersal of blowfly populations', *J. Anim. Ecol.* 32: 1-32.

314. MADLE, H. 1934. 'Zur Kenntnis der Morphologie, Ökologie und Physiologie von *Aphodius rufipes* Lin. und einigen verwandten Arten', *Zool. Jahrb. Abt. Anat.* 58: 303-96.

315. MARQUARDT, G. 1950. 'Die Schleswig-Holsteinische Knicklandschaft', *Schr. Geogr. Inst. Univ. Kiel*, 13(3): 1-90.

316. MARR, J. W. 1961. 'Ecosystems of the east slope of the Front Range in Colorado', *Univ. Colorado Stud.*, Ser. in Biol. 8: 1-134.

317. MARSHALL, J. F. 1938. *The British mosquitoes*, London.

318. MASSEE, A. M. 1937. *The pests of fruit and hops*, London.

319. MATTHEWS, J. K. 1946. 'Lepidoptera of the coastal sandhills of Lancashire', *Proc. S. Lond. Ent. Nat. Hist. Soc.* for 1945-6: 72-8.

320. MIDDLETON, A. D. 1930. 'The ecology of the American grey squirrel (*Sciurus carolinensis Gmelin*) in the British Isles', *Proc. Zool. Soc. Lond.*: 809-43.

321. MIDDLETON, A. D. 1935. 'The food of a badger (*Meles meles*)', *J. Anim. Ecol.* 4: 291.

322. MIDDLETON, A. D. & CHITTY, H. M. 1937. 'The food of adult partridges, *Perdix perdix* and *Alectoris rufa*, in Great Britain', *J. Anim. Ecol.* 6: 322-36.

323. MILLER, R. S. 1951. 'Activity patterns in small mammals with special reference to their use of natural resources', D.Phil. Thesis, Oxford University.

324. MILLER, R. S. 1954. 'Food habits of the wood-mouse, *Apodemus sylvaticus* (Linné, 1758), and the bank vole *Clethrionomys glareolus* (Schreber, 1780), in Wytham Woods, Berkshire', *Säugetierk. Mitt.* 2: 109-14.

325. MILLER, R. S. 1955. 'Activity rhythms in the wood mouse, *Apodemus sylvaticus* and the bank vole, *Clethrionomys glareolus*', *Proc. Zool. Soc. Lond.* 125: 505-19.

326. MILLER, R. S. 1958. 'A study of a wood mouse population in Wytham Woods, Berkshire', *J. Mammal.* 39: 477-93.

327. MILNE, A. 1944. 'The ecology of the sheep tick, *Ixodes ricinus* L. Distribution of the tick in relation to geology, soil and vegetation in northern England', *Parasitology*, 35: 186-96.

328. MILNE, A. 1950. 'The ecology of the sheep tick, *Ixodes ricinus* L. Microhabitat economy of the adult tick', *Parasitology*, 40: 14-34.

329. MITFORD, R. L. S. B. 1940. 'The excavations at Seacourt, Berks., 1939', *Oxoniensia*, 5: 31-41.

330. MOHR, C. O. 1943. 'Cattle droppings as ecological units', *Ecol. Monogr.* 13: 275-98.

331. MOON, F. E. & PAL, A. K. 1949. 'The composition and nutritive value of bracken', *J. Agric. Res.* 39: 296-301.

332. MOORE, B. P. 1955. 'Notes on carrion Coleoptera in the Oxford district', *Ent. Mon. Mag.* 91: 292-5.

333. MOORE, N. W. 1962. 'The heaths of Dorset and their conservation', *J. Ecol.* 50: 369-91.

334. MORISON, G. D. 1963. 'The heather beetle (*Lochmaea suturalis* Thomson)', N. Scotland Coll. Agric., Aberdeen.

335. MORLEY, C. 1935. 'A beech-tree's insects and their parasites', *Ent. Mon. Mag.* 71: 90-1.

336. MORRIS, J. 1960. *Hired to kill*, London. P. 237.

337. MOULE, G. R. 1957. 'The biology of blowfly control in Australia', [Penguin] *New Biology*, 22: 91-103.

338. MÜLLER, H. 1883. *The fertilisation of flowers* (transl. D'A. W. Thompson), London.

339. MURDOCH, W. 1963. 'The population ecology of certain Carabid beetles living in marshes and near fresh water', D.Phil. Thesis, Oxford University.

340. MURPHY, P. W. 1954. 'Soil faunal investigations', *Rep. For. Res., Lond.* for year ending March 1953: 110-16.

341. MURPHY, P. W. 1955. 'Ecology in the fauna of forest soils', in *Soil Zoology . .* , (ed. D. K. McE. Kevan), London. Pp. 99-124.

342. MURTFELDT, M. E. 1894. 'Acorn insects, primary and secondary', *Insect Life* (*Period. Bull. U.S. Div. Ent.*), 6: 318-24.

343. NASH, O. 1956. *Good intentions*, London (orig. publ. 1942).

344. NATURE CONSERVANCY. 1958. *Rep. for year ended 30 September 1958*.

345. NATURE CONSERVANCY. 1960. *Rep. for year ended 30 September 1960*.

346. NATURE CONSERVANCY. 1962. *Rep. for year ended 30 September 1962*.

347. NATURE CONSERVANCY. 1963. *Rep. for year ended 30 September 1963*.

348. NAYLOR, G. R. 1963. 'The status of the rock pipit (*Anthus spinoletta* ssp.) in the West Riding of Yorkshire', *Naturalist*, 1963: 37-9.

349. NEAL, E. 1948. *The badger*, London.

350. NICHOLLS, A. G. 1946. 'Syncarida in relation to the interstitial habitat', *Nature, Lond.* 158: 934-6.

351. NIELSEN, C. OVERGAARD. 1949. 'Studies on the soil microfauna. II. The soil inhabiting nematodes', *Natura Jutlandica*, 2: 1-131.

352. NIELSEN, C. OVERGAARD. 1952-3. 'Studies on Enchytraeidae. 1. A technique for extracting Enchytraeidae from soil samples', *Oikos*, 4: 187-96.

353. NIELSEN, C. OVERGAARD. 1955. 'Studies on Enchytraeidae. 2. Field studies', *Natura Jutlandica*, 5: 1-58.

354. NIELSEN, C. OVERGAARD. 1962. 'Carbohydrases in soil and litter invertebrates', *Oikos*, 13: 200-15.

355. NIELSEN, C. OVERGAARD & CHRISTENSEN, B. 1959. 'The Enchytraeidae: critical revision and taxonomy of European species. (Studies on Enchytraeidae VII)', *Natura Jutlandica*, 8-9, 1-160. (Also Suppl. in *Natura Jutlandica*, 1961, 10: 1-19.)

356. NIELSEN, E. 1932. *The biology of spiders with especial reference to the Danish fauna*, Copenhagen. Vol. 2.

357. NORDBERG, S. 1936. 'Biologisch-Ökologische Untersuchungen über die Vogel-nidicolen', *Acta Zool. Fenn.* 21: 1-170.

358. NØRGAARD, E. 1956. 'Environment and behaviour of *Theridion saxatile*', *Oikos*, 7: 159-92.

359. ODUM, E. P. & PONTIN, A. J. 1961. 'Population density of the underground ant, *Lasius flavus*, as determined by tagging with P^{32}', *Ecology*, 42: 186-8.

360. OLDHAM, C. 1899. 'Climbing powers of the long-tailed field mouse', *Zoologist*, Ser. 4, 3: 27.

361. OLSEN, C. 1916. 'Studier over epifyt-mossernes indvandringsfølge (succession) paa barken af forskellige traeer . . .,' *Bot. Tidsskr.* 34: 313-42.

362. OSBORNE, P. J. 1956. 'Insects other than Lepidoptera at a Mercury-vapour light trap', *Ent. Mon. Mag.* 92: 19.

363. OSMASTON, F. C. 1959. 'The revised working plan for the Wytham Woods or the Woods of Hazel for the period 1959/60 to 1968/69', Imperial Forestry Institute, Oxford. 2 vols., mimeographed.

364. OVINGTON, J. D. 1963. 'Flower and seed production. A source of error in estimating woodland production, energy flow and mineral cycling', *Oikos*, 14: 148-53.

365. OWEN, D. F. 1953. 'Records of *Protocalliphora azurea* Fall. from bird's nests in Berkshire', *Ent. Rec.* 65: 31-2.

366. OWEN, D. F. 1954. '*Protocalliphora* in birds' nests', *Brit. Birds*, 47: 236-43.

367. OWEN, D. F. 1955. 'The food of the heron *Ardea cinerea* in the breeding season', *Ibis*, 97: 276-95.

368. OWEN, D. F. 1956. 'The food of nestling jays and magpies', *Bird Study*, 3: 257-265.

369. OWEN, D. F. 1960. 'The nesting success of the heron *Ardea cinerea* in relation to the availability of food', *Proc. Zool. Soc. Lond.* 133: 597-617.

370. OWEN, D. F. and ASH, J. S. 1955. 'Additional records of *Protocalliphora* (Diptera) in birds nests', *Brit. Birds.* 48: 225-9.

371. OXFORD UNIVERSITY FORESTRY DEPARTMENT. 1950. 'Working plan for 1949/50-1959/60 for the Woods of Hazel, Wytham, Berks' (Mimeographed).

372. PARIS, O. H. & PITELKA, F. A. 1962. 'Population characteristics of the terrestrial isopod *Armadillidium vulgare* in California grassland', *Ecology*, 43: 229-48.

373. PARK, T. 1961. 'An ecologist's view', *Bull. Ecol. Soc. Amer.* 42(1): 4-10.

373a. PARMENTER, L. 1952. 'Flies at ivy-bloom', *Ent. Rec.* 64: 90-1.

374. PARMENTER, L. 1960. 'Scatopsidae (Dipt.) reared from a wasp's nest', *Ent. Rec.* 72: 274-5.

375. PARRY, D. W. & SMITHSON, P. 1958. 'Silicification of branched cells in the leaves of *Nardus stricta* L.', *Nature, Lond.* 182: 1460-1.

376. PEARCE, E. J. 1948. 'The invertebrate fauna of grass-tussocks: a suggested line for ecological study', *Ent. Mon. Mag.* 84: 169-74.

377. PEARSALL, W. H. 1950. *Mountains and moorlands*, London.

378. PENNANT, T. 1784. *Arctic zoology. Vol. I. Introduction. Class I. Quadrupeds*, London.

379. PERRING, F. H. & WALTERS, S. M. (eds.) 1962. *Atlas of the British Flora*, London.

380. PERRINS, C. 1963. 'Survival in the great tit, *Parus major*', *Proc. 13th Int. Orn. Congr.*: 717-28.

381. [PERRINS, C. M.] 1963. *Rep. Oxf. Orn. Soc. on the Birds of Oxfordshire and Berkshire* for 1963: 54-5.

382. PETERSEN, C. G. J. 1918. 'The sea bottom and its production of fish-food. A survey of the work done in connection with valuation of the Danish waters from 1883-1917', *Rep. Danish Biol. Sta.* 25: 1-62.

383. PETERSEN, C. G. J. & BOYSEN JENSEN, P. 1911. 'Valuation of the sea. I. Animal life of the sea-bottom, its food and quantity. (Quantitative studies)', *Rep. Danish Biol. Sta.* 20: 1-81.

384. PHILLIPS, E. A. 1951. 'The associations of bark-inhabiting bryophytes in Michigan', *Ecol. Monogr.* 21: 301-16.

385. PIGOTT, C. D. 1955. 'Biological Flora of the British Isles. *Thymus* L.', *J. Ecol.* 43: 365-87.

386. PIMENTEL, D. 1961. 'Animal population regulation by the genetic feed-back mechanism', *Amer. Nat.* 95: 65-79.

387. PIMENTEL, D. 1961. 'The influence of plant spatial patterns on insect populations', *Ann. Ent. Soc. Amer.* 54: 61-9.

388. PIMENTEL, D. 1961. 'Species diversity and insect population outbreaks', *Ann. Ent. Soc. Amer.* 54: 76-86.

389. PIMENTEL, D. 1961. 'Competition and the species-per-genus structure of communities', *Ann. Ent. Soc. Amer.* 54: 323-33.

390. PONTIN, A. J. 1958. 'A preliminary note on the eating of aphids by ants of the genus *Lasius* (Hym., Formicidae)', *Ent. Mon. Mag.* 94: 9-11.

391. PONTIN, A. J. 1960. 'Observations on the keeping of aphid eggs by ants of the genus *Lasius* (Hym., Formicidae)', *Ent. Mon. Mag.* 96: 198-9.

392. PONTIN, A. J. 1961. 'Population stabilization and competition between the ants *Lasius flavus* (F.) and *L. niger* (L.)', *J. Anim. Ecol.* 30: 47-54.

393. PONTIN, A. J. 1961. 'The prey of *Lasius niger* (L.) and *L. flavus* (F.) (Hym., Formicidae)', *Ent. Mon. Mag.* 97: 135-7.

394. PONTIN, A. J. 1963. 'Further considerations of competition and the ecology of the ants *Lasius flavus* (F.) and *L. niger* (L.)', *J. Anim. Ecol.* 32: 565-74.

395. PRIESNER, E. 1961. 'Nahrungswahl und Nahrungsverarbeitung bei der Larve von *Tipula maxima*', *Pedobiologia* 1: 25-37.

396. PRIME, C. T. 1960. *Lords and ladies*, London.

397. PUKOWSKI, E. 1933. 'Ökologische Untersuchungen an *Necrophorus* F.', *Z. Morph. Ökol. Tiere*, 27: 518-86.

398. RAMSBOTTOM, J. 1951. *A Handbook of the larger British Fungi*, London.

399. RAMSBOTTOM, J. 1953. *Mushrooms and toadstools: a study of the activities of Fungi*, London.

400. RANWELL, D. S. 1960. 'Newborough Warren, Anglesey. III. Changes in the vegetation on parts of the dune system after the loss of rabbits by myxomatosis', *J. Ecol.* 48: 385-95.

401. RAWSE, M. 1961. 'The problem of *Nardus* and its productivity in relation to sheep grazing at Moor House, Westmorland', *J. Brit. Grassl. Soc.* 16: 190-3.

402. REYNOLDSON, T. B. 1955. 'Observations on the earthworms of North Wales', *Northw. Nat.* N.S. 3: 291-304.

403. RICHARDS, O. W., in SUMMERHAYES, V. S., COLE, L. W. & WILLAMS, P. H. 1924. 'Studies on the ecology of English heaths. I. The vegetation of the unfelled portions of Oxshott Heath and Esher Common, Surrey. With notes on the animals', *J. Ecol.* 12: 287-306.

404. RICHARDS, O. W. 1926. 'Studies on the ecology of English heaths. III. Animal communities of the felling and burn successions at Oxshott Heath, Surrey', *J. Ecol.* 14: 244-81.

405. RICHARDS, O. W. 1930. 'The animal community inhabiting rotten posts at Bagley Wood, near Oxford', *J. Ecol.* 18: 131-8.

406. RICHARDS, O. W. 1939. 'Hymenoptera Aculeata (ants, bees, and wasps)', in *The Victoria History of the County of Oxford* (ed. by L. F. Salzman), Oxford. Vol. 1.

407. RICHARDS, O. W. & WALOFF, N. 1954. 'Studies on the biology and population dynamics of British grasshoppers', *Anti-Locust Bull.* 17: 1-182.

408. RICHARDS, P. W. 1952. *The tropical rain forest: an ecological study*, Cambridge.

409. RIDER, N. E. 1952. 'The effect of a hedge on the flow of air,' *Quart. J. R. Met. Soc.* 78: 98-101.

410. RIDLEY, H. N. 1930. *The dispersal of plants throughout the world*, London.

411. ROBERTS, H. 1956. 'An ecological survey of the arthropods of a mixed beech–oak deciduous woodland, with particular reference to the Lithobiidae', D.Phil. Thesis, Southampton University.

412. ROBERTSON, A. G. 1939. 'The nocturnal activity of crane-flies (Tipulinae) as indicated by captures in a light trap at Rothamsted', *J. Anim. Ecol.* 8: 300-22.

413. ROBINSON, I. 1953. 'On the fauna of a brown flux of an elm tree, *Ulmus procera* Salisb.', *J. Anim. Ecol.* 22: 149-53.

414. ROTHSCHILD, M. & CLAY, T. 1952. *Fleas, flukes and cuckoos: a study of bird parasites*, London.

415. ROYDS, T. F. 1930. *The beasts, birds and bees of Virgil: a naturalist's handbook to the Georgics*, Oxford.

416. RUSSELL, E. J. 1957. *The world of the soil*, London.

417. RUTTNER, F. 1953. *Fundamentals of limnology* (transl. D. G. Frey and F. E. J. Fry), Toronto.

418. SALISBURY, E. J. 1934. 'On the day temperatures of sand dunes in relation to the vegetation at Blakeney Point, Norfolk', *Trans. Norfolk Norw. Nat. Soc.* 13: 333-55.

419. SALISBURY, E. J. 1952. *Downs and dunes: their plant life and its environment*, London.

420. SALISBURY, E. 1961. *Weeds and aliens*, London.

421. SANDARS, E. 1939. *A butterfly book for the pocket*, Oxford.

422. SANDHOLM, H. A. 1952. 'Field observations on the nectar feeding habits of some Minnesota mosquitoes', *Mosquito News*, 22: 346-9.

423. SANDS, W. A. 1957. 'The immature stages of some British Anthocoridae (Hemiptera', *Trans. R. Ent. Soc. Lond.* 109: 295-310.

424. SATCHELL, G. H. 1947. 'The ecology of the British species of *Psychoda* (Diptera: Psychodidae)', *Ann. Appl. Biol.* 34: 611-21.

425. SATCHELL, J. E. 1958. 'Earthworm biology and soil fertility', *Soils & Fert.* 21: 209-219.

426. SATCHELL, J. E. 1962. 'Resistance in oak (*Quercus* spp.) to defoliation by *Tortrix viridana* L. in Roudsea Wood National Nature Reserve', *Ann. Appl. Biol.* 50: 431-42.

427. SATCHELL, J. E. & MOUNTFORD, M. D. 1962. 'A method of assessing caterpillar population on large forest trees, using a systemic insecticide', *Ann. Appl. Biol.* 50: 443-50.

428. SATCHELL, J. E. & SOUTHWOOD, T. R. E. 'The Heteroptera of some woodlands in the English Lake District', *Trans. Soc. Brit. Ent.* 15: 117-34.

429. SAVELY, H. E. 1939. 'Ecological relations of certain animals in dead pine and oak logs', *Ecol. Monogr.* 9: 321-85.

430. SAVORY, T. H. 1935. *The spiders and allied orders of the British Isles*, London.

431. SCHEERPELTZ, O. & HÖFLER, K. 1948. *Käfer und Pilze*, Vienna.

432. SCHNEIDER, F. 1948. 'Beitrag zur Kenntnis der Generationsverhältnisse und Diapause räuberischer Schwebfliegen (Syrphidae, Dipt.)', *Mitt. Schweiz. Ent. Ges.* 21: 249-85.

433. SCORER, A. G. 1913. *The entomologist's log-book*, London.

434. SCOURFIELD, D. J. 1915. 'A new copepod found in water from hollows on tree trunks', *J. Quekett Micr. Club*, Ser. 2, 12: 431-40.

435. SCOURFIELD, D. J. 1939. 'Entomostraca in strange places', *J. Quekett Micr. Club*, Ser. 4, 1: 116-22.

436. SÉGUY, E. 1934. 'Diptères (Brachycères) (Muscidae Acalypterae et Scatophagidae)', *Faune de France*, Vol. 28.

437. SHANKS, R. E. & OLSON, J. S. 1961. 'First-year breakdown of leaf litter in Southern Appalachian forests', *Science*, 134: 194-5.

438. SHARP, W. E. 1908. *The Coleoptera of Lancashire and Cheshire*, St Alban's.

439. SHELFORD, V. E. 1913. *Animal communities in temperate America as illustrated in the Chicago region: A study in animal ecology*, Chicago.

440. SHORTEN, M. 1951. 'Some aspects of the biology of the grey squirrel (*Sciurus carolinensis*) in Great Britain', *Proc. Zool. Soc. Lond.* 121: 427-59.

441. SHORTEN, M. & COURTIER, F. A. 1955. 'A population study of the grey squirrel *Sciurus carolinensis*) in May 1954', *Ann. Appl. Biol.* 43: 494-510.

442. SIDE, K. C. 1955. 'A study of the insects living on the wayfaring tree', *Bull. Amat. Ent. Soc.* 14: 3-5, 11-14, 19-22, 28-31, 43, 47-50.

442a. SIMMONDS, S. P. 1964. '*Chirosia crassiseta* Stein (Dipt., Muscidae) on bracken in Lancashire', *Ent. Mon. Mag.* 100: 80.

443. SIMPSON, J. F. HOPE-. 1940. 'The utilization and improvement of chalk down pastures', *J. R. Agric. Soc.* 100: 44-9.

444. SIMPSON, J. F. HOPE-. 1941. 'Studies of the vegetation of the English chalk. VIII. A second survey of the chalk grassland of the South Downs', *J. Ecol.* 29: 217-67.

445. SKIDMORE, P. 1962. 'Notes on the Helomyzidae of Lancashire and Cheshire . . .', *Entomologist*, 95: 226-36.

446. SKOCZEŃ, S. 1961. 'On food storage of the mole, *Talpa europaea* Linnaeus 1758', *Acta Theriol.* 5: 23-43.

447. SLADEN, F. W. L. 1912. *The humble-bee . . .*, London.

448. SMART, J. 1944. 'The British Simuliidae . . .', *Sci. Publ. Freshw. Biol. Ass.* 9: 1-57.

449. SMITH, F. 1865. 'Notes on *Cynthia cardui* and *Vanessa antiopa*', *Ent. Mon. Mag.* 2: 160-1.

450. SMITH, K. G. V. 1956. 'On the Diptera associated with the stinkhorn (*Phallus impudicus* Pers.) with notes on other insects and invertebrates found on this fungus', *Proc. R. Ent. Soc. Lond.* A, 31: 49-55.

451. SMITH, K. G. V. 1957. 'A preliminary list of the Thysanoptera of Oxfordshire and Berkshire', *Proc. Ashmol. Nat. Hist. Soc.* 1951-6: 19-26.

452. SMITH, K. PAVIOUR-. 1959. 'The ecology of the fauna associated with macrofungi growing on dead and decaying trees', D.Phil. Thesis, Oxford University.

453. SMITH, K. PAVIOUR-. 1960. 'The invasion of Britain by *Cis bilamellatus* Fowler (Coleoptera: Ciidae)', *Proc. R. Ent. Soc. Lond.* A, 35: 145-55.

454. SMITH, K. PAVIOUR-. 1960. 'The fruiting-bodies of macrofungi as habitats for beetles of the family Ciidae (Coleoptera)', *Oikos*, 11: 43-71.

455. SMITH, K. PAVIOUR-. 1960. 'Insect succession in the "birch-bracket fungus", *Polyporus betulinus*', *Verh. 11th Int. Kongr. Ent. Wien* 1960, 1: 792-6.

456. SMITH, K. PAVIOUR-. 1963. 'The night–day activity of *Tetratoma fungorum* F. (Col., Tetratomidae)', *Ent. Mon. Mag.* 99: 234-40.

457. SMITH, K. PAVIOUR-. 1964. 'The life history of *Tetratoma fungorum* F. (Col., Tetratomidae) in relation to habitat requirements, with an account of eggs and larval stages', *Ent. Mon. Mag.* 100: 118-34.

458. SMITH, K. PAVIOUR-. 1964. 'Habitats, headquarters and distribution of *Tetratoma fungorum* (Col., Tetratomidae)', *Ent. Mon. Mag.* 100: 71-80.

458a. SMITH, K. PAVIOR-. 1965. 'Some factors affecting numbers of the fungus beetle *Tetratoma fungorum* F.', *J. Anim. Ecol.* 34: 699-724.

459. SMITH, P. GRIEG-. 1961. 'Data on pattern within communities. II. *Ammophila arenaria* (L.) Link', *J. Ecol.* 49: 703-08.

460. SMUTS, J. C. 1936. *Holism and evolution*, London. (Orig. publ. 1926.) P. 16.

461. SOUTH, A. 1961. 'The taxonomy of the British species of *Entomobrya* (Collembola)', *Trans. R. Ent. Soc. Lond.* 113: 387-416.

462. SOUTH, R. 1961. *The moths of the British Isles*, (revised by H. M. Edelsten & D. S. Fletcher), London etc. Vol. 1.

463. SOUTHERN, H. N. 1954. 'Tawny owls and their prey', *Ibis*, 96: 384-410.

464. SOUTHERN, H. N. 1959. 'Mortality and population control', *Ibis*, 101: 429-36.

465. SOUTHERN, H. N. & LINN, I. 1964. 'Distribution, range and habitat', Ch. 4 in *The Handbook of British Mammals* (ed. H. N. Southern), Oxford.

466. SOUTHWOOD, T. R. E. 1961. 'The number of species of insect associated with various trees', *J. Anim. Ecol.* 30: 1-8.

467. SOUTHWOOD, T. R. E. 1962. 'Migration of terrestrial arthropods in relation to habitat', *Biol. Rev.* 37: 171-214.

468. SOUTHWOOD, T. R. E. & JEPSON, W. F. 1962. 'The productivity of grasslands in England for *Oscinella frit* (L.) (Chloropidae) and other stem-boring Diptera', *Bull. Ent. Res.* 53: 395-407.

469. SOUTHWOOD, T. R. E. & LESTON, D. 1959. *Land and water bugs of the British Isles*, London, etc.

470. SOUTHWOOD, T. R. E. & SCUDDER, G. G. E. 1956. 'The immature stages of the Hemiptera-Heteroptera associated with the stinging nettle (*Urtica dioica* L.)', *Ent. Mon. Mag.* 92: 313-25.

471. SPARKS, B. W. 1957. 'The non-marine Mollusca of the Interglacial deposits at Bobbitshole, Ipswich', *Phil. Trans.* Ser. B, 241: 33-44.

472. SPECTOR, W. S. (Ed.) 1956. *Handbook of biological data*, Philadelphia & London.

473. SPITTLE, R. J. 1947. 'The coleopterous fauna of herons' nests', *Ent. Mon. Mag.* 83: 204.

474. SPITTLE, R. J. 1947. 'The coleopterous fauna of carrion-crows' nests', *Ent. Mon. Mag.* 83: 270.

475. SPITTLE, R. J. 1948. 'The coleopterous fauna of sand-martins' nests', *Ent. Mon. Mag.* 84: 260.

476. SPITTLE, R. J. 1949. 'The coleopterous fauna of owls' nests', *Ent. Mon. Mag.* 85: 78-9.

477. SPITTLE, R. J. 1951. 'The coleopterous fauna of red squirrels' dreys', *Ent. Mon. Mag.* 87: 184.

478. SPITTLE, R. J. 1952. 'The coleopterous fauna of grey squirrels' dreys', *Ent. Mon. Mag.* 88: 163-4.

479. SPOONER, G. M. 1961. '*Bathynella* and other interstitial Crustacea in southern England', *Nature, Lond.* 190: 104-5.

480. STEERS, J. A. 1944. 'Coastal preservation and planning', *Geogr. J.* 104: 7-27.

481. STEERS, J. A. (ed.) 1960. *Scolt Head Island*, Cambridge. 2nd ed.

482. STEGMAN, LE R. C. 1960. 'A preliminary survey of earthworms of the Tully forest in central New York', *Ecology*, 41: 779-82.

483. STEP, E. 1908. *Wayside and woodland ferns . . .*, London & New York.

484. STOTT, F. C. 1936. 'The marine foods of birds in an inland fjord region in West Spitsbergen. Part 1. Plankton and in shore benthos', *J. Anim. Ecol.* 5: 356-69.

485. STROYAN, H. G. L. 1955. 'Recent additions to the British aphid fauna. Part II', *Trans. R. Ent. Soc. Lond.* 106: 283-340.

486. STYLES, J. H. 1960. '*Syndemis musculana* Hübner (Lep., Tortricidae) in conifer plantations and forest nurseries in the British Isles', *Ent. Gaz.* 11: 144-8.

487. SUMMERHAYES, V. S. 1941. 'The effect of voles (*Microtus agrestis*) on vegetation', *J. Ecol.* 29: 14-48.

488. SUMMERHAYES, V. S., COLE, L. W. & WILLIAMS, P. H. 1924. 'Studies on the ecology of English heaths. I. The vegetation of the unfelled portions of Oxshott Heath and Esher Common, Surrey', *J. Ecol.* 12: 287-306.

489. SUMMERHAYES, V. S. & ELTON, C. S. 1923. 'Contributions to the ecology of Spitsbergen and Bear Island', *J. Ecol.* 11: 214-86.

490. SUMMERHAYES, V. S. & ELTON, C. S. 1928. 'Further contributions to the ecology of Spitsbergen', *J. Ecol.* 16: 193-268.

491. SVENDSEN, J. A. 1957. 'The distribution of Lumbricidae in an area of Pennine moorland (Moor House Nature Reserve)', *J. Anim. Ecol.* 26: 411-21.

492. SVENDSEN, J. A. 1957. 'The behaviour of Lumbricids under moorland conditions', *J. Anim. Ecol.* 26: 423-39.

493. TANSLEY, A. G. 1939. *The British Islands and their vegetation*, Cambridge.

494. TAYLOR, L. R. 1960. 'Mortality and viability of insect migrants high in the air', *Nature, Lond.* 186: 410.

495. TEAL, J. M. 1957. 'Community metabolism in a temperate cold spring', *Ecol. Monogr.* 27: 283-302.

496. TESTER, J. R. & MARSHALL, W. H. 1961. 'A study of certain plant and animal interrelations on a native prairie in northwestern Minnesota', *Occ. Pap. Univ. Minn. Mus. Nat. Hist.* 8: 1-51.

497. THOMAS, A. S. 1960. 'Changes in vegetation since the advent of myxomatosis', *J. Ecol.* 48: 287-306.

498. THOMAS, A. S. 1962. 'Anthills and termite mounds in pastures', *J. Brit. Grassl. Soc.* 17: 103-8.

499. THOMPSON, D'A. W. 1910. 'Vol. IV. Historia Animalium', in *The works of Aristotle translated into English* (ed. by J. A. Smith & W. D. Ross), Oxford.

500. THOMPSON, G. B. 1955. 'The parasites of British birds and mammals. IV. Records of mammal parasites', *Ent. Mon. Mag.* 71: 214-19.

501. THOMPSON, H. S. 1925. 'Flowering plants as epiphytes on willows and alders', *Nature, Lond.* 116: 710-11.

502. THOMPSON, H. V. & WORDEN, A. N. 1956. *The rabbit*, London.

503. THOMPSON, J. L. CLOUDSLEY-. 1959. 'Notes on Arachnida. 32. The fauna of sand-dunes', *Ent. Mon. Mag.* 95: 24.

504. THOMPSON, W. R. (ed.) 1954. *A catalogue of the parasites and predators of insect*

pests. Sect. 2. Host parasite catalogue. Pt 3. Host of the Hymenoptera (Calliceratid to Evaniid), Ottawa.

505. TISCHLER, W. 1955. 'Influence of soil types on the epigeic fauna of agricultural land', in *Soil Zoology* (ed. by D. K. McE. Kevan), London. Pp. 125-37.

506. TISCHLER, W. 1955. *Synkölogie der Landtiere*, Stuttgart. Chs. 17 & 18.

507. TODD, V. 1949. 'The habits and ecology of the British harvestmen (Arachnida, Opiliones), with special reference to those of the Oxford District', *J. Anim. Ecol.* 18: 209-29.

508. TURNBULL, A. L. 1957. 'The ecology of some woodland spiders', D.Phil. Thesis, Oxford University.

509. TURNBULL, A. L. 1960. 'The prey of the spider *Linyphia triangularis* (Clerck) (Araneae, Linyphiidae)', *Canad. J. Zool.* 38: 859-73.

510. TURNBULL, A. L. 1960. 'The spider population of a stand of oak (*Quercus robur* L.) in Wytham Wood, Berks. England', *Canad. Ent.* 92: 110-24.

511. TURNER, G. J. 1901. *Select pleas of the Forest*, Selden Society, London.

512. TYLER, P. S. 1961. 'Cluster flies and swarming flies: their behaviour and control', *Sanitarian*, 69: 285-90.

513. URBAIN, A.-J. & MARTY, P. 1920. 'Influence du travail souterrain des taupes sur la flore des pâturages du Cantal', *C. R. Acad. Sci., Paris*, 171: 581-3.

514. VACHON, M. 1957. 'Remarques sur les Chernetidae (Pseudoscorpions) de la faune britannique', *Ann. Mag. Nat. Hist.* Ser. 12, 10: 389-94.

515. VAN DER DRIFT, J. 1950. 'Analysis of the animal community in a beech forest floor', *Tijdschr. Ent.* 94: 1-168.

516. VAN DER DRIFT, J. & WITKAMP, M. 1958. 'The significance of the break-down of oak litter by *Enoicyla pusilla* Burm', *Arch. Néerl. Zool.* 13: 486-92.

517. VAN EMDEN, F. I. 1945. 'Larvae of British beetles. V. Elateridae', *Ent. Mon. Mag.* 81: 13-37.

518. VAN HEERDT, P. F. & MÖRZER BRUYNS, M. F. 1960. 'A biocenological investigation in the yellow dune region of Terschelling', *Tijdschr. Ent.* 103: 225-73.

519. VARLEY, G. C. & GRADWELL, G. R. 1958. 'Balance in insect populations', *Proc. 10th Int. Congr. Ent.* 2: 619-24.

520. VARLEY, G. C. & GRADWELL, G. R. 1958. 'Oak defoliators in England', *Proc. 10th Int. Congr. Ent.* 4: 134-6.

521. VARLEY, G. C. & GRADWELL, G. R. 1962. 'The effect of partial defoliation by caterpillars on the timber production of oak trees in England', *Proc. 11th Int. Congr. Ent.* 2: 211-14.

522. VENABLES, L. S. V. 1939. 'Bird distribution on the South Downs, and a comparison with that of Surrey Greensand heaths', *J. Anim. Ecol.* 8: 227-37.

523. VERDCOURT, B. 1947. 'A note on the food of *Acrydium* Geoff. (Orthopt.)', *Ent. Mon. Mag.* 83: 190.

524. VERE, D. W. 1947. 'The hornets of Epping Forest', *London Nat.* for 1946 (26): 99-109.

525. VON BOCHMANN, G. 1941-42. 'Die Spinnenfauna der Strandhaferdünen an der deutschen Küsten', *Kieler Meeresforsch.* 4: 38-69.

526. VON LENGERKEN, H. 1954. *Die Brutfürsorge- und Brutpflegeinstinkte der Käfer*, Leipzig.

527. VON MARILAUN, A. K. 1895. *The natural history of plants: their forms, growth, reproduction, and distribution. Vol. II. The history of plants*, (transl. F. W. Oliver), London.

528. WADDELL, H. 1952. *Mediaeval Latin lyrics*, Harmondsworth, Middlesex.

529. WAKELY, S. 1958. 'Notes on the Tineina', *Ent. Rec.* 70: 81-2.

530. WALKER, J. J. 1907. 'Preliminary list of Coleoptera observed in the neighbourhood of Oxford from 1819 to 1907', *Proc. Ashmol. Nat. Hist. Soc.* for 1906: 49-99.

531. WALKER, J. J. 1908. 'Coleoptera in flood-refuse at Oxford', *Ent. Mon. Mag.* 44: 135-6.

532. WALKER, J. J. 1935. 'New localities for *Cis bilamellatus* Wood', *Ent. Mon. Mag.* 71: 245.

533. WALLACE, A. R. 1890 ed. *A narrative of travels on the Amazon and Rio Negro . . .*, London etc. P. 4. (Orig. publ. 1853.)

534. WALLACE, D. B. JOHNSTONE- & KENNEDY, K. 1944. 'Grazing management practices and their relationship to the behaviour and grazing habits of cattle', *J. Agric. Sci.* 34: 190-7.

535. WALLACE, H. R. 1953. 'The ecology of the insect fauna of pine stumps', *J. Anim. Ecol.* 22: 154-71.

536. WALOFF, N. & BLACKITH, R. E. 1962. 'The growth and distribution of the mounds of *Lasius flavus* (Fabricius) (Hym: Formicidae) in Silwood Park, Berkshire', *J. Anim. Ecol.* 31: 421-37.

537. WARDLE, P. 1961. 'Biological Flora of the British Isles. *Fraxinus excelsior* L.', *J. Ecol.* 49: 739-51.

538. WATERHOUSE, D. F. 1947. 'The relative importance of live sheep and of carrion as breeding grounds for the Australian sheep blowfly *Lucilia cuprina*', *Bull. Coun. Sci. Industr. Res., Aust.* 217: 1-31.

539. WATERHOUSE, D. F. & PARAMONOV, S. J. 1950. 'The status of the two species of *Lucilia* (Diptera, Calliphoridae) attacking sheep in Australia', *Aust. J. Sci. Res.* Ser. B, 3: 310-36.

540. WATERHOUSE, F. L. 1955. 'Microclimatological profiles in grass cover in relation to biological problems', *Quart. J. R. Met. Soc.* 81: 63-71.

541. WATLING, R. 1962. 'Fungal succession on kestrel pellets', *Naturalist*: 41-3.

542. WATNEY, V. J. 1910. *Cornbury and the Forest of Wychwood*, London.

543. WATT, A. S. 1947. 'Pattern and process in the plant community', *J. Ecol.* 35: 1-22.

544. WEBER, N. A. 1935. 'The biology of the thatching ant, *Formica rufa obscuripes* Forel, in North Dakota', *Ecol. Monogr.* 5: 164-206.

545. WELLINGTON, P. S. 1960. 'Assessment and control of the dissemination of weeds by crop seeds', in *The biology of weeds* (ed. J. L. Harper), Oxford. Pp. 94-107.

546. WHITE, D. J. B. 1961. 'Some observations on the vegetation of Blakeney Point, Norfolk, following the disappearance of the rabbits in 1954', *J. Ecol.* 49: 113-18.

547. WHITE, E. 1960. 'The natural history of some species of *Aphodius* (Col., Scarabaeidae) in the Northern Pennines', *Ent. Mon. Mag.* 96: 25-30.

548. WILLIAMS, C. M., BARNESS, L. A. & SAWYER, W. H. 1943. 'The utilization of

glycogen by flies during flight and some aspects of the physiological ageing of *Drosophila*', *Biol. Bull., Wood's Hole*, 84: 263-72.

549. WILSON, G. F. 1926. 'Insect visitors to sap-exudations of trees', *Trans. Ent. Soc. Lond.* 74: 243-54.

550. WILSON, G. F. 1929. 'Pollination of hardy fruits: insect visitors to fruit blossoms', *Ann. Appl. Biol.* 16: 602-29.

551. WILSON, G. F. 1933. 'Contributions from the Wisley Laboratory. LXV. Pollination in orchards (VIII). Insect visitors to fruit blossom', *J. R. Hort. Soc.* 58: 125-38.

552. WINSTON, P. W. 1956. 'The acorn microsere, with special reference to arthropods', *Ecology*, 37: 120-32.

553. WITHYCOMBE, C. L. 1923. 'Notes on the biology of some British Neuroptera (Planipennia)', *Trans. Ent. Soc. Lond.* 1922: 501-94.

554. WOLCOTT, G. N. 1937. 'An animal census of two pastures and a meadow in northern New York', *Ecol. Monogr.* 7: 1-90.

555. WOODROFFE, G. E. 1953. 'An ecological study of the insects and mites in the nests of certain birds in Britain', *Bull. Ent. Res.* 44: 739-72.

556. WOODROFFE, G. E. & SOUTHGATE, B. J. 1951. 'Birds' nests as a source of domestic pests', *Proc. Zool. Soc. Lond.* 121: 55-62.

557. WOODROFFE, G. E. & SOUTHGATE, B. J. 1954. 'An investigation of the distribution and field habits of the varied carpet beetle, *Anthrenus verbasci* (L.) (Col., Dermestidae) in Britain . . .', *Bull. Ent. Res.* 45: 575-83.

558. WORTHINGTON, E. B. 1941. 'Rainbow trout in Britain', *Salm. Trout. Mag.* 100: 241-60; 101: 16 & 62-99.

559. YAPP, W. B. 1955. 'A classification of the habitats of British birds', *Bird Study*, 2: 111-21.

560. YAPP, W. B. 1962. *Birds and woods*, London etc.

561. ZAHAR, A. R. 1951. 'The ecology and distribution of black-flies (Simuliidae) in south-east Scotland', *J. Anim. Ecol.* 20: 33-62.

562. ZOEBELEIN, G. 1956. 'Der Honigtau als Nahrung der Insekten', *Z. Ges. Ent.* 38: 369-416; 39: 129-67.

Notes

Note numbers in the text are in square brackets

1 (p. 65). John Morris[336] writes of the way polo was being played in 1927 at a remote part of the North-West Frontier: 'Polo, as played in Hunza, is very different from the game as it is known in India and England. It takes place in a gravelled and walled enclosure rather smaller than a hockey-field. Any number of people may play at a time, and the game generally results in a free-for-all scramble to hit the ball. There appear to be no rules. I imagine this is the original form of the game. It is still played in this way in the remote parts of Central Asia and is exactly as portrayed in early Persian paintings.' The phrase 'there appear to be no rules' might well stand for the outlook of a conventional experimental zoologist upon the difficult problems of community ecology in the field.

2 (p. 100). *Rubus vestitus* was named by Dr E. F. Warburg.

3 (p. 109). Identification of the fauna of grassland on The Dell was done by a number of experts who will be acknowledged in detail when the full results are published. The largest task was naming the beetles, done by Mr P. J. Osborne.

4 (p. 113). Prof. D. Pimentel has allowed me to consult his unpublished report on the food of voles on Rough Common, an investigation done in cooperation with D. H. Chitty's population study of *Microtus agrestis* there.

5 (p. 148). *Cochlicella acuta.* The map in Fig. 15 is mainly constructed from the table and map of vice-county distribution in the Conchological Society's Census,[78] published in 1951 but with the following corrections and additions. The inland locality in Wiltshire is omitted since it is almost certainly a temporary introduction.[219] Later work extended the distribution to the whole coast of Kent.[92] It is to be noted that each stretch of vice-county is marked completely (as in the Census maps) but the actual localities are of course much more restricted within the vice-county.

6 (p. 152). Dr J. Morton Boyd has given me the heights of the two grass areas on Tiree, not included in his papers.

7 (p. 155). The ants were named by Dr A. J. Pontin.

8 (p. 163). Animals were named as follows: *Achorutes reuteri* by Dr A. Macfadyen; *Stenus ossium* by Mr P. J. Osborne; *Theridium bimaculatum* by Dr E. Duffey; the rest by myself. Dr E. W. Jones examined the moss.

9 (p. 165). Animals were named as follows: *Calocoris norvegicus* by Dr G. G. E. Scudder; beetles by Mr P. J. Osborne; *Bombus lapidarius* by Dr I. H. H. Yarrow; the rest by myself.

9A (p. 173). Mr H. N. Southern informs me that bank voles (*Clethrionomys glareolus*) gnaw the bark of elders in Wytham Woods in some winters.

10 (p. 174). Assistance in the field survey at Sheep Drove was given by the following people, who came from time to time, and to whom I am grateful. Dr J. F. Hope Simpson inspected the vegetation; Mr (now Professor) Francis C. Evans and the late Mr G. Swynnerton trapped small mammals in the neighbourhood; Dr B. M. Hobby and the late Mr J. R. Carpenter collected some insects; Mr L. S. V. Venables and the late Mrs Fraser Darling (then Miss Averil Morley) did bird counts. Most of the collections of insects were mounted by Mr E. Taylor and Mr E. W. Aubrook. Help in naming specimens was given by several people, especially: Dr Hobby (Psocoptera), Prof. O. W. Richards (bumble-bees), the late Prof. L. W. Grensted (Diptera) and *Simulium* by the late Dr F. W. Edwards; Mr P. J. Osborne (Coleoptera); Dr G. G. E. Scudder (Hemiptera Heteroptera) and *Anthocoris* by Mr W. J. LeQuesne. The field notes and a large sample of the collections are deposited with the Ecological Survey in the Bureau of Animal Population. My wife made careful notes of all the trees, shrubs and climbers, recording their times of leafing, flowering and fruiting; and helped me considerably with the mapping of habitats.

11 (p. 178). *Corticaria fuscula* was named by Dr J. Balfour-Browne; the other beetles (except *Phyllotreta nemorum* identified by myself) by Mr P. J. Osborne.

12 (p. 179). The insects from hawthorn were named as follows: beetles by Mr P. J. Osborne; ants by Dr A. J. Pontin; Hemiptera by Dr G. G. E. Scudder. *Rhynchites aequatus* and *R. caeruleus* are mentioned by Massee[318] as pests of fruit trees, especially apple. The latter is known as the 'apple twig cutter' from its habit of cutting off the shoot in which it lays the egg. It has also been recorded on oaks.

13 (p. 182). *Ceruraphis eriophori* named by Dr H. L. G. Stroyan; *Hemerobius humulinus.* by Mr C. A. Elbourn; *Chrysopa perla* by myself.

14 (p. 182). All these moths occur on both *Viburnum* species, *Lithocolletis lantanella* occasionally also on the rowan, *Sorbus aucuparia*, and *Coleophora ahenella* also on buckthorn, *Rhamnus*, and dogwood, *Cornus sanguinea*.[161]

15 (p. 183). *Entomobrya nivalis*, on flowers of *Viburnum lantana*, 2–6 ft, deciduous woodland edge, Wytham Woods, 10 June 1962. Named by Mr A. Macfadyen and Mr I. Healey.

16 (p. 183). Lichen named by Miss Ursula Duncan.

17 (p. 183). Pscoptera from hawthorn were named by Dr B. M. Hobby.

17A (p. 186). Since this chapter was completed for press an excellent study of the feeding sites of birds in grassland with thick scrub by Bevan[24] has been published. This was done on Bookham Common in Surrey, and a comparison made with an earlier survey of feeding habitats in dense oak wood there. This analysis gives many instances of the effects of habitat structure on feeding possibilities for birds.

18 (p. 199). Prof. G. C. Varley and Dr G. D. Gradwell have provided me with some original figures, as they cannot be read accurately from the published graphs. There is a correction in the total figure for five trees, 1952.

19 (p. 200). Dr H. L. G. Stroyan has given me the following information about sycamore aphids. *Drepanosiphum platanoides* is much more common on sycamore than on common maple, on which it is not found to any great extent. *Periphyllus testudinatus* is a highly polyphagous aphid whose main host plant is the common maple. *Periphyllus aceris* ssp. *acericola* seems to live exclusively on sycamore, and Dr A. F. G. Dixon informs me that he has found this but not the next species in Wytham Woods. *Drepanosiphum* *gracilis* appears to live only on sycamore, and on the lower leaves of saplings growing in dense shade. The first record in Britain was at Harpenden, Hertfordshire, in 1949.[485]

20 (p. 202). Mr M. Brown has provided me with information from literature about the beech species in Europe and the Black Sea. There is still a good deal of doubt about the status and distribution of *Fagus sylvatica* and *F. orientalis*, since the two forms overlap and cannot always be easily separated. *F. orientalis* had a wider European range in the Tertiary Period. Probably both forms occur in the Crimea.

21 (p. 212). Dr R. R. Askew informs me that the food-webs given in his oak gall-fly paper[13] combine records from two separate areas in Wytham Woods, about 1300 yards apart: (1) a young plantation of oaks (mainly *Quercus robur*) of average height about 10 ft, mixed with young ash, beech, spruce and cypress, (2) scattered large oak trees with canopy sweeping near the ground, with dense field layer between them of bramble, bracken and honeysuckle, and with sallow trees and bushes.

22 (p. 214). A recent summary of the food-habits of *Cantharis* and *Rhagonycha* species by Janssen[244] in Germany suggests that they are really omnivores. Adults have been found eating other insects and sometimes other Cantharids, young shoots of forest trees, flowers and young fruits of fruit trees, and both pollen and nectar of herbs and shrubs. The larvae in the ground zone or soil have been found eating snails and slugs, worms and insect larvae, and also attacking wheat seeds and crop vegetables that have already been opened by other damage. In Poland[5] adult *Cantharis livida, fusca* and *rustica* visit the crops of rape (*Brassica napus*) during the flowering period from the end of May to mid-June, and there prey on a number of insects, including Bibionid and other flies, hive-bees and small Nitidulid and other beetles (including weevils). *Malachius aeneus* attacks aphids, also small beetles, flies and Hymenoptera.

22A (p. 222). Mr (now the Rev.) P. H. T. Hartley's unusual width of ecological interest led him, in the course of his systematic patrols for observation of birds, to collect information also about insects (including a complete record of butterflies seen over two years in Wytham Woods). All the information and many specimens, especially of Diptera, with their correct habitat context, are deposited with the Ecological Survey.

23 (p. 227). Mrs Vizoso informs me that in a wide experience of grey squirrels she only had three nests in ash, one in sycamore, none in Norway maple (*Acer platanoides*) – though they often use common maple (*Acer campestre*) – and something over six in elm. Shorten and Courtier[441] give a list of nest trees (including summer and winter records) on a 46-acre mixed woodland near Petersfield, Hampshire, visited in May. 266 dreys were noted, in a large number of different kinds of trees, but none in ash or sycamore, although these, as Mrs Vizoso informs me, were both present and the squirrel population was crowded. They frequently obtained seeds from sycamore and elm, the latter being little used for nesting.

23A (p. 229). Mr H. N. Southern has also noted rook roosts in several parts of Wytham Woods at one time or another.

24 (p. 232). The extensive surveys of the British woodland litter fauna by Dr J. E. Satchell and his colleagues based on Merlewood Research Station of the Nature Conservancy, and their analysis in collaboration with Mr M. D. Mountford of the Conservancy's Biometrics Unit in London have not been published and are therefore not taken into account in the figures given here. They will not only add a certain number of animal species, but give for the first time a quantitative comparison of a number of woods with different dominant trees and a variety of soils. Similarly, I have not included an important survey and analysis of the beech litter community in Wytham Woods, carried out by Professor M. Lloyd and Dr R. J. Ghelardi, the results of which are being worked out in California.

25 (p. 238). The collecting trays, made of muslin on frames, were at ground level but not much in contact with the soil surface. The leaves were brought in and dried at room temperature, stored, and weighed later on. From information that Mr K. L. Bocock has given me it seems likely that the losses from leaching and microbial activity before the leaves were brought in was probably quite small. Losses during drying and storage would not be more than about 10%. For the comparative treatment I have used, this error is not important.

26 (p. 247). Bornebusch used the name *Allolobophora turgidus*, which is a synonym for *A. caliginosa*.[178]

27 (p. 255). The food of the mole (*Talpa europaea*) can be determined in two ways: by looking at stomach contents and by the stores of earthworms that are sometimes found underground. Godfrey and Crowcroft[190] ascertained, from an examination of stomachs of moles from Suffolk farmland, that earthworms not only occurred in nearly all of them but also formed by far the greater part of the bulk of food. Insects, adult and larval, were commonly encountered but were small in bulk – less than 10% of the whole. Earthworm egg cocoons were common in the pasture moles. Other even smaller items were molluscs and myriapods. Although mole diet varies with the seasons, earthworms are predominant all round the year. Moles sometimes (it is not known how commonly) make large stores of live worms that have mostly had the heads bitten off, but may otherwise be relatively uninjured – which Evans[140] suggested might be through their being collected in underground runs. Skoczen[446] in Poland has assembled enough evidence to show not only that *Lumbricus terrestris* is the chief species taken (as in England), but that it is selected in preference to others.

28 (p. 268). In *Historia Animalium* of Aristotle (translated by D'Arcy Thompson[499]), section 554b: 'In Pontus are found bees exceedingly white in colour, and these bees produce their honey twice a month. . . . But this is not always the case with these bees, but only in the winter season; for in Pontus the ivy is abundant, and it flowers at this time of the year, and it is from the ivy-flower that they derive their honey.' Thompson states that Aristotle probably did most of his natural history studies in middle age (this would place them in the region of 300 B.C.), and that he had more interest in the wild life of Macedonia and the coast of Asia Minor than in Greece itself. Pontus was a region on the Black Sea coast of Asia Minor. The ivy would apparently be the same as our species.[71]

29 (p. 273). The insects visiting *Viburnum lantana* were collected by Miss B. MacPherson (now Mrs Sladen), who named the flies. Mr J. L. Perkins named the Ichneumonidae and Prof. O. W. Richards *Mellinus*.

30 (p. 274). The insects visiting blackberries were studied by Mr V. P. W. Lowe and Miss S. Middleton during a field class exercise. The flies were named partly by Miss

MacPherson (now Mrs Sladen) the rest (*Sarcophaga, Lucilia, Muscina*) by Mr K. G. V. Smith.

31 (p. 284). The parasites of *Hylesinus fraxini* were named by the following experts: Braconidae by Mr G. Nixon, 1950; *Eurytoma morio* by Dr J. F. Claridge, 1958; other Chalcids by Mr G. J. Kerrich, 1950. Earlier records of '*Eurytoma flavoscapularis*' are probably *E. morio*.

32 (p. 290). Of the beech log insects, *Conosomus testaceus* was named by Mr P. J. Osborne; the larvae of *Denticollis lineatus* by Prof. E. W. Fager; *Ichneumon gracilentus* by Mr R. D. Eady; and *Coelocrabro leucostomoides* by Prof. O. W. Richards; the rest by myself.

33 (p. 291). Of the species from the rotten ash branch mentioned, *Coelocrabro ambiguus* was named by Dr I. H. H. Yarrow; the rest by myself.

34 (p. 295). *Phlaeothrips* (= *Hoplothrips*) *ulmi* was named by Dr G. D. Morison. It was breeding in the *Grynobius* galleries.

35 (p. 297). The totals given here are derived from the tables in Fager's thesis, which are very slightly different from those given in his thesis text.

36 (p. 297). Of the four largest insect tunnellers only 14 *Tipula flavolineata* occurred, distributed in 6 natural logs. But *Denticollis linearis* was common: 216 larvae in 24 natural logs.

36A (p. 297). Comparison between log and litter communities has been facilitated by some preliminary lists of mites and Collembola in beech litter at Wytham, supplied to me by Prof. M. Lloyd [24]. He considers that a good many more resemblances will be found when the litter community identifications are complete, though at the same time there are some striking differences especially among the microfauna and among mites in particular.

37 (p. 301). All identifications of the difficult family Ichneumonidae have been made by Mr J. L. Perkins or Mr R. D. Eady at the British Museum (Natural History).

38 (p. 303). In compiling the list of breeding birds in the Wytham area, I have relied greatly on the knowledge of Mr H. N. Southern, as well as upon information given me from time to time by members of the Edward Grey Institute of Field Ornithology, especially Dr C. M. Perrins.

39 (p. 309). *Gyrophaena strictula* was named by Mr C. E. Tottenham; *Aceosejus muricatus* by Dr G. Owen Evans.

40 (p. 322). Long-eared owl pellets were collected by me in a young larch plantation on Beinn Lagan, Argyll, 18 April 1939, and the moths bred out and named by Mr E. W. Aubrook. *Monopis weaverella* was bred out by me from the following bird pellets collected by Mr V. P. W. Lowe in Wytham Woods: 15 adults from an old tawny owl pellet, 19 April 1956, and 8 from heron pellets, 24 April 1956; named with the help of Mr E. Taylor. *Monopis rusticella* is reported to be common in winter birds' nests (e.g. those of thrushes and blackbirds),[529] also in dried dung and 'animal refuse'.[161] I have bred *M. weaverella* from nest debris (not carrion) of a tawny owl, *Strix aluco*, in a natural hole in a beech tree at 20 ft, in deciduous woodland at Wytham; the nest collected by J. Pollack and J. M. Cherrett.

41 (p. 324). A further 61 species on the general carrion list have been recorded in the Wytham Woods area, though not actually at carrion. 46 were beetles, and half of these Staphylinidae.

42 (p. 324). The carrion beetles were collected from this dead tawny owl by Mr H. N. Southern, Miss K. Paviour-Smith (Mrs Southern) and Professor M. Lloyd. The owl was on the ground in an oak-sycamore wood, 6 August 1959. Dr J. Balfour-Browne named the *Sciodrepa*, *Gnathoncus*, *Oxytelus* and *Aleochara*; Professor Lloyd *Philonthus succicola* and *P. fimetarius*. The rest were named by myself.

43 (p. 330). 2♂ *Lucilia caesar* on *Pastinaca sativa* flowers at deciduous woodland edge, August 1948. Rev. P. H. T. Hartley coll., Mr G. R. Gradwell det.; 1♂ *L. ampullacea*, coll. by field class on over-ripe blackberries at deciduous woodland edge, September 1954. Mr K. G. V. Smith det.

44 (p. 332). In many hot dry countries of the world dung is assiduously collected by the inhabitants for fuel. J. D. Hooker in his *Himalayan Journals*[235] described a visit in 1849 to the edge of Tibet, where yaks were pastured. 'All their droppings are removed from near the tents, and piled in heaps. . . . These heaps swarm with the maggots of two large flies, a yellow and a black, affording abundant food to red-legged crows, ravens and swallows.'

45 (p. 332). Dr M. H. R. Soper of the Department of Agriculture, Oxford, has guided me to the literature on cow behaviour and dung production.

46 (p. 333). The chemistry and microbiology of nutrition in dung insects has not been far explored, especially the roles played by bacteria as intermediate converters, as against direct digestion of the solid or liquid dung constituents. The chief work has been done by Madle,[314] with the beetles *Aphodius*, whose larvae feed on albumins.

47 (p. 336). At Rothamsted it was proved by experiments that cattle, horse or sheep dung greatly stimulated the rate of cocoon production in the earthworm *Allolobophora chlorotica*;[141] and it was also found that earthworms were five times as abundant on patches where dung had lain some months before as on ordinary neighbouring pasture patches.[416] In the wet conditions of Moor House National Nature Reserve in the Pennine Hills, Svendsen[491, 492] discovered that four species of earthworms – *Lumbricus rubellus* and *Dendrobaena rubida* on alluvial soils and *D. octoedra* and *Bimastus eiseni* on wet moor and bog – were highly aggregated in sheep dung, which they consumed.

48 (p. 336). In Tullgren funnel extracts from 6 small tussocks of grass, *Deschampsia caespitosa*, in oak–ash–sycamore wood at Wytham, 5 December 1956, there were 216 beetles belonging to at least 36 species (64 of them being Aleocharine Staphylinidae that were not named). Among these were specimens of *Sphaeridium lunulatum*, *Cercyon atomarius*, *Oxytelus laqueatus* and *Aleochara lanuginosa*, all of which have also been taken in cow or sheep dung, or both, in the Wytham area. *A. lanuginosa* also visits carrion there; Donisthorpe,[102] for Windsor Forest, gives its habitats as manure heaps, cow dung and deer dung (very abundant in the last). Extracts from litter alongside these tussocks produced 27 beetles belonging to 19 species (including 5 un-named Aleocharines), of which only 6 occurred also in the tussocks. Most of the beetles were litter forms. All these species were named by Mr P. J. Osborne.

48A (p. 338). *Formica aquilonia* from the nest shown in Plate 57 were named by Dr I. H. H. Yarrow.

49 (p. 339). The information about *Cyphodurus albinos* was supplied by Dr A. J. Pontin.

50 (p. 340). The main field work on ant numbers and population structure by Pontin, including that with Odum, was not done on the 'ant reserve' shown in Plate 56, but in The Bowling Alley, a tree-sheltered place already described in Ch. 6 in connection with grassland spiders.

51 (p. 341). From tawny owl nests at Wytham, *Philonthus subulicornis* and *Dendrophilus punctatus* were named by Mr P. J. Osborne; *Trox scaber* by myself; *Ceratophyllus gallinae* by Mr R. B. Freeman.

52 (p. 345). In the mapping of water bodies on Wytham Hill I did the main reconnaissance, receiving some help from Mr S. W. Hurry in 1960, and latterly considerable help from Mr C. A. Elbourn. The map in Fig. 27 was largely assembled by the latter, partly with the aid of air photos taken by Hunting Surveys Ltd in 1953 and 1960. The map was drawn by Mr A. J. Dunford, with technical advice from Mr D. A. Kempson, who undertook much difficult photographic processing.

53 (p. 349). Mr L. Parmenter has helped me with useful references to tree-hole Diptera.

54 (p. 350). *Batrachospermum moniliforme* was named by Professor J. L. Harper.

55 (p. 351). In 1963 a quantitative investigation of productivity (especially of the part played by *Gammarus pulex*) in a woodland stream at Wytham was begun by Mr C. P. Mathews, at the Bureau of Animal Population.

55A (p. 352). A detailed list of species identified from Stream 5 has now been published by Elbourn.[121a]

55B (p. 353). Crisp and Lloyd's survey[89] of the insects living in the dead leaves and mud around a small woodland stream in Roundhay Park, Leeds, revealed a similar richness in species, especially of flies. But the habitat from which they were mainly bred out was Transition zone, not the stream itself. It formed a sloping system of clay flats with black soil and a blanket of dead leaves for most of the year, with virtually no green plants growing in it.

56 (p. 355). Adults of *Nemurella inconspicua* (= *picteti*) were found at Wormstall Duck Pond, Wytham Park, after my 1956 paper was published, by Mr S. W. Hurry and myself on 26 April 1960. Nymphs of this species were also taken by Dr H. B. N. Hynes at the same place.

57 (p. 357). The records of heron censuses in Wytham Woods are scattered in a series of published reports. Mr D. F. Owen and Dr C. M. Perrins have provided me with the information given here.

58 (p. 359). At this date (1964) Dr W. W. Murdoch's research has not been published but he has allowed me to cite a few points from his Thesis,[339] which contains a full population analysis of selected species of marsh Carabidae.

59 (p. 360). J. D. Hooker[235] mentioned some of the conspicuous epiphytes that he saw in the temperate forests of the Himalayan hills during his journeys in 1848. These forests were at heights of 7000-8500 ft. 'A magnificent forest of chestnut, walnut, oaks and laurels . . . literally clothed for yards with a continuous garment of epiphytes, one mass of blossoms, especially the white Orchids, which bloom in a profuse manner, whitening their trunks like snow.' In another damp forest of oak, magnolias, laurels, horse-chestnut and walnut, 'scarlet flowers of *Vaccinium serpens*, an epiphytical species, were strewed about'; again, an epiphytic currant; in great forests of oak, magnolias and rhododendron near Darjeeling, *Rhododendron dalhousiae* grew as an epiphyte on a huge magnolia and also on oaks and laurels – a slender shrub with several lemon-scented flowers 4½ in. long and wide, at the end of each branch. And of course many ferns and mosses also grow on trees there.

60 (p. 366). Dr M. J. Cotton has given me the records of fleas in Wytham Woods: the rabbit flea collected in very large numbers in April–May 1960, and the grey squirrel flea (both sexes) in February 1960.

61 (p. 367). Middleton's first survey[320] of the spread of grey squirrels gives 1916 as its earliest arrival in Oxford City. It was first recorded in St John's College garden in 1916–17. By 1921 it was common round Oxford, e.g. at Marston, Radley, Bagley and Headington (unpublished notes, Bureau of Animal Population archives). I noted at this time (about 1920-2) the change from a red squirrel to a grey squirrel population in Magdalen College Park, Oxford.

62 (p. 368). It is not implied that sycamore alone is seriously damaged by grey squirrels. Beech is also attacked, and occasionally oak, ash, birch and larch.[164] But it is not clear how far these records of damage relate chiefly to young forest plantations. So far as Wytham Woods are concerned, sycamore damage is spectacular and that to other trees in established woodland negligible.

63 (p. 370). The Ecological Survey contains the following records of *Lathridius bifasciatus* from Wytham Woods: on a *Polyporus betulinus* bracket on a dead birch at the edge of deciduous woodland, 5 May 1960, Miss K. Paviour-Smith coll.; and swept from the field layer at the edge of deciduous woodland, 31 July 1962, Mr E. Lewis and K. P.-S. coll. The latter also found it in the Botanic Garden, Oxford, 13 Oct. 1962.

64 (p. 371). In May 1952 I found a larva of *Tetropium gabrieli* (named by Mr E. A. J. Duffy), under bark of an almost dead larch in mainly deciduous woodland at Wytham. This species can live on other conifers as well. *Urocerus gigas* was recorded in Wytham Woods by Miss V. Todd (now Mrs Davies) in July 1946 and has since been noted by others. *Rhyssa persuasoria* was found by Mr H. Probitts in May 1949; and by Professor G. C. Varley in larch logs in May 1964.

65 (p. 383). My son Robert and I have spent much time studying the natural history of another large gravel-pit at Cassington, near Oxford. This is shown in Plate 65 and from the air on the left-hand side of Plate 8. It is shallow water with many residual gravel islands that are important for birds, visiting or nesting. Round the margins is great variety of tall meadow type vegetation, as well as open ground gravel edges, and transition habitats that include reeds (*Phragmites*) and reed-mace (*Typha latifolia*). There is further variety of hedgerow and much scrub of crack willow (*Salix fragilis*) – greatly increased since photo 65 was taken. Altogether there are preserved at least 40 habitat components (including the boundaries). Our own records, together with others published by the Oxford Ornithological Society, give over 50 species of birds as visitors or residents. Although some of these are passage migrants, it is remarkable how the creation of such a varied water complex and its ring of surrounding habitats in the heart of England can enrich the fauna. In so far as such gravel workings often become exploited for recreation or are filled again for other purposes, it is a shifting fauna that moves on to other pits that are being made anew, or has just moved in from surrounding land and water.

Index

Species of woody plants and of animals are mostly indexed by their Latin genus and also by their English name where in common use; other plants mostly by Latin genus only. Larger animal groups, e.g. 'spiders' or 'Dytiscidae' or 'Diptera', are seldom indexed but can be found where their habitats are mentioned in the text. The Notes are only indexed (by figures in square brackets) where the subject does not follow from the text. The numerous references to Wytham Woods, the Wytham Ecological Survey and the Bureau of Animal Population have not been separately indexed.